Alan

Advance Praise for

teach yourself

"As we all prepare to make the transition from Computer Aided Drafting to Engineering Enterprise Modeling, we are truly fortunate to have an author and engineer of Ranjit's caliber to help lead the way."

Ray Bentley, Executive Vice President, Bentley Systems, Inc.

"Every MicroStation user, administrator, and programmer should read this outstanding book."

Morteza Tadayon, Team Leader, Maryland SHA

"After finishing the chapter (Chapter 15: Fixing Corrupt Files), I wrote a couple of command files from the instructions and ran them on ten design files. The results—outstanding!"

Garett Tunison, CAD Operator, PEPCO (Potomac Electric Power Co.)

"Ranjit Sahai is an excellent author. His publications are very well written and I am looking forward to reading Teach Yourself MicroStation/J."

Greg Cooley, Manager, Highway Mapping Team, Maryland SHA

"In Teach Yourself MicroStation/J, Ranjit expertly communicates all facets of MicroStation, that can overwhelm the novice and expert alike, in a truly engaging manner. Being a programmer, I am particularly envious of those who will start their programming journey with this book—it will take months off their learning curve."

Michael Colynuck, AScT, Software Developer, Pacific International Mapping, BC, Canada

PUBLISHED BY

Alpha Press
A Division of Alpha Corporation
45665 Willow Pond Plaza
Sterling, VA 20164-4453

10 9 8 7 6 5 4 3 2 1

Printed in the United States of America

Library of Congress Cataloging-in-Publication Data

Sahai, Ranjit S.
Includes index

1. MicroStation (computer software)

2. Computer Aided Design I. Title

ISBN 1-892658-00-3

Library of Congress Catalog Card Number: 99-60978

teach yourself

MicroStation J™

by
Ranjit S. Sahai, P.E.

Trademarks

MicroStation is a registered trademark and the stylized Bentley B logo is a trademark of Bentley Systems, Inc. The Bentley B logo and the MicroStation logo are used on the cover of this book with permission.

Alpha Press is a trademark of Alpha Corporation. Microsoft Windows NT is a registered trademark of Microsoft Corporation. Other products and services mentioned in this book are either trademarks or registered trademarks of their respective owners. Alpha Press and the author make no claims on these trademarks.

Warning and Disclaimer

This book is designed to teach you, at your own pace, various aspects of Bentley's MicroStation software through discussions and exercises. Every effort has been made to make this book as complete and accurate as possible; nevertheless, no warranty or fitness is implied.

Information is provided in this book on an as-is basis. Neither Alpha Press, nor the author, shall have any liability or responsibility to any person or entity with respect to any loss or damages in connection with or arising from the information contained in this book.

About the Author

Ranjit S. Sahai is a vice president with Alpha Corporation, an engineering and technology consulting company based in Sterling, Virginia. He works on both Information Technology projects, particularly CAD and GIS, and engineering design projects such as bridges, commercial buildings, waste water structures, tunnels and the like. Drawings for all his projects are done in MicroStation.

Ranjit earned a Bachelors degree in Civil Engineering and a Masters degree in Structural Engineering from the prestigious Indian Institute of Technology in New Delhi, India. He then went on to earn another Masters in Mechanical Engineering from the University of Houston at the Central Campus in Houston, Texas.

He was first introduced to CAD in 1987 when he joined Alpha. All drawing production was done at Alpha on a DEC VAX 750-based Intergraph system running IGDS, MicroStation's precursor. Of course, the original computer hardware has long since been replaced with a Microsoft Windows 2000 Server-based network environment.

Information technology in general, and CAD in particular, along with GIS, began as a passionate hobby with him and are now a part of his professional life as well. He has written over 200 articles for several computer magazines, including over six dozen MicroStation-related articles in the *MicroStation Manager* magazine. His *MDL Class* and *MDL Corner* columns, that ran from October 1996 through August 1998, and now the *Java/MDL Workshop* column that started in October 1998, have proved to be the most popular series he has written for the magazine.

In addition to writing, Ranjit also lectures and provides training, either on-site or at workshops around the country. He has conducted training on several topics, including Windows NT for the beginner; integration of office applications with MicroStation in a Windows environment using DDE and OLE technology; basic, intermediate, and advanced levels of MicroStation; and using ArcView.

Ranjit at work on Teach Yourself MicroStation/J.

He facilitated the development of CAD standards and custom MDL tools for various divisions and departments at government agencies, including the Maryland State Highway Administration and the New York City Transit Authority. He finds the shift to object technology in today's CAD systems a milestone in the evolution of CAD. This will be evident when you read the *Introduction*.

In his spare time Ranjit dabbles in photography. He also enjoys reading and listening to music.

How This Book Is Organized

This book is divided into the following four parts.

- **Using:** This section of the book is for beginners who haven't used MicroStation before, or for those who have used it for some time but need to explore areas they may not have used thus far, such as dimension-driven design and three-dimensional modeling. Exercises help you throughout the book.

- **Administering:** This section is for those of you who manage the deployment of MicroStation within your organization. Here you learn how to fix corrupt design files, how to translate files between different CAD platforms, how to implement standards, and set up workspaces.

- **Customizing:** This section is for the power user who wants to customize MicroStation to fit specific task needs. Here you learn about the tools and interfaces available for creating custom menus, cells, line styles, and for data exchange between MicroStation and other applications.

- **Programming:** This section is for the corporate developer who wants to create custom applications for MicroStation users at his firm. You learn the four programming languages MicroStation supports: User Command language, MicroStation BASIC, MDL, and Java-based JMDL.

Each chapter, no matter where in the book, is self-contained by way of concepts discussed and exercises that reinforce those concepts. Depending on your previous experience with MicroStation and your specific area of interest, you can read chapters in the sequence that make sense for you. However, if you are a new MicroStation user, I strongly urge you to read the chapters in sequence.

Typographical Conventions

While reading this book you will come across variations in font and other conventions. The following table lists these conventions to help you understand the context in which they are used.

Type Style	Sample	Description
Italic	when you read the *Introduction*	Chapter and section names and figure captions appear in italic type, as do terms when they are defined.
Initial capital letters	select Save Settings from the File menu	Names of commands, menus and dialogs appear with initial capital letters.

Type Style	Sample	Description
Fixed pitch font	open the `00index.txt` file	File and directory names, text to be typed in, and source code appear in a fixed pitch font.
All capital letters	the following URL	Acronyms and some MicroStation specific terms appear in all capital letters.

Notes and Tips

An icon with a feather and an ink bottle offsets a gray shaded area containing text to designate notes as shown below.

NOTE: Notes highlight concepts worth emphasizing and present information that might otherwise be overlooked.

An icon with a light bulb offsets a gray shaded area containing text to designate tips as shown below.

TIP: Tips present hints and shortcuts you may want to become familiar with as they help you be more productive.

The Companion CD-ROM

This book comes with a bonus CD-ROM that contains:

- Exercise files and cell libraries to help you learn how to use the various features in MicroStation.
- Macro code in UCM and BASIC to help automate tasks and provide a framework for your own macros.
- Program code in MDL and JMDL designed to serve as an introduction to professional application development for MicroStation.
- RS Tools LE, an MDL application, to simplify many common drafting tasks.
- Demos of applications you might find useful.

Acknowledgments

I would like to take this opportunity to thank Keith Bentley, the CEO of Bentley Systems, Inc. for making it possible for me to spend several days at Bentley Systems talking to the developers, project leads, and programmers, as they were working on MicroStation/J. The interview he granted me helped make the introduction what it is now—a captivating tour of MicroStation's history along with its future.

I would also like to thank Jeffrey Lindsey, the CEO of Alpha Corporation, for recognizing that my passion for Information Technology had a business potential. Consequently, Alpha Press serves as a vehicle to get my writings to you.

Several chapters in this book showcase projects users created in MicroStation. I acknowledged the source of such images directly under the figures. A sincere thank you to all who contributed images and drawings. Those of you who would like to contribute drawings and/or renderings for the next edition of this book, feel free to contact me via e-mail at **Ranjit.Sahai@AlphaCorporation.com**.

Credits

Task	Responsibility
Production	Ranjit S. Sahai
Marketing and Public Relations	Joanne Roehling
Preface	Ray Bentley
Technical review of programming chapters	Michael Colynuck, Mark Anderson
Printing and binding	United Press
Indexing	RAM Indexing Services
Copyediting and proofreading	Carrie Smoot
Cover design	Bruce Gibson
Cover image	Bentley Systems, Inc.

Dedication

I dedicate this book to my loving wife Manjit, and to our son Amar. This book would not have been possible without your support and love. Thank you for the gift of time. I also dedicate this book to my parents—my father Onkar and my mother Gobinder—for raising their children in a caring environment and supporting us in every way. I think of you constantly.

Preface by Ray Bentley

Over the last dozen years, MicroStation has evolved from a relatively simple drafting program to become a mission-critical platform for the creation of design information for large engineering projects throughout the world. The introductory chapter of *Teach Yourself MicroStation/J* does an outstanding job of chronicling this evolution. With the release of MicroStation/J, and the impending delivery of ProjectBank and Engineering Component Modeling, we are poised to make a more revolutionary step with benefits that far exceed those realized when computers first replaced the tee-squares and drafting boards.

I have reviewed the manuscript of *Teach Yourself MicroStation/J* and am truly impressed with the attention to detail, and the breadth of coverage it provides. It takes new users by the hand and teaches them basic concepts through step-by-step exercises. It addresses the needs of CAD administrators with detailed information on everything from translation to standards implementation. *Teach Yourself MicroStation/J* can also serve as a corporate programmer's introduction to all the programming interfaces in MicroStation, including JMDL.

The author, Ranjit S. Sahai, a professional engineer, has been authoring MicroStation texts since 1992. His knowledge of MicroStation, versatility as a writer, and experience as a workshop leader and trainer at Bentley FORUMs is clearly evident throughout the book. As we all prepare to make the transition from Computer Aided Drafting to Engineering Enterprise Modeling, we are truly fortunate to have an author and engineer of Ranjit's caliber to help lead the way.

Raymond B. Bentley
Executive Vice President
Bentley Systems, Inc.
Exton, Pennsylvania
December 11, 1998

Contents

Introduction

The Object Revolution
From Geometry to Component Modeling

What do the state of transportation at the turn of the twentieth century and the state of CAD today have in common?

Don't misunderstand me. This is no pop quiz. I mean it in all earnestness. And I envy the discovery you are about to make about the future of CAD in general and MicroStation in particular.

On December 17, 1903 the sustained flight in a heavier-than-air vehicle by the Wright brothers at Kitty Hawk, North Carolina broke the shackles of earthbound transportation and led to the birth of the aviation industry. Similarly, at the dawn of the twenty-first century CAD is poised to break the shackles of geometric modeling.

Ever since I began my career in the CAD industry as an author and analyst, I haven't seen the undercurrent of massive impending change that pervades our industry today. Professional CAD is moving from geometric modeling to component modeling through the use of software objects.

What do the state of transportation at the beginning of the twentieth century and the state of CAD today have in common? Revolution!

What is this revolution? I invite you to stay with me through the rest of this introduction as we explore both the history of CAD and its future—with an emphasis on MicroStation.

This chapter is organized into the following sections.

- **Geometric Modeling** discusses the history of CAD, the birth of MicroStation and its evolution. It also discusses the concept of geometric modeling as the basis of today's CAD systems.
- **Design Applications** highlights how the needs of the engineering and architectural design community have been met through add-ons to CAD that maintain nongraphic attribute data, either within or external to the design file, to enable discipline specific functionality.
- **Engineering Component Modeling** discusses the concept of software objects, called engineering component models by Bentley, and the role JMDL is to play in their implementation in the upcoming releases of MicroStation/J. Here you learn about ProjectBank, Bentley's upcoming transaction and component management system that is to be the repository for engineering component models.

I'm excited about what MicroStation/J stands for, and its future path. Though the initial release of MicroStation/J appears virtually indistinguishable from a user's point of view when compared to MicroStation SE, under the hood it represents a remarkable remake of the software's core.

But I'm getting ahead of myself. Let's go back in time to when CAD started. This historical journey will help you put things in perspective and better appreciate the object revolution that is upon us. As Hendrick Willem van Loon said in the introduction to his classic book, *The Story of Mankind*, history gives you "the benefit of the full view."

After you have read this introduction, you too will appreciate why I look forward to what the future holds for CAD and the role MicroStation is playing in shaping it.

The last section in this chapter showcases component modeling technology—the future of professional CAD. The rest of the book focuses on helping you maximize your investment in Bentley's

MicroStation software. You learn its basic features. In addition, you learn how to manage the software's use within your organization, how to customize it for your needs, and finally, how to develop custom macros and add-on applications that extend the software's functionality.

Geometric Modeling

Blueprints have been for centuries, and still are, the most significant deliverables produced by an engineering or architectural firm for their clients. These technical drawings are a dimensionally scaled graphical representation of design concepts for the construction, manufacture, or inventory of man-made assets.

The term man-made assets refers to such artifacts as buildings, bridges, industrial plants, automobiles, submarines, aircraft components, spaceships, underground utilities, and so on.

The focus of technical drawings, as opposed to sketching and painting, is to convey accurate and definitive information about all parts of the asset and how they come together. Many views of the asset under design are typically drawn. Plan, elevation, section, and isometric views are commonly used to convey design information.

Technical drawing, or engineering drawing, has its own set of accepted standards, conventions, terms and abbreviations.

Thomas E. French (1871-1944), head of the engineering drawing department at Ohio State University, was a pioneer in the field. Revised editions of his original work, such as the book *Engineering Drawing and Graphic Technology*, Fourteenth Edition (1993), McGraw-Hill, are still in print and used for instruction at technical schools today.

Basic concepts of drafting standards and good graphic communication practices taught in French's book are still essential for the successful creation of quality engineering drawings, whether prepared by hand, or through the use of computer software.

Tee-Squares to Computers

Engineering drawings have traditionally been done by draftspersons using a drafting table, tee-squares, triangles, templates, irregular curves, pens, pencils, and erasers. Tee-squares and triangles have largely been replaced by Computer Aided Design and Drafting (CADD, more commonly referred to as CAD) software in the professional engineering and architectural industry.

Much like the drafting board and tee-square helped draftspersons create drawings through the use of geometric shapes, CAD today helps create drawings through the use of geometric modeling tools. This means that the core data structure that defines the CAD file format is focused on the geometric properties and attributes of entities drawn.

All drawings created in popular CAD packages today use geometric shapes such as lines, arcs, and circles as their basic building block. These geometric shapes have attributes such as coordinates, level, color, weight, style, and optional nongraphic data.

To take CAD beyond the creation of drawings with geometric tools to the simulation of assets such that these simulations are useful beyond just the design stage of a project will mean the adoption of file formats and systems of a different nature. That is what component modeling is all about, and is discussed later in this introduction.

History of CAD

Considering that CAD came into widespread use after the introduction of the IBM-compatible personal computer in 1981, many believe that CAD originated with the PC. Nothing could be further from the truth.

The work of Dr. Ivan Sutherland in the early 1960s was a milestone in the development of vector-based computer graphics software. His 1963 doctoral dissertation at the Massachusetts Institute of Technology (MIT) described Sketch-Pad, an interactive CRT graphics system that could be used to draw a line on screen when a light pen was tapped to identify its start and end points. His thesis described data structures for storing geometric entities that formed the basis upon which today's CAD systems are based.

At about the same time, several large companies in various industries also began experimenting with computer graphics as a means of developing design drawings. Aerospace companies such as Boeing, McDonnell Douglas, and Lockheed began to explore ways to exploit computer graphics technology for the design of aircrafts and missiles. Automobile manufacturing firms such as General Motors began work to apply computer graphics technology to design cars. Electronics companies such as Motorola, and Fairchild began to use this technology for the design and manufacture of printed circuit boards.

Computer graphics systems at the time could only run on mainframe computers. Only large companies with dedicated computer support staff could afford to invest in the research and development of systems for such use. One thing was clear though. The use of interactive computer graphics was indeed helping these companies save time and money.

In an effort to bring the technology to a wider audience a new generation of companies known as turnkey computer graphics vendors, came into being. Silicon Graphics, Inc. and ComputerVision were among the first in this genre of companies. These companies independently developed high-performance computer graphics systems and bundled hardware, software, support, and peripherals (graphics terminals, disk drives, memory, floating-point processors, pointing devices, printers and plotters) in a value-added package available from a single source.

The philosophy that drove turnkey computer graphics vendors was that many companies and government agencies have a need for computer graphics, but not all have either the technical or financial resources to develop such systems in-house. By investing in the development of this technology for a wider audience the cost per site would be much lower than if the system were developed for a single site. This proved to be a sound business principle, and such companies thrived.

Intergraph as Turnkey CAD Vendor

In the late 1960s during the Apollo moon mission years a few managers at IBM, led by Jim Meadlock, left the company to form M&S Computing and entered the computer graphics world. The company got its start as a consultant for NASA developing real-time software and it developed a printed circuit board design and a mapping software package. Of these packages the mapping software was more general purpose in nature and useful to other industries.

M&S Computing had success in marketing its mapping package to oil companies that relied on geophysical sciences for their business. This success led the company in the mid-1970s to enhance the system and call it IGDS, an acronym for Interactive Graphics Design System. This system was flexible and able to support the creation of drawings in virtually any engineering design discipline.

In the beginning IGDS ran on 16-bit PDP11 minicomputers manufactured by Digital, a company that was recently acquired by Compaq Corporation. M&S Computing was an OEM (original equipment manufacturer) of Digital computers. The company specialized in modifying these computers with its own graphics subsystems for fast graphics performance and bundled its IGDS software, peripherals and support to become a turnkey vendor of interactive graphics systems.

In 1980 the company changed its name from M&S Computing to Intergraph, a word formed by combining parts of the two words *interactive* and *graphics*, the company's primary business. During this time, Intergraph also switched its product line from the 16-bit PDP11 to Digital's more powerful 32-bit VAX minicomputer line.

Intergraph built upon its initial success by continuing to expand its user base. The company marketed its turnkey systems to various industries with discipline-specific add-on solutions that enhanced IGDS. Intergraph built its reputation as a vendor of powerful CAD systems for government agencies and large companies. In fact, an overwhelming majority of State Departments of Transportation (DOTs) and Fortune 100 companies began using Intergraph systems to make it a firm with over a billion dollars in annual revenues.

Bentley Writes MicroStation

DuPont, a global chemical company, was a large user of Intergraph CAD systems. In 1978, at its Delaware plant, the company hired Keith Bentley to support its CAD operations. Keith was still in college studying toward his graduate engineering degree and was assigned the task of developing an application to automate the creation of P&ID—piping and instrumentation diagrams—schematic drawings in batch mode.

While developing his application Keith quickly discovered that access to IGDS, though vital to his efforts, was not easy. Intergraph CAD workstations, at nearly $75,000 per seat were at a premium and were kept busy round the clock with three shifts.

To open IGDS design files so he could develop his application more expeditiously, Keith wrote, primarily on his own time, a piece of software he called PseudoStation. The software was written in FORTRAN on the VAX and was designed to provide read-only access to IGDS drawings on inexpensive VT-100 terminals equipped with a graphics card.

The name PseudoStation referred to the fact that the graphics card equipped terminal was not really a CAD station, but a pseudo CAD station. Little did Keith realize at the time that his work would lead to a fantastic journey putting him on top of a company with world-wide operations that supports over 1,000 employees!

The software, though not officially sanctioned by DuPont, became an unqualified hit at the plant where Keith worked. And gradually, it found its way to other plants that used IGDS. While Keith was writing CAD software, his four brothers were also making their mark in the software business.

Greg, graduated from the University of Pennsylvania with an MBA degree and worked at the Yardley Group, an actuarial consulting company in Philadelphia. He soon left the firm to found Devon Systems, Inc., a successful developer of securities exchange software, which he later left to join Bentley Systems, Inc.

Barry graduated from Cal Tech with a Ph.D. in chemical engineering and founded Dynamic Solutions with two college friends. They developed chemical analysis software for the Apple II in assembly language.

Scott earned a degree in economics and worked in the software business. He was employed at Scientific Time-Sharing Corporation in Philadelphia as an APL programmer. Ray earned a degree in mechanical engineering and worked on jet engines at another large company, General Electric. He is particularly strong in mathematics and was to take on the challenge of enhancing MicroStation's 3D tools.

The Bentley brothers, clockwise from rear left: Scott, Barry, Ray, Greg, and Keith.

About the time when Keith wrote PseudoStation, Barry was looking to diversify his chemical analysis software portfolio and invited Keith to join him in California. Keith agreed to quit his job at DuPont to try his hand at business and PseudoStation figured in his thoughts.

Before leaving DuPont, Keith acquired the rights to PseudoStation in exchange for his promise to support the software that had become very popular at the company. Today DuPont has several thousand MicroStation licenses as a result of that agreement.

On his way to California, Keith stopped at Intergraph headquarters in Huntsville, Alabama with the intention of selling PseudoStation for a few thousand dollars. That Intergraph was not interested proved to be a disappointment for the moment, but a thankful coincidence that would lead to riches beyond Keith's wildest dreams.

Though the software Barry's Dynamic Solutions developed was of excellent quality, it did not do very well as a business. Meanwhile, Keith was convinced that there was a future in PseudoStation. If DuPont saw value in the relatively inexpensive terminal-based software, scores of other Intergraph customers would be interested in the software. This led to the formation by Keith and Barry of Bentley Systems, Inc. in 1984 to pursue the future of PseudoStation. The early success of the software that was sold at $7,500 a copy led them to bring in Scott to run the business side of the company.

By the time the brothers decided to move to the East Coast in 1986, they had sold 350 copies of the software.

The remarkable success of the personal computer in businesses and the growing acceptance of relatively under-powered CAD software running on PCs convinced Keith that the future of PseudoStation lay in a feature-complete version of the software running on microcomputers. Thus was born MicroStation: a full-featured Intergraph IGDS-compatible CAD station running on microcomputers.

At this point in the history of CAD the focus shifted from turnkey systems to the development of computer graphics software that could run on workstations and personal computers customers already had. This has led to an even lower cost of entry to the world of professional CAD.

MicroStation Versions

Whereas PseudoStation was designed to provide IGDS design file access for viewing and printing purposes, MicroStation was to be a superset of IGDS with full editing capabilities. PseudoStation was terminal-based and required a VAX minicomputer. MicroStation was to be a stand-alone program that would run on a multitude of platforms including DOS-based personal computers and UNIX workstations.

Considering the power of the minicomputer and the limited processing power and resources in the personal computer, implementing all features in IGDS on the PC was no minor undertaking. That Bentley was able to develop a DOS version of MicroStation in 1986 that offered a remarkably rich feature set that included 3D modeling capabilities is testimony to their programming prowess. Though version 2 was a capable system, it wasn't widely distributed.

At about the time when version 3 was ready for DOS-based personal computers and Intergraph's UNIX-based Clipper workstations, Bentley had reached a business arrangement with Intergraph. For a 50-percent stake in Bentley, Intergraph would be the exclusive distributor of MicroStation, and Bentley would concentrate on research and development. The software came to be known as Intergraph MicroStation. This arrangement, with virtually no modifications, remained in place until the end of 1994.

Greg Bentley, the founder of Devon Systems, joined Bentley Systems, Inc. (BSI) in 1991 with a goal of aggressively developing the business. This arrangement would relieve Keith from day-to-day business operations and allow him to focus more intently on product development—something he enjoys most.

Knowing the personal computer market would continue to more aggressively challenge the workstation market as time went on, Bentley wanted to be a major player in the CAD software market. Their goal was to deliver MicroStation on any and all hardware platforms a sufficient number of customers wanted it to run on. Realizing that Intergraph's CAD business model was focused on hardware sales tied to the software, Bentley initiated a renegotiation of its contract with Intergraph.

In 1995, Bentley became responsible for the development of MicroStation and its distribution, sales, and support. From then on the software came to be known as Bentley MicroStation. The following screenshots of early versions of MicroStation give you a brief overview of the enhancements implemented in the software over the years.

I was unable to locate a screenshot of MicroStation version 2 at Bentley's archives. If you happen to have one, I'd love to get a copy to include in the next edition of this book. Version 2 was remarkable in its support for 3D modeling and reference files.

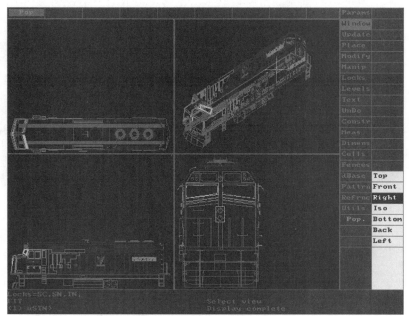

Version 3 (1989) ran on MS-DOS and introduced screen menus.

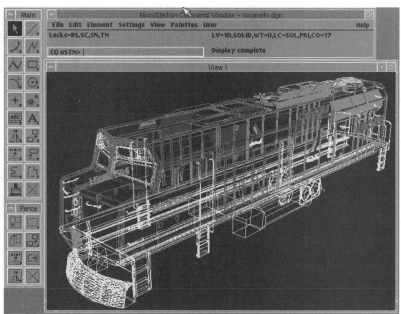

Version 4 (1991) introduced MDL and a modern graphical interface.

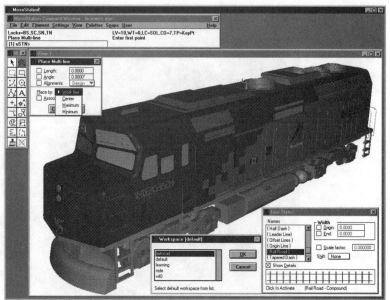

Version 5 (1993) improved usability through consolidated icon palettes, workspaces, and scores of other enhancements.

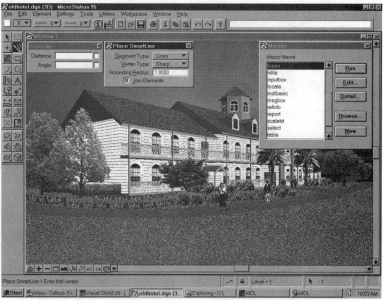

MicroStation 95 (1995) introduced the BASIC macro language, AccuDraw, status bar, and other enhancements.

MicroStation SE (1997) introduced colored icons, Internet technologies, batch plotting, and rolled Masterpiece functionality into the software.

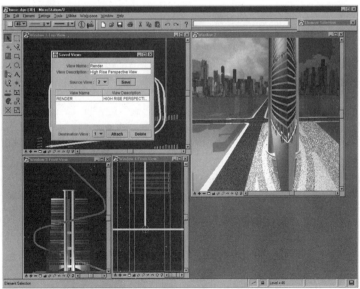

MicroStation/J (1998) introduces the Java-based JMDL environment and lays the foundation for component modeling.

The following table summarizes MicroStation's timeline.

Version	Year	Significant Features
2	1987	IGDS Compatible file editor with 2D and 3D modeling capabilities
3	1989	Screen menus, database links, rendering module
4	1991	MDL, Motif-based graphical interface on all platforms
5	1993	Workspaces, consolidated palettes, custom line styles
95 (or 5.5)	1995	BASIC macros, AccuDraw, status bar, SmartLine, raster reference files
SE (or 5.7)	1997	Colored icons, batch plotting, Internet technologies, ray-traced rendering
/J (or 7)	1998	Java-based JMDL, Parasolid 3D modeling technology, engineering configurations

CAD has indeed come a long way from its humble beginnings as Sketch-Pad, described by Dr. Ivan Sutherland. It is now a mature software category with vendors offering products ranging from under $50 for the hobbyist to thousands of dollars for the professional. Today, MicroStation is one of the premier discipline-independent professional CAD software packages on the market with an ever-growing user base that exceeds 250,000.

Gallery of MicroStation-Based Projects

Though engineering and architectural firms primarily use MicroStation, the software is also in use by many other markets. The software is used to create plan drawings for a variety of infrastructure assets such as buildings, waste water treatment facilities, bridges, industrial plants, mechanical parts, underground utilities, tunnels, and others. The software is also used to study design alternatives through comparison of three-dimensional models. NASA has extensively used MicroStation to create beautifully detailed and fully rendered models of fantastic projects such as space stations.

This section is designed to give you an idea of what engineers and architects use MicroStation for. The drawings and images featured here are reproduced with permission from their respective owners. I thank all of you who graciously agreed to let me feature your works on these pages. Credits for images appear under them in parentheses.

Rendering of an offshore refinery platform designed with PDS and MicroStation. (Courtesy of Amoco Oil and Fluor Daniel, Inc.)

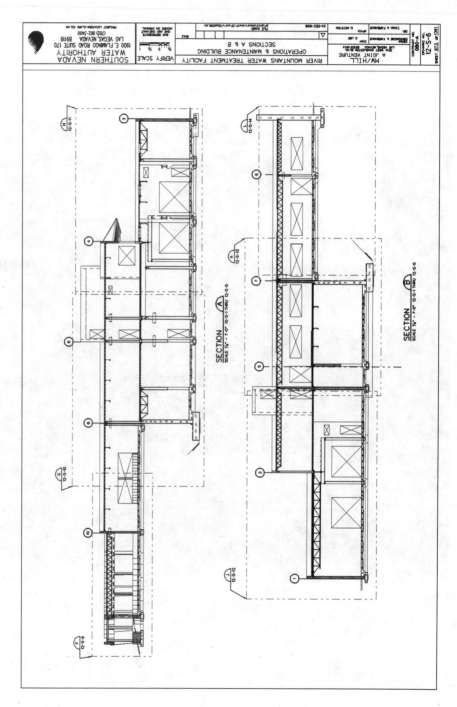

Operations and Maintenance Building section. (Courtesy of SNWA and MW/Hill.)

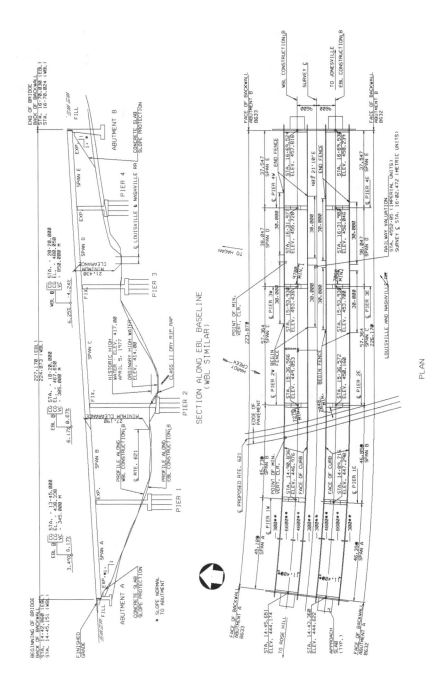

Proposed bridge over Hardy Creek. (Courtesy of Alpha Corporation.)

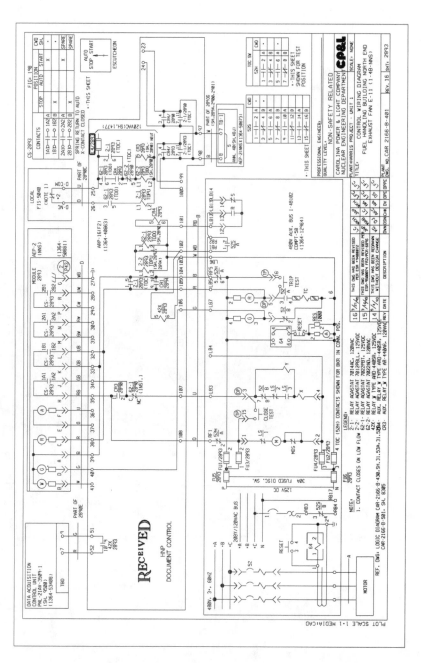

*Control Wiring Diagram for Fuel Handling Building
North End Exhaust Fan E-11 (1-4B-NNS). (Courtesy of Carolina Power & Light.)*

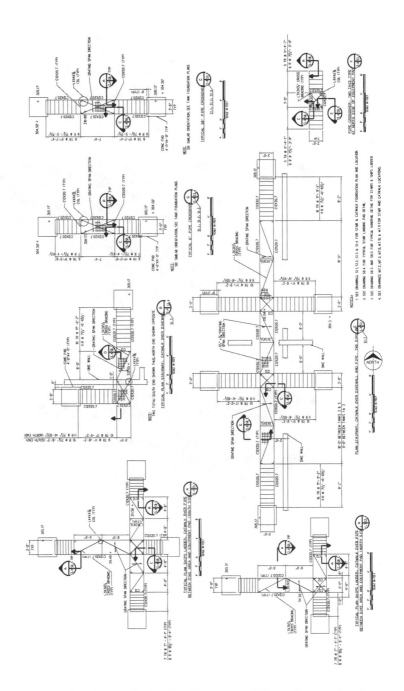

Steel catwalk details. (Courtesy of Alpha Corporation.)

River Mountains Water Treatment Facility, Process Area.
(Courtesy of SNWA and MW/Hill.)

River Mountains Water Treatment Facility, Operations and Maintenance Building.
(Courtesy of SNWA and MW/Hill.)

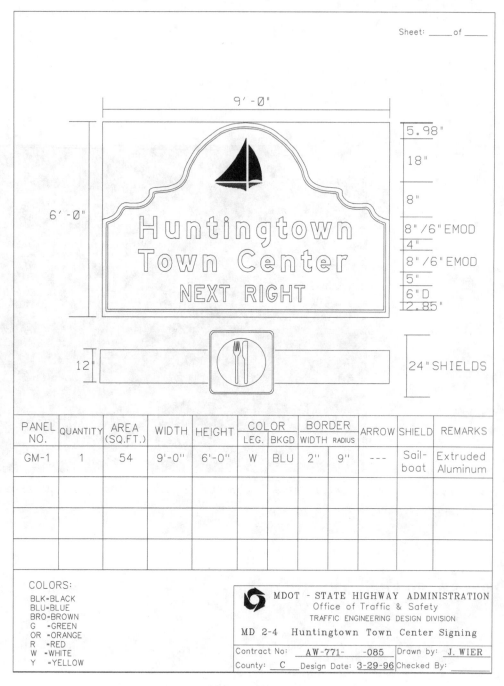

Sheet: _____ of _____

9'-0"

6'-0"

5.98"

18"

8"

8"/6" EMOD

4"

8"/6" EMOD

5"

6"D

2.85"

Huntingtown
Town Center
NEXT RIGHT

12'

24" SHIELDS

| PANEL NO. | QUANTITY | AREA (SQ.FT.) | WIDTH | HEIGHT | COLOR | | BORDER | | ARROW | SHIELD | REMARKS |
					LEG.	BKGD	WIDTH	RADIUS			
GM-1	1	54	9'-0"	6'-0"	W	BLU	2"	9"	---	Sail-boat	Extruded Aluminum

COLORS:
BLK=BLACK
BLU=BLUE
BRO=BROWN
G =GREEN
OR =ORANGE
R =RED
W =WHITE
Y =YELLOW

MDOT - STATE HIGHWAY ADMINISTRATION
Office of Traffic & Safety
TRAFFIC ENGINEERING DESIGN DIVISION
MD 2-4 Huntingtown Town Center Signing

Contract No: AW-771-   -085   Drawn by: J. WIER
County: C   Design Date: 3-29-96   Checked By: _____

Huntington Town Center sign detail. (Courtesy of Maryland SHA.)

Design Applications

As you will have noticed from the showcase of drawings in the previous section, MicroStation is used to create drawings and images for a wide range of projects.

The larger a project, the greater the number of resources needed to tackle it and more numerous the quantity of drawings generated. Such projects require far more coordination of effort, not only between designers but also between different design tasks. CAD as a geometric modeler does little to alleviate the extensive coordination efforts necessary in paper-based drafting projects.

Early on, Intergraph realized that to better serve the needs of its large clients working on massive projects MicroStation would have to do more than draw geometric shapes interactively.

Extending Drafting to Design

With the goal of automating engineering design tasks within the CAD environment, Intergraph devoted its energies in the early 1980s to begin developing several suites of industry-specific solutions. These solutions extended the geometric modeling tool to perform design tasks.

For the transportation industry, Intergraph developed InRoads. For the structural engineering community it developed MicasPlus and FrameWorks. For the industrial plant design community it developed PDS. For the municipal government sector it developed InSewer. For the architect it developed Project Architect. For the electrical engineer it developed PE/Elec. For the mechanical engineer it developed PE/HVAC.

Several other independent software vendors (ISVs) developed applications to extend MicroStation for engineering design. There are presently over a hundred vendors with nearly a thousand tools, utilities, and applications designed to extend MicroStation.

Among the more prominent vendors in which Bentley has an equity stake are GEOPAK with civil engineering solutions, HMR with imaging solutions, and Jacobus with plant design solutions.

Most MicroStation add-on applications are written in MicroStation Development Language (MDL), its professional development environment. These applications offer tools to create models or perform engineering calculations and generate, either automatically or semi-automatically, traditional 2D drawings as a by-product.

Engineering Configurations

The use of design applications on top of MicroStation has the potential of significantly increasing your CAD productivity. To encourage their use, Bentley offers those who license new copies of MicroStation/J, at no extra cost, a choice of the following four design applications:

- **GeoGraphics:** a GIS (Geographic Information Systems) application for earth-scale projects. Municipalities and utility companies can use it to manage geoengineering assets such as underground water networks and transmission towers.

- **CivilPAK:** a civil engineering application for site-scale projects. Design firms can use it to create survey alignments, layout subdivisions and generate plats, design highways, and do other tasks.

- **TriForma:** an architectural and plant/building engineering application for building-scale projects. Design firms can use it for 3D building modeling and from the model extract plan, elevation, and section drawings along with specification and bill of material documents.

- **Modeler:** a manufacturing/mechanical engineering application for equipment scale projects. Equipment manufacturers can use it to create feature-based solid models and assemblies from which can be extracted plan, elevation, section, and exploded view drawings.

NOTE: Bentley calls the above applications *Engineering Configurations*. A complete chapter is devoted to these applications later in the book.

Bentley is expected to add to this list of applications for distribution as engineering configurations to users of MicroStation/J. If none of the above applications seems to fit your design needs, check with your MicroStation dealer—a more suitable application may have become available.

How Design Applications Work

As was noted earlier, the MicroStation design file format primarily stores geometric information such as entity type, element coordinates, color, level, style, and weight. A design application or an engineering configuration, on the other hand, requires that it operate upon more than just this geometric data.

For instance, in order to create a bill of materials, TriForma needs a way to determine that the set of lines and arcs that looks like a door is somehow tagged as a door and stores nongraphic data attributes it needs. Similarly, in order to implement COGO (coordinate geometry) functions, CivilPAK needs a way to store monument points and other alignment information.

Design applications store nongraphic attribute data, often referred to as intelligence, in either data files external to the MicroStation design file, or as *user data* within the design file. User data refers to nondisplayable attributes application developers can associate with elements in a design file.

There are two key components to a design application: nongraphic attribute data and the add-on software that operates upon the data. Design applications work by interacting with both the attribute data and the MicroStation CAD engine.

Engineering Component Modeling

Through all the changes the CAD industry has undergone over the last three decades, one thing remains unchanged: the core data structure that defines the CAD file format. The CAD file data structure has focused on the geometric properties and attributes of entities drawn. All drawings are created through the use of geometric shapes such as lines, arcs, and circles. Geometric shapes have attributes such as coordinates, level, color, weight, style, and optional nongraphic data.

The late-1990s represent a shift in focus by Bentley from geometry, and even design applications, to a more data-rich, inter-operable and transaction-based component model.

Research, development, and marketing efforts to nurture this technology to maturity and to see its user-base continue to grow. The widespread deployment and use of the component modeling technology is still a few years away, but we must follow this technology, as it will have a dramatic impact on how we think of CAD.

Component modeling refers to the creation of models that are governed by physical laws and design principles as are the real-world projects they represent.

Limitations of Design Applications

One might argue that existing design applications already create geometric models that follow design principles. For instance, TriForma already knows about walls and their relationship to doors and windows. When you place a door in a TriForma wall, the wall knows to create an opening to accommodate the door.

If existing design applications already implement such relationships, what then is the big deal about component modeling?

The answer to this question lies in understanding the implementation of design applications and their limitations.

Design applications operate by tagging MicroStation geometric elements with nongraphic user data and operating upon the data for design needs. So long as the design application responsible for the tagged user data is loaded within MicroStation, it will ensure that the tagged data remains consistent to design rules. Should you ever edit the drawing without the associated application loaded, the design file can easily become corrupt.

What drove the creation of the CAD software category and its data structure was the need to automate and impart greater precision to the process of creating drawings. It emulated the drawing creation process, nothing more. Nobody quite thought of, or had developed a means to capture design information in a way that would focus on the value of the data rather than just its representation on the screen, the plotter or the drawing.

This is where component modeling comes in. It is based on the premise that systems that focus on the value of the data in enterprise-wide terms offer far greater utility than geometric or other representations, which can be derived from the model on demand.

Java As Basis of JMDL OOP Environment

The word *object* has many connotations. It can mean one thing to a programmer, and quite another to a software user. Programmers who use object oriented programming (OOP) methodologies may claim their software is object-oriented. A user, on the other hand, may not notice the difference between software developed using OOP and software developed using a more traditional programming language, if both applications approach the problem in the same way.

For example, when calculating the area of a rectangle, whether you use a function (traditional programming concept) or use a method in a class (OOP concept) the user gets the same answer and couldn't care less what technique the programmer used.

How code is written and organized within a program is immaterial from a user's perspective. It is the approach to solving, or even looking at the problem, that can make all the difference to the value the software offers a user. An object to a user is an intelligent software component that understands the rules it must follow for a specific purpose.

Because of the confusion in the use of the word *object*, Bentley chose not to rechristen the software Objective MicroStation, as was the initial intent. Rather, it chose to keep the focus on MicroStation with a J suffix to designate the open Java programming environment it now supports.

Initially, all programming was procedural in nature. You wrote a monolithic piece of code that sequentially prompted the user for input and then went on to finish its task and displayed the results. This is how MicroStation User Commands and MicroStation BASIC macros work.

Then came along event-driven programming that is the basis of all windowing environments such as Microsoft Windows, Apple Macintosh and others. Here you write modular code that is organized into functions that handle specific user events such as mouse click, cursor movement, command key-in, or tool selection. Once your program loads, it waits for events and acts appropriately. This is how MDL programs work.

The difference between a procedural program and an event-driven program is immediately apparent to a user. In the first type of program all command input must initially be supplied in sequential order before it will begin processing. In the latter type of program, command input need not be sequential and user interface is graphical in nature.

The release of MicroStation/J signifies a shift in the Bentley software model, that of transaction-based systems. As MicroStation stands today, even when used on a network, it is a peer system. All computers running MicroStation perform the same role. The transaction-based system, on the other hand, requires a gatekeeper. The initial release of MicroStation/J is not transaction-based. ProjectBank, MicroStation's transaction manager, will make its debut later. An overview of ProjectBank is provided later in this chapter.

Bentley began development of OMDL, an acronym for Objective MicroStation Development Language, to support the requirements of a transaction manager in 1995/96. At about the same time, the Java programming environment came out from Sun Microsystems. Java had many of the same features and the design philosophy Bentley needed. In 1997 Bentley decided to adopt Java and extend it for its transaction management needs and call the language JMDL (Java MicroStation Development Language).

Java is the foundation upon which the new JMDL language is based. The language is object-oriented, making it better suited to the development of engineering components—the core of where MicroStation/J is headed.

Engineering Components

Object-oriented programming is an approach to solving more complex problems through the definition of a higher level abstraction concept called an object. However, simply using OOP does not mean that the software automatically becomes a component modeling system.

In Bentley terminology a *component model* is what a user might refer to as an object, such as a P&ID valve in a schematic diagram or a door in a wall. An engineering component encapsulates data and behavior relevant to that object as a coherent whole.

Rather than approach the process of engineering drawing production as a geometric modeling problem, component modeling approaches the process as a transaction-based database problem. Drawing production then becomes one of the representations engineering components can generate from the database.

There are three concepts that are relevant to understanding the implementation of engineering components in the upcoming releases of MicroStation. These concepts are listed below.

- **Transaction Manager:** This term refers to a server resident program that is the gatekeeper of all transactions designers make on components. It supports the concept of creating a project and having to check in and check out components during various stages of design.

- **Persistence:** Objects as defined in OOP languages are transient in nature—they are alive only during the session in which the program is active. Engineering components can be programmatically represented as objects but have a need to maintain their state of data between sessions because design transactions can be long and can span multiple sessions. There needs to be a mechanism to save the state of engineering components between sessions. This is called persistence.

- **Schema:** This term refers to the rules components must follow for a specific purpose. Each MicroStation application domain will have its own schema. In MicroStation's component modeling mode each schema must have a core set of methods or properties that are saved in the transaction manager along with the component. Bentley implements this requirement to ensure that models have no zombies or proxies that can occur in other object modeling environments.

Each of these concepts is implemented in Bentley's ProjectBank, a transaction management and component modeling environment scheduled to be delivered at no cost to MicroStation/J users some time in 1999.

ProjectBank

Thus far in its history MicroStation has been a desktop technical drawing production system. There is no concept of a system that is in charge of managing a project. Of course, there is TeamMate, a file management system that can simplify the organization of files on a project-by-project basis. However, it only deals with files, not components.

ProjectBank is a server resident component modeling environment that supports transaction management. It is the gatekeeper for projects that use components. Its purpose is to store and maintain project data and to coordinate its interaction with other relevant information systems.

When you begin using ProjectBank, you create a project and check your work into it. Now ProjectBank has a project and associated data. This data will initially be your electronic drawings in either `.dgn` or `.dwg` format. Over time however, as engineering component modeling applications become available and you make use of them, you also will check in engineering components into the project.

To work on the project, you log on to ProjectBank and check out the files and components you need. You will then have begun a transaction against ProjectBank.

The design session you start on the data you have checked out can last a single day, or it can last a week or more. Once you have completed the design task on the data you had checked out, you first synchronize your work with the current state of the data in ProjectBank as many people could be working on the same project. If the changes you made conflict with changes made by others on the project, you can adjust your design or have others coordinate their work with yours prior to checking your work back in. You have now completed a transaction against ProjectBank.

After your work is checked for consistency and validity against design rules, only the changes you made are returned to ProjectBank. This is change management.

Change management in ProjectBank is similar to version control used to manage software builds. Its purpose is to let you re-create an old state of a project at any time.

ProjectBank provides a mechanism to store engineering components and CAD files. It provides a mechanism to store the basic set of rules, called a schema, that define how engineering components behave in a model. It provides a mechanism to store a historical journal of changes to components during transactions and their reasons. It provides a mechanism to store for each component a list of dependent components thus permitting the enforcement of dependency rules.

ProjectBank was designed with component modeling in mind. Nevertheless, it has an important role to play for projects that are still file-based and use .dgn and .dwg format CAD files.

ProjectBank implements a mechanism to store and manage CAD drawings and to assign each entity in the drawing a project-wide unique component ID. To import MicroStation elements as components, ProjectBank uses the DGN Schema, and to import AutoCAD elements as components it uses the DWG Schema.

The key benefit to using ProjectBank for managing .dgn and .dwg projects is its ability to easily permit the editing of different parts of the same drawing by two users and to help synchronize and resolve conflicts when two users edit the same component in a file. Another benefit is ProjectBank's ability to manage the who, what, and why of changes to drawings at the element, not the file, level.

The fact that both DGN and DWG file types can harmoniously reside in the ProjectBank reflects the reality of current project workflows where both MicroStation and AutoCAD are used for drawing production. However, the fact that both file types can reside in the ProjectBank does nothing to change the fact that both formats are different and will need to be mapped when translated from one format to another.

ECM Applications

In line with the ongoing development efforts at Bentley, you can expect to see ECM applications emerge from them and from its third-party software developers. These applications will exploit the JMDL architecture of MicroStation/J and the server-based ProjectBank transaction manager to fulfill the promise of modeling enterprise-scale projects in a way that serves assets throughout their life cycle, including their operation and maintenance phases, not just the design phase.

As of this writing, there is word of three upcoming JMDL-based applications from Bentley. These are expected to work in conjunction with ProjectBank and add value to current CAD workflows. The applications are listed below.

- **DWG Schema:** This schema will allow ProjectBank to support `.dwg` drawings for projects where both MicroStation and AutoCAD are used to create drawings.
- **Expressions:** This application will permit the representation of engineering components in a variety of ways: as drawings or as tabular data. It will help *express* engineering components in different ways.
- **Custom Objects:** Think of these as intelligent cells. Just as custom geometric symbols can be transformed into cells for reuse without programming, engineering components will be transformed into custom objects without programming. Of course, custom objects are necessarily simpler in scope than engineering components that can be developed through JMDL programming.

What type of engineering component modeling (ECM) systems will you be using in the future? They will initially be JMDL versions of what are now design applications. Over time they will evolve into life cycle systems that will interact with data outside CAD systems and will be useful over the life of an asset.

Because schematic applications for network diagramming, process and instrumentation diagrams, and the like are programmatically well defined, these applications are likely to initially mature as ECM applications.

After that, the sky is the limit! I am convinced that an electronic simulation object model is such a logical progression for CAD that a few years from now we will wonder what took us so long to get to it.

Part 1

Using MicroStation
How To Create CAD Drawings

Chapter 1

Getting to Know MicroStation

How to Get Started

Did you read the *Introduction*?

Though most of this book is designed so you could start reading it from any chapter, the *Introduction* is special. If you're new to MicroStation, you will appreciate its historical perspective. If you're an experienced MicroStation user, you will benefit from the discussion on engineering component modeling and its role in the evolution of MicroStation/J. Though you may continue to use MicroStation as a traditional Computer Aided Design (CAD) system with the current release of the software, at some point you'll want to take advantage of the enterprise-wide data connectivity and continuity MicroStation/J promises. With this release of MicroStation, Bentley lays the groundwork for its vision of making MicroStation an enterprise engineering solution. You will not learn about these concepts in this chapter. Guess what? For a discussion of these concepts, you will need to read the *Introduction*!

MicroStation is one of the best general purpose professional CAD software available today that runs on more than a dozen operating system platforms. MicroStation is the standard at many government agencies and at large engineering design firms around the United States and the world. It's also used by small engineering consulting companies. Over eighty percent of the State Departments of Transportation (DOTs) in the United States have standardized on MicroStation as their CAD software of choice. If you provide engineering consulting services to State DOTs you are likely required to make electronic drawing deliverables in the MicroStation DGN file format.

Over the years Bentley has progressively added useful and timesaving features to its flagship software. This software release is no exception. Parasolid the solid modeling engine is new; so is the Java development environment. If you are acquiring a new copy of MicroStation/J, you get to pick an add-on of your choice: Modeler for feature-based mechanical modeling, TriForma for building and plant design, CivilPAK for civil site design work, or GeoGraphics for Geographic Information System (GIS) projects. These features are covered later in the book.

This chapter introduces you to MicroStation. As you read it, you will become familiar with the following topics:

- Installation and Directory Structure
- Starting MicroStation
- Understanding the Interface
- Interacting with MicroStation
- Getting Help
- File Operations

If you are new to MicroStation, this chapter will help you get familiar with all the basics. If you have been using earlier versions of the software, you may skip this chapter, with the exception of two topics: directory structure and command line options. The directory structure for MicroStation/J departs from previous versions, particularly the workspace module directory. The command line options aren't new, but you may find their tabular presentation a helpful reference if you ever create shortcuts to invoke MicroStation in different ways.

Installation and Directory Structure

If you work at a larger firm or government agency, MicroStation is probably already installed for you. In this case you need not worry about setting up the software or the license registration process you would otherwise need to complete. If you are installing a copy by yourself, the following paragraphs give you an overview of the installation process.

Installing MicroStation

MicroStation includes a Setup program that installs the software in a directory of your choice. It also offers multiple installation choices. The Typical option is the default. This option installs the most common components from all MicroStation modules, except MDE Programming (MDL and JMDL). For most situations this is perfectly acceptable, even desirable, as the development tools take up room on the hard drive. Why install them if you won't tackle them? If you plan to develop applications in MDL and JMDL, you will need to either click the Complete installation option, or enable the checkbox next to the MDE Programming tools option.

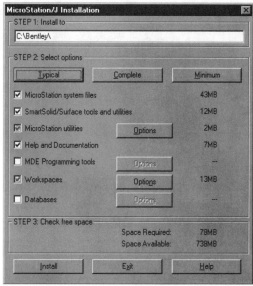

If you intend to develop MDL and JMDL applications, you need to select the checkbox next to the MDE Programming tools option.

Feel free to select the Typical installation option if you are not sure whether you will get involved with application development. You can always add components you do not initially install by running the Setup program again. To add components on an existing MicroStation install, simply run Setup and make selections using the checkboxes next to components. To see additional installation options, click the appropriate Options button next to the module. Each of the four dialog boxes invoked when you click the Options button is shown in the composite image below.

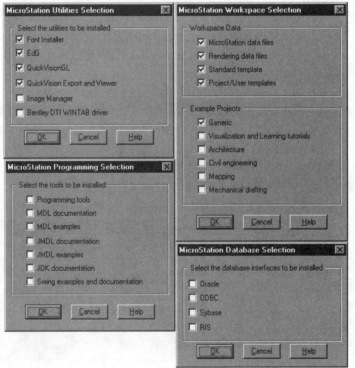

This is a composite image of all installation options offered by MicroStation.

Upon installation, the Setup program will create a MicroStation_J program group in your Windows environment. This program group contains several icons for applications and help files, including an icon to invoke MicroStation. This program group and all its icons are accessible from the Start button.

If you find navigating the Start button to invoke MicroStation a bit tedious, you can create a desktop shortcut for the software. The process of creating a shortcut is explained in the next section, along with a list of command line options supported by MicroStation.

NOTE: Bentley SELECT, an annual support subscription, permits network license pooling, and offers a home-use license for every registered copy.

Once the software is installed, you must register it with Bentley to obtain a license number. This license number is unique to a combination of user name, company name, and product serial number. Should you need to reinstall the software after a hard disk upgrade or other reason, you will need to use *exactly the same user name, company name, and serial number information* to be able to use the license number originally generated for you.

NOTE: The user name, company name and serial number information you use during registration is case sensitive.

On starting the software for the first time, you are presented with the Registration Information dialog box. Here you key in the information requested and click the Continue button. MicroStation uses the information you entered to create a registration number for you in the License Information dialog box that pops up. You then either e-mail, fax, or phone this information to Bentley, including the generated registration number to obtain your license number.

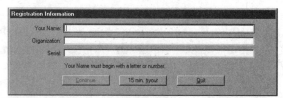

The Registration Information dialog box generates an interim registration number that Bentley uses to create a unique license number for you.

TIP: If you mistyped any of the registration information and have already generated a registration number, do not yet send it in to Bentley for processing. Delete the file **msj.lic** from the **c:\Bentley\Program\Licensing** folder and start MicroStation again to get another chance at creating new registration information.

On keying in the license number that Bentley supplies you in the License Information dialog box, the Register button will become available. Clicking the Register button completes the basic MicroStation setup procedure. If you wish to implement a customized MicroStation environment, you will need to invest effort in setting up custom workspaces. This topic is covered later in chapter 17.

For purposes of this book, I will assume you chose a typical installation with default options. Most chapters and exercises make this assumption. When concepts and exercises are introduced that deviate from this assumption, I will clearly state so at that time. This is particularly true of the chapter on workspaces and for chapters that deal with MDL and JMDL programming.

Directory Structure Used by MicroStation

The set of folders MicroStation uses for its components and utilities has changed significantly from previous versions. This change was made for two reasons. First, Bentley is no longer the single-product vendor it used to be. Second, the workspace module directory hierarchy of old did not clearly set down rules for the separation of Bentley-supplied workspace components, company-wide drawing standards, and project-specific standards.

The new directory structure introduced in MicroStation/J branches from a folder called Bentley. I expect this base folder to serve as the common repository for all Bentley products in the future. You may recall that Bentley was the default base folder name in the MicroStation/J Installation dialog box. The Setup program creates several other subdirectories under this folder. MicroStation system files get installed in the directory:

`c:\Bentley\Program\MicroStation`

The non-graphical DGN file editing utility called EdG (this utility is covered later in chapter 15) is in the folder:

`c:\Bentley\Program\Edg`

The workspace modules that are used to implement drawing standards and other configurations are stored in the folder:

`c:\Bentley\Workspace`

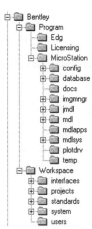

The directory hierarchy for MicroStation.

The most significant of the folders shown in the above screenshot are listed in the table below. Each folder name has an associated description regarding its content and purpose.

Folder Name	Description
/Bentley/Program/Edg	Non-graphical DGN File Editor
/Bentley/Program/Licensing	License files
/Bentley/Program/MicroStation/config	Add-on application (MasterPiece, Image Manager, QuickVisionGL), database, and MicroStation system configuration files
/Bentley/Program/MicroStation/database	Database catalog and example files
/Bentley/Program/MicroStation/docs	Help files and online books
/Bentley/Program/MicroStation/imgmngr	Image Manager application files
/Bentley/Program/MicroStation/jmdl	JMDL environment and development platform
/Bentley/Program/MicroStation/mdl	MDL development environment
/Bentley/Program/MicroStation/mdlapps	MDL applications folder
/Bentley/Program/MicroStation/mdlsys	MDL system files
/Bentley/Program/MicroStation/plotdrv	Printer and plotter driver files

Folder Name	Description
/Bentley/Program/MicroStation/temp	Folder for scratch files
/Bentley/Workspace/interfaces	Function key menu and user interface modification files
/Bentley/Workspace/projects	Project configuration files and examples
/Bentley/Workspace/standards	Site configuration files
/Bentley/Workspace/system	System configuration files
/Bentley/Workspace/users	User configuration files

As an end user whose focus is on using default MicroStation settings to get the job done as quickly as possible, you never have to deal with the above directory structure. MicroStation is preconfigured to call default components when needed. However, if you are a power user or the designated CAD administrator at your office, an understanding of the above directory structure, along with a knowledge of how MicroStation can be configured, is necessary to make the software use your own custom components.

Starting MicroStation

MicroStation runs on many different operating system platforms, including Microsoft Windows. The Windows version of MicroStation is the most popular and the first one available from Bentley. Consequently, it is the version used for all screenshots in this book. Though differences exist among operating systems, they all offer similar graphical interfaces.

What you learn about starting MicroStation in the following sections applies specifically to Windows 95/98 and Windows NT. However, the information presented here is applicable, with minor modifications, to other graphical operating systems as well.

Selecting Shortcuts from the Start Button

During the MicroStation installation process, the Setup program creates the MicroStation_J cascading menu under the Programs menu on the Start button. To invoke MicroStation, click the Start button on the task bar and navigate to the Programs menu. This will open a submenu that will contain the MicroStation_J submenu. From this menu select the MicroStation icon to invoke the software.

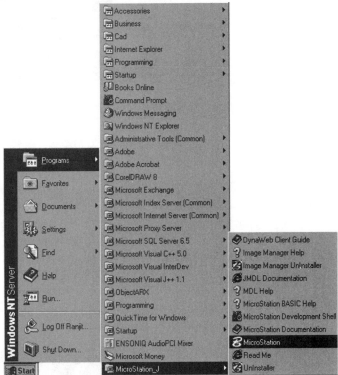

Select MicroStation from the MicroStation_J cascading menu on the Start button to invoke MicroStation.

Double-Clicking Icon in Folder

When you install MicroStation, the Setup program extracts relevant program and support files from the software delivery media to your computer's local or network disk storage space. The Setup program also creates the MicroStation_J program group with icons as shown below.

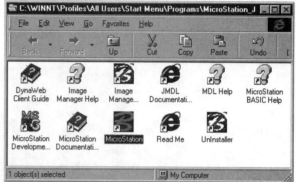

Double-click the MicroStation icon in the MicroStation_J
program folder to invoke the software.

The location of the MicroStation_J program group on your computer hard disk isn't quite obvious. On Windows NT it is located in the folder `C:\Winnt\Profiles\All Users\Start Menu\Programs\MicroStation_J`. I keep a shortcut to this folder on my Windows desktop to open it easily when needed.

To invoke MicroStation, open the MicroStation_J program group folder and double-click its icon. Or, you may highlight the MicroStation icon in this folder and press the Enter key.

NOTE: MicroStation/J for Windows is a 32-bit application that uses the same executables for Windows 95/98 and Windows NT on Intel processors. The software will not run on Windows 3.11.

Another way to start MicroStation is through the Windows Explorer file navigation utility. Navigate your local or network disk storage media where MicroStation is installed and locate the MicroStation executable file `ustation.exe`. For a default installation, the file is located in the folder `c:\Bentley\Program\MicroStation`. You can double-click this file to start MicroStation.

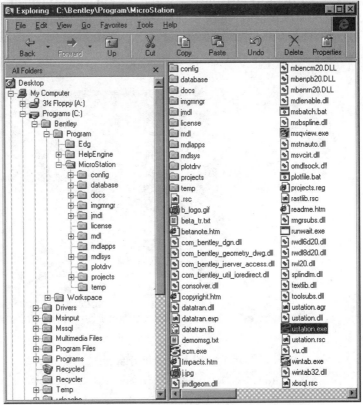

Double-click the ustation.exe file in the
MicroStation folder to invoke the software.

You can also invoke MicroStation by double-clicking any design file with the filename extension of `.dgn`. This works because during installation MicroStation registers the `.dgn` filename extension as associated with it.

NOTE: You can verify that the .dgn filename extension is registered to MicroStation by selecting Folder Options from the View menu in Windows Explorer. When the Folder Options dialog box opens, click the File Types tab to find the MicroStation Design File entry in the Registered File Types list box.

From Desktop Icon

The most convenient way to invoke MicroStation is by creating an icon for it on your Windows desktop. You create such an icon by clicking the right mouse button while the cursor is on an empty area of the desktop. This opens a context-sensitive menu window. From this menu window, select Shortcut from the New menu option. This will open the Create Shortcut dialog box.

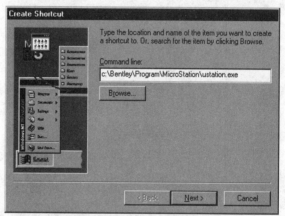

Use the Create Shortcut dialog box to create a MicroStation icon on the desktop.

In the Command Line field type
`c:\Bentley\MicroStation\ustation.exe` and click the Next button to open the Select a Title for the Program dialog box. On this dialog box key in MicroStation as a name for the shortcut, and click the Finish button. This will leave a shortcut icon on your desktop that you can double-click to invoke MicroStation.

The shortcut you create by following the above steps starts MicroStation with default settings. To invoke MicroStation differently for different projects, you can create several shortcuts. Each shortcut would use appropriate command line switches.

For example, if you need to work on two projects and each project has a separate project workspace, the command line to invoke MicroStation with ProjectA workspace active would be:

`c:\Bentley\MicroStation\ustation -wpProjectA`

And for invoking MicroStation with ProjectB workspace active it would be:

```
c:\Bentley\MicroStation\ustation -wpProjectB
```

MicroStation supports many other command line switches. These are discussed in the next section.

NOTE: For Windows 95 or Windows NT with Internet Explorer 4.0 installed, or for Windows 98, the task bar along the bottom edge of the screen offers a program icon area to the right of the Start button where you can drag shortcuts so they do not get obscured by open applications.

Command Line Switches

Yet another way to start MicroStation is from the command prompt, also know as the shell prompt or console window on UNIX systems. Select Command Prompt from the Programs menu on the Windows Start button. Then, switch to the MicroStation folder on your computer's local or network disk storage space and key in `ustation`. Of course, if you have the MicroStation folder on your system's path variable, you need not switch to the MicroStation folder when keying in the command.

When invoking MicroStation from the command prompt, or specifying the command line to be used by a shortcut, you must use the following syntax:

```
ustation <switch 1> ... <switch n> <design file name>
```

The angle bracket above indicates that the command line switches are optional and so is the name of a design file. You may combine several switches on the same command line. The following table lists command line switches MicroStation makes available.

Switch	Description
-Aappname	Starts the MicroCSL application specified as `appname`
-Ccache	Specifies the `cache` limit in KB for MicroStation to use
-DEBUG	Dumps configuration variables to `msdebug.txt` and exits

Switch	Description
-DISPLAYdisplayname	Directs output to the X Windows display device indicated by `displayname` (UNIX with X Windows only)
-Iparameters	Passes through `parameters` to INITAPPS
-MICROCSLappname	Starts the offline MicroCSL application specified as `appname` (DOS Protected Mode Only)
-O	Does not open any reference files
-Q	Enables the ! command in MicroStation for creating a shell window (UNIX Only)
-R	Starts MicroStation in read-only mode
-Sscriptfile	Runs the script file specified as `scriptfile` after loading a design file
-Uundobuffersize	Specifies the undo buffer size in bytes
-WAappname	Starts the MDL application specified as `appname` during MicroStation initialization as a replacement for the MicroStation Manager dialog box
-WCsystem	Specifies the `system` configuration file to load first
-WDdatabase	Specifies the `database` configuration to use
-WIinterface	Specifies the user `interface` modification files to load at startup
-WPproject	Specifies the `project` configuration file to load at startup
-WUuser	Specifies the `user` configuration file to load at startup

The following examples illustrate the use of some of these switches. To invoke MicroStation with the autocad interface that lists AutoCAD terminology next to MicroStation menu items, key in:

ustation -WIautocad

To invoke MicroStation with the tutorials user workspace, the visualization project workspace, and the desklite drawing in read-only mode, key in:

ustation -WUtutorials -WPvisualization -R desklite

MicroStation Manager as Gateway to Design Files

The first window you see when you start MicroStation without specifying a design file name on the command line is the MicroStation Manager dialog box. It's your gateway to the world of design files. From this dialog box you can create new design files, navigate your computer's local or network disk storage space to pick the desired design file, compress files, merge files, manage files or directories, or select the desired workspace components.

The MicroStation Manager dialog box lets you manage design files and select workspace components.

To open a design file, locate it in the MicroStation Manager dialog box and click the OK button. You may also double-click the design file to open it.

The File menu on the MicroStation Manager dialog box lists the most recently used files for easy selection. It lets you copy, rename, delete or display information about design files. It also lets you merge several design files into a single file, or to compress design files. The word *compress* as used by MicroStation is very similar to the term *purge* used by database software. When you compress a design file, you purge the drawing elements that had been marked for deletion but were still in the file to enable you to undelete them. Of course, if you compress a design file, you can no longer undo elements you may have deleted during your drawing session.

The Directory menu lists the most recently accessed directories for easy selection. It also lets you create new directories, copy directories, or compress all design files in a directory.

In addition to the file, directory, and drive navigation controls on the MicroStation Manager dialog box, there is an option button titled List Files of Type. Click it to see the various types of files MicroStation supports. The design, sheet and hidden line file types have their own unique filename extensions. Sheet files are created by the Drawing Composition utility in MicroStation. Hidden line files are created when rendering three-dimensional models to remove hidden lines. MicroStation can also open AutoCAD DWG, DXF, and DXB drawing files. When you open an AutoCAD drawing in MicroStation, the file is translated on the fly to a native MicroStation file. MicroStation can also open CGM (Computer Graphics Metafile) file types and MicroStation PowerScope Redline RDL files. MicroStation PowerScope is a design file review package from Bentley.

MicroStation can open a variety of file types.

The MicroStation Manager dialog box lets you select workspace components, such as user workspace, project workspace, user interface, and status bar style, whether Windows style or Command Window style that was used in Versions 4 and 5 of MicroStation. Don't worry if you don't yet understand what workspaces are. Chapter 17 is devoted to this topic.

Understanding the Interface

On selecting a file in MicroStation Manager, and clicking the OK button, you enter the MicroStation graphics environment. You will spend most of your time here creating drawings. As you saw in the *Introduction*, what you draw in MicroStation is limited only by your imagination.

MicroStation offers the tools you need to make your job easier. You can create bid drawings for a contractor to build bridges, roads, buildings, or cars. You can also create photo-realistic images for presentations and visualization, or develop maps for geographic information systems.

The more familiar you become with the software, the better will you be able to use it to serve your needs. This section introduces you to the most visible of all software components—its interface. You will learn how the MicroStation interface is organized. These and other questions will be answered:

- Where can I find drawing commands?
- Where do I key in element coordinate data?
- How many view windows does MicroStation support?
- What function do the buttons on a mouse perform?
- What do the different cursor shapes mean?
- Which part of the MicroStation screen gives me directions during command operation?
- How do I learn each tools function?
- How do I create new design files?
- How do I exit MicroStation?

After reading this section you will understand the name and purpose of MicroStation's interface components. It is important you understand these terms; the rest of the book assumes you know them.

The figure below identifies each of the interface components such as menu bar, status bar, toolboxes, Key-in window, Tool Settings window, and others explained in this section.

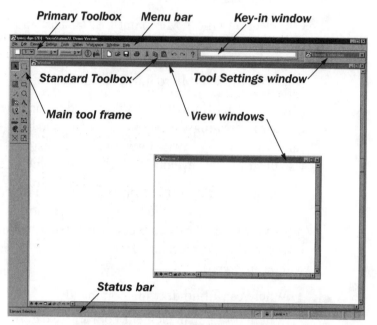

The MicroStation interface components.

The MicroStation application window shown above is highly configurable. If your computer screen does not quite look the same as that shown, your preferences and settings are different from those I used while taking these screenshots. I have used default MicroStation settings except for the activation of the Key-in window.

Title Bar and Menu Bar

Along the top of the MicroStation application window is the title bar. It displays the name of the design file that is currently open along with its dimensional status (2D or 3D) in parentheses, followed by the name of the software, MicroStation/J. To the left of the title bar is the Bentley logo that opens the application control menu when clicked. To the right of the title bar are three icons: Minimize, Maximize/Restore, and Close. These icons have the same function as they do in any other Windows application.

Directly below the title bar is the menu bar. The menu bar provides access to a variety of commands, settings, and dialog boxes through an easy pull-down menu system. To display a menu, choose one of the menu options or press the underlined letter in conjunction with the Alt key on the keyboard. To display the Element menu, either click it on the menu bar or press Alt+L on the keyboard. The figure below shows the Element pull-down menu.

Choose Element on the menu bar, or press Alt+L to open the Element menu.

NOTE: The MicroStation menu bar is customizable through the Customize dialog box that is invoked from the Workspace menu. This topic is covered later in *Part 3* of the book.

Several example workspace interfaces come standard with MicroStation. I invite you to take a look at the MicroStation Manager dialog box that lets you select workspace components before entering the MicroStation graphics environment. The following figure shows the sample interfaces delivered with MicroStation. Each uses a custom menu bar. The *newuser* interface provides fewer menu choices than does the default interface.

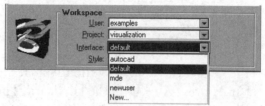

*Several workspace interface components
delivered with MicroStation use custom menus.*

Status Bar and Command Window

Along the bottom of the MicroStation application window is the status bar. It displays the active command name, command prompts, error messages, snap and lock settings, active level, number of drawing entities selected, the save status of a file, and other helpful messages. MicroStation uses the status bar to communicate with you. Always keep an eye on the status bar and the Tool Settings window, discussed later, to see what MicroStation is expecting by way of feedback from you.

A vertical line splits the status bar into two areas. The left side is used to display three types of messages: the name of the active command, a prompt requesting input or an action from you, and error messages. The active command name and prompt messages are displayed together and are separated by the > symbol. Error messages appear when necessary and overwrite the command name and prompt field. The right side of the status bar has six fields. When listed in order from left to right, these are: *active snap mode*, *lock icon*, *active level*, *selected element status*, *fence status*, and *file save status*. MicroStation will occasionally overwrite the fields on the right of the status bar with information or status messages.

In addition to displaying messages, the status bar has hot spots you can click to open menus or dialog boxes. Clicking the active snap mode icon on the status bar opens the Snaps menu. Clicking the lock icon opens the Locks menu. Clicking the active level field displays the Set Active Level dialog box. Clicking the element selection field of the status bar opens the Selection menu.

NOTE: If you select Command Window under the Style field in the MicroStation Manager dialog box, the status bar is replaced with a floating Command Window.

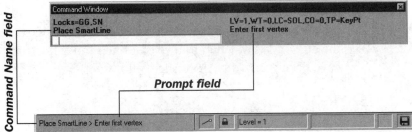

This figure identifies two status bar fields and associates them with corresponding Command Window fields.

The last field on the right of the status bar displays a disk icon when the active design file has changed. If you open a design file in read-only mode, the disk icon appears in red with an X through it.

Tool Frames and Toolboxes

While the menu bar provides access to file operations, settings, and attributes, it's the palettes containing icons that provide access to all the drawing, editing and element manipulation commands. MicroStation offers two types of icon palettes called *tool frames* and *toolboxes*.

Toolboxes are resizable windows that contain icon commands. You can dock toolboxes along any edge of the MicroStation application window, or you can have them float on your screen. When you resize a toolbox by dragging its edge with the mouse, it may take on a different shape, but it will always maintain a minimum size so that all icons are visible.

A tool frame, on the other hand, is not resizable and it can contain either icon commands or toolboxes. You can dock tool frames along any edge of the MicroStation application window, or you can place them as floating windows anywhere on your screen.

When you drag the edge of a tool frame, rather than resize it, as is the case with toolboxes, the action lets you move the tool frame to another location on your screen. Tool frames display icons as do toolboxes. However, there is a subtle difference. If the lower right corner of an icon displays a tiny right-headed arrowhead, it means the icon represents a toolbox you can tear away from the tool frame.

To tear away a toolbox from a tool frame, click and hold down the mouse button on its icon until it opens. With the mouse still held down, drag the cursor away from the tool frame till a floating rectangle attaches to the cursor. Now, when you release the mouse button, the toolbox will have been torn away from the tool frame.

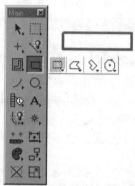

You can tear away toolboxes from tool frames by simply dragging them with your mouse.

Command icons when located in tool frames display one other difference when compared to what they look like when located in toolboxes. If the command icon implements options that display in the Tool Settings window, the tool frame icon displays a tiny down arrow on its lower right corner.

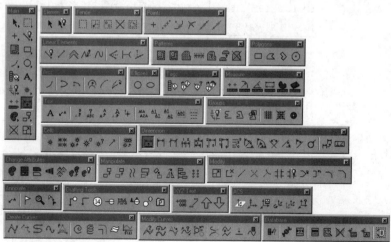

MicroStation implements several dozen toolboxes and tool frames.

To see a complete list of tool frames and toolboxes click the Tools menu. Or, browse the Tool Boxes dialog box by selecting Tool Boxes from the Tools menu.

For icons in tool frames and toolboxes, MicroStation implements tool tips and mouse-over help. When you pause the cursor on top of an icon, a small rectangle containing the name of the command appears. This rectangle is called a tool tip. Now move the cursor over icon commands and take a look at the status bar. As the mouse moves over an icon, the status bar displays a single line help about the command the icon implements. This help line in the status bar is called mouse-over help.

The rest of this section discusses three icon palettes: the Main tool frame, the Primary toolbox, and the Standard toolbox. You are likely to always have these three icon palettes open on your screen.

Main Tool Frame

The Main tool frame, by default, is docked along the left edge of the MicroStation application window. It contains eighteen icons displayed in two columns by nine rows. As you will notice, seventeen of the icons in the Main tool frame display an arrowhead in their lower right corners. These icons represent the seventeen toolboxes contained in the Main tool frame.

The Main tool frame contains seventeen toolboxes and one icon command.

The single most significant reason why MicroStation implements tool frames is that they save screen space. The Main tool frame contains over ten dozen icons in the space taken by only eighteen icons.

If you prefer not to have the Main tool frame docked along the left edge of the MicroStation application window, you can move it. To move the Main tool frame, click and hold the mouse button along any of its edges and move the cursor away till you see a bounding rectangle attached to it. Now when you leave the cursor, the tool frame will float there.

When the Main tool frame is floating, it gains a title bar along with a Close button to the right of its title bar. Clicking the Close button will close the tool frame. Should you accidentally close the tool frame, all is not lost. You can bring it back at will. Simply select Main, followed by Main from the Tools menu.

Primary Toolbox

The Primary toolbox is docked by default directly under the menu bar and to the left. It contains six controls in two groups. The first group consists of four controls: Active Color, Active Level, Active Line Style, and Active Line Weight. The second group consists of two icon commands: Analyze Element, and Start AccuDraw. The purpose of this toolbox is to keep you aware of the active element symbology and property settings (color, level, line style, line weight) and to help invoke the element information tool and AccuDraw. Don't worry if the concept of element symbology is new to you; it is covered in detail in chapter 3. Our focus in this chapter is to get familiar with MicroStation's interface.

NOTE: You can change the symbology of existing elements by first selecting the elements with the Element Selection tool and then changing the active symbology in the Primary toolbox.

The Element Information tool is invoked when you click the Analyze Element icon on the Primary toolbox. This tool displays more information than you may care to know about an element you identify. When you click the Analyze Element icon, the prompt on the status bar requests that you identify an element. On clicking an element, you are further prompted to either accept the highlighted element or reject it if you wish to pick another. A left mouse button click accepts the selection. A right mouse button rejects the selection. The process of highlighting an element and following up with an accept/reject step is prevalent throughout MicroStation. We will discuss this further in the *Interacting With MicroStation* section later in the chapter.

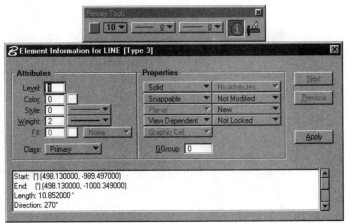

The Analyze Element icon on the Primary toolbox invokes the Element Information dialog box when you identify an element.

The title bar of the Element Information dialog box displays the type of element you have requested information on. This dialog box displays all attributes and properties of the element and its coordinate data. You can use this dialog box to change some of the information displayed. To edit an element, simply change the information displayed in any of the edit fields and click the Apply button.

AccuDraw is another useful data point entry tool. It is discussed in a separate section later in this chapter, and throughout the book.

Standard Toolbox

The Standard toolbox is docked by default directly under the menu bar and to the right of the Primary toolbox. It contains ten icon commands in five groups. The first group consists of three icon commands related to file operations: New File, Open File, Save Design. The second group consists of a single icon command: Print. The third group contains three icons for Windows clipboard related commands: Cut, Copy, and Paste. The fourth group contains two icons: Undo and Redo. The last group contains a single icon for invoking Help.

The Standard toolbox offers ten icon commands separated into five groups.

The purpose of the Standard toolbox is to provide access to the most common file, clipboard, and other operations. Some icons invoke commands that perform an action immediately, such as the Save Design, Undo and Redo icons. Other icons, such as New File and Open File, invoke dialog boxes with items you need to choose before the command will take effect.

Tool Settings Window

As its name implies, MicroStation's Tool Settings window displays the settings, or options, relevant to the active command or tool. This window is like a chameleon; it changes depending on the tool you select. When you click the Element Selection tool, its title bar reads *Element Selection*. When you activate the Place SmartLine command, its title bar reads *Place SmartLine*. Options available in this dialog box change depending on the tool selected.

The Tool Settings window is a floating dialog box that changes in size to accommodate the controls it needs to display. Depending where on the screen you place the dialog box, its edges move as it resizes itself. When it is placed in the upper right corner of the application window, its left and bottom edges move as it resizes. When it is placed in the lower left corner, its right and top edges move as you switch tools. I prefer keeping this window in the upper right corner of the screen.

The Tool Settings window when the Mirror tool is active.

MicroStation can display checkboxes, text fields, option buttons, the color picker, or any other type of control that may be needed to support the tool options it displays.

Because of the sheer quantity of toolboxes and icon commands available in MicroStation, you may not realize that Bentley has gone to considerable length to reduce the number of icons it needs to implement.

The most common technique used by MicroStation to reduce the number of icons is the Method option button to group related commands.

MicroStation uses the Method option button to consolidate several commands into one icon.

Consider the Place Circle command. Rather than implement three different icons for each of the circle placement methods it supports, MicroStation uses the Method option button in the Tool Settings window as shown in the figure above.

NOTE: Always keep an eye on the Tool Settings window to keep track of the options you have available for the active command.

View Windows

The largest area on the screen in the MicroStation application window is the drawing area called the *view window*. MicroStation supports the concurrent display of up to eight view windows. These windows use the names *Window 1* through *Window 8* in their title bars. You open or close view windows from the Open/Close submenu under the Window menu on the menu bar.

A view window is like a porthole to your entire drawing area, also known as the design plane or cube, which can be very large. You can control how much of your drawing area to display in a particular view window by using the view control commands. You can minimize, maximize, restore, or close view windows.

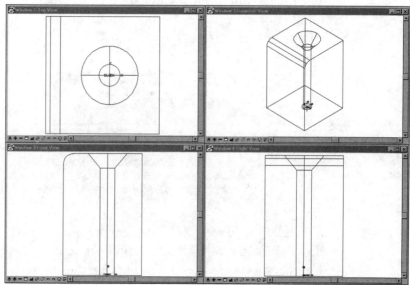

MicroStation supports multiple view windows.

Each view window is enclosed within a rectangular border. You can resize a view window by dragging the border with the mouse cursor. You can *drag*, that is, click on and move while holding the mouse button down, an edge of a view window to resize it horizontally or vertically. You can also drag its corner to resize the window in both horizontal and vertical dimensions simultaneously.

To move a floating view window to another location, drag it by its title bar. To the right of the title bar are the three standard window icons: Minimize, Restore/Maximize, and Close. Clicking the Minimize button shrinks the view window to its minimum size. Clicking the Restore button while a view window is maximized restores it to its former location and size. Clicking the Close button closes the view window.

The Bentley logo in the title bar of the view window provides access to several standard window control menu options, and to four MicroStation view-specific menu options shown in the table below.

Menu Name	Description
View Attributes	Invokes the View Attributes dialog box to control the display in the view window.

Menu Name	Description
Rendering View Attributes	Invokes the Rendering View Attributes to control the display of rendering related display attributes in a view window.
Level Display	Invokes the Level Manager dialog box to turn on or off the display of levels in a view window.
View Save/Recall	Invokes the Saved Views dialog box to manage saved views.

To the right and bottom of the view window are scroll bars to let you pan its contents horizontally or vertically. You can choose to turn off the scroll bars by invoking the Preferences dialog box from the Workspace menu and turning off the Scroll Bars on View Windows checkbox from the View Windows category.

To the left of the bottom scroll bar in each view window is a set of icons called the *view control bar*. With these icons you can control the display inside the view window. The nine icons that comprise the view control bar in 2D design files are, from left to right: Update View, Zoom In, Zoom Out, Window Area, Fit View, Rotate View, Pan View, View Previous, and View Next. We will discuss these commands in chapter 4.

Interacting with MicroStation

Now that you recognize most of the interface components in MicroStation, it is time to learn the different aspects of interacting with the software. I assume you are already familiar with your operating system and do not need to learn how to select menu items and interact with dialog boxes.

This section discusses MicroStation-specific user interaction. You learn about the function of the different mouse buttons because this aspect differs from most other Windows applications. You also learn about the different cursor shapes the mouse pointer can take on and what they mean. Additionally, you will learn the syntax for keying in coordinate data, and you will be briefly introduced to AccuDraw as a useful coordinate input tool.

Pointing Devices

It is worth noting that there are two types of cursors in any computer operating system graphical environment such as Windows, Macintosh, UNIX, or other. First, the keyboard cursor is used typically to capture input from the keyboard. Second, the mouse cursor is used to select menu items, click on icons, interact with dialog boxes, and move the keyboard cursor to the desired location in a document.

The term *pointing device* as a subsection heading here refers to the computer peripheral, known as a mouse, that moves what I called the mouse cursor in the paragraph above. There are two types of pointing devices MicroStation can use: the mouse and the digitizing tablet.

Mouse

A *mouse* is a relative pointing device that moves well on any flat solid surface. It's called a relative device because the position of the mouse cursor on the screen has a relative, as opposed to an absolute, correspondence with the position of the mouse on the tabletop. In other words, it is possible to move the mouse from point A to point B on the table without moving the mouse cursor on the screen.

In addition to the mouse cursor movement, MicroStation has a need for three actions from a pointing device: Data point, Reset, and Tentative point. Most mice (the computer peripheral, not the rodent!) available for personal computers and workstations have either two or three buttons. Thus each of the mouse button clicks is assigned a specific default action by MicroStation.

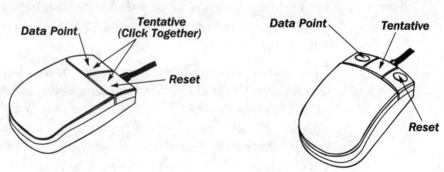

Default button assignments for a two- and a three-button mouse.

The default mouse button assignments shown in the figure above are customizable. You can change mouse button assignments in the Button Assignments dialog box that is invoked from the Workspace menu. Now you know the names of the actions MicroStation performs when you click a mouse button. What do the actions mean? The following table describes the three MicroStation mouse button actions.

Action	Description
Data point	Used to select menus and interact with dialog boxes. Also used to identify elements, accept elements, or click locations on the design plane in a view window.
Tentative point	Used to snap to key points on an element, or to temporarily locate a data point in a view window. You must click the data point button to accept a tentative point. You may also click the reset button to reject a tentative point.
Reset	Used to reject highlighted elements, or to restart or terminate the active command.

NOTE: The Apple Macintosh mouse has a single button that is assigned the data point action. You need to click it in conjunction with Command and Control keys to invoke the reset and tentative point actions.

Digitizing Tablet

A digitizing tablet is an absolute pointing device that consists of a puck in addition to the tablet. The puck is a mouse-like device with four to sixteen buttons that slides on a tablet. Digitizing tablets come in varying sizes, from 9 inch by 9 inch to E size (3 feet by 4 feet) and are suitable for tracing over paper drawings when converting them to vector CAD file format.

The digitizing tablet is an absolute pointing device because the position of the cursor on the screen has an absolute, as opposed to relative, correspondence with the position of the puck on the tablet. In other words, when the puck is placed on a specific point on the tablet, it corresponds to a specific coordinate in the design plane. You must configure and calibrate the tablet before starting digitization. The Digitizing option on the Workspace menu invokes the Digitizing dialog box to let you set up the tablet.

Though you can configure the tablet to become a relative pointing device, you may not want to do this as it defeats the purpose of what a tablet is designed for. Besides, if you use the tablet as a mouse, you end up with a very expensive mouse. The WinTab driver specification for the Microsoft Windows operating system allows for the coexistence of a mouse and a tablet on the same computer.

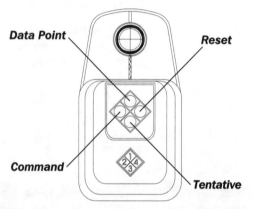

Default button functions for a four-button digitizing tablet puck.

The command button on a puck invokes a new action specific to digitizing tablets. This action is not available on a mouse. Its purpose is to invoke MicroStation commands from a menu attached to the tablet. If you wish to use a tablet menu, you must first partition the tablet into a digitizing area and a menu area, and then attach a tablet menu.

Cursor Shapes

MicroStation communicates with you in many ways. You learned about tool tips, mouse-over help, and the prompts it displays in the status bar. Here we look at the several cursor shapes MicroStation displays depending on the state it is in. Knowing what the shape of the mouse cursor indicates about the software can help you work better and avoid mistakes.

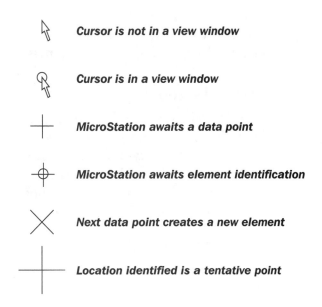

	Cursor is not in a view window
	Cursor is in a view window
	MicroStation awaits a data point
	MicroStation awaits element identification
	Next data point creates a new element
	Location identified is a tentative point

MicroStation's cursor shapes and their meanings.

Let me take a moment and describe how understanding the cursor shapes can help you avoid mistakes.

You wish to move a single element and invoke the Move command. As you get ready to identify the element you notice that the cursor shape indicates that MicroStation awaits a data point, not element identification. You had thought no element was selected and meant to move an element by identifying it. Your knowledge of the cursor shapes alerts you immediately that either a fence is active or elements are already selected—a situation you must address before you can click that data point. To fully appreciate this example, I suggest you come back to it later when you have had some experience with MicroStation.

Coordinate Input

The key difference between business graphics packages and CAD software is its emphasis on precision. In CAD you can snap to element key points, such as vertex, midpoint, or quadrant, and you can specify exact coordinates for data points in a variety of coordinate systems.

To snap to key points on existing elements click the tentative button to locate the key point, then accept it with a data point. To specify an exact coordinate input value for data points, you can either use a precision key in at the Key-in window, or you can use the AccuDraw tool.

Key-in Window

In order to key in coordinate data, you will need to open the MicroStation Key-in window if it is not already open. To open the Key-in window, select Key-in from the Utilities menu. The Key-in window can assume three sizes. In its most unobtrusive size, it offers a single text field when docked along the top or bottom edge of the MicroStation application window.

MicroStation supports six precision key ins, as shown in the table below.

Key-in	Description
XY=x,y	Absolute: Cartesian coordinates from the design plane origin.
DL=dx,dy	Delta: horizontal and vertical distances from the last data point entered.
DX=dx,dy	View Delta: distances aligned to the view axes from the last data point entered.
DI=dr,a	Distance: radial distance and angle from last data point entered in polar coordinates.
AX=x,y	ACS: similar to Absolute except that the origin is a user defined Auxiliary Coordinate System.
AD=dx,dy	ACS Delta: similar to Delta except that it is referenced to an Auxiliary Coordinate System.

Let me explain the use of the key-ins with the help of an example. To draw a line that is 4 units in the X direction and 5 units in the Y direction, invoke the Place Line command by keying in PLACE LINE in the Key-in window. At the enter first point prompt click the left mouse button, called the data point button, at any point in a view window and MicroStation will prompt you with enter end point while showing a line attached to the cursor. Now rather than clicking a point with the mouse, go to the Key-in window and key in DL=4,5 and press the Enter key. This will place the line you wanted in the design file. Now click the right mouse button—the Reset button—to restart the command.

When keying in coordinates, a knowledge of MicroStation's working units is helpful. MicroStation expresses its working units in `mu:su:pu` (master units, subunits, and positional units) format. See chapter 3 for details. Thus if your master and subunits are feet and inches MicroStation interprets the key ins 3:6 and 3.5 as the same distance—3 feet 6 inches or 3.5 feet. Just remember, when keying in coordinates you use the colon (`:`) symbol to separate working unit components.

AccuDraw

Think of AccuDraw as your coordinate data input helper. This utility is designed to simplify the creation of complex geometry by minimizing the placement of construction lines and the use of snaps. We will cover this tool in greater detail later.

To invoke AccuDraw, click the Start AccuDraw icon in the Primary toolbox. This opens the AccuDraw window that displays two key-in fields: X and Y. Make sure that the AccuDraw window has the input focus and press the letter P on the keyboard to open the Data Point Keyin window. You can tell whether or not AccuDraw has the input focus by looking at its title bar: If the title bar is dark in color, it has the focus, if it is gray in color, it does not have the focus. To switch the input focus to AccuDraw, if it is not active, click its title bar or press the Esc key on the keyboard.

The Data Point Keyin window has an option button to let you select any one of the precision data point key-in methods discussed earlier. It also has an input field to accept numbers separated by a comma. The advantage of using the Data Point Keyin window is that you do not have to key-in a coordinate data prefix such as `DL=`. As soon as you enter a number and press the Enter key, the Data Point Keyin window closes.

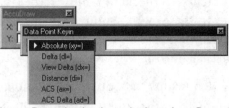

*Pressing the letter P on the keyboard when AccuDraw has the focus
invokes the Data Point Keyin window.*

To draw the same line we drew when discussing the Key-in window
coordinate input, invoke the Place Line command by keying in PLACE
LINE in the Key-in window. At the enter first point prompt click the left
mouse button, called the data point button, at any point in a view
window and MicroStation will prompt you with enter end point while
showing a line attached to the cursor. Now rather than clicking a point
with the mouse, switch focus to AccuDraw and press the letter P to open
the Data Point Keyin window. From this window select the choice Delta
(dl=) from the option button and key in 4,5 in the text field and press
the Enter key. This will place the line you wanted in the design file. Now
click the Reset button to restart the command.

To close the AccuDraw window, press the letter Q on the keyboard while
the AccuDraw window has the focus.

Getting Help

MicroStation implements a good help system that makes use of several
technologies and document formats. For online help while you are using
the software it uses the built-in Windows Help engine. Bentley is
expected to shortly include the DynaWeb SGML engine to publish pages
on-the-fly in an HTML browser such as Microsoft Internet Explorer or
Netscape Navigator.

For reference documentation on aspects of MicroStation you do not need to use frequently, such as programming in the User Command language, it provides documents in Adobe's PDF format that requires the use of the free Adobe Acrobat Reader provided on the MicroStation delivery CD-ROM media, or available on the Internet at the URL:

`http://www.adobe.com`

Even if you are an experienced MicroStation user who knows its many features and capabilities, you are probably unfamiliar with some aspects you seldom use. As an example, you might be an accomplished designer of two-dimensional design files, but may have rarely explored its three-dimensional features. When you are treading new ground, knowing where and how to get help can mean the difference between a quick online lookup while still drawing on the computer, or having to close your drawing session to go look for the information in the printed manuals.

Help Files and Documents

MicroStation online help files that use the Windows Help engine are located in the `c:\Bentley\Program\MicroStation\Docs` folder for a default installation. These files have the HLP filename extension and include help on the following topics.

- MicroStation BASIC macro programming language (`basichlp.hlp`)
- EdG, the non-graphical design file editor (`edg.hlp`)
- Image Manager (`imgmngr.hlp`)
- MDL programming language (`mdehelp.hlp`)
- Basics of MicroStation (`ustnhelp.hlp`)

You can invoke these help files from the MicroStation_J menu on the Start button in Windows. Or, you can double-click the appropriate help filename after locating it in the Windows Explorer file navigation utility.

If you are new to MicroStation, or are exploring a new area of MicroStation, you will find it helpful to enable help tracking. To do this select Tracking on the Help menu. With tracking enabled, when you invoke any MicroStation command by selecting it from the Main tool frame or other toolbox, MicroStation opens Windows Help with information about the command ready for you to read and apply.

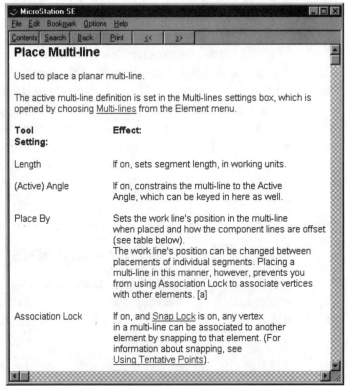

With Tracking enabled on the Help menu, MicroStation displays help about commands as you invoke them.

In addition to the files in Windows Help format, MicroStation provides a complete set of manuals in Adobe PDF file format on your MicroStation CD-ROM delivery media. All MicroStation manuals, even those that you would need to purchase separately in print version, are included in this format. When a section of Bentley manuals sends you to the Reference Guide and you do not have it, your best bet is to look it up in PDF format from the CD-ROM MicroStation was delivered with.

SGML Help Engine

MicroStation is expected to soon include the DynaWeb SGML help engine to publishes electronic online help within a Web browser. When available, selecting Contents from the Help menu will load the SGML help engine and invoke the Web browser installed on your computer. Bentley chose this technology in an effort to migrate its entire documentation to the SGML file format so as to be able to generate hardcopy manuals and online interactive hyper-linked help from the same source. SGML, an acronym for simple generic markup language, is a superset of HTML, an acronym for hyper text markup language, the language of the Web.

The SGML help engine will use frames to display online help in a Web browser. The left frame will display the online books available. The right frame will display the contents of the book or topic link selected in the left frame. The bottom frame will display help navigation and search icons and controls.

Key-in Browser

As you get more familiar with MicroStation you will have a need to discover the key-ins supported by the software. The primary reason for this is likely to be your desire to customize function keys, or to create custom menus and macros. To help you browse through all the key-ins active in your design environment, MicroStation provides the Key-in Browser option on the Help menu.

When you select Key-in Browser from the Help menu, the Key-in window opens to its maximum size. You may recall that I mentioned earlier that the Key-in window can take on three different sizes. When the Key-in window is docked, it is in its smallest size and displays only the key in field. If you drag this window from its docked position, it gains a title bar but still retains its single key-in field size. When you drag its lower edge downward, the Key-in window grows in size to display four scrollable lists and two buttons. This is where you browse MicroStation's key-ins. When you drag the lower edge downward even further, the Key-in window grows to its maximum size and adds a scrollable key-in history field. To summarize, the top pane of this window is the key-in field, the middle is the command table browser, and the lower pane is the history field.

You use the Key in button on the Key-in window to invoke the command that is displayed in the key-in field. You can build commands in the key-in field by directly typing them, by selecting them from the command table browser section of the window, or by selecting them from the history field.

The MicroStation command table is hierarchical. When building command tables for their applications, MDL developers take care that their tables are no deeper than four levels. This is the reason you have four fields in the command table browser section of the Key-in window.

Exercise: Using the Key-in Browser

This exercise helps you discover how the command table browser works. Follow along with me on your computer with the following steps.

1. If the Key-in window is not already open to its maximum size on your screen, select Key-in Browser from the Help menu. This will open the Key-in window to its maximum size.

2. From the command table browser section in the middle of the window, select the word **accudraw** that appears in the top of the first vertical scrollable list. When you click the first level of a command table in the first scrollable list, its second level displays in the adjoining scrollable list, and so on. As you can see, the first word of the command **accudraw** offers several second-word options starting from **activate** through **shortcuts**.

3. Click the word **activate** in the second field and notice that it has no further options that display in the adjoining field to the right. Also notice that your selections have been entered in the key-in field as well.

4. Click the Key in button and notice that the AccuDraw window opens as a result of this action.

Through this exercise you have learned that the key-in to activate the AccuDraw window is `accudraw activate`. Thus, when you click the Start AccuDraw icon in the Primary toolbox, it actually sends the `accudraw activate` key-in to MicroStation to process.

Let me emphasize that the Key-in window lets you browse all key-ins active in your design environment, not just those implemented in the core of MicroStation. Thus, there is another use for the Key-in Browser. Not only can you discover MicroStation's key-ins by using it, you can also discover key-ins for any add-on application that you load within MicroStation. You use the Tables button for this. The following figure shows the Key-in Tables dialog box that opens when you click the Tables button.

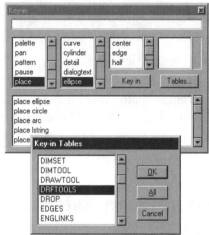

The Key-in Tables dialog box lets you display only the key-ins supported by a MicroStation component or another loaded application.

Because this is an introductory chapter, I will not go into the process of loading, using, and discovering the key-ins for add-on applications. An example of how to do this is provided in chapter 25.

File Operations

Like database software, MicroStation is file-based. It saves your drawing and editing actions to the design file as soon as you perform them. Thus, you can safely exit MicroStation at any time without first having to use the Save command. All the work you do in your drawing session is automatically saved.

 NOTE: The default save-as-you-go operation of MicroStation can be over-ridden in the Preferences dialog box invoked from the Workspace menu. Look for checkboxes in the Operation category in the Preferences dialog box.

On starting MicroStation, the MicroStation Manager dialog box opens to let you select a design file to open or to create a new design file. The Preferences dialog box allows you to over-ride this behavior as well. If you would rather have MicroStation come up directly into an unnamed drawing file, you can enable a checkbox in the Operation category in the Preferences dialog box.

Opening an Existing Design File

There are three ways in which you can open an existing design file in MicroStation. The first method is by using the MicroStation Manager dialog box to locate the desired file and clicking the OK button when MicroStation starts. And if a design file is already open in MicroStation, you can select Close from the File menu, or press the Ctrl+W keystroke combination, to close the active design file and display the MicroStation Manager dialog box.

The second method is to select Open from the File menu when you are already working on a design in MicroStation. This invokes the Open Design File dialog box to let you locate and identify the desired file and click the OK button to open it.

The third method is to use the short key-in IGDS users will recognize. In the Key-in window, key in `RD=filename`, where filename is the name of the design file you wish to open with the complete path specification and filename extension.

Creating a New Design File

The process you use to create new design files is very similar to that used when opening existing design files. You can use either the MicroStation Manager dialog box during startup, or select an option on the File menu when you are already in MicroStation.

To create a new design file, select New from the File menu in either the MicroStation Manager dialog box, or the MicroStation application menu. Either action invokes the Create Design File dialog box shown below.

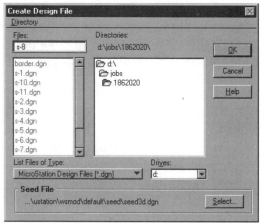

The Create Design File dialog box is invoked by selecting New from the File menu.

Simply type the name for the design file you need, navigate to the folder you want the file created in, and click the OK button. One thing I'd like to point out is the Seed File groupbox along the bottom of the dialog box. When creating new design files, MicroStation copies the contents of a seed file into the new file. Seed files are templates, either the standard ones you get with MicroStation, or custom ones you create yourself. You will learn more about seed files in a later chapter.

NOTE: If you need to exchange design files with users still running older versions of MicroStation on the DOS platform, you will want to continue to use the familiar **8.3** file naming convention.

Quitting MicroStation

To exit MicroStation when the MicroStation Manager dialog box is displayed, either click the Close button or press the Esc key. And if you are working on a design file in MicroStation, select Exit from the File menu. You can also key in EXIT or QUIT in the Key-in window.

NOTE: If you a veteran MicroStation or IGDS user and prefer the Ctrl+Z shortcut, you can enable its checkbox under the Operation category in the Preferences dialog box that is invoked from the Workspace menu.

This concludes our chapter. You learned about MicroStation installation options and its directory structure, how to start the software, its interface components, and how to interact with it. You also learned about the supported help engines and available online documentation, along with how to open and create new design files.

The rest of the book is designed to fill you in on the details of the software, its tools and operations, including customization. The next chapter walks you through a sample design session. This is followed by an introduction to the MicroStation CAD environment. There are exercises throughout the book, and I encourage you to work through them. This will help you reinforce what you read so it stays with you longer.

Chapter 2
Your First Drawing Session
Laying Out an Apartment Unit

This chapter's series of simple exercises make up a project similar to those you might actually do with MicroStation. The exercises are designed to make you feel comfortable with the tools you are likely to use most frequently. You've probably heard of the 80/20 rule, which states that 80 percent of most work can be accomplished by using 20 percent of the features found in any software. The purpose of this chapter is to provide you a guided tour of that 20 percent of the software.

Did I say guided tour? Yes, and I mean this in its strictest sense. You are guided through every tool selection and mouse button click operation in each of the exercises. I realize that none of the tools you'll be asked to use in this chapter has been formally introduced just yet, so you will need a helping hand. That's what this guided tour is all about. You will learn more about the tools in chapter 5.

You'll get the most out of this chapter by working through the exercises on your own computer. You will want to work through each exercise in sequential order from the beginning of the chapter to the end. Each exercise works on a different aspect of the project and requires you to use the file from the previous exercise. Instructions are provided on how to set up your design file and the MicroStation environment before you start work on the exercises.

Exercise files for this chapter are provided on the accompanying CD-ROM in the \Exercise\Ch02 folder. You have a choice when starting the exercises: Either use the exercise file supplied with this book, or re-create each exercise file on your own. The former approach lets you pick any exercise in the chapter and have a design file to work with. The latter approach makes you work through all exercises in sequence.

Your task in this chapter is to lay out an apartment unit. While completing this task, you will undertake several exercises that will introduce you to the following concepts:

- Creating a New Design File
- Setting Design File Parameters
- Creating, Manipulating, and Modifying Geometry
- Using Cells
- Printing a Design File

For those of you new to MicroStation and CAD in general, this chapter will serve as an introduction to the cycle of tasks you would go through when working on an actual project. I hope that by having you participate this early in the book in the use of tools that take a design concept from vision to hardcopy, the exercises will help you approach the rest of the book with a sense of excitement about what lies ahead.

If you are an experienced MicroStation user, this chapter offers a series of structured exercises you can use to teach basic concepts to clients or to others in your office. Though you may not pick up much that is new in this chapter, using it as a teaching aid will save you the effort of having to come up with carefully designed exercises.

Understanding the Project

In this chapter you work on a project most of us can easily relate to: the layout of an apartment floor plan. You will draw the walls, insert doors and windows, label the rooms, and assign dimensions to a few walls.

The apartment is a single bedroom unit with a bathroom, a kitchen, and a living room. The following figure shows the layout you will have created when you finish this chapter.

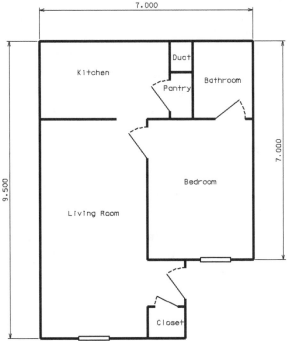

The apartment unit layout you will create in this chapter.

Much like you organize your computer hard disk in directories and subdirectories to facilitate data retrieval, a good MicroStation drawing organizes various graphic elements in levels. A *level* in MicroStation is the equivalent of an overlay sheet in traditional drafting.

Because we will be drawing walls, doors and windows, text, and dimensions, one way to organize this information might be to have a different level for each of these drawing components.

Let's take a moment to summarize the levels we will be using, along with element attributes like color, weight, and style for the elements we will be drawing.

Types of graphic elements	Level	Color	Weight	Style
walls: exterior and interior	1	white	4	0
doors and windows	2	yellow	1	0
labels	3	green	0	0
dimensions	4	red	0	0

Creating an architectural plan layout like the one shown in the figure above requires you to have room dimensions. Were you actually doing a similar project at an architectural firm, you would visit the site and take measurements to define the space completely. For purposes of this chapter, the dimensions are provided in the figure above and in the explanations accompanying each exercise.

NOTE: For a discussion on organizing drawing elements by levels, color, line thickness, and style, see chapter 14 on implementing CAD standards.

All exercises in this chapter are detailed in both metric and US English units. No matter what your preferred dimensional unit of measure, you will be able to work through the exercises in this chapter and throughout the book.

Creating a New Design File

The first step in creating a drawing in MicroStation is to create an empty new design file with the dimensional status (2D or 3D) desired. Because the electronic drawing you create in this chapter will emulate the two-dimensional paper-based drafting environment, you will use a 2D seed file to create this blank drawing.

The term *seed file* in MicroStation is similar to the term *template* in a word processor. You use a seed file as a template when creating a new design file. You can use seed files delivered with MicroStation, or you can create your own library of seed files.

For this chapter we'll use seed files delivered on the enclosed CD-ROM as listed in the table below.

Seed File Name	Description
2DseedM.dgn	Use for the metric version of the exercises.
2DseedE.dgn	Use for the US English version of the exercises.

For those of you who are familiar with MicroStation and who are curious about the settings used in the seed files, or wish to re-create the seed files because you have misplaced the accompanying CD-ROM, the following table summarizes them.

Setting	Metric Seed File	English Seed File
Coordinate Readout	Master Units; Accuracy 0.123	Sub Units; Accuracy 0
Text Size	150 mm	6 in
Working Units	1 m: 1000 mm: 100 pu	1 ft: 12 in: 2000 pu
Grid	250 mm; Grid Reference 4	6 in; Grid Reference 2

Exercise: Create New Drawing

The purpose of this exercise is to create a new design file called either **aptunite.dgn** or **aptunitm.dgn**. You will use the appropriate seed file, metric or English, for this purpose depending on the units you wish to work in.

The following steps guide you through this exercise.

1. Start MicroStation if it's not already running. See chapter 1 if you need help.

The MicroStation Manager dialog box helps you create new design files or open existing ones.

2. If you had previously opened a design file in MicroStation, the Files text field in the MicroStation Manager dialog box will contain that file name. Otherwise, it will be blank. MicroStation remembers the name of the design file last edited, assuming you might want to edit it again.

3. Select New from the File menu in the MicroStation Manager dialog box. The Create Design File dialog box opens.

The Select button in the Seed File groupbox lets you identify the seed file to use for the new file you create.

4. Click the Select button in the Seed File groupbox. The Select Seed File dialog box opens. Navigate to the drive and directory where you copied the exercise files from the accompanying CD-ROM. Identify the seed file `2dseede.dgn` if you intend to do the exercise in English units, or the file `2dseedm.dgn` if you intend to do the exercise in metric units, then click the OK button. The Select Seed File dialog box closes, and the name of the seed file you selected appears in the Seed File groupbox in the Create Design File dialog box.

Select either the metric or the English units seed file.

5. Key in the new design file name `aptunite` for English units, or `aptunitm` for metric units in the Files text field in the Create Design File dialog box and click the OK button.

6. The Create Design File dialog box closes as the new design file gets created. The design file you just created appears in the MicroStation Manager dialog box and is highlighted for you to begin editing.

Click OK after selecting the desired file to begin editing it.

7. You are ready to begin an editing session with the file you just created. With your new file highlighted in the MicroStation Manager dialog box, click the OK button to start your editing session.

NOTE: Another way to open the desired design file is to double-click its name in the Files list box.

Setting Design File Parameters

After you create a new design file, you need to make sure that its *settings*, also know as design file parameters, meet your needs. There are many settings in a design file. The ones that impact your work in this chapter have already been set in the seed files you used earlier.

Our goal here is to interact with the Design File Settings dialog box to get a sense of how they are organized and how you set them.

The settings you will examine include *coordinate readout* (these determine how dimensions are written), *element attributes* (these help set the default level, color, style and weight), *grid* (these help set the spacing for grid lines in the design file), and *working units* (these help set the desired unit of measure and accuracy).

NOTE: Design file settings are discussed in detail in chapter 3. The purpose of the exercise below is to make you aware of their presence and show how to change them.

In the following exercise we will also explore the Text dialog box where you set the size of text to draw.

Exercise: Design File Settings

If you created a new design file in the previous exercise, you will use that file for this exercise.

If you skipped the previous exercise and wish to do this one, copy the file `apt-01e.dgn` from the `\exercise\ch02` folder on the accompanying CD-ROM to your computer's hard drive and rename it `aptunite.dgn` for the English units version of this exercise. Similarly, for the metric units version, copy the file `apt-01m.dgn` and rename it `aptunitm.dgn`.

The following steps guide you through some of the more important design file settings relevant to this chapter's exercise files.

1. Start MicroStation if it's not already running. If you need help, see chapter 1.

2. Select the file `aptunite.dgn` (English units), or the file `aptunit1m.dgn` (metric units) in the MicroStation Manager dialog box and click the OK button to open that file.

3. Invoke the Design File Settings dialog box by selecting Design File from the Settings menu in MicroStation.

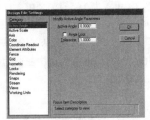

The Design File Settings dialog box.

This dialog box is divided into two panes. The left pane lists the setting categories available. The right pane displays the options for the selected category.

Coordinate Readout

4. Select the Coordinate Readout category in the left pane of the Design File Settings dialog box. The right pane of the dialog box will display two groupboxes. One is titled Coordinates and the other Angles.

The set of options in the Coordinates groupbox determine how distances and coordinates display in the status bar, in dimension elements, and in dialog boxes. The set of options in the Angles groupbox determines how angular measurements are displayed.

The following table lists the settings your new drawing took from the exercise seed file. Both the English and the metric settings are shown.

Option Name	Value (English units)	Value (metric units)
Coordinates Format	Sub Units	Master Units
Coordinates Accuracy	0	0.123
Angles Format	DD.DDDD	DD.DDDD
Angles Mode	Conventional	Conventional
Angles Accuracy	0.1	0.1

5. Make sure your design file has the settings shown above. If not, change the values accordingly.

Element Attributes

6. Select the Element Attributes category in the left pane of the Design File Settings dialog box. The right pane of the dialog box will display the available options. These options specify the default attributes, also referred to as symbology, elements are to be drawn with.

   The following table lists the settings your new drawing took from the exercise seed file.

Option Name	Value
Level	1
Color	0
Style	0
Weight	4
Class	Primary

7. Make sure your design file has the settings shown above. If not, change the values accordingly.

Grid

8. Select the Grid category in the left pane of the Design File Settings dialog box. The right pane displays the available options.

   A *grid* refers to a set of evenly spaced dots like those found on engineering grid paper designed to visually aid the creation of orthographic or isometric drawings. These options let you set the spacing of grid lines and the MicroStation environment such that the cursor is restricted to move only along grid points.

   The following table lists the settings your new drawing took from the exercise seed file.

Option Name	Value (English units)	Value (metric units)
Grid Lock	Enabled	Enabled
Grid Master	0:6	0.250

Option Name	Value (English units)	Value (metric units)
Grid Reference	2	4
Grid Config	Ortho	Ortho
Grid Aspect	1	1

9. Make sure your design file has the settings shown above. If not, change the values accordingly.

NOTE: If the grid lines do not display on your screen, you have either zoomed out too far from the working area, or the Grid checkbox is disabled in the View Attributes dialog box. Make sure you use the supplied seed files for this exercise to avoid these issues. View control issues are covered in chapter 4.

Working Units

10. Select the Grid category in the left pane of the Design File Settings dialog box. The right pane displays the available options. These options determine the settings for the units of measurement you wish to use in your drawing.

The following table lists the settings your new drawing took from the exercise seed file.

Option Name	Value (English units)	Value (metric units)
Master Units (MU)	'	m
Sub Units (SU)	"	mm
Resolution (MU:SU)	12" per '	1000 mm per m
Resolution (SU:PU)	2000 PU per "	100 PU per mm

11. Make sure your design file has the settings shown above. If not, change the values accordingly.

12. Click OK to exit the dialog box.

13. Select Save Settings from the File menu if you changed any of the settings in the design file.

NOTE: You must invoke the Save Settings command if you want the settings you change in a design session to stay intact when you later bring up the file to edit.

Text

14. Select Text from the Element menu to display the Text dialog box as shown below.

The Text dialog box is used for text settings.

15. Make sure your design file has the settings shown above. If not, change the values accordingly.

16. Close the Text dialog box. This concludes the exercise.

Creating Geometry

The first two exercises set the stage for creating geometry. You created a blank design file and made sure it has the parameters appropriate for the exercise. The phrase *creating geometry* refers to placing lines, arcs, circles, and other shapes in your drawing.

Exercise: Drawing Exterior Walls

Our first task when creating the apartment unit layout is to create the walls.

The following steps walk you through the process of drawing walls.

1. Start MicroStation if it's not already running. If you need help refer to chapter 1.

2. Select the file `aptunite.dgn` (English units), or the file `aptunitm.dgn` (metric units) in the MicroStation Manager dialog box and click the OK button to open that file.

This is the same file you created in the first exercise. If you did not work through the earlier exercises, see the previous exercise for instructions on copying and renaming a file from the accompanying CD-ROM.

3. Verify that the Primary toolbox reflects the exercise specifications. Namely, color is white, level is 1, line style is solid (value of 0), and line weight is 4.

4. Invoke the Place Line command. You can do this by either keying in `place line constrained` in the Key-in window or by selecting the Place Line tool from the Main tool frame as shown in the figure below.

Select Place Line from the Main tool frame.

The status bar displays Place Line in the command name field and "Enter first point" in the prompt field. The Tool Settings window title bar reads Place Line and displays the Length and Angle checkboxes and text fields. Make sure the checkboxes are unchecked.

5. Enter a data point at the location identified as number **1** on the screenshot below.

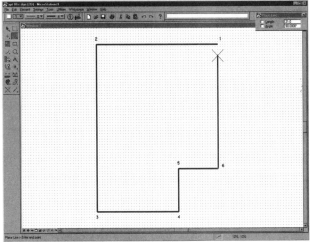

You draw six lines in this exercise to represent the exterior walls.

As soon as you enter the first data point, a line starting from that point follows your cursor. This dynamic movement of an element before it is actually made a part of the design file is called *rubberbanding* or *dynamics*.

6. Move the cursor straight to the left and watch the Length and Angle fields in the Tool Settings window. The Length field displays the distance and the Angle field displays the rotation of your cursor from the first point. When the Length and Angle fields display 23:00 and 180.0 respectively for English units and 7.000 and 180.0 respectively for metric units, you have reached the location identified as number **2** in the figure above. Enter a data point to complete the first line connecting points **1** and **2**.

NOTE: The sequence numbers shown in the screenshot above are only for your reference and are used to identify the location and order in which to enter data points. Do not use the Place Text command to enter the numbers in your design file. Also, note that the cursor is restricted to move only between grid points to facilitate precision placement of data points.

Continue locating the remaining points in sequence at the distances and angles shown in the table below by watching the Length and Angle fields in the Tool Settings window. Enter a data point when you locate the point and continue to locate the next point until you have drawn all six wall lines.

Line Segment	Length; Angle (English)	Length; Angle (metric)
1 to 2	23:0; 180.0	7.000; 180.0
2 to 3	31:0; 270.0	9.500; 270.0
3 to 4	15:6; 0.0	4.750; 0.0
4 to 5	8:0; 90.0	2.500; 90.0
5 to 6	7:6; 0.0	2.250; 0.0
6 to 1	23:0; 90.0	7.000; 90.0

7. When you enter the last data point at the location identified with the number **1** for the line segment between points **6** and **1**, you have drawn all the perimeter walls. However, the Place Line command's "Enter end

point" prompt is still active, evident by the line following your cursor. Click the Reset button (the right mouse button) to terminate the command's request for the next end point.

TIP: If you have accidentally drawn a few lines you don't want, feel free to use the Delete command located in the lower left corner of the Main tool frame. When using the delete command, first identify the line to delete with a data point, then accept it with another data point. This sequence of first identifying and then accepting elements is inherent to how MicroStation works.

This concludes the exercise on creating geometry. You may terminate your MicroStation session by selecting Exit from the File menu, or continue with the next exercise.

Manipulating Geometry

In the previous exercise you placed the exterior perimeter walls of the apartment unit. It's now time to create new geometry based on existing geometry. You will use MicroStation's manipulation commands to draw the interior walls.

MicroStation's manipulation commands are located in the Manipulate toolbox that is located to the right in the eighth row of the Main tool frame. You will use the Copy Parallel command from the Manipulate toolbox for the following exercise.

Exercise: Using Exterior Walls to Create Interior Walls

If you worked through the previous exercise, you will use that same file on your hard drive for this exercise.

If you skipped the previous exercise and wish to do this one, copy the file `apt-02e.dgn` from the `\Exercise\Ch02` folder on the accompanying CD-ROM to your computer's hard drive and rename it `aptunite.dgn` for the English units version of this exercise. Similarly, for the metric units version, copy the file `apt-02m.dgn` and rename it `aptunitm.dgn`.

The following steps guide you through the creation of interior walls.

1. Start MicroStation if it is not already running. If you need help, refer to chapter 1.

2. Select the file `aptunite.dgn` (English units), or the file `aptunitm.dgn` (metric units) in the MicroStation Manager dialog box and click the OK button to open that file.

3. Verify that the active element attributes in the Primary toolbox reflect the specifications we are to follow. Namely, color is white, level is 1, line style is solid (value of 0), and line weight is 4.

4. Invoke the Copy Parallel command. You can do this by either keying in `move parallel icon` in the Key-in window or by selecting the Move Parallel tool from the Main tool frame as shown in the figure below.

Ensure that the Make Copy checkbox is enabled.

The status bar displays Copy Parallel by Distance in the command name field and "Identify element" in the prompt field. The Tool Settings window title bar reads Move Parallel and displays the Distance and Make Copy checkboxes and a text field. Make sure the Make Copy checkbox is checked.

5. Identify the line designated with the number **1** in the figure below. MicroStation attaches a copy of the identified line to the cursor.

6. Move the cursor to the left by 6.5 feet for the English exercise and 2 m for the metric exercise and click a data point at the location designated with the number **2**. This places a copy of the exterior wall at the location you just clicked.

NOTE: For the English units exercise the cursor is set to move in 6 inch increments, so to measure 6.5 feet it must move by 13 increments. For the metric units exercise the cursor is set to move in 250 mm increments, so to measure 2 m it must move by 8 increments.

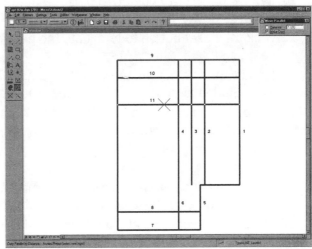

Copy of line from point 9 to point 11 can be seen in progress here.

7. Move the cursor further to the left from point **2** by 2.5 feet (English) or .75 m (metric) to locate point **3** and click a data point to place another copy of the exterior wall. See the table below for the distances between points.

Point to point	Distance (ft)	Distance (m)
1 to 2	6.5	2
2 to 3	2.5	0.75
3 to 4	2.5	0.75
5 to 6	4	3.5
7 to 8	3.5	1
9 to 10	3.5	1
10 to 11	4.5	1.5

8. Continue moving the cursor to the left to locate point **4** and click a data point to place the last copy of the same wall at this point.

9. Click the Reset button to terminate the next input prompt and the command starts over. MicroStation prompts you to identify an element.

10. Identify the line designated with the number **5** in the figure above. MicroStation attaches a copy of the identified line to the cursor.

11. Move the cursor to point **6** and click a data point. This places a copy of the exterior wall at the location you just clicked.

12. Click the Reset button to terminate the next input prompt and restart the command.

13. Identify the line designated with the number **7** in the figure above. MicroStation attaches a copy of the identified line to the cursor.

14. Move the cursor to point **8**. This places a copy of the exterior wall at the location you just clicked.

15. Click the Reset button to terminate the next input prompt and restart the command.

16. Identify the line designated with the number **9** in the figure above. MicroStation attaches a copy of the identified line to the cursor.

17. Move the cursor to point **10** and click a data point. This places a copy of the exterior wall at the location you just clicked.

18. Move the cursor to point **10** and click a data point. This places a copy of the exterior wall at the location you just clicked.

19. Click the Reset button to terminate the command.

20. This concludes our element manipulation exercise. You may terminate your MicroStation session by selecting Exit from the File menu, or continue with the next exercise.

Modifying Geometry

You now have all the walls, both interior and exterior, in place. In this section you will learn a few element modification tools to help clean up wall intersections.

MicroStation's element modification commands are located in the Modify toolbox, located to the right in the last row of the Main tool frame.

Exercise: Extending Two Walls To Intersection

If you worked through the previous exercise, you will use that same file on your hard drive for this exercise.

If you skipped the previous exercise and wish to do this one, copy the file `apt-03e.dgn` from the `\Exercise\Ch02` folder on the accompanying CD-ROM to your computer's hard drive and rename it `aptunite.dgn` for the English units version of this exercise. Similarly, for the metric units version copy the file `apt-03m.dgn` and rename it `aptunitm.dgn`.

The following steps guide you through the cleanup of intersections for two sets of interior walls.

1. Start MicroStation if it is not already running. If you need help refer to chapter 1.

2. Select the file `aptunite.dgn` (English units), or the file `aptunitm.dgn` (metric units) in the MicroStation Manager dialog box and click the OK button to open that file.

3. Invoke the Extend Elements to Intersection command. You can do this by either keying in `extend element 2` in the Key-in window or by selecting the Extend Elements to Intersection tool from the Main tool frame as shown in the figure below.

The Modify toolbox is to the right of the Delete icon.

The status bar displays Extend 2 Elements to Intersection in the command name field and "Select first element for extension" in the prompt field. The Tool Settings window title bar reads Extend 2 Elements to Intersection and displays no options.

4. Identify the line designated with the number **1** in the figure below. MicroStation displays it in the highlight color and displays the prompt "Select element for intersection" in the status bar prompt field.

5. Identify the line designated with the number **2** in the figure below. MicroStation displays the cleaned up intersection in the highlight color and displays the prompt "Accept - Initiate intersection" in the status bar prompt field.

NOTE: The data points 1 and 2 must identify, with respect to the intersection, the element segments you intend to keep. The element segments on the other side of the intersection are deleted when you accept the command with a data point. If you identified the elements on the wrong side of the intersection, simply click the Reset button and start over from step 4.

6. Accept the intersection by clicking a data point anywhere in the view window such as the location designated with the number **3** in the figure below.

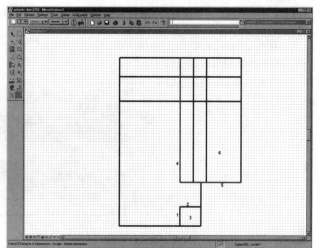

*Extend Elements to Intersection is used to clean up
the intersections of walls 1 and 2 and of walls 4 and 5.*

7. MicroStation starts the command over and prompts you for the first element to extend. Identify the line designated with the number **4** in the figure above. The element displays in the highlight color and prompts you to identify the element for intersection.

8. Identify the line designated with the number **5** in the figure above. MicroStation displays the cleaned up intersection in the highlight color and prompts you to accept the intersection cleanup as displayed.

9. Accept the intersection by clicking a data point anywhere in the view window such as the location designated with the number **6** in the figure above.

10. This concludes the first of two line extension exercises.Don't end your MicroStation session now. I suggest you continue to clean up all your wall intersections before taking a break.

Exercise: Extending Wall to Intersection

In the previous exercise, you used a command that modifies both lines selected. In this exercise you use a similar command that modifies only the line you identify first.

The following steps guide you through the cleanup of intersections of the remaining interior walls.

1. Invoke the Extend Element to Intersection command. You can do this by either keying in `extend element` in the Key-in window or by selecting the Extend Element to Intersection tool from the Main tool frame as shown in the figure below.

The tool for this exercise is adjacent to the tool used in the previous exercise.

The status bar displays Extend Elements to Intersection in the command name field and "Select first element for extension" in the prompt field. The Tool Settings window title bar reads Extend Element to Intersection and displays no options.

2. Identify the line designated with the number **1** in the figure below. MicroStation displays it in the highlight color and displays the prompt "Select element for intersection" in the status bar prompt field.

3. Identify the line designated with the number **2** in the figure below. MicroStation displays the cleaned up intersection in the highlight color and displays the prompt "Accept - Initiate intersection" in the status bar prompt field.

4. Accept the intersection by clicking a data point anywhere in the view window such as the location designated with the number **3** in the figure below.

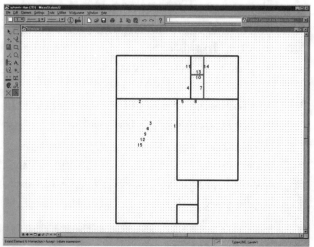

Extend Element to Intersection trims the first wall against the second wall.

5. MicroStation starts the command over and prompts you for the first element to extend. Identify the line designated with the number **4** in the figure above. The element displays in the highlight color and prompts you to identify the element for intersection.

6. Identify the line designated with the number **5** in the figure above. MicroStation displays the cleaned up intersection in the highlight color and prompts you to accept the intersection clean up as displayed.

7. Accept the intersection by clicking a data point anywhere in the view window, such as the location designated with the number **6** in the figure above.

8. Repeat steps 5, 6 and 7 above with the data points **7**, **8**, and **9** for one wall, data points **10**, **11**, and **12** for one end of the remaining wall, and data points **13**, **14**, and **15** for the other end of the wall.

9. This concludes our exercise that demonstrates the use of the Extend Element to Intersection command. You may terminate your MicroStation session by selecting Exit from the File menu, or continue with the next exercise.

Exercise: Deleting Segments of Wall For Openings

Now that all the walls for the apartment unit are in place, we need to delete segments of walls to accommodate doors and windows. For this task we will use MicroStation's Partial Delete command from the Modify toolbox.

If you skipped the previous exercises and wish to do this one, copy the file `apt-05e.dgn` from the `\Exercise\Ch02` folder on the accompanying CD-ROM to your computer's hard drive and rename it `aptunite.dgn` for the English units version of this exercise. Similarly, for the metric units version copy the file `apt-05m.dgn` and rename it `aptunitm.dgn`.

The following steps guide you through the deletion of wall segments.

1. Start MicroStation if it is not already in use. If you need help, refer to chapter 1.

2. Select the file `aptunite.dgn` (English units), or the file `aptunitm.dgn` (metric units) in the MicroStation Manager dialog box and click the OK button to open that file.

3. Invoke the Partial Delete command. You can do this by either keying in `delete partial` in the Key-in window or by selecting the Partial Delete tool from the Modify toolbox in the Main tool frame, as shown in the following screenshot.

Invoking the Partial Delete tool.

The status bar displays Delete Part of Element in the command name field and "Select start pnt for partial delete" in the prompt field. The Tool Settings window title bar reads Delete Part of Element and displays no options.

4. Identify the location on the wall designated as number **1** in the figure below. This point is located 4 feet from the lower left corner of the apartment unit. Use the distance 1.25 m for the metric version of the exercise. It's easy to locate this point because the cursor is restricted to move only along grid points and each grid increment is set up as 6 inch and 250 mm for the English and metric versions, respectively.

   MicroStation displays the prompt "Select end pnt of partial delete" and starts deleting a part of the wall as you move your cursor to the right.

5. Locate point **2** at a distance of 3.5 feet (English) or 1 m (metric) from point **1** and click a data point. This creates your first wall opening. MicroStation restarts the Partial Delete command by prompting for a start point for the next partial delete operation.

6. Locate point **3** at a 6 inch (English) or 250 mm (metric) distance from the upper left corner of the closet. MicroStation starts deleting a part of the closet wall as you move your cursor to the right.

7. Locate point **4** at a distance of 3 feet (English) or 750 mm (metric) from point **3** and click a data point to specify the end point for the wall opening.

   Remember, the design file parameters were set such that 3 feet means six grid increments, and 750 mm means three grid increments.

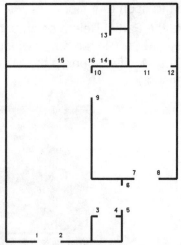

This figure shows the sequence of data points to be used for creating wall openings using the Partial Delete tool.

8. Use the figure above showing the sequence of data points to create all the remaining wall openings. The pair of data points to click for a wall opening should now be obvious. All the remaining six openings are 3.5 feet for the English units version of the exercise and 1 m for the metric units version.

> **NOTE:** All openings in the above figure were created with a 6 inch (English) and 250 mm (metric) jamb from a wall edge or corner. If you accidentally create an opening you do not want, you can use the Undo command from the Edit menu to close the opening and start over.

9. This concludes our element modification exercises. You may end your MicroStation session by selecting Exit from the File menu or continue with the next exercise.

Working With Cells

Congratulations on having come this far in the chapter! You are very close to completing the apartment unit layout we started with. In fact, after you finish this exercise, the entire unit will look complete. The remaining exercises deal with *annotation*: labeling rooms and placing a few dimensions.

The following exercise demonstrates the use of pre-built symbols—doors and windows—that you pick from a supplied cell library and drop in at the desired location with the proper orientation.

Exercise: Placing Windows and Doors

If you worked through the previous exercise, you will use that same file on your hard drive for this exercise.

If you skipped the previous exercise and wish to do this one, copy the file `apt-06e.dgn` from the `\Exercise\Ch02` folder on the accompanying CD-ROM to your computer's hard drive and rename it `aptunite.dgn` for the English units version of this exercise. Similarly, for the metric units version copy the file `apt-06m.dgn` and rename it `aptunitm.dgn`.

In addition to the exercise design file you'll need to copy from the CD-ROM to your hard drive a cell library that contains the needed door and window symbols. The cell library file for the metric units version of the exercise is called `aptm.cel` and `apte.cel` for the English units version.

The following steps guide you through the placement of doors and windows in the apartment unit.

1. Start MicroStation if it's not already running. If you need help, refer to chapter 1.
2. Select the file `aptunite.dgn` (English units), or the file `aptunitm.dgn` (metric units) in the MicroStation Manager dialog box and click the OK button to open that file.
3. Verify that the active element attributes in the Primary toolbox reflect the specifications we are to follow. Namely, color is yellow, level is 2, line style is solid (value of 0), and line weight is 1.
4. Select Cells from the Element menu to invoke the Cell Library dialog box.
5. From the Cell Library dialog box's File menu select Attach. This opens the Attach Cell Library dialog box shown below.

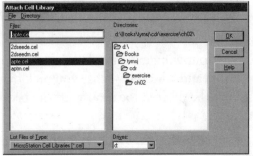

Navigate to the directory where you copied the exercise cell library.

6. Navigate to the location on your hard drive where you copied the cell library that accompanies this exercise. Select `apte.cel` if you're working on the English version of the exercise, or select `aptm.cel` if you're working on the metric version, and click OK to open the cell library in the Cell Library dialog box.

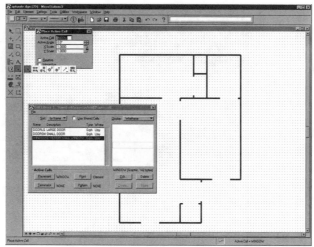

The Window cell is active and ready for placement.

7. The title bar of the Cell Library dialog box displays the name of the cell library open. The dialog box should list the three cells that are contained in the cell library: WINDOW, DOORSM, DOORLG.

8. Highlight the WINDOW cell in the Cell Library dialog box and click the Placement button in the Active Cells groupbox of the dialog box. This activates the highlighted cell as a placement cell.

9. Invoke the Place Active Cell command from the Main tool frame as shown in the figure above. The Window cell attaches to your cursor as you move it.

10. The Tool Settings window displays Place Active Cell in its title bar and WINDOW as the active cell. Verify that the active angle is zero and the X and Y active scales are 1.0 each.

11. Move the cursor to locate point **1** shown in the above figure and click a data point. This places the first window cell in your drawing.

12. Move the cursor to locate point **2** and click another data point. This places the second window cell in your drawing.

13. Highlight the DOORSM cell in the Cell Library dialog box and click the Placement button to make this the new placement cell.

14. Invoke the Place Active Cell command from the Main tool frame. The small door cell now follows your cursor. Click the right end of the closet opening to place the small door, as shown in the screenshot below.

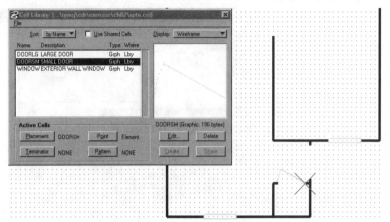

Click the right end of the closet to place the small door cell.

15. Highlight the DOORLG cell in the Cell Library dialog box and click the Placement button to make this the new placement cell.

16. Invoke the Place Active Cell command from the Main tool frame. The large door cell now follows your cursor. Sequentially click the locations identified as points **1, 2,** and **3** to place the large door, as shown in the figure below.

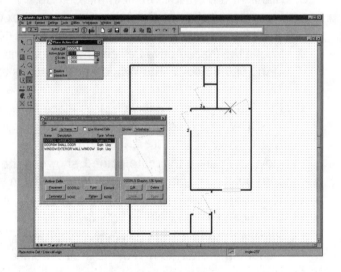

17. The fourth large door for the bathroom will need to be rotated by 270 degrees to be properly oriented for the wall opening. To change the door's orientation, edit the Active Angle field in the Tool Settings window to 270 and press the Tab key to have the new value take effect. Now the door is oriented properly.

18. Click a data point at the location designated as number **4** in the above figure.

19. This completes this exercise. Before you click the Reset button to terminate the Place Active Cell command, make sure you return the active angle value from 270 back to 0. You may now end your MicroStation session or continue with the next exercise.

Using Annotation Tools

This section introduces you to two annotation commands. The first demonstrates the Place Text command to label the rooms. The second demonstrates the Dimension Element command to place a few dimension lines in the drawing.

Exercise: Labeling Rooms

If you worked through the previous exercise, you will use that same file on your hard drive for this exercise.

If you skipped the previous exercise and wish to do this one, copy the file `apt-07e.dgn` from the `\Exercise\Ch02` folder on the accompanying CD-ROM to your computer's hard drive and rename it `aptunite.dgn` for the English units version of this exercise. Similarly, for the metric units version copy the file `apt-07m.dgn` and rename it `aptunitm.dgn`.

The following steps guide you through placing room labels.

1. Start MicroStation if it is not already running. If you need help, refer to chapter 1.

2. Select the file `aptunite.dgn` (English units), or the file `aptunitm.dgn` (metric units) in the MicroStation Manager dialog box and click the OK button to open that file.

3. Verify that the active element attributes in the Primary toolbox reflect the specifications we are to follow. Namely, color is green, level is 3, line style is solid (value of 0), and line weight is 0.

4. Invoke the Place Text command from the Text toolbox. Several options appear in the Tool Settings window. The Text Editor window appears on your screen.

   The Place Text command is the first icon from the right column in the fifth row of the Main tool frame. Look at the screenshot below if you need help in determining its location. The Place Text icon appears activated in the figure.

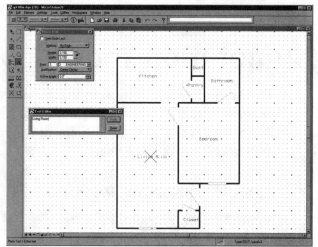

*Text typed in the Text Editor window is attached to
the cursor ready for placement as a room label.*

5. Type the label "Living Room" in the Text Editor window and move the cursor to the center of the room, as shown in the above figure, and click a data point to place it.

6. Click the Reset button to clear the text in the Text Editor window and type the label "Bedroom" and move the cursor to the center of the room. Click a data point to place it.

7. Repeat the above step to place labels for the Closet, Bathroom, Kitchen, Pantry, and Duct. The above screenshot shows each room location.

8. Click Reset to clear the Text Editor window.

9. This concludes the room labeling exercise. You may now terminate your MicroStation session by selecting Exit from the File menu. You may also continue with the next exercise.

Exercise: Dimensioning

This exercise will use the Dimension Element tool to place a few dimensions in your drawing.

If you worked through the previous exercise, you will use that same file on your hard drive for this exercise.

If you skipped the previous exercise and wish to do this one, copy the file `apt-08e.dgn` from the `\Exercise\Ch02` folder on the accompanying CD-ROM to your computer's hard drive and rename it `aptunite.dgn` for the English units version of this exercise. Similarly, for the metric units version copy the file `apt-08m.dgn` and rename it `aptunitm.dgn`.

The following steps guide you through the placement of wall dimensions.

1. Start MicroStation if it is not already in use. If you need help, refer to chapter 1.

2. Select the file `aptunite.dgn` (English units), or the file `aptunitm.dgn` (metric units) in the MicroStation Manager dialog box and click the OK button to open that file.

3. Verify that the active element attributes in the Primary toolbox reflect the specifications we are to follow. Namely, color is red, level is 4, line style is solid (value of 0), and line weight is 0.

4. Invoke the Dimension Element command from the Dimension toolbox. The command name Dimension Element appears in the status bar along with the prompt "Select element to dimension." Several options also appear in the Tool Settings window.

    The Dimension Element command is the first icon from the right column in the seventh row of the Main tool frame. Look at the screenshot below if you need help in determining its location. The Dimension Element icon appears selected in the figure.

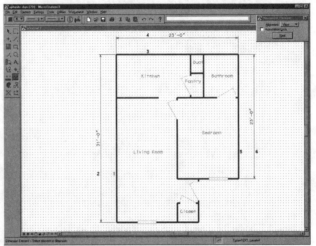

You will place the three dimensions shown.

5. Identify the left exterior wall at the number **1** shown in the above figure. A dimension line appears and follows the cursor. Also the prompt on the status bar changes to read "Accept (Press Return to switch command)."

6. Move the cursor to the left and click a data point at the location designated as number **2** in the above figure.

7. Repeat steps 5 and 6 to dimension the top exterior wall using the points **3** and **4**.

8. Repeat steps 5 and 6 to dimension the right exterior wall using the points **5** and **6**.

9. This concludes the dimensioning exercise. You may now terminate your MicroStation session by selecting Exit from the File menu. You may also continue with the last exercise in this chapter.

Printing Your Drawing

The apartment unit layout we started is now complete. The only thing remaining is a hardcopy of the drawing for your files, or for submittal to the client, were this a real-world project. In the following exercise, you will print the drawing. Feel free to skip the following exercise if you don't have a printer.

Exercise: Previewing and Printing the Drawing

If you completed the previous exercise, you will use that same file on your hard drive for this exercise.

If you skipped the previous exercise and wish to complete this one, copy the file `apt-09e.dgn` from the `\Exercise\Ch02` folder on the accompanying CD-ROM to your computer's hard drive and rename it `aptunite.dgn` for the English units version of this exercise. Similarly, for the metric units version copy the file `apt-09m.dgn` and rename it `aptunitm.dgn`.

The following steps guide you through the task of printing the drawing.

1. Start MicroStation if it is not already in use. If you need help, refer to chapter 1.

2. Select the file `aptunite.dgn` (English units), or the file `aptunitm.dgn` (metric units) in the MicroStation Manager dialog box and click the OK button to open that file.

3. Make sure the drawing fits completely within your view window. If the drawing does not completely fit within the view window, invoke the Fit View command by clicking the Fit View icon, located to the left of the horizontal scroll bars, as shown in the following figure.

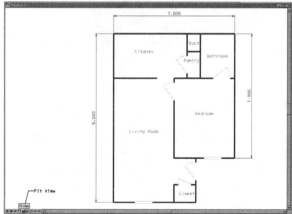

Click the Fit View icon to fit the entire drawing within the view window.

4. Select Print/Plot from the File menu to invoke the Plot window. (The plot you generate won't be to scale. To learn more about plotting and how to create scaled plots, you are referred to chapter 7.)

5. Select Driver from the Setup menu in the Plot window. This opens the Select Plotter Driver File dialog box. Choose the `printer.plt` file and click the OK button. This configures MicroStation to use the default Windows printer driver.

6. Select Page from the Setup menu in the Plot window. This opens the Print Setup dialog box. Verify that the paper size and orientation are the way you want them. A selection of letter-size paper in portrait orientation will suffice for our purposes.

7. Select Preview from the File menu in the Plot window. This enlarges the Plot window to display a preview of your drawing, as shown in the figure below.

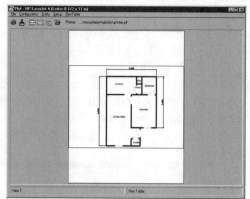

The Plot window grows to display a preview of
the plot when you select Preview from its File menu.

8. Once you are satisfied that the page size and orientation are what you need them to be, select Plot from the File menu in the Plot window. This tells MicroStation to send the drawing to the printer.

9. Close the Plot window. This completes the printing exercise, the last exercise in this chapter. You may now terminate your MicroStation session by selecting Exit from the File menu.

Details Ahead

Now that you've completed all the exercises in this chapter, you probably feel comfortable with how MicroStation's basic geometry creation, manipulation, and modification commands work.

If you feel like experimenting, you can add furniture and appliances to this apartment unit layout. You have only used a few of the repertoire of available commands. Your knowledge of how MicroStation's commands are organized, and the meaning of some MicroStation-specific terms, such as *data point* and *Reset button* makes you ready to explore its other commands.

Considering that you had only learned and used MicroStation's interface components and other simple file operations, you've covered a lot of ground in this chapter. It can be difficult to understand the logic and sequence of commands without a grounding in fundamentals. Don't worry if you did not understand all the details of the tools and concepts presented. The rest of the book covers this.

In the next three chapters you will explore MicroStation's basic drawing environment, how to navigate and use its many view windows and view control commands. You will also discover scores of other drawing and editing tools.

Chapter 3
The MicroStation Environment
Understanding the CAD Medium

CAD is often referred to as an electronic pencil. But is it?

The pencil is such a ubiquitous tool, you need no training on how to use it. You can use it to write, sketch, or draw anything on paper. If you make a mistake, an eraser can rub out the improperly placed linework so you can place it again with greater care.

The skill of the person using the pencil determines the quality of the generated linework. If your handwriting is good, your letters will be attractive and legible. And the freehand straight line you draw will be straighter than the one drawn by a child.

CAD software does not attempt to be a pencil. Though you can write and sketch on a computer screen with the software, it is specifically geared toward the creation of architectural and engineering drawings.

CAD software creates technical drawings using geometric shapes such as lines, arcs, circles, and curves a draftsperson uses. These geometric shapes are represented in the electronic CAD file in mathematical terms.

The line you draw in MicroStation will be exactly as straight as that a child draws. This is because you do not draw the line as you do with a pencil. You simply identify the two points the line needs to connect and the software takes care of drawing the line between those two points.

NOTE: MicroStation stores all geometric shapes in terms of the cardinal points necessary to define it in mathematical terms. For a line, the coordinates of its two end points are stored. For an ellipse, the length of its two axes, the rotation angle of its primary axis, and the coordinates of its center are stored. MicroStation re-creates these shapes in real time on the screen as you navigate the drawing.

This chapter introduces you to MicroStation's electronic drawing environment. The topics we cover in this chapter are listed below.

- Comparison of a MicroStation drawing with other drawing mediums, along with a discussion of its advantages.
- The nature of a MicroStation design file and its settings.
- Discussion of seed files and workspaces to facilitate reuse.
- Displaying information about and the attributes of MicroStation's geometric shapes, known as elements, and the tools used to manipulate them in a group.

For the new MicroStation user the information presented in this chapter is vital if you are to understand the variety of settings and tools MicroStation provides to control your drawing environment.

For the experienced MicroStation user, this chapter can serve as a reference you can turn to for a discussion of topics that may not be very clear because you use them infrequently.

The CAD Model

The purpose of CAD was to computerize the drafting process. CAD has certainly accomplished that goal. Clients expect computer-generated drawings and even request electronic deliverables in addition to the blueprints. Virtually no engineering and architectural firm today, whether a single-person office or multinational organization, creates bid documents on the drafting board. They use CAD software to create bid drawings used by contractors for project construction.

The electronic file that represents a MicroStation drawing has the filename extension .dgn, and is referred to as a design file. The rest of this chapter is devoted to exploring various aspects of a MicroStation design file and the drafting environment it provides for the creation of drawings.

In order to better understand the CAD drafting environment, we need to compare it with some of the other drawing mediums. To this end let us reconsider the apartment unit layout you created in chapter 2.

Suppose you hand over the task of creating the apartment unit layout to two different people who are to use different tools. The first will use the traditional drafting board with pencils and other tools such as tee-squares and shape templates. The second will re-create the drawing using a raster drawing program such as Windows Paint that is bundled with Windows as an accessory application. Click Start, Programs, Accessories, Paint on the Windows task bar to locate Paint.

Though the drawings you get back from the two people may look virtually the same as the one you printed from MicroStation in chapter 2, the process each person went through to create the drawing with the tools they used would be very different.

Let's closely examine how the apartment unit layout might have been created using traditional drafting tools. We will follow that with a discussion on its creation with a raster drawing program. The purpose of this comparison in to gain a sharper understanding of the MicroStation drawing environment.

Compared to Traditional Drafting

Before you even sit in front of a drafting table to begin a drawing you must decide on the size of paper to draw on. Then you must determine the size of the apartment unit in order to compute the scale it will need to be to fit on the paper.

For standard letter-size paper, and for the apartment unit length of 9.5 m (metric exercise) or 31 feet (English exercise) a choice for drawing scales might be 1:50 (metric) or 1/4"=1'-0" (English). This scale selection would mean that the apartment unit length would take up 190 mm (=9500/50) on paper for the metric exercise and 7.75 inch (=31X12/48) on paper for the English exercise. This scale selection ensures enough space around the room layout to accommodate dimensions and other labels that may be required.

To draw the exterior walls, you will either need a scaled ruler appropriate for the chosen drawing scale, or you will need to convert the length of each wall segment to its appropriate length on paper.

Contrast this to the exercise to create a design file in chapter 2. You set neither the size of paper, nor the scale. All walls were drawn to actual dimensions. You did set the unit of measure for the drawing—English or metric. This was set in the Working Units category of the Design File Settings dialog box.

NOTE: In CAD, you create full scale models. These can be plotted on any paper size paper to an appropriate scale. On a drafting board, you must first select the paper size, then draw a scaled representation of the model.

To create thick exterior walls with a pencil, you would draw several lines side by side to build up the line thickness. In MicroStation, to draw thicker lines, you set the line weight to a value of 4. In this sense a MicroStation line is smarter than a line drawn by hand. You can request the line to display and plot itself thicker.

To draw interior walls on a drafting board, you would first compute their scaled offset distance from exterior walls. Then, you would use a tee-square and triangles to draw parallel and perpendicular lines. In chapter 2, you used the Copy Parallel tool. The software computed end point coordinates from the specified offset value and created the new lines.

NOTE: In CAD, the geometric shapes you draw have associated attributes, such as end point coordinates. The software uses these to compute coordinates for new elements. The drafting board environment has you perform all such computations.

To draw door and window symbols in the chapter 2 exercise, you had conveniently used a pre-built cell library to place the symbols at the appropriate location with a single data point click. On a drafting board, you use templates of common shapes. These guide your pencil for quick and clean linework. However, you must trace every line of the shape for all its instances.

NOTE: CAD permits the effortless reuse of existing geometry, no matter how complex. It implements tools such as Copy Element and Place Cell. The drafting board offers templates of shapes for consistency, but each shape must be redrawn.

The above discussion has highlighted the most significant issues relevant to the understanding of the CAD environment: full scale modeling, the concept of elements and their attributes, and reusability.

Compared to Raster Graphics Programs

There are two types of graphics software: vector and raster. CAD, drawing, and illustration software are vector-based. Examples of vector graphics software are: MicroStation, CorelDRAW, Micrografx Designer, and Adobe Illustrator. Photo editing and imaging category of software is raster-based. Examples of raster software are: Adobe Photoshop, Corel Photo-Paint, and Micrografx Picture Publisher.

The most significant difference between raster and vector graphics software is how each stores graphics data. The former stores graphics as an array of dots, or a bit-map. The latter stores graphics as a collection of supported element types that have specific coordinates and attributes.

An image size in Windows Paint is measured in pels, an acronym for picture elements. Contrast this to MicroStation's design plane that is fixed in size and is defined in terms of a *positional unit*. Positional units are covered later in this chapter.

Windows Paint measures its image area in pixels, or pels.

An image with a width of 10 pels and a height of 12 pels will consist of a total of 120 pels (=10X12). The raster file maintains each pel's color information. The basic unit of information stored in a raster program is a pel. In contrast, the basic unit of information in MicroStation is an element with its own set of attributes, depending on element type.

NOTE: The basic unit of information in a raster program is the pixel. Raster files store color attributes about each pixel with no concept of a line or arc. In CAD software the basic unit of information is a geometric element. Drawing files store element type information, whether line or arc, and coordinate and display attribute for each element.

Though both raster and vector programs are designed to handle graphics, each does it in a fundamentally different way.

Like vector programs, raster programs provide tools to draw lines, circles, and arcs. However, unlike CAD, the raster program's tools do not create such elements; they simply change the color attributes of pixels along a path representing the shape.

In CAD, you have tools to operate upon existing elements in a design file. Remember how the Copy Parallel tool was used in chapter 2 to offset exterior walls to create interior walls. In raster programs such as Windows Paint, if you draw a line, you cannot erase it by identifying it; you must erase each individual pixel on the screen that represents it.

Despite their differences, raster images and vector graphics can coexist. Many of you, especially when dealing with photogrammetry and GIS applications, have a need to work in a hybrid raster and vector environment. MicroStation supports the use of raster images in two ways. It can embed an image file as a non-editable raster element. It can also attach an external image file as a background *reference file*. Reference files are covered in chapter 6.

Advantages of the Electronic Medium

Why has CAD become the medium of choice for the creation of architectural and engineering drawings? This section attempts to answer the question.

Full Scale Modeling

The geometry you draw in CAD is typically done to full scale. Thus an exterior wall of a commercial building may be drawn as a line 100 m long, and a stretch of highway may be drawn as a line 15 miles long. Each of these lines would be drawn to full scale in its proper units, not to a scaled representation on paper, as is done on the drafting board.

This full scale modeling offers a more natural environment in which you do not have to use the equivalent of an architectural or engineering scale to determine the actual size of an element. Another advantage of full scale modeling is that the same model can be plotted to different scales on paper of any size.

Precision

When you draw on paper, the length of a line will vary depending on the accuracy of your scale and the care with which you draw it. It is possible for two people to measure the same line and come up with slightly different lengths. In the electronic CAD medium the length of the line is precisely defined to the accuracy available in the design file format. No matter who measures the line, the line will always measure exactly the same.

Element and Attribute Data

Because a CAD file stores drawings as elements and their attributes electronically, you can perform operations not possible otherwise. For example, you can dimension an element in MicroStation by simply identifying it with the Element Dimension tool as shown in the chapter 2 exercise.

If you organize elements in a design file using some convention of element attribute and level usage, you can easily isolate them for group operations. This is described later in the chapter when introducing MicroStation's Select By tool.

Reusability

The concept of cells (remember the use of door and window cells in the chapter 2 exercise) and reference files promotes the effortless reuse of common symbols and details. You only spend time initially creating the symbol or detail. It can then be used over and over in any design file.

Extensibility

MicroStation's support for macros and a variety of development languages such as the UCM Language, MicroStation BASIC, MDL and JMDL means that the core software functionality can be extended to meet specialized needs. This is what MicroStation's engineering configurations are all about.

Chapter 13 covers three engineering configurations: TriForma for architectural and building design, GeoGraphics for GIS projects, and Modeler for the manufacturing industry.

Undo and Redo

The ability to undo an operation, or redo it after performing an undo is unique to electronic files. During conceptual design your drawing may explore an alternative only to abandon it, and later revisit it. Like other software programs, MicroStation addresses this need through undo and redo commands located in the Edit menu. MicroStation also supports the ability to set an undo mark in a design file. All work after an undo mark is set can be undone in a single step. Remember, operations before selecting Compress from the File menu can't be undone.

Backup

When working on a drafting board, you work on the original paper or mylar until the drawing is complete, which may take a week or several months. Were something to happen to the original, all the valuable time you spent on it would be lost. You'd have to start over.

CAD being an electronic medium, you can backup the design file every day. In fact, nightly backups of data on corporate servers is a norm. This gives you a level of protection not otherwise possible. Should a design file become corrupt, or otherwise unusable, an earlier version that is still in good condition can be easily restored from a prior backup to help salvage time already spent on the project.

TIP: Always backup your design files at least daily. You never know when you might have a need to restore a file, whether to fix a corrupt file, or to begin work on a new phase of an old project.

The MicroStation Design File

A design file is similar in many ways to a database file. A MicroStation element may be thought of as a database record. Whereas database records are of a fixed length, records in a design file that represent elements are of variable length. In other words, the amount of information stored about an element depends on its type. Thus the record that stores a line element differs in size when compared to the record that store an arc element.

The structure of a design file is covered in greater detail in chapter 15. The next section lists the most common element types supported in the design file format.

Repository for Elements

A MicroStation design file is a repository for elements and design file settings. The file is binary and stores information in sequential order. The later an element is created in a session, the closer to the end of the file it is stored.

In this section we discuss the most common element types, listed in alphabetical order, the design file format supports. An element's unique type number is also listed in what follows. As a MicroStation user, you need not concern yourself with the element type ID. However, if you develop applications to manipulate elements, a knowledge of an element's type ID is helpful.

Arc

An arc element is a partial segment of a circle or an ellipse. It is a Type 16 element.

B-spline Curve

A B-spline curve is short for Non-Uniform Rational B-splines (NURBS), a sophisticated mathematical representation for smooth curves. In MicroStation, B-spline curves can have an order from 2 to 15, with 4 being the default. The higher the order of a B-spline curve, the more smooth its representation, and consequently the more expensive it is in terms of computing power needed to create it. The default value of 4 is suitable for most uses. It is a Type 27 element.

B-spline Surface

A B-spline surface is only valid within 3D design files and is used to represent free-form curved surfaces. It is a Type 24 element.

Cell

A cell is a complex element in that it is a container for other element types. It is a Type 2 element. MicroStation SmartSolids are stored in the design file as cells.

Complex Chain

A complex chain is a complex element in that it is stored in the design file as a container for a series of connected lines and arcs to be treated as a single unit. It is a Type 12 element.

Complex Shape

A complex shape is a complex element because it is stored in the design file as a container for a closed shape made up of connected lines and arcs. It is a Type 14 element.

Cone

A cone is only valid within 3D design files. It is a Type 23 element. In MicroStation a cylinder is a special case of a cone.

Curve

A point curve, simply referred to as a curve, is a mathematically simple curve definition. It is a Type 11 element.

Dimension

A dimension element consists of witness lines, arrowhead symbols, extension lines and text. It is used to show the length or angle of other elements. It is a Type 33 element.

Ellipse and Circle

An ellipse is a closed element with a primary and a secondary axis. A circle is a special case of an ellipse where the primary and secondary axes are equal. It is a Type 15 element.

Line and Point

A line is the shortest distance between two points. It is a Type 3 element. Points in MicroStation are zero-length lines.

Line String

A line string is a series of connected lines that are treated as a single unit. It can have a maximum of 101 vertices. It is a Type 4 element.

Multi-Line

A multi-line is a group of up to 16 parallel lines of different attributes and optional end caps. It is a Type 36 element.

Raster Data

A raster element is an embedded bit-map image in the design file. It is a complex element with the header being a Type 87 element and the data being a Type 88 element.

Shape

A shape is a closed element made up of lines that can have up to 101 vertices. It is a Type 6 element.

Surface and 3D Primitive

A surface is only valid in a 3D design file and represents a zero thickness element. 3D primitives, such as slabs, spheres, and tori are stored in the design file as surfaces. It is a Type 18 element.

Text

A single line of text is stored in a design file as a text element. It is a Type 17 element.

Text Node

A text node is a text element with a unique, searchable node number. Text that spans multiple lines is automatically assigned a node number. It is therefore a text node. It is a Type 7 element.

Attributes of Elements

The term element attribute refers to the subset of element properties stored in the design file that can be used to control their display in one way or another. Following is a list of these attributes, what they mean and how they can control the display of an element.

Class

An element can belong to one of two classes: primary and construction. Elements you draw as part of the electronic model belong to the primary class. Elements you draw to help construct geometry belong to the construction class. The construction class corresponds to construction lines you would use in traditional drafting. You can hide the display of construction class elements using the View Attributes dialog box.

Color

The MicroStation color table supports 255 colors that are numbered from color 0 through color 254. When you draw an element it takes on the active color as displayed in the Primary toolbox. You can override the display color of an element by using MicroStation's level symbology override feature.

Note that when you use MicroStation's rendering capabilities that can generate photo-realistic images from 3D models, it can display up to 16.7 million colors, provided your display hardware can handle it.

Level

A *level* is the equivalent of an overlay sheet in drafting. It is used to organize elements for a specific purpose, as demonstrated in the chapter 2 exercise. MicroStation design files have 63 levels, from level 1 through level 63. When you draw an element it is placed on the active level as displayed in the Primary toolbox. You control the display of levels using the View Levels dialog box.

Style

MicroStation supports eight standard line styles, also referred to as line codes, and custom line styles for greater flexibility. When you draw an element it takes on the active line style as displayed in the Primary toolbox. You can override the screen display of element line styles by using MicroStation's level symbology override feature.

The following table lists the eight standard line styles.

Line Weight	Description
0	solid
1	dot
2	medium dash
3	long dash
4	dot dash
5	short dash
6	dot dash dot
7	long dash short dash

Weight

MicroStation supports thirty-two line weights from weight 0 through weight 31. When you draw an element it takes on the active line weight as displayed in the Primary toolbox. The Primary toolbox provides easy access to the first sixteen weights. To use any supported line weight you must use the `WT=nn` key in, where `nn` is a number from 0 through 31. You can override the screen display of element line weights by using MicroStation's level symbology override feature.

Other Element Properties

In addition to the element attributes mentioned above, a MicroStation design file stores many other element properties. Coordinates of cardinal points of elements, the graphic group number they belong to, data tags, and user data are some of these properties.

Exercise: Creating and Hiding Constructions

The purpose of this exercise is to help you create and use construction class elements. You use construction class elements to help simplify the construction of primary class elements.

For this exercise you will need the file `conclass.dgn` from the `\Exercise\Ch03` folder on the accompanying CD-ROM. Make a copy of this file on your computer's hard drive before proceeding.

The following steps guide you through this exercise.

1. Start MicroStation if it is not already running. The MicroStation Manager dialog box appears on your screen.
2. Use the MicroStation Manager dialog box to browse your computer's hard disk and locate the folder where you copied the exercise file.
3. Double-click the exercise file `conclass.dgn` to open it in MicroStation. You will see the cross section of a circular pipe in your view window.
4. Open the Element Attributes dialog box by selecting Attributes from the Element menu.
5. Select Construction from the Class option button in the Element Attributes dialog box, as shown in the figure below. Every element you place while this class is active will be tagged as a construction class element.

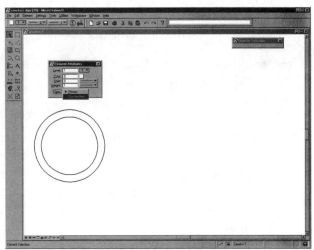

The Element Attributes dialog box includes a Class option button.

6. Invoke the Place Line tool from the Main tool frame. Having used it in chapter 2, you should be familiar with the tool now. It is the second icon in the Linear Elements toolbox, located in the right column of the second row of the Main tool frame. The Tool Settings window displays Length and Angle fields to help you constrain the line's length and angle.

7. Enable the Length checkbox and key in the length 20.0 in the text field next to it. Enable the Angle checkbox and key in the angle 0.0 in the text field next to it. The Tool Settings window for the Place Line tool is shown in the figure below. A 20-unit long horizontal line tracks your cursor awaiting placement in the drawing.

Enable both checkboxes and key in the values shown.

8. With the cursor close to the top of the outer circle click the tentative button on your mouse. For a two-button mouse click both the left and the right buttons together. For a three-button mouse that has been properly configured, click the middle button. The cursor jumps to locate the top quadrant keypoint of the circle, and the circle is highlighted. Click a data point to place the first construction line.

NOTE: If the tentative cursor does not snap to the desired location, move the cursor close to the top quadrant of the circle and try clicking the tentative button again.

9. With the cursor close to the top of the inner circle, click the tentative button to snap to the top quadrant of the circle. Click a data point to place the second construction line.

10. With the cursor close to the bottom of the inner circle, click the tentative button to snap to the bottom quadrant of the circle. Click a data point to place the third construction line.

11. With the cursor close to the bottom of the outer circle, click the tentative button to snap to the bottom quadrant of the circle. Click a data point to place the last construction line.

12. Click the Reset button to terminate the Place Line command. Your screen should look similar to the screenshot shown below.

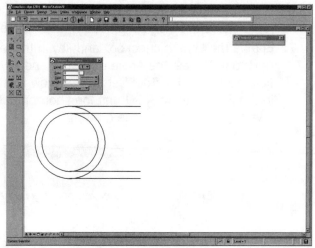

The construction lines shown will help draw the side view.

13. Select Primary from the Class option button in the Element Attributes dialog box to switch to placing primary elements.

14. Invoke the Place Line tool again. If the Length and Angle checkboxes in the Tool Settings window are enabled, uncheck them. This will remove the constraints from the line's placement.

15. Snap to the right endpoint, designated as the number **1** in the figure below, of the first construction line by clicking the tentative button while the cursor is close to that point. Accept the snapped location with a data point to start the placement of the line.

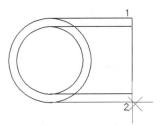

Snap to locations 1 and 2 to draw the left end of the pipe's side view.

16. Snap to the right endpoint, designated as the number **2** in the figure above, of the fourth construction line and accept it with a data point to place the line.

17. Click the Reset button to restart the Place Line tool. You have drawn the left end of the side view of the pipe.

18. Place four 25.0 unit long horizontal lines by snapping to the right ends of the four construction lines. If you are not sure how to do this, reread steps 6 and 7 of this exercise. Make sure you use the Length and Angle fields in the Tool Settings window to apply the given length and angle constraints.

TIP: Enable the Length checkbox and key in 25 in the text field next to it. Also, to make the line horizontal enable the Angle checkbox and key in 0 in the associated text field.

19. Click the Reset button to terminate the Place Line tool. Your screen should look similar to the following figure.

20. Now draw the right end of the pipe's side view. You can do this by invoking the Place Line tool again. If the Length and Angle checkboxes in the Tool Settings window are enabled, uncheck them. This removes constraints from the line's placement.

21. Snap to the right endpoint of the top line by clicking the tentative button while the cursor is close to that point. Accept the snapped location with a data point to start the placement of the line.

22. Snap to the right endpoint of the bottom line by clicking the tentative button while the cursor is close to that point. Accept it with a data point to place the line.

23. Click the Reset button to restart the Place Line tool. Your screen should look similar to the following figure.

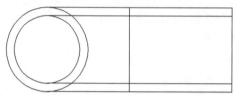

The pipe's side view before turning off the construction lines.

24. Turn off the display of construction class elements. You do this by first invoking the View Attributes dialog box. Select View Attributes from the Settings menu. Then turn off the checkbox labeled Constructions, as shown in the figure below. Finally, click the Apply button to make your change to the View Attributes dialog box take effect.

Use the View Attributes dialog box to control
the display of construction class elements.

This concludes the exercise. Here you learned how to use the Element Attributes dialog box to make the construction class active before placing construction lines. You also learned how to use the View Attributes dialog box to turn off the display of construction class elements.

NOTE: If you do not delete construction class elements from your drawings, make sure you turn their display off when plotting; otherwise, the construction lines will be plotted as well.

Design File Settings

Now that you have worked with a few design files; you probably realize that MicroStation continuously saves elements as your session progresses. However, not all changes you make in MicroStation are saved as they are made. Design file settings, such as active element and view attributes, the state of locks and other settings must be explicitly saved if you want them remembered between sessions.

You save design file settings by selecting Save Settings from the File menu.

The rest of this section explains the various design file settings that affect the MicroStation drawing environment. To follow along, invoke the Design File Settings dialog box shown in the figure below by selecting Design File from the Settings menu.

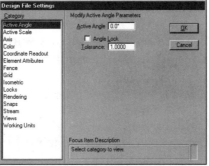

The Design File Settings dialog box is modal in nature.

The Design File Settings dialog box is modal in nature. The term *modal* refers to those dialog boxes that must be dismissed before you can perform another action in MicroStation. You can spot modal dialog boxes by looking for the ellipsis symbol (...) next to their name in the menu bar. Note that the name Design File has the ellipsis symbol next to it in the Settings menu.

Active Angle

Several commands in MicroStation require an angle to be specified for their operation. These commands use the value assigned to a setting known as the *active angle*. A few examples of commands that use the active angle are Construct Line at Active Angle, Place Cell and Place Text.

In a situation where you may want the active angle to be rounded to the nearest multiple of a number, MicroStation implements an angle lock and a tolerance value.

Active Scale

Several commands in MicroStation require a scale factor to be specified for their operation. These commands use the value assigned to a setting known as the active scale. A few examples of commands that use the active angle are Place Cell and Scale Element. MicroStation allows you to scale the X, Y and Z axes disproportionately.

In a situation where you may want the active scale to be rounded to the nearest multiple of a number, MicroStation implements a scale lock and a tolerance value.

Axis

When you wish to constrain the placement of data points so that they lie at a specified angle with respect to the previous data point, you can enable the axis lock setting. The axis lock setting is affected by two variables, the start angle with respect to the view axis and the increment angle with respect to the start angle.

Color

There are three color settings in addition to the active color setting. When you identify elements for modification, they are highlighted in the highlight color. The drawing pointer color determines the color of the cursor when it is moved in a view window. When you add elements to a selection set and set the MicroStation preference to use highlighting rather than handles, they are highlighted in the selection set color.

Coordinate Readout

You can control how units are displayed in text fields, in dialog boxes, or in status bar messages by using the coordinate readout settings. Settings for both linear and angular units of measure are included.

Element Attributes

The subset of displayable element properties are referred to as element attributes. It's the combination of level, color, line style, line weight, and class discussed earlier in this chapter.

Fence

A *fence* is a method of grouping elements for manipulation or modification. With this setting, you can control how fence operations affect the elements in and around it. Additional details on fence operations are covered later in this chapter.

Grid

A *grid* is an imaginary array of dots to assist drawing operations. When grid lock is enabled, data points are forced to lie on grid points. The grid master setting determines the spacing in working units between grid points. The grid reference setting is the distance between the heavier grid reference dots expressed as multiples of the grid master setting. You can also configure the grid to be orthogonal or isometric. MicroStation lets you create an irregular grid where the spacing between dots along the X and Y axes is different.

Isometric

To assist in the creation of isometric drawings, MicroStation provides an isometric lock setting. When it is enabled, data points are forced to lie on the top, left, or right isometric planes.

Locks

The Locks category on the Design File Settings dialog box provides access to miscellaneous locks that are not covered elsewhere. When the *text node* lock is on, new text elements are placed at locations where empty text nodes exist. If no empty text nodes are present, new text elements cannot be placed. When *level lock* is enabled you can only select elements on the active level. When the *graphic group lock* is enabled, element manipulation commands operate upon all members of a graphic group.

Rendering

The Rendering category on the Design File Settings dialog box provides access to a variety of rendering related settings such as stroke tolerance, shadow filter size, and fog color among others.

Snaps

When enabled, the snap lock setting forces tentative points to locate snappable points on nearby elements. This setting must be enabled if you wish your tentative button clicks to locate snappable points. MicroStation implements a variety of snap modes, such as keypoint, endpoint, midpoint, and so on. The keypoint snap mode is the default, and it is recommended for normal operations. You can temporarily override the default snap mode while performing a drawing operation by selecting the desired snap mode from a pop-up menu that appears when you click the snap field in the status bar.

Stream

The stream settings affect the Place Stream Line String and Place Stream Curve commands. There are settings to control the minimum distance between sampled points, the stream tolerance, angle, and area. You can also enable the display on the status bar of the stream acceptance criteria as line string or curve stream vertices are placed.

Views

The view settings allow you to define precisely the size in pixels of a view window, to restrict window resizing operations to maintain proportionality, and to specify a raster image as a view window background.

Working Units

MicroStation's working units are flexible. They let you create an electronic model of a product in any desired measurement system. If you wish to lay out a property survey line in rods and chains, you can adjust MicroStation's working units to accommodate this need. If you decide you would rather use meters, adjust the working units. Whether you need to draw the map of your country in miles, or the model of an atomic structure in angstroms, you can adjust MicroStation's working units to accommodate the measurement system you need.

An understanding of the MicroStation design plane (2D) or design cube (3D) is helpful when manipulating working units.

MicroStation's design plane, or drawing area, when measured in terms of a positional unit, is also referred to as the unit of resolution (UOR). A positional unit is indivisible, is fixed in size, and represents the smallest distance MicroStation can measure.

What is the size of MicroStation's design plane? It's a square with each side measuring over 4.2 billion positional units. If you are working in a three-dimensional design file, it is a cube with each side measuring over 4.2 billion positional units. To be exact, the side of a design plane or cube measures 4,294,967,295 positional units.

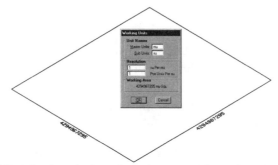

The MicroStation design plane for a two-dimensional drawing is a square with sides over 4.2 billion positional units long.

You probably have heard that MicroStation's design plane is based on a 32-bit integer address space. This is correct. If you take a 32-bit long address space and compute the largest number $(=2^{32})$ it can accommodate, you will come up with the size of the design plane.

NOTE: The size of the design plane is just one of many areas where the binary nature of a computer's address space manifests itself in MicroStation. The eight line styles $(=2^3)$, the 32 line weights $(=2^5)$ and the 64 levels $(=2^7)$ are other examples.

Did you notice the above note says there are 64 levels, while the level map in the Primary toolbox only displays 63? Actually there are 64 levels, from level 0 through level 63, but only levels 1 through 63 are available to you for use. Level 0 is reserved for the placement of headers, such as a cell header.

With this background information on the design plane or cube, you are now ready to tackle working units.

MicroStation implements the concept of working units to accommodate any possible system of measurement. A working unit is a collection of the following three component units:

- positional unit
- sub unit
- master unit

You group several positional units to make up a sub unit. Then you group several sub units to make up a master unit. You can name a master and a sub unit whatever you want, such as a foot and an inch, or a meter and a millimeter. The number of positional units you group together to make a sub unit determines the accuracy of the measurement system you set in your design file.

Think about this for a minute. As you increase the number of positional units (PU) that make up a sub unit (SU), the size of the design plane when measured in terms of master units (MU) shrinks. This fact can be expressed with the following equation:

```
size of design plane in MU = 4294967295 / (no. of SU per MU x no. of PU per SU)
```

As is evident, there is a trade-off between the size of the design plane in master units and the accuracy of measurement in the design file.

TIP: When setting working units for your design file think of the smallest unit of measure you need to dimension, whether a sixteenth of an inch or a mm, then provide for accuracy of at least one-hundredth (even smaller if practical) that dimension to minimize rounding errors.

Exercise: Setting Working Units

The purpose of this exercise is to help you get a sense of the inverse relationship between the size of the design plane and the accuracy of measurement in a design file.

For this exercise you will need the file `workunit.dgn` from the `\Exercise\Ch03` folder on the accompanying CD-ROM. Make a copy of this file on your computer's hard drive before proceeding.

The following steps guide you through this exercise.

1. Start MicroStation if it's not already running. The MicroStation Manager dialog box appears on your screen.
2. Use the MicroStation Manager dialog box to browse your computer's hard disk and locate the folder where you copied the exercise file.
3. Double-click the exercise file `workunit.dgn` to open it in MicroStation. It is an empty design file with no elements.
4. Open the Design File Settings dialog box by selecting Design File from the Settings menu.
5. Select the Working Units category in the Design File Settings dialog box. The dialog box should look similar to that shown in the figure below.

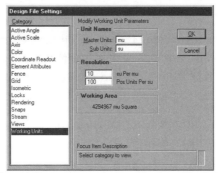

Select the Working Units category in the Design File Settings dialog box.

6. Change the master units designation from `mu` to `ft` for feet and the sub units designation from `su` to `in` for inch. As you tab into the Resolution groupbox, notice how the label next to the first text field changed from `su per mu` to `in per ft`.

7. Change the resolution to `12` in per ft and watch the working area section of the dialog box as you press the tab key to move to the next field. The working area changes from 4294967 to 3579139.

8. Change the second resolution field to 1000 positional units per inch. This means that your design file can accurately measure a distance up to one-thousandth of an inch. Now watch the working area section of the dialog box as you press the tab key to make this change take effect. The working area reduces to 357193.

9. Click the OK button to close the Design File Settings dialog box. MicroStation displays an alert message that the size of any existing elements in the design file will change. Click OK to accept the change.

This concludes the exercise. Here you saw that as you increase the number of sub units per master unit or positional units per sub unit, the size of the working area in master units reduces. Any time you change working units MicroStation displays the alert message you saw in the exercise.

NOTE: To have MicroStation save changes between sessions to the working units in a design file, you must choose Save Settings from the File menu.

Packaging Elements and Attributes in Templates

MicroStation offers a flexible environment suitable for any architectural or engineering design discipline. Considering this flexibility, there needs to be a way to standardize the use of working units and other settings for consistency between drawings created by different designers within the same organization.

To this end MicroStation implements the concept of seed files and workspaces.

Seed Files

A *seed file* is similar to a document template in a word processor. When you create a new drawing, you select a seed file to use as a template for its creation. This was discussed in chapter 1.

A seed file need not be blank. In addition to the design file settings you may have saved in it, you can store graphics such as a border and company logo. This way, when a new drawing is created from this seed file, it will always contain the desired standard graphics as well.

MicroStation comes with several sample seed files you can use as is. Or you can create your own set of seed files for your work place. The system seed files are located in the following directory:

`C:\Bentley\Workspace\System\Seed`

This directory has a collection of `.dgn` (for creating new design files) `.cel` (for creating new cell libraries) and `.sht` (for composing drawing sheets using the Drawing Composition tool) seed files.

Should you create your own seed files that will be adopted as an organization-wide standard, you'll want to save them in the following directory on all computers:

`C:\Bentley\Workspace\Standards\Seed`

Don't be content with the seed files delivered with MicroStation. Create your own. As your experience with MicroStation grows and you find yourself changing the same settings over and over, simply create a new seed file and use it as a template for new drawings.

Workspaces

Whereas seed files deal with the creation of new design files and cell libraries, workspaces deal with all the other customizable aspects of MicroStation.

MicroStation implements a host of customizable settings and tools, such as the settings manager, glossary files, menu bar, color tables, collection of cell libraries, level naming conventions, macros, and applications. A *workspace* is a mechanism to help organize several sets of customizable settings to serve varying design needs within an organization.

For example, your organization might want to implement different workspaces for its design disciplines. There might be a civil workspace for the civil engineering discipline and there might be an electrical workspace for the electrical engineering discipline.

The implementation and creation of workspaces is a CAD administrative task and is discussed in a separate chapter later in this book.

Working with Elements

Earlier in this chapter you learned about the different element types MicroStation supports. A design file stores these elements. MicroStation provides a variety of tools you can use to display information about elements and their linear and angular relationship to other elements. It also provides tools to help you manipulate a group of elements as a set in a single step. This section of the chapter helps you discover those tools.

Displaying Information About

You can display information about elements in your design file by using the Element Information tool. You invoke this tool by clicking the Analyze Element icon on the Primary toolbox as shown in the figure below.

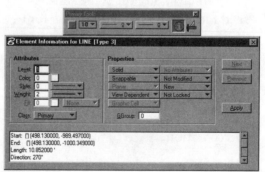

Click the Analyze Element icon in the Primary toolbox, identify an element in the design file, and accept it to invoke the Element Information dialog box.

When you click the Analyze Element icon in the Primary toolbox, MicroStation prompts you to identify an element. On identifying an element with a data point you are further prompted to either accept the highlighted element, or reject it. A data point accepts the selection, a Reset button click rejects the selection letting you identify another one. When you accept an element, the Element Information dialog box appears.

The Element Information dialog box analyzes the element you identify and displays its element type ID in the title bar. The figure above shows that the element identified is a line and that it's a Type 3 element.

This dialog box also displays all element attributes, properties and coordinate information. It is worth noting that you can use this dialog box to change element attributes and properties. To edit an element's attributes or properties, simply change the information displayed in any of the edit fields and click the Apply button.

Measuring Elements

To help you determine an element's linear, angular, and other measurements MicroStation provides the Measure toolbox. This toolbox also contains tools to compute distances between points and elements and angles between elements.

The Measure toolbox is located in the left column on the seventh row of the Main tool frame. The figure below shows the toolbox torn away from the Main tool frame.

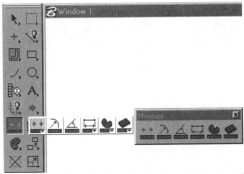

The Measure toolbox is located in the Main tool frame.

The Measure toolbox implements six measurement tools. We will use each of these six tools in the following exercise.

Exercise: Using the Measure Toolbox

The purpose of this exercise is to help you become familiar with the Measure toolbox.

For this exercise you will need the file `measure.dgn` from the `\Exercise\Ch03` folder on the accompanying CD-ROM. Make a copy of this file on your computer's hard drive before proceeding.

The following steps guide you through this exercise.

1. Start MicroStation if it's not already running. The MicroStation Manager dialog box appears on your screen.
2. Use the MicroStation Manager dialog box to browse your computer's hard disk and locate the folder where you copied the exercise file.
3. Double-click the exercise file `measure.dgn` to open it in MicroStation. Your view window will display an arc, a circle, two lines, and a sphere along with a few numbers to guide your data point sequence.

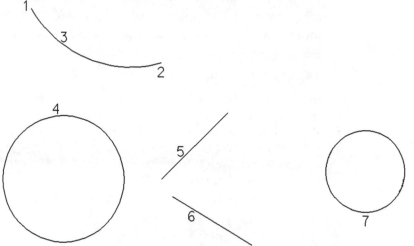

The exercise file should look like this figure on your screen.

4. Invoke the Measure Distance tool, the first icon on the Measure toolbox. Make sure the Distance option button in the Tool Settings window is set to Between Points. Snap to the arc end point **1** by first clicking the tentative

button and then accepting it with a data point. Follow this by similarly snapping and accepting the end point **2** of the arc. The right side of the status bar will display the message, "Dist = 2.2902m." This is the straight line distance between the two end points of the arc.

5. With the Measure Distance tool still selected, change the Distance option button in the Tool Settings window to Along Element. Snap to the end points **1** and **2** of the arc as was done in step 4 above. The status bar will display the message "Dist = 2.4627m." This is the distance between the two endpoints when measured along the arc.

6. With the Measure Distance tool still selected, change the Distance option button in the Tool Settings window to Perpendicular. Identify the arc close to the location identified as the number 3. A dynamic line that stays perpendicular to the arc follows your cursor. Snap to the top quadrant point of the circle by clicking the tentative button when the cursor is close to the location identified as the number 4. The cursor will jump to the top quadrant, and the circle will be highlighted. Accept the snapped location with a data point. The status bar will display the message, "Dist = 0.9774m." This is the distance of a line from the top quadrant of the circle and perpendicular to the arc.

7. With the Measure Distance tool still selected, change the Distance option button in the Tool Settings window to Minimum Between. Identify the arc with a data point close to the location identified as the number 3. Then identify the circle with a data point close to the location identified as the number 4. Then accept the selection with a data point. A line representing the minimum distance between the two elements will be drawn in the highlight color and the status bar will display the message, "Dist = 0.9256m."

8. Click Reset.

9. Invoke the Measure Radius tool from the Measure toolbox and identify the circle with a data point close to the location identified as the number 4. The circle displays in the highlight color and waits for you to accept this selection with a data point before displaying in the status bar the message, "Radius = 1.0000." This is the radius of the circle.

10. Invoke the Measure Angle tool from the Measure toolbox. You are prompted to identify the first element. Identify line 5 followed by line 6. Accept the selection with a data point. The status bar will display the message, "Angle = 75°." This is the angle between the two lines.

11. Invoke the Measure Length tool from the Measure toolbox. You are prompted to identify an element. Identify line 5 followed by a data point to accept the selection. The status bar will display the message, "Length:

1.5000m, Angle = 45°." This is the length of the line and its inclination to the view axis. You may want to try identifying the arc to see if will measure the length of the arc element. (Hint: It will.)

12. Invoke the Measure Area tool from the Measure toolbox. Make sure the Method option button in the Tool Settings window is set to Element. You are prompted to identify an element. Identify circle 4 followed by a data point to accept the selection. The status bar will display the message, "A = 3.1416 SQ m, P = 6.2832." These are the enclosed area and perimeter of the circle.

13. Invoke the Measure Volume tool from the Measure toolbox. You are prompted to identify an element. Identify the sphere 7 followed by a data point to accept the selection. The status bar will display the message, "Volume: 1.12417 Cubic m, Surface Area: 5.22844."

This concludes the exercise. Here you discovered MicroStation's measuring tools and how they can help you measure geometric attributes of elements.

Grouping for Operations

In chapter 2 you learned a few element manipulation commands. You operated upon each element one at a time. As design files get larger and you have a need to manipulate several elements together, MicroStation provides the tools to make your work simpler.

In this section we discover MicroStation's tools that let you group elements together for many operations.

Element Selector

The Element Selection tool is the top left icon with the shape of an arrow in the Main tool frame. It is the default tool that activates when you terminate certain commands. When you identify an element with the Element Selection tool it gets selected and MicroStation displays handles around it, or if you set a workspace preference, MicroStation displays the element in the selection set color.

You can add elements to the selection set by holding down the Ctrl key and clicking additional elements. Should you identify an element that is already selected, that element will be unselected.

NOTE: The third field from the right on the status bar is called the element selection field. It displays the number of elements in the current selection set.

You can add several elements to the selection set by clicking and holding down the data point button while dragging the cursor diagonally to enclose the desired elements in a rectangular area. If you wish to keep the existing selection set and add several elements to it, hold down the Ctrl key while you drag the cursor diagonally to create the selection rectangle.

Many MicroStation commands change their behavior when a selection set is active. For instance when you invoke the Delete Element tool, MicroStation prompts you to identify an element and then accept it. However, if a selection set is active when the command is invoked, all elements in the selection set are deleted without any prompts.

To unselect all elements from the current selection set, with the Element Selection tool still active, click an empty area in the view window.

PowerSelector

The PowerSelector tool is the second icon in the Element Selection toolbox to the right of the Element Selection tool, as shown in the figure below.

PowerSelector offers several Tool Settings window options.

PowerSelector offers far greater flexibility in element selection than its older cousin, the Element Selection tool. It offers four methods for drawing a temporary selection shape and four modes of operation. In addition, a set of selection information drop-down fields help control element selection by element type and its attributes.

The four PowerSelector methods are Individual, Block, Shape, and Line. When PowerSelector is active, you can quickly switch between them by pressing the keys Q, W, E, and R or the keys U, I, O, and P.

The four PowerSelector modes are Add, Subtract, Invert, and Select All. You can quickly switch between them by pressing the keys A, S, D, and F or the keys J, K, L, and ";".

When you have the Individual method and Invert mode set for PowerSelector it operates similar to the Element Selection tool when you have the Ctrl key pressed.

To add elements that cross an imaginary line set PowerSelector's method to Line and mode to Add and click two data points to identify the line's end points. All elements that cross the line will be added to the selection set.

The Block and Shape methods help you draw a rectangular or polygon selection shape. All elements fully enclosed within the block or shape are added, subtracted or inverted from the selection set depending on the mode. If you click the Block or Shape method icon twice, the icon changes shape and the tool begins to operate upon all elements that cross the block or shape.

PowerSelector's Select All mode selects all elements in the design file if no elements are selected. If some elements are selected, clicking the Select All mode unselects all elements.

The downward pointing arrow in the lower right corner of the PowerSelector's Tool Settings window, when clicked, makes the Selection Information fields available. Here you can key in an element type or any of its attributes you would like to have PowerSelector use to filter out selected elements.

NOTE: When the Selection Information fields are active in the PowerSelector's Tool Settings window, the method and mode shortcut keys are disabled.

Select All

To select all elements in the design file from the Edit menu, choose Select All.

Select By Attributes

To add elements to the selection set, filter MicroStation's ability to identify or locate elements you click on, and to control their display based on their type and attributes, invoke the Select By Attributes dialog box shown in the figure below by choosing Select By Attributes from the Edit menu.

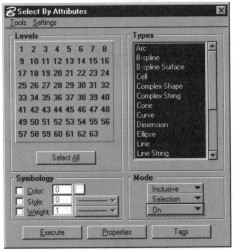

The Select By Attributes dialog box.

The Levels section in the dialog box is used to identify the levels you wish to include in your search criteria. You can individually click the levels of interest, or drag the mouse over a group of levels, or use the Select All/Clear All button.

The Types section in the dialog box lets you select the element types you wish to include in your search criteria. If you only want to operate upon arc elements, select Arc in the Types list box and deselect all other element types.

The Symbology section in the dialog box lets you specify the color, line style or line weight to include in your search criteria. If you wish to ignore the symbology of all elements during the search operation, leave the checkboxes unchecked.

The Mode section in the dialog box has three option buttons. The first option button lets you include or exclude the elements the tool retrieves from its search. The second option button lets you operate on the elements in three ways: Selection adds elements to the selection set, Location restricts element location tools to operate on elements searched, and Display restricts the display of elements to those that meet the search criteria. The third option button offers two choices: On implies that the search criteria is effective, Off implies that the search criteria is ignored.

The Properties button on the dialog box lets you specify values for element properties to include in the search, and the Tags button on the dialog box lets you specify values for tag data to be used in the search.

When you click the Execute button this tool selects, locates, or displays elements in accordance with the search criteria you have specified.

Group/Ungroup/Lock/Unlock

This collection of four commands on the Edit menu is normally disabled. However, these commands become available the moment you add elements to the selection set using either the Element Selection tool, PowerSelector, Select All, or Select By Attributes.

After adding elements to a selection set when you invoke the Group command from the Edit menu you associate the elements together into an *orphan cell*. The term *orphan* implies that the cell has no name and was created on the fly and not imported from a cell library. From now on, this group of elements will behave as a single unit.

The Ungroup command on the Edit menu breaks previously grouped elements into their component elements.

The Lock command on the Edit menu freezes selected elements in place so they cannot be modified. This is helpful when you wish to protect elements from inadvertent modifications.

Again, the Unlock command on the Edit menu reverses the action of the Lock command. To unlock locked elements, first select them and then invoke the Unlock command.

Fence Operations

Before there was the Element Selection tool or any of the other selection set tools discussed above, there were fence operations. The concept of fence in MicroStation goes back to the days when the software was called IGDS and ran on minicomputers from Intergraph.

A *fence* is a closed shape you draw around elements to group them. A fence needs to be already in place before MicroStation can work with its contents. Though you can see a fence on screen when you place it, it is not an element that is a part of the design file. It is simply a temporary shape displayed on screen to help you isolate elements you wish to work with.

Many of MicroStation's element manipulation tools such as Copy, Move, Scale, Rotate and Mirror display a checkbox labeled Use Fence in their Tool Settings window. To have MicroStation use the contents of the fence for these operations, you must enable the Use Fence checkbox.

TIP: In order to undo fence operations that manipulate a large number of elements, your Undo Buffer may need to be larger than the default. Change the value of the Undo Buffer in the Preferences dialog box, accessed from the Workspace menu.

The Fence toolbox is located to the right of the Element Selection toolbox in the first row of the Main tool frame. See the figure below.

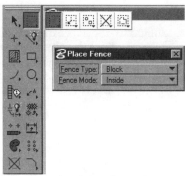

The Fence toolbox is to the right of the Element Selection tool.

The Fence toolbox contains five tools: Place Fence, Modify Fence, Manipulate Fence Contents, Delete Fence Contents, and Drop Fence Contents.

To place a fence in a view window, use the Place Fence tool. The Tool Settings window associated with this tool displays two option buttons: Fence Type and Fence Mode. The Fence Type option determines the fence shape and the method of placement, the Fence Mode option determines which elements in the fence, and how, they should be manipulated by fence operations.

The following table describes the available fence types.

Fence Type	Description
Block	Rectangular fence placed by identifying its diagonal points
Shape	Polygon fence placed by identifying its vertices
Circle	Circular fence placed by identifying its center and radius point
Element	Polygon fence placed by tracing the identified closed shape in a design file
From View	Rectangular fence placed around the perimeter of a view window
From Design File	Rectangular fence placed around the extents of all elements in the design file

The following table describes the available fence modes.

Fence Mode	Fence Operation Manipulates
Inside	Elements completely enclosed within the fence
Overlap	Elements completely enclosed within and crossing the fence boundary
Clip	Elements completely enclosed within and inside portions of elements crossing the fence boundary
Void	Elements completely outside the fence
Void-Overlap	Elements completely outside and crossing the fence boundary
Void-Clip	Elements completely outside and outside portions of elements crossing the fence boundary

To remove a fence from your view window, simply invoke the Place Fence command and proceed with another command without placing the fence.

To manipulate the shape or change the location of an existing fence on screen use the Modify Fence tool. The Tool Settings window associated with this tool offers the familiar Fence Mode option button and the new Modify Mode option button. The Modify Mode option button offers two choices: Vertex and Position.

To modify the vertex of a fence select the Vertex option from the Modify Mode option button, identify the fence vertex to modify and click a data point to define its new location. To move the fence to another location, select the Position option from the Modify Mode option button, identify the origin point for the fence move operation and click a data point to define the distance and direction with respect to the origin point.

To manipulate the elements in a fence use the Manipulate Fence Contents tool. The Tool Settings window associated with this tool offers the familiar Fence Mode option button and the new Operation option button. The Operation option button offers six choices: Copy, Move, Rotate, Scale, Mirror, and Stretch.

The following table describes the available fence manipulation operations.

Operation	Action Performed by Operation
Copy	Copies fence contents when you identify an origin and a destination point
Move	Moves fence contents when you identify an origin and a destination point
Rotate	Rotates fence contents by active angle or when you identify a pivot point and the rotation angle
Scale	Scales fence contents by the active scale when you click a data point

Operation	Action Performed by Operation
Mirror	Mirrors fence contents about a horizontal or a vertical line when you click a data point, or about an arbitrary line when you identify the two points for the mirror line
Stretch	Moves the vertices of elements completely enclosed within the fence and stretches the sides of elements that cross the fence boundary when you identify an origin and a destination point

To delete the contents of a fence, use the Delete Fence Contents tool. On invoking the tool you are prompted to accept or reject the fence contents. You accept the deletion of fence contents, based on the Fence Mode qualifier, by clicking a data point in the view window.

To drop the complex status of fence contents, you select the Drop Fence Contents tool. On invoking the tool you are prompted to accept or reject the fence contents. You accept the modification of complex elements in the fence by clicking a data point in the view window. The term *drop complex status* refers to the modification of complex elements such as cells and complex chains to their component elements.

Groups Toolbox

MicroStation dedicates a separate toolbox for its other tools that relate to grouping elements. The Groups toolbox is in the left column of the sixth row of the Main tool frame, as shown in the figure below.

The Groups toolbox.

The following table describes, in sequential order, from left to right, the seven tools found in this toolbox.

Tool Name	Description
Drop Element	Drops the grouped status of complex, dimension, line string, shape, multiline, shared cell, solid and text into component elements
Create Complex Chain	Creates a complex chain from a series of elements connected end to end at their vertices
Create Complex Shape	Creates a closed complex shape from a series of elements connected end to end at their vertices
Create Region	Creates a closed complex shape by performing boolean operations such as intersection, union, difference on overlapping closed elements
Add To Graphic Group	Tags identified elements with a unique graphic group number so they may be manipulated as a group when desired
Drop From Graphic Group	Removes elements from a graphic group
Group Hole	Creates an orphan cell from an outer closed shape (solid) with interior closed shapes (holes)

Elements in a graphic group can be manipulated either individually or as a group. To manipulate them individually, disable the Graphic Group lock. To manipulate them as a group, enable the Graphic Group lock.

You can toggle the Graphic Group lock from the locks menu that pops up when you click the lock icon on the status bar. Or, you can toggle it from the Locks submenu in the Settings menu on MicroStation's menu bar.

Snapping for Precision

The name of the game in CAD is precision. To precisely locate data points by their coordinate values in the design plane, use the precision key-ins listed in tabular format under the *Coordinate Input* section in chapter 1. To precisely locate the keypoints on an element—endpoint, midpoint, intersection, and others—click the tentative button.

As its name implies, the tentative button is used to tentatively locate a keypoint on an element. If it does not snap to the desired location, simply move the cursor and click the tentative button again. The tentative button does not pass the coordinates of its location to a command waiting for coordinate input until you accept its location with a data point.

NOTE: A tentative point must be followed by a data point for the coordinates of its location to be passed as input to a command.

The keypoint snap mode is the default, with a value of 2 for the snap divisor. When you click a data point near an element, the tentative cursor will jump to find element keypoints and the midpoints between the keypoints. A line has two keypoints: its two endpoints. A circle has five keypoints: its center and four quadrants. The keypoint snap is an intelligent snap mode—it adjusts based on the element type identified. You will find it convenient to leave the snap mode to keypoint for normal operations.

TIP: To have the tentative button jump to third-points between keypoints, change the snap divisor value to 3 by keying in KY=3. To locate quarter points between keypoints, key in KY=4.

When snapping, if you can't locate element keypoints, make sure the snap lock is enabled. Click the locks field in the status bar (look for the lock icon) to display the locks pop-up menu. Select Toggles to display the Lock Toggles dialog box, then enable the Snap Lock checkbox.

You can temporarily override the default snap mode at any time by invoking the snap menu.

To invoke the snaps menu, do one of the following:

- Click the snaps field on the status bar. It is located to the left of the lock icon.
- Click the tentative button in a view window while holding down the Shift key.
- Select Settings, then Snaps from the menu bar.

The first option in the Snaps menu reads Button Bar. If you frequently switch between snap modes, you may want to keep this button bar open.

Selecting a snap mode from the Snaps menu overrides the default snap mode for the duration of a single coordinate input. To change the default snap mode, select it from the Snaps menu while pressing the Shift key.

The following table lists the snap modes in sequence, from left to right, available in the Snap Mode button bar.

Snap Mode	Tentative Click
Nearest	snaps to point on element closest to cursor
Keypoint	snaps to keypoint on an element (number of snappable points depends on the snap divisor value)
Midpoint	snaps to midpoint of an element or segment of a complex element
Center	snaps to centroid of an element
Origin	snaps to origin of a cell
Bisector	snaps to midpoint of an entire element
Intersection	snaps to intersection of two elements
Tangent	constrains element to be tangent to another element (not valid for all commands)
Tangent From	constrains element to be tangent to a specified point on another element (not valid for all commands)
Perpendicular	constrains element to be perpendicular to another element (not valid for all commands)
Perpendicular From	constrains element to be perpendicular from a specified point on another element (not valid for all commands)
Parallel	constrains element to be parallel to another element (not valid for all commands)
Through Point	constrains element to pass through designated point in design plane (not valid for all commands)
Point On	constrains element to begin or end at designated point on another element (not valid for all commands)

TIP: New MicroStation users have difficulty using the intersection snap mode because it requires two tentative button clicks. Here is a tip to using it successfully. With the intersection snap active, tentative click the first element followed by a tentative click on the second intersecting element. The cursor will jump to the intersection of both elements. Now you can accept the tentative cursor's location with a data point.

Controlling the Cursor

The pointing device, whether mouse or digitizing tablet, is the primary tool for interacting with MicroStation. With it you select choices from menus, invoke pop-up menus, identify points in the design plane, select elements, snap to keypoints on elements, and select commands from a tablet menu.

MicroStation offers several settings to constrain the movement of the cursor in a view window. It also offers settings that affect the appearance of the cursor.

Constraining Cursor Movement

You might recall that while working through the exercises in chapter 2 the cursor was constrained to only move from one grid point to another. This was very convenient for the exercises. Rather than using precision key ins, which can be tedious when used over and over, you could simply count the number of jumps the cursor made and know its exact position.

To constrain the cursor to move on grid points, enable the grid lock. Do this by clicking the locks field in the status bar to open the Locks pop-up menu and select Grid. If a check mark appears next to Grid when you invoke the Locks pop-up menu, grid lock is already enabled. Alternatively, key in LOCK=GR in the Key-in window to toggle the status of the grid lock.

To set up grid parameters see the discussion on grid in the *Design File Settings* section in this chapter. To turn on or off the display of a grid use the View Attributes dialog box. See the last exercise in chapter 4 on invoking and using this dialog box.

You can also constrain the cursor to move along the horizontal and vertical axes. This is useful when you are drawing orthogonal shapes

To constrain the cursor to move along the axis parameters defined in the Axis category in the Design File Settings dialog box, enable axis lock. Do this by clicking the locks field in the status bar to open the Locks pop-up menu and select Axis. If a check mark appears next to Axis when you invoke the Locks pop-up menu, axis lock is already enabled. Alternatively, key in LOCK=AX in the Key-in window to toggle the status of the axis lock. To constrain the cursor to move along isometric axes, select Isometric from the Locks pop-up menu, or key in LOCK=IS to toggle the isometric lock status.

NOTE: AccuDraw, discussed in detail later, is designed to reduce, among other things, the need to toggle cursor locks during drawing operations.

Changing Cursor Display

MicroStation lets you change its crosshair cursor. The default crosshair size is small. Key in SET CURSOR FULL for a crosshair that runs across the full screen. This mode is convenient when aligning elements visually. Key in SET CURSOR SMALL to restore the crosshair to its default value. Alternatively, invoke the Preferences dialog box from the Workspace menu and select Normal for the small crosshair, or Full View for the full cursor from the Pointer Size option button in the Operation category of the dialog box.

While you have the Preferences dialog box open, notice the Pointer Type option directly beneath Pointer Size. There are two choices for Pointer Type: Orthogonal and Isometric. The default pointer type is orthogonal that aligns with the horizontal and vertical axes. Switch it to isometric when creating isometric drawings.

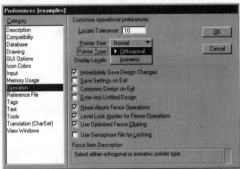

Control the cursor in the Operation category on the Preferences dialog box.

This concludes our introduction to the MicroStation CAD environment. In the next chapter you learn how to navigate a drawing.

Chapter 4

Mastering View Control
How to Navigate a Drawing

Unlike the paper you draw on at a drafting table, the MicroStation design plane is vast. You create full scale geometric models on it. When you model a commercial building, it could span several hundred feet. When you model the map of a country, it could span several thousand kilometers. When you model an atom, it would span a microscopic distance. Clearly, you need *view control* tools to navigate the design plane.

The view navigation tools MicroStation provides can be considered modes of transportation we use to travel from one place to another. They also can be compared to optical devices, like the microscope and telescope you use to get a better view of things, depending on their size and distance.

To obtain a bird's-eye view of Earth, you would have to fly high in a spaceship. In MicroStation you use the Fit View and Zoom Out commands to see the bird's-eye view of your model. To go from one town to another, you would likely drive. In MicroStation you use the scroll bars or the Pan command to move from one area of the model to another.

Let's revisit the paper on the drafting table. Because of the paper's limited size and the relatively wide angle of your vision, you are always aware of the entire drawing area no matter which part of it you may be working on.

This is certainly not the case in CAD, where you work on a vast design plane. When you are working up close on a detail of your model, the rest of the model is simply not visible. This is very much like gazing at the skies with a telescope. When you are focused on a specific star, you lose awareness of the rest of the sky. This is *tunnel vision*.

To help you cope with tunnel vision, MicroStation supports eight view windows. It's like having eight pairs of eyes with variable magnifications so you can look at the same model from different perspectives.

In this chapter we cover everything you need to know to keep your bearings straight within the design plane. You learn how to move from one part to another of the electronic drawing model. You also learn, through an exercise, how to exploit the benefits multiple view windows provide.

The primary focus in this chapter is 2D. We will cover 3D view control issues in the 3D modeling and rendering chapter.

Following is a list of topics covered in this chapter.

- The role of a view window in MicroStation's drawing environment
- Anatomy of a view window
- Introduction to view control commands
- Exercises to help you master MicroStation's view controls

For the new MicroStation user, an understanding of the above information is vital. Much like the freedom you experienced when you got your driver's license, a good working knowledge of view controls will help you explore all facets of your model.

For the experienced MicroStation user, the exercises demonstrating the use of multiple view windows and view rotation may be helpful if you have not explored these features before. If you installed the JMDL examples on your computer, you will invoke your first JMDL dialog box immediately following the saved view exercise.

Understanding View Windows

In the exercises from previous chapters, you worked within the confines of a single view window labeled *Window 1*. MicroStation, however, implements the use of up to eight view windows.

View windows in MicroStation are simply portholes to the design plane you draw on, just like a telescope is a porthole to the sky. When you open multiple view windows during a design session, they all display the contents of the same design file—much like eight telescopes, when pointed towards heaven at the same time, would display the same cosmic event.

To discuss view windows further, imagine yourself in a window seat in a train car while a companion sits in a window seat in another car. As the train travels through wide open spaces, both of you see the same view: the distant mountains, or farmland.

However, while the train waits at a station, the view from your window may be very different from your companion's view at their window. You might see a billboard and a light pole. Your companion may see passengers waiting on a bench. While both of you are looking at the same station, each has a different view. This is the same tunnel vision mentioned earlier.

MicroStation's view windows are similar to train windows; they provide a view of the world (or design file) around you. One significant difference exists between a train window and a MicroStation view window. In a MicroStation view window, you can increase or decrease the magnification of your view when needed.

Exercise: Working with Views

In this exercise you will open several view windows, use view control commands, and use an element placement command across views. You will need to copy to your computer's hard drive the file `openview.dgn` from the `\Exercise\Ch04` folder on the accompanying CD-ROM.

The following steps guide you through this exercise.

1. Start MicroStation if it is not already running. If you need help starting MicroStation, refer to chapter 1.

2. Select the file `openview.dgn` in the MicroStation Manager dialog box and click the OK button. If the file does not appear in the dialog box, use its Directories list box to locate the folder where you saved it.

3. MicroStation opens the design file and displays the name of the file in the title bar. Notice that although the design file is open, no view window displays on your screen. It is your task to open view window 1.

4. From the Window menu, select Open/Close, then Dialog. The Open/Close dialog box opens. This dialog box has eight toggle buttons representing each of the eight supported view windows. Notice that none of the buttons is on; thus, no view window is active.

5. Click the button labeled **1** in the Open/Close dialog box. View window 1 opens, as shown in the following figure.

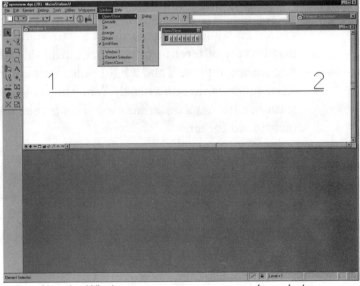

Use the Window menu to open a new view window.

Alternatively, from the Window menu, select Open/Close, then 1, to open view window 1 without using the Open/Close dialog box. Let's now open view windows 2 and 3.

6. Click the buttons labeled **2** and **3** in the Open/Close dialog box to open view windows 2 and 3. Your screen should look like the following figure.

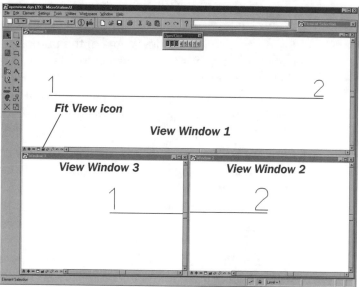

Open view windows 1, 2 and 3 for this exercise.

7. The design file contains a single line element and two text elements that label the two end points of the line. View window 1 at the top displays the entire line. Window 2 on the right displays the right end of the same line. Window 3 on the left displays only the left end of the line.

8. Each of the three view windows has a vertical scroll bar and a horizontal scroll bar. To the left of the horizontal scroll bar is a set of nine icons called the *view control bar*. To navigate the design file through a specific window, use its view control bar.

9. Click the top arrow in the vertical scroll bar of view window 1 several times. Notice that the line scrolls downward until it vanishes from view. The line still exists in the design file, but you positioned the view window so that it can no longer display the line.

10. Click the Fit View icon, the fifth icon from the left, in the view control bar of view window 1. The Fit View command displays the entire contents of the design file in the view.

11. Invoke the Place Line command, the second icon in the Linear Elements toolbox in the Main tool frame. You are prompted to enter the first point for the line. In view window 1 click a point directly above the text label designating endpoint 1 of the line. A line segment follows your cursor. Move the cursor in window 1 toward the text label 2 and notice the display in windows 2 and 3. Keep moving the cursor while watching the other two view windows. Don't click the second data point yet.

12. Position the cursor in view window 3 and move the cursor while watching the other two view windows. Again, the purpose here is to get used to the cursor movement and the associated display in the other windows. Don't click the second data point yet.

13. Position the cursor in view window 2 below the text label designating endpoint 2 of the line and click a data point to place the line. Click the Reset button to restart the Place Line command.

14. Click the Fit View icon in view window 2's view control bar. The view's magnification changes to fit the entire design file within the boundaries of the view window.

15. Click a data point anywhere in view window 3. The view magnification changes to fit the design file within its boundaries. Notice that you did not have to click the Fit View icon in the view window's view control bar. As long as the Fit View command is active you simply click inside the view where you will apply the command.

16. Close view windows 2 and 3 by toggling buttons 2 and 3 in the Open/Close dialog box.

17. Maximize view window 1 by clicking the Maximize button in the view window's title bar.

18. Fit the design file in the view by clicking the Fit View icon in the window's view control bar.

This concludes the exercise. You may now close the file and exit MicroStation. If you wish to practice more, try using the other commands under the Window menu. The following table describes the five commands under the Window menu.

Command in Window Menu	Action Performed by Command
Cascade	Arranges open view windows in an overlapping arrangement.
Tile	Arranges open view windows side by side.

Command in Window Menu	Action Performed by Command
Arrange	Cleans up window arrangement to remove overlaps.
Groups	Invokes Window Groups dialog box to let you organize and operate upon windows in a group.
Scroll Bars	Toggles the display of scroll bars in view windows.

In addition to window-related commands, MicroStation's Window menu displays the names of active view windows and dialog boxes. As you open more windows and dialog boxes, the list grows to display each. This list of open windows and dialog boxes lets you know what is open and to help you switch to one of them even if it is obscured or hidden under another window.

As you moved the cursor between view windows in the above exercise you probably noticed that the cursor movement and associated element display was seamless. Unlike dialog boxes that must first be made active so they get the focus before you can interact with them, MicroStation's view windows are always active. You do not have to click inside a view window to make it active before entering a data point in the view, as must be done in a dialog box if several are open concurrently. This is a subtle but important difference, because not all CAD packages implement concurrently active view windows.

Components of a View Window

Having used several view windows in the last section's exercise, let's take a closer look at the view window.

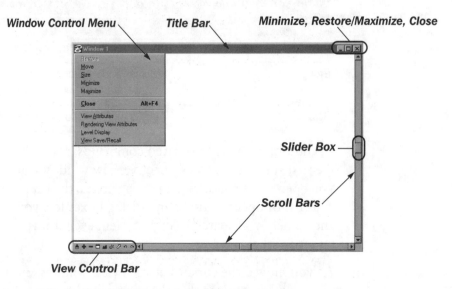

The anatomy of a view window.

Window Control Menu

When you click the Bentley B logo in a view window's title bar, the menu that drops down is called the Window Control Menu. The options in this menu are listed below.

- **Restore:** Restores the view window to its former location and size after a maximize or minimize operation.

- **Move:** Permits you to move the view window using the arrow keys on the keyboard.

- **Size:** Permits you to resize the view window using the arrow keys on the keyboard.

- **Minimize:** Minimizes the view window to a short title bar and places it along the bottom edge of the application window.

- **Maximize:** Maximizes the view window to occupy the maximum view area.

- **Close:** Closes the view window.

- **View Attributes:** Invokes the View Attributes dialog box to control the display in the view window.

- **Rendering View Attributes:** Invokes the Rendering View Attributes dialog box to control rendering-related display attributes for the view.
- **Level Display:** Invokes the Level Manager dialog box to turn on or off the display of levels in a view window.
- **View Save/Recall:** Invokes the Saved Views dialog box to manage saved views. You can save the display setting in a view and assign it a name for later recall.

Title Bar

Along the top of the view window is its title bar. It displays the name of the view window, such as *Window 1*.

The Minimize, Restore/Maximize, Close Buttons

To the right of the view window title bar are three icons representing the four most common operations from the window control menu. The center icon becomes the restore icon when the view is maximized, and it becomes the maximize icon when the view is restored.

The Scroll Bars

Along the right edge of the view window is the vertical scroll bar. You use it to scroll through the design file vertically up or down. Similarly, along the bottom edge of the view window is a horizontal scroll bar to navigate to the left or right. You used the vertical scroll bars in the earlier exercise.

NOTE: You can toggle the display of both the vertical and horizontal scroll bars by selecting Scroll Bars from the Window menu.

When you click the arrowhead on the scroll bar, your view window scrolls in the direction of the arrowhead by one-tenth the size of the view window. When you click the scroll bar between the slider box and the arrowhead, your view window scrolls by a complete screen.

The View Control Bar

Every view window has nine icons to the left of the horizontal scroll bar in an icon palette called the *view control bar.* You use these icons to control the magnification and location of the view window within the design plane. The individual commands on the view control bar, along with others, are discussed in the next section.

View Control Commands

All drawing and editing takes place within view windows. There are two categories of view commands. The first category of commands lets you manipulate the view windows themselves, such as *move*, *size*, *tile*, *maximize* and *close*. The second category of commands lets you control the display within the view windows. This section deals with the latter category of commands, called the *view control commands.*

NOTE: View control commands are special because they do not abort active element placement and editing commands when invoked. For instance, if you are in the middle of drawing a circle and find that zooming out would help you complete the operation more conveniently, you need not abort the command. Simply perform the Zoom Out operation and click the Reset button to resume the circle command where you left it.

MicroStation's view control commands are available in two locations: in the view control bar to the left of the horizontal scroll bar, and in the 2D View Control toolbox. You open the 2D View Control toolbox by selecting Tools, View Control, then 2D from MicroStation's menu bar. The following figure shows both.

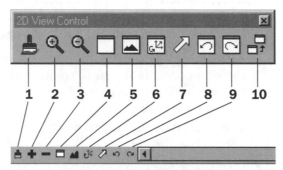

1. *Update View* 2. *Zoom In* 3. *Zoom Out* 4. *Window Area* 5. *Fit View*
6. *Rotate View* 7. *Pan View* 8. *View Previous* 9. *View Next* 10. *Copy View*

Following is a brief description of each of the view control commands.

- **Update View:** Repaints the contents in a view window. When invoked from the toolbox, and several view windows are open, you are prompted to identify the view window to update. Or, you can click the Update All Views button or press the space bar to update the contents of all open view windows.

- **Zoom In:** Increases a view window's magnification by a default factor of two so contents appear larger. You can change the magnification factor in the Tool Settings window. You can also key in the magnification factor as ZOOM IN 4.

- **Zoom Out:** Decreases a view window's magnification by a factor of two so contents appear smaller. You can change the magnification factor in the Tool Settings window. You can also key in the magnification factor as ZOOM OUT 4.

- **Window Area:** Requests the diagonal points defining a rectangular area in the design plane to display in a view window. When invoked from the view control bar, the Apply to Window checkbox is turned on for the view. When invoked from the toolbox, the checkbox is turned off.

- **Fit View:** Adjusts the magnification of a view window so that all elements in the design file are visible. The Tool Settings window offers four choices: All, Active, Reference, and Raster. All fits the contents of the design file and all attached reference files in the view window. Active ignores attached reference files when computing the area to display. Reference ignores the active design file and uses the extents of reference files when computing the area to display. Raster uses raster reference files instead of DGN reference files.

- **Rotate View:** Adjusts the orientation of a view window's axes so that the view contents appear to rotate within the window. You can negate a view rotation by selecting Unrotated from the Tool Settings window. Identify a data point in the view window to restore to unrotated state. Be sure to work through the *Rotating a View* exercise later in the chapter.

- **Pan View:** Scrolls the contents of a view window without changing its magnification by identifying an origin point and a destination point. This command supplements the panning capabilities provided by scroll bars.

While on the subject of scrolling views, let's discuss MicroStation's **Dynamic Pan** feature. To activate dynamic panning, press the Shift key on your keyboard and drag the mouse while keeping the left button pressed. The view within your window starts moving. Once dynamic panning activates, you can release the Shift key, but you need to keep holding the left mouse button down. Dynamic panning stops when you release the left mouse button. Dynamic panning is a very useful feature. It brings into view distant portions of a model without repeated panning. I encourage you to practice it.

You control the direction and speed of dynamic panning with the mouse. The farther you move the mouse from the initial location where you started dragging it, the faster the panning speed. The direction in which you drag the mouse from the starting point determines the panning direction.

- **View Previous:** Restores the contents and attributes of a view window to their previous state after a view control operation. When invoked from the toolbox, you need to identify the view window to operate upon.

- **View Next:** Reverses the action of the View Previous command. When invoked from the toolbox, you need to identify the view window the command should operate upon.

- **Copy View:** Copies the view attributes from one view to another. On invoking the command, you are first prompted to select a source view and then asked to identify destination view(s). Do not confuse this command with the Copy Element command used to copy elements in a design file. This is strictly a view control operation that simply copies the configuration of one view window to another.

NOTE: When you are working in a 3D design file, the View Control Bar displays two additional icons: Change View Perspective and Change View Display Mode.

- **Change View Perspective:** Changes the perspective displayed in a view window. Available only in 3D design files.
- **Change View Display Mode:** Changes the dynamic rendering display mode in a view window. Available only in 3D design files.

MicroStation also provides key-ins for view control commands. The following table lists a few view control commands that you can't invoke otherwise.

Key In Command	Action Performed by Command
Move Up	Scrolls upwards the view identified with a data point by a quarter of the view window height.
Move Down	Scrolls downwards the view identified with a data point by a quarter of the view window height.
Move Left	Scrolls to the left the view identified with a data point by a quarter of the view window width.
Move Right	Scrolls to the right the view identified with a data point by a quarter of the view window width.
Swap View	Swaps between the two video pages on display adapters that support it to emulate Intergraph's older dual-screen UNIX workstations. You get the error *SWAP Illegal on this hardware* if your hardware does not support this feature.
Update Grid	Repaints the grid dots, if enabled, in the view window.
Update Fence	Repaints the contents within a fence in a view window. Obviously, a fence must exist for this command to work.
Update Fence Outside	Repaints the contents outside a fence in a view window. Obviously, a fence must exist for this command to work.
View Off All	Closes all open view windows.
View On All	Opens all eight view windows.

There is one more way of invoking view control commands. With the cursor in a view window, hold the Shift key and click the Reset button. A pop-up view control menu opens at the screen location you clicked.

NOTE: The pop-up view control menu that opens when you hold the Shift key and click the Reset button, was first implemented in MicroStation V5 and has not been updated since. This will be obvious when you display the menu and read the command names and their sequence.

You've been introduced to all the view control commands implemented in MicroStation when working in two-dimensional design files. You also learned about a couple more view control commands MicroStation makes available when working in three-dimensional design files. These commands will be covered in greater detail in chapter 11, which discusses 3D modeling and rendering.

Let's practice what you've learned in the exercises that follow.

Exercise: Viewing Details in Another Window

In this exercise you will navigate a busy drawing by setting up two views. The first view will be small and to the lower left of the screen to display the entire design file. The second view will occupy most of the screen and will be used to display parts of the design file in detail for close-up work. You may find this view arrangement, one to display the entire drawing and another to display magnified portions of it, an effective antidote to tunnel vision discussed earlier.

For this exercise, you will need to copy to your computer's hard drive the file `twoviews.dgn` from the `\Exercise\Ch04` folder on the CD-ROM.

The following steps guide you through this exercise.

1. Start MicroStation if it is not already running. If you need help starting MicroStation, refer to chapter 1.
2. Select the file `twoviews.dgn` in the MicroStation Manager dialog box and click the OK button. If the file does not appear in the dialog box use its Directories list box to locate the folder where you saved it.

3. MicroStation opens the design file and displays its contents in the large view window titled *Window 1*.

4. Open view window 5. You can do this by selecting Window, Open/Close, then 5 from the menu bar. A smaller new view opens and displays a portion of the design file. You can resize this window by dragging its border like you would any other resizable window in Windows.

5. Move Window 5 from its current location in the top right corner of your screen to the lower left corner. Your screen should look similar to the figure below.

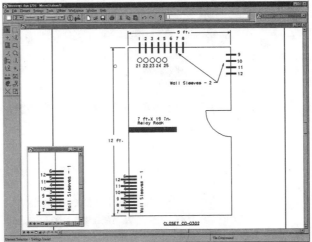

Open a small window at the lower left corner of your screen.

6. Click the Fit View icon from Window 5's view control bar. The entire design file displays in the view.

7. Click the Reset button to terminate the Fit View command.

   You have now set up two views in a configuration many designers prefer while working in drawings that are busy with detail. The smaller view in the lower left corner of the screen is used to display the entire drawing at all times. The larger view is used to display portions of the design file you need to be working on. Your task now is to edit the title block in the drawing. To do this, you must display the title block area in the larger Window 1.

8. Click the Window Area icon from Window 1's view control bar. It is important you invoke the command from the larger window's view control bar. The Tool Settings window displays the option Apply to Window 1 with its checkbox enabled. You are prompted to identify the first corner point of the proposed display area.

9. Click a data point in the smaller Window 5 close to the upper left corner of the title block, as shown in the figure below.

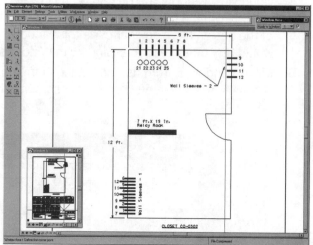

Identify upper left corner of title block in Window 5.

10. Click another data point in Window 5 to identify the lower right corner of the title block.

11. The title block area displays in the larger Window 1. Click the Reset button to terminate the Window Area command.

12. If a portion of the title block is obscured behind a window edge, you can fine-tune the display by using the scroll bars or the Dynamic Pan feature discussed earlier.

This concludes the exercise. You may now close the file and exit MicroStation. If you wish to practice more, try using the other view control commands such as Zoom In, Zoom Out, Pan and View Previous. If Window 5 accidentally gets obscured behind Window 1, bring it in front by selecting Window 5 from the Window menu.

Exercise: Rotating a View

The Rotate View command changes the orientation of a view window's axes so that view contents appear to rotate within the window. The operative phrase here is *appear to rotate*. The elements in the design file remain exactly as they are; it's only their display in the view window that is transformed by the rotation you specify.

Why would you want to rotate a view for display purposes?

Civil engineers will relate well to the answer because they use this feature most often. Consider the design of a highway that runs along the north-west direction. The survey data you received is based on the magnetic north, and it makes sense to use the data as is to draw the highway on the design plane. However, when you wish to plot the highway plan, rather than lay it out diagonally on the plot, it is conventional to have it run horizontally from left to right. This is easily accomplished by rotating the view while preserving the actual survey coordinate data.

In this exercise you will display the plan of a highway running in the north-west direction in two views. You will then rotate one of the two views so that the highway appears to run horizontally from left to right. Then you will copy the rotated view's attributes to the second window. Finally, you will negate the second view's rotation.

For this exercise you will need to copy to your computer's hard drive the file `highway.dgn` from the `\Exercise\Ch04` folder on the CD-ROM.

The following steps guide you through this exercise.

1. Start MicroStation if it is not already running. If you need help starting MicroStation, refer to chapter 1.
2. Select the file `highway.dgn` in the MicroStation Manager dialog box and click the OK button. If the file does not appear in the dialog box, use its Directories list box to locate the folder where you saved it.
3. MicroStation opens the design file and displays its contents in two tiled view windows.

   The view of the highway in both views is oriented with the north direction pointing directly upward, evident by the direction of the north arrow.
4. Click the Rotate View icon in Window 1's view control bar. The Tool Settings window displays an option button with the label "Method." Select the option "2 Points." MicroStation prompts you to identify the first point for the view's X axis. Snap to the location labeled **1** in the figure below and accept it with a data point. You are prompted to define the X axis of the view as a temporary view outline rotates around the first data point.

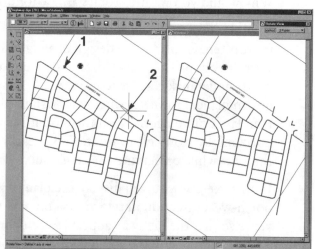

*Snap to locations identified as **1** and **2** to rotate the view axes of Window 1.*

5. Snap to the location labeled **2** in the above figure and accept it with a data point. The view rotates such that the line from 1 to 2 becomes the X axis for Window 1. Click the Reset button to terminate the Rotate View command. Note that while Window 1 displays a rotated view of the highway, Window 2 still displays the unrotated view.

You will now copy the rotated view attributes of Window 1 to Window 2.

6. Open the 2D View Control toolbox from the Tools menu by selecting View Control, followed by 2D. From this toolbox, invoke the Copy View command. Alternatively, you could have keyed in COPY VIEW in the Key-in window. You are prompted to select the source view.

7. Click a data point in Window 1. You are prompted to select destination view(s). Click a data point in Window 2. The view in Window 2 also rotates by the same amount as in Window 1. Click the Reset button to terminate the Copy View command.

You will now unrotate the view in Window 2.

8. Click the Rotate View icon in Window 2's view control bar. The Tool Settings window displays an option button with the label Method. Select the option Unrotated. MicroStation prompts you to select the view to restore to unrotated state.

9. Click a data point anywhere in Window 2. The view is restored to its original state, as shown in the figure below. (Window 2 is the one to the right.)

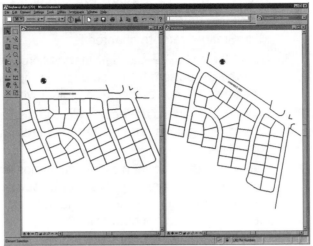

Your screen looks like this after rotating Window 1.

10. Click the Reset button to terminate the Rotate View command.

This concludes the exercise. You may now close the file and exit MicroStation or continue with the next exercise demonstrating MicroStation's Saved Views feature.

Exercise: Save and Recall a View

Earlier in the chapter you saw the View Save/Recall option under the Window Control Menu. This option invokes the Saved Views dialog box to help you save the display setting in a view and assign it a name for later recall.

In this exercise you will save the display of different parts of a drawing as named views. You will then recall these saved views. When drawings grow large and you constantly need to visit the same parts of a drawing during different editing sessions, saved views can help you get to those drawing areas quickly.

For this exercise you will need to copy to your computer's hard drive the file **saveview.dgn** from the **\Exercise\Ch04** folder on the CD-ROM.

The following steps guide you through this exercise.

1. Start MicroStation if it is not already running. If you need help starting MicroStation, refer to chapter 1.

2. Select the file `saveview.dgn` in the MicroStation Manager dialog box and click the OK button. If the file does not appear in the dialog box, use its Directories list box to locate the folder where you saved it.

3. MicroStation opens the design file and displays its contents in Window 1. If the drawing does not display the entire drawing, use the Fit View command.

   The view of this communication closet has enough detail information that it cannot be conveniently edited at its current magnification. To edit the wall and floor sleeve tables and the title block, you will need to zoom in to these areas to gain a better view.

4. Use the Window Area command to zoom in on the group of wall sleeve tables, as shown in the figure below. You will need to click two data points in response to the Window Area command's prompts to specify the rectangular area to zoom in on. You may have to use Pan or other view control commands if the Window Area operation did not display the desired view.

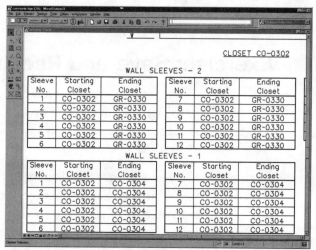

Zoom in on the Wall Sleeves - 2 table as shown here.

You will now save this view for later recall.

5. Invoke the Saved Views dialog box by selecting View Save/Recall from Window 1's Window Control Menu. Alternatively, you can select Saved Views from the Utilities menu. The following figure shows the Saved Views dialog box.

The Saved Views dialog box.

6. Key in **WST** in the Name field, **Wall Sleeve Tables** in the Description field and click the Save button. A new line is added to the Saved section of the dialog box.

7. Use the horizontal scroll bar to display the floor sleeve table directly to the right.

8. Save this view display with the name of **FST** and description of **Floor Sleeve Table**, described in step 6.

9. Use the vertical scroll bar to display the title block area directly underneath the tables.

10. Save this view display with the name of **TITLE** and description of **Title Block**, described in step 6. Now the Saved Views dialog box displays three lines in the Saved section of the dialog box, as shown in the figure below.

The three saved views in the dialog box.

11. Select Close from the File menu to return to the MicroStation Manager dialog box.
12. Reselect the `saveview.dgn` file and click the OK button. The design file opens to occupy the entire view.
13. Invoke the Saved Views dialog box, as described in step 5.
14. Highlight the TITLE saved view and click the Attach button. The view changes to display the title block area as you had it displayed onscreen when you saved the view.

This concludes the exercise. Before you close the file and exit MicroStation, let's take a moment to invoke a saved view JMDL example application delivered with MicroStation/J.

To invoke the Java-based Saved Views dialog box:

1. In the Key-in Window, key in `java examples.dgn.SavedView`. Note that the command is case sensitive and the word SavedView must be typed with the letters S and V capitalized.
2. MicroStation loads the `savedview.mclass` file from the `C:\Bentley\Program\MicroStation\JMDL\Examples\dgn` folder and displays the dialog box shown below.

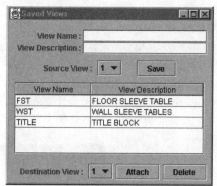

The Saved Views JMDL application.

You must have installed the JMDL development environment for the above dialog box to appear on your system. If you install JMDL examples and are still having trouble, you may want to read the JMDL configuration issues discussed in chapter 26.

The next exercise is the last one in this chapter. In it you will explore the View Attributes and Level Display options on the Window Control Menu.

Exercise: View Attributes and Level Display

The View Attributes and Level Display options under the Window Control Menu were briefly described in the beginning of this chapter. These options invoke the View Attributes and Level Manager dialog boxes to help you control the display of elements based on their attributes or levels.

In this exercise you will see some of the features implemented in these dialog boxes.

For this exercise you will need to copy to your computer's hard drive the file `aptunit.dgn` from the `\Exercise\Ch04` folder on the CD-ROM.

The following steps guide you through this exercise.

1. Start MicroStation if it is not already running. If you need help starting MicroStation, refer to chapter 1.
2. Select the file `aptunit.dgn` in the MicroStation Manager dialog box and click the OK button. If the file does not appear in the dialog box, use its Directories list box to locate the folder where you saved it.
3. MicroStation opens the design file and displays its contents in Window 1. If the window does not display the entire drawing, use the Fit View command.

    This design file contains the plan view of the apartment unit you had drawn in chapter 2. This drawing has several types of elements and is organized in levels—walls being on one level and text on another—making it ideal for our purposes here.
4. Invoke the View Attributes dialog box from the view's Window Control Menu.

    This dialog box is shown in the figure below and is used to toggle the display of certain view attributes, such as the grid, and types of elements, such as dimensions and text in a specified view or in all the eight views related to the design file.

To toggle the display of a view attribute or element type, click the checkbox associated with it and click the Apply button. The View Number displayed in the top of the dialog box changes when you click Apply. To have the change appear in all eight view windows, you must click the All button instead.

Each of the eight views maintains its own set of view attributes that can be set independently.

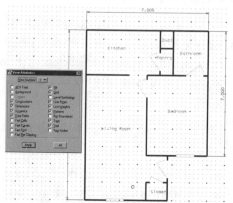

Each of the eight views maintains its own set of view attributes.

5. Disable the checkbox labeled Grid and click Apply to turn off the display of the grid in the view.

6. Disable the checkbox labeled Line Weights and click Apply to display all lines with a weight of zero.

7. Disable the checkboxes labeled Text and Dimensions and click Apply to turn off the display of all dimensions and text in the design file. Close the View Attributes dialog box.

8. Select Close from the File menu to return to the MicroStation Manager dialog box. Because we did not save the settings, when you reopen this file the view attributes you changed above will no longer be in effect.

9. Select the file `aptunit.dgn` in the MicroStation Manager dialog box and click the OK button to reopen the file.

10. Invoke the Level Manager dialog box by selecting Level Display from the view's Window Control Menu.

The Level Manager opens with a single tab called Numbers. The Level Manager implements a tabbed dialog box interface. To turn on the other tabs in the dialog box, select the desired tab name in the Tabs menu item in the Level Manager dialog box.

The tab labeled Numbers includes a level map control that displays all 63 levels. Notice that level 4 has a circle around it. This circle indicates that level 4 is the active level, as you can see from the Primary toolbox setting. To make another level active, double-click it in the level map. To turn off a level, click it in the level map and click the Apply button. Each of the eight views independently maintains its own set of level display attributes.

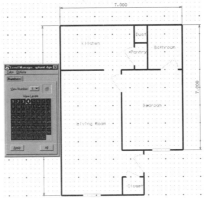

The circle around level 4 indicates that it is the active level.

11. Click the number 1 in the level map to turn it off (the box containing the number turns gray) and click the Apply button. All the walls in the view vanish from the screen. You might recall we had drawn walls on level 1, so when you turn off the level, its contents vanish from the view.

12. Click the number 3 in the level map to turn it off and click the Apply button. All text labels for rooms vanish from the screen.

13. Click the number 1 in the level map again to turn it back on and click the Apply button. The walls come back in the view. As an aside, try turning off level 4, the active level. You can't! An active level cannot be turned off. To turn off level 4, you will need to switch to another level before turning it off.

This concludes the exercise and the chapter. You may now close the file and exit MicroStation.

NOTE: If you wish to retain the View Attributes and Level Display settings between sessions, you must invoke Save Settings from the File menu before closing the design file.

Having come this far, by now you should have a good understanding of how MicroStation works. You also should be able to create simple drawings on your own. The next chapter provides a formal introduction to the element drawing, manipulation, and modification tools you've used in exercises for earlier chapters. You will be introduced to a large number of tools and commands along with exercises to help you practice the use of these commands.

Chapter 5

Drawing and Editing Elements

MicroStation's 2D Drafting Tools

Welcome to the road map to MicroStation's two-dimensional drawing and editing tools!

So far, you've used MicroStation without a formal guide to its drawing and editing tools. This wasn't an oversight. Since the best way to learn is by doing, chapter 2 focused on a series of assisted exercises. Later chapters introduced CAD and drawing navigation concepts with the help of exercises. I hope you are now eager to discover all the drafting tools, and the flexibility in drawing creation, MicroStation has to offer.

This chapter covers a lot of ground. Use it as a guide to MicroStation's 2D drawing tools in the Main tool frame. You can also use the chapter as a source for exercises while practicing or teaching the drawing and editing tools.

This chapter assumes you are comfortable with creating and opening design files, setting up working units, using the mouse for identifying, snapping to and selecting elements, and entering data point coordinates, either interactively with a mouse, or through key-ins.

The chapter begins with a summary of relevant concepts covered in earlier chapters. The intent is to make this a self-contained reference to the element placement, manipulation, and modification tools you will use most when creating two-dimensional drawings.

A list of chapter sections and a description of what is covered follows.

- **Summarizing the Basics** outlines the coordinate input, element selection, and cursor control concepts from earlier chapters.
- **Element Placement Tools** discusses tools from the Main tool frame used to place new elements in a design file.
- **Element Manipulation Tools** discusses tools from the Main tool frame used to change the location and scale of existing elements.
- **Element Modification Tools** discusses tools from the Main tool frame used to modify the shape or extent of existing elements.
- **Exercises** helps you understand the use of tools discussed in a step-by-step format.

To quickly discover the names of toolboxes covered, look for the annotated screenshot in the beginning of a section. To discover what a tool does, read its description under the associated toolbox. To practice using a tool, check out the exercises toward the end of the chapter.

Summarizing the Basics

To use MicroStation's drawing and editing tools, you must understand the concept of elements and know how to work with them. You create elements by clicking data points. You identify elements to edit with the element selection tools. You control the cursor and snap mode while working with elements.

This section covers these basics in a nutshell.

Coordinate Input

Data points you clicked in previous exercises were either interactive, or constrained using grid lock or a value in the Tool Settings window. To enter precise coordinate data, use precision key-ins or AccuDraw. To place data points relative to existing elements, use element snaps.

A knowledge of precision key-ins, element snaps, and AccuDraw will help you avoid moments of frustration that arise when simple geometric constructions seem difficult to draw in MicroStation.

Precision Key-Ins

To enter precision key-ins, use the Key-in window or AccuDraw. To open the Key-in window, select Key-in from the Utilities menu. To open the AccuDraw dialog box, click the Start AccuDraw icon in the Primary toolbox.

The following table lists the four common key-ins you type in the Key-in window. Note that the lowercase place holders to the right of the '=' symbol in the table are numeric values you type.

Key-in	Description
XY=x,y	Absolute: Cartesian coordinates from the design plane origin.
DL=dx,dy	Delta: horizontal and vertical distances from the last data point entered.
DX=dx,dy	View Delta: distances aligned to the view axes from the last data point entered.
DI=dr,a	Distance: radial distance and angle from last data point entered in polar coordinates.

To enter precision key-ins using AccuDraw, press the letter P when AccuDraw has the focus. This opens the Data Point Keyin window. Select the precision key-in mode from an option button on this window and enter coordinates followed by the Enter key. Pressing the Enter key sends the coordinate input to MicroStation and closes the Data Point Keyin window.

When keying in coordinate data, use the colon (:) symbol to separate working unit components., for example 26:4 for 26 feet and 4 inches.

Element Snaps

To *snap to* an element, use the *tentative button* on your mouse. With a two-button mouse, click both the left and right buttons together when the cursor is within the target range of the element to snap to it; on a three-button mouse with default configuration, use the middle button.

A tentative point click places a tentative cursor at the location snapped. If the tentative point did not snap to the desired location, continue to click tentative points or change the snap mode and try again. To accept the snapped location, you must click a data point. See the section *Snapping for Precision* in chapter 3 for different snap modes and additional terms, such as *snap divisor*.

The *keypoint snap mode* is the default, and you will use it the most. You can override the default snap mode for a single snap operation by using the Snaps menu or Snap Mode button bar. To change the default snap mode, hold the Shift key down when selecting the snap mode.

To open the Snaps pop-up menu, click the active snap field in the status bar, or press the shift key and click the tentative button in a view window. Alternatively, select Settings, then Snaps from the MicroStation menu bar. To invoke the Snap Mode button bar, select Button Bar from the Snaps menu.

NOTE: The active snap field in the status bar displays an icon representing the snap mode currently active. If snap lock is off, the active snap field is empty. To turn on snap lock if it is off, click the locks field in the status bar to open the Locks menu, select Toggles to open the Lock Toggles dialog box and click the Snap Lock checkbox.

Element Selection

Lines, arcs, circles, curves, multi-lines, text, dimensions, and other items you place in a design file are referred to as *elements*. They behave as individual entities, or *vectors*, that can be modified or manipulated. This is why CAD is referred to as a *vector graphics program*.

You can edit elements individually or in a group. MicroStation supports selection sets and fence operations to edit elements in a group. MicroStation changes the behavior of its element manipulation tools when a selection set is active.

Selection Set

To select an element, click it with the element selection tool or PowerSelector. When selected, either handles appear around it, or it displays in the highlight color—depending on your workspace preference settings.

To add elements to the selection set with the element selection tool, hold the Ctrl key down while clicking other elements. To remove elements from the selection set, simply click them again while holding down the Ctrl key. To remove all elements from the selection set, click an empty area in a view window.

When using PowerSelector, you don't have to hold the Ctrl key down while identifying elements. You either click elements or draw temporary constructions (such as a line, rectangle, or polygon) to designate elements to be selected. The mode selected in the Tool Settings window determines what PowerSelector does—add, remove, or invert—with the identified elements.

The selection set field in the status bar displays the number of elements in the selection set. You can also click the selection set field to display a pop-up menu of selection set tools.

To select all elements in a design file, use Select All from the Edit menu. To select elements based upon their type and attributes, use the Select By Attributes dialog box invoked from the Edit menu.

Fence

A *fence* is another method for grouping elements for manipulation. You place a fence in a view window with the Place Fence tool in the Fence toolbox. The associated Tool Settings window offers several ways to place a fence: Block, Shape, Circle, Element, From View, and From Design File. A fence is a temporary construction that is visible on the screen but is not a part of the design file and does not plot.

The Fence Mode option in the Tool Settings window determines which elements—Inside, Overlap, Clip, Void, Void-Overlap, Void-Clip—to process when a manipulation tool is instructed to use the fence.

A fence can be edited after placement. You can either change its location on screen or edit its vertices by using the Modify Fence tool in the Fence toolbox. Make sure you have the appropriate Modify Mode option, Vertex or Position, selected in the Tool Settings window.

When a fence is active, the active fence field in the status bar displays a rectangular dashed icon. Another indication of an active fence is the cursor shape when using an element manipulation tool. If the cursor shape indicates that MicroStation awaits a data point, not element identification, when you invoke an element manipulation tool, either a selection set or a fence is active. See the *Cursor Shapes* section in chapter 1 for additional details.

NOTE: Fence operations can manipulate a large number of elements. To undo fence operations, be sure to set an adequate Undo Buffer size in the Memory Usage category of the Preferences dialog box invoked from the Workspace menu.

Cursor Control

As your experience with MicroStation grows you will appreciate the ways you can control cursor movement. You can control the cursor to move in increments from one grid point to another, or to move along a view or isometric axis.

To control cursor movement you use locks: grid lock, axis lock and isometric lock. You can also use AccuDraw, discussed in chapter 8.

Grid Lock

A technical stationery store carries many different types of grid paper. Similarly, MicroStation implements a flexible grid system. You control the spacing between grid points, their aspect ratio, and orientation under the Grid category of the Design File Settings dialog box that is invoked from the Settings menu.

To set a grid with points spaced 4 inches apart, set the Grid Master field to 4 inch. To have larger grid reference dots appear at one-foot spacing, set the Grid Reference field to 3 because *3* grid spaces make up a foot. Grid Reference is measured in multiples of Grid Master.

You can also set the grid spacing via key-ins. The example in the previous paragraph could also be set up by keying in `GU=:4` to specify the Grid Master spacing and by keying in `GR=3` to specify the Grid Reference multiplier.

Even though you may have set up a grid, it may not be visible. To display the grid, enable the Grid checkbox in the View Attributes dialog box accessed from the Settings menu. Note that grid points also do not display if you are zoomed out too far. In this case, zoom in to see the grid points or change their spacing.

To constrain the cursor to lie only on grid points, enable the grid lock. Click the lock icon in the status bar to display the Locks menu on which to change the status of the lock for grid. Alternatively, you may key in `LOCK GRID ON` or `LOCK GRID OFF` to set a specific grid lock status, or `LOCK GRID` to toggle the current status.

Axis Lock

When drawing horizontal or vertical lines, it is helpful to constrain data points to lie parallel to view axes. You set up axis constraint parameters in the Axis category of the Design File Settings dialog box accessed from the Settings menu.

If your needs so dictate, the axis increment can differ from the default 90°. If you set the axis increment in the Design File Settings dialog box to 45°, data points will be constrained to move by increments of the specified angle.

To constrain the cursor to lie along axis angles, enable the axis lock. Click the lock icon in the status bar to display the Locks menu on which to change the status of the lock for axis. Alternatively, you may key in `LOCK AXIS ON` or `LOCK AXIS OFF` to set a specific grid lock status, or `LOCK AXIS` to toggle the current status.

Isometric Lock

When drawing isometric views, it is helpful to constrain data points to lie parallel to isometric axes. You select the isometric plane in the Isometric category of the Design File Settings dialog box accessed from the Settings menu.

You can restrict the cursor to these isometric planes: Top, Left, and Right. You will want to change the default orthogonal cursor to an isometric cursor when drawing isometric views. Change the cursor to isometric by selecting Isometric for Pointer Type from the Operation category of the Preferences dialog box, accessed from the Workspace menu.

NOTE: The isometric toolbox accessed from the Tools menu complements the isometric lock and the isometric cursor for the creation of isometric drawings.

To constrain the cursor to lie along isometric axes, enable the isometric lock. Click the lock icon in the status bar to display the Locks menu to change the status of the lock for isometric axes. Alternatively, you may key in LOCK ISOMETRIC ON or LOCK ISOMETRIC OFF to set a specific lock status, or LOCK ISOMETRIC to toggle the current status.

Main Tool Frame

The Main tool frame contains the seventeen most frequently used toolboxes and the Delete Element tool.

The rest of this chapter explores all the tools in the Main tool frame used to create, manipulate, and modify elements. To invoke the Main tool frame from the Tools menu, select Main for the submenu, followed by another Main for the tool frame. (It's two Mains!)

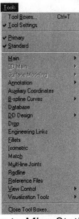

The Tools menu provides access to MicroStation's tool frames and toolboxes.

As you see on the Tools menu, MicroStation has many more tool frames and toolboxes. Many of these will be covered in later chapters.

Four sections follow this fast-paced summary of MicroStation's 2D drawing environment. An annotated figure of the Main tool frame highlighting the toolboxes covered begins each of the next three sections. The fourth is devoted exclusively to exercises that help you practice what you learn.

Element Placement Tools

As the name suggests, these tools are used to place, i.e. create, new elements in a design file. You used some of these tools for the first time in chapter 2. This section provides a road map to those tools and others.

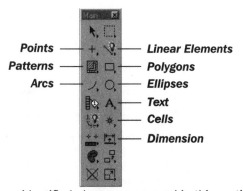

The toolboxes identified above are covered in this section.

Despite the number of element placement toolboxes there are only a few unique element types. That's right! Even the most complex drawings are made up primarily of lines, arcs, circles, and a few other elements.

The number of tools available is indicative of the flexibility in the set of data you can use as input to create new elements. For example, whether you know the offset distance from an existing line; the length, angle, and start point; or tangency to an arc, you have a tool to draw that line in a few steps.

If one icon were implemented for one unique way an element could be created, MicroStation would have to implement over a thousand. In order to reduce the number of icons and to simplify its interface, MicroStation implements the Method field in the Tool Settings window. Thus, one tool can incorporate the functionality of several commands. Activate the desired command by choosing the appropriate method in the Tool Settings window associated with a tool.

Points Toolbox

This toolbox is used to place an active point in the design file. The *active point* is not a basic element type. It refers to one of three element types—a zero-length line, a single text character, or a cell—that can be designated as an active point. You use the Point Type option button in the Tool Settings window to designate the element type to use as the active point.

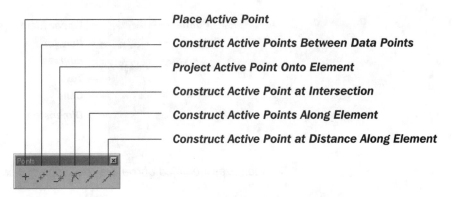

The tools in the Points toolbox.

You can use these tools to place cells, points, or characters at or between data points, or along existing elements.

There are many uses for points in your drawing work. Should you need to draw a series of equidistant light pole symbols along the edge of a roadway, the Construct Active Points Along Element tool when used in conjunction with a cell would help. For placing a snappable point on an element a certain distance long a monument point, use the Construct Active Point at Distance Along Element tool.

Place Active Point

This tool places a single instance of the active point at the location specified.

To use the tool:

1. Click its icon. The Tool Settings window displays three fields: Point Type, Character, and Cell.
2. Select the desired type of active point.

   To use a zero-length line as the active point, select Element from the Point Type option. A thick line weight, such as 7, ensures zero-length lines are visible on screen.

   To use a text character as the active point, select Character from the Point Type option and key in a letter in the Character field.

   To use a cell as the active point from an attached cell library, select Cell from the Point Type option and key in the name of the cell to use in the Cell field.

NOTE: If the Cell field appears dimmed, you don't have a cell library attached. See the Cells toolbox description later in the chapter on how to attach a cell library.

3. Click a data point at the location you want the active point placed.

After placing the active point, the command restarts itself. Clicking the Reset button exits the command and activates the default tool, the element selection tool.

Construct Active Points Between Data Points

This tool is used to place several instances of the active point between two data points.

To use the tool:

1. Click its icon. The Tool Settings window displays these fields: Point Type, Character, Cell, and Points.
2. Select the desired type of active point. See step 2 under Place Active Point for details.
3. Use the Points field to specify the number of points to place.
4. Specify the first point. You are prompted for the next data point.

5. Specify the second point. The tool places the number of active points specified.

   Two active points are placed at the two data points you clicked, and the remaining are placed equally spaced between them. If you request only one point to be drawn, it is placed in the center of the two data points and the tool continues requesting the next data point, assuming you wish to place more points between the previous point and the next one.

6. Click the next data point if you wish to continue placing more points. Or, click Reset to restart the command, and it prompts for the first data point again.

Project Active Point Onto Element

Use this tool to place the active point on an element at a location closest to the data point you click to accept the element.

To use the tool:

1. Click its icon. The Tool Settings window displays these fields: Point Type, Character, and Cell.

2. Select the desired type of active point. See step 2 under Place Active Point for details. You are prompted to identify an element.

3. Click a data point on the desired element. It highlights and you are prompted accept or reject the element.

4. If you accept the element, the location on the element closest to the data point receives the active point. If you reject the element, the command restarts and you are prompted to identify an element.

Construct Active Point at Intersection

Use this tool to place the active point at the point of intersection between two elements.

To use the tool:

1. Click its icon. The Tool Settings window displays the fields: Point Type, Character, and Cell.

2. Select the desired type of active point. See step 2 under Place Active Point for details. You are prompted to select an element for intersection.

3. Click a data point on the desired element. It highlights, and you are prompted to select another element for intersection.

4. Click a data point on the second intersecting element. Highlighting from the first element is removed, and the second element highlights. You are prompted to accept the intersection point.

5. On accepting the intersection of the two elements, the intersecting point that is closest—if there are more than one—to the first data point receives the active point. If the elements do not intersect, an error message appears on the status bar.

NOTE: The two elements you identify do not have to actually intersect for this tool to work successfully. For two lines that do not meet, but would meet were they extended far enough, the tool will find the apparent intersection and place the active point there.

Construct Active Points Along Element

This tool places several instances of the active point along an element between the two data points you identify.

To use the tool:

1. Click its icon. The Tool Settings window displays the fields: Point Type, Character, Cell, and Points.

2. Select the desired type of active point. See step 2 under Place Active Point for details.

3. Use the Points field to specify the number of points to place. You are prompted to identify an element.

4. Click a data point on the element to identify it. It highlights. The location you clicked to identify the element will be the starting point for the construction of active points. You are prompted for the end point.

5. Click a second data point on the element. This location is used as the ending point for the construction of active points along the element. The number of points specified in step 3 are drawn.

   Two active points are placed at the two data points you clicked, and the remaining ones are placed equally spaced between them. If you request only one point be drawn, it is placed in the center of the two data points.

6. The command restarts and prompts you to identify an element. You can either continue the operation for another element, or switch to another tool.

Construct Active Point at Distance Along Element

This tool places the active point on an element at the distance you specify from the point of element identification.

To use the tool:

1. Click its icon. The Tool Settings window displays these fields: Point Type, Character, Cell, and Distance.
2. Select the desired type of active point. See step 2 under Place Active Point for details.
3. Use the Distance field to specify a distance value. You are prompted to identify an element.
4. Click a point on an element to specify the origin for distance measurement. You are prompted to accept, or reject.
5. If you click a data point, an active point is placed on the element at the specified distance from origin when measured along the element and the command restarts. If you click Reset, no active point is placed and the command restarts.

Linear Elements Toolbox

This toolbox is used to place lines, line strings, chains, closed shapes and point curves in the design file. The *Place SmartLine* tool is the most versatile, as it can place different types of elements depending on the Tool Settings options you select.

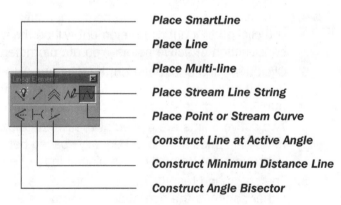

- *Place SmartLine*
- *Place Line*
- *Place Multi-line*
- *Place Stream Line String*
- *Place Point or Stream Curve*
- *Construct Line at Active Angle*
- *Construct Minimum Distance Line*
- *Construct Angle Bisector*

The tools in the Linear Elements toolbox.

This toolbox has two different groups of tools: placement and construction. The former group of tools take data points for input. The latter group requires you to identify existing elements as input.

Place SmartLine

This flexible tool draws a variety of element types: lines, line strings, arcs, complex chains, and complex shapes. See chapter 3 for definitions of these element types. Depending on the options you select for the tool, with it you can create complex chains and shapes with chamfered and filleted corners.

With default settings, it connects the data points you click with a line string. You must click the Reset button after specifying the last vertex to complete the creation of the element.

> **NOTE:** Place SmartLine is one of the few tools that requires a Reset button click to signal the end of data points and to initiate the creation of an element.

Because a Reset will not abort the command—except right after the first data point—you must use the Undo command from the Edit menu, or the Delete Element tool, if you change your mind about using the tool after initiating it.

SmartLine makes sense when you need to draw interconnected line segments with sharp or rounded corners that are to maintain their vertex connections during edit operations.

Tool Options: Before getting into step-by-step instructions on how to use this tool, you will find a discussion of its options helpful. The Tool Settings window for Place SmartLine offers the following four fields:

- *Segment Type*: An option button that lets you choose between Lines and Arcs as segments for the connected shape you draw. You can switch between segment types at any time during command operation.

- *Vertex Type*: An option button that lets you choose between Sharp, Rounded, and Chamfered for the corners of your shape. You can switch between vertex type at any time during command operation.

The Sharp option, the default, makes corners sharp. *Rounded* fillets adjacent line segments with a tangential arc. *Chamfered* chamfers adjacent line segments with a line.

- *Rounding Radius/Chamfer Offset*: When Vertex Type is Rounded, this field is named Rounding Radius. When Vertex Type is Chamfered, this field is named Chamfer Offset. The value you key in here determines the radius of the fillet or offset of chamfer.

- *Join Elements*: A checkbox, enabled by default, draws connected segments. To draw individual elements for segments, turn this checkbox off.

To use the tool:

1. Click its icon. You are prompted for the first vertex.
2. Select either Lines or Arcs for Segment Type from the Tool Settings window and click the first data point to start segment creation.
3. Follow status bar prompts and click the required number of data points to complete the first segment. You are prompted to enter the next vertex or click Reset to stop adding new segments.
4. Select the next segment type and repeat step 3. If the segment type is a line you can also choose to have the corner filleted or rounded with the value you key in the Tool Settings window.
5. The Reset button creates the element and restarts the command.

Place Line

Use this tool to draw individual line elements by specifying either their endpoints, or their length, orientation, and location. A line might be the element you use most.

To use the tool:

1. Click its icon. You are prompted for the first point.
2. If you know the length of the line, enable the Length checkbox and key in its length in the Tool Settings window.
3. If you know the orientation of the line with respect to the view axis, enable the Angle checkbox and key in the angle.

4. If you enabled both checkboxes in steps 2 and 3, a dynamic line attaches to the cursor and the first data point places it and restarts the command. If none of the checkboxes were enabled, or only one were enabled, the first data point click starts rubberbanding the line to your cursor and you are prompted for the end point.

5. If you enabled only one checkbox, the second data point determines either the line's length (if Angle was constrained) or its orientation (if Length were constrained), creates the line and restarts the command.

Continuing to supply data points in response to the prompt for end points creates on screen what looks like a line string (series of connected line segments). Nevertheless, each segment is individual. Should you try to move the shape, only the segment identified will move, not the whole.

Place Multi-line

Many times you need to draw a well-defined combination of parallel lines to represent objects such as HVAC ductwork and architectural walls. MicroStation implements Place Multi-line to address this need.

Because this tool creates connected elements, a Reset button click is used to signal the end of segments and complete the element. As you enter data points that designate vertices for multi-line segments, several parallel lines are drawn in one step for each segment.

You control multi-line parameters—number of parallel lines, their symbology and offset distance, and status of end caps and joint display—in the Multi-lines dialog box accessed from the Element menu. Only one multi-line definition may be active at a time. You can save different multi-line definitions in the Settings Manager, discussed in chapter 14.

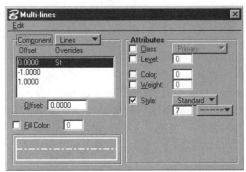

The Multi-lines dialog box controls multi-line parameters.

The Component groupbox in the Multi-lines dialog box uses an option button to let you switch between parameters for Lines, Start Cap, End Cap, and Joints. When using this dialog box you will first select the component to edit from the Component option button. The options in the Component groupbox change depending on the component you select.

The default multi-line definition consists of three parallel lines. A line with a line code of seven is drawn along the data points you click. Two parallel lines are drawn as well. One is offset a distance of 1 master unit from the line connecting the data points. The other is offset the same distance, but on the other side. Thus the offset distance for one is 1.000, and for the other it is -1.000. Additionally, a line is specified as a cap at both the start and end of the multi-line.

NOTE: A multi-line can incorporate up to sixteen parallel lines in its definition.

To edit the definition of the multi-line, use the Edit menu on the Multi-lines dialog box. This menu offers three choices: Insert, Delete, Duplicate. To add a new parallel line, select Insert; to delete the highlighted line, select Delete; to copy an existing line for edit, select Duplicate.

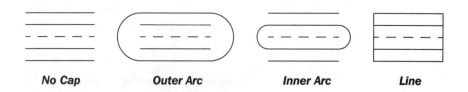

No Cap   **Outer Arc**   **Inner Arc**   **Line**

The different types of caps at the ends of multi-lines.

The start and end of multi-line elements can have caps. The different types of caps are shown in the above figure. Caps link various parallel line segments with lines or arcs. You can enable more than one type of cap for a multi-line end. You can also specify an angle for the caps to achieve a beveled effect.

The joint component of a multi-line controls the display of vertex joints. When enabled, every interior vertex displays a line. This option is popular with those laying HVAC ductwork to help them visually determine the number of joints in a run of ductwork for cost estimate purposes.

I'd like to call your attention to one other option in the Multi-lines dialog box: the Fill checkbox. You can enable this checkbox and select a fill color for the area bounded by the exterior lines of a multi-line definition, regardless of the cap status.

TIP: You can change the parameters of an existing multi-line to match the ones you define in the Multi-lines dialog box by using the Change Multi-line Definition tool in the Change Attributes toolbox.

To modify multi-lines you can use many of MicroStation's modification tools such as Extend Line, Partial Delete, and more. However, you cannot use others, such as Extend 2 Elements to Intersection. To work with multi-line intersections and other editing operations, MicroStation implements the Multi-line Joints toolbox accessed from the Tools menu.

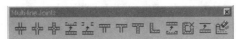

Use the Multi-line Joints toolbox to clean up multi-line intersections.

To use the tool:

1. Click its icon. You are prompted to enter the first point.

   The parameters in the Multi-lines dialog box will be used to draw the multi-line. If needed, you can change the parameters at this time.

2. If you know the length of the multi-line segment, enable the Length checkbox and key in its length in the Tool Settings window.

3. If you know the orientation of the multi-line with respect to the view axis, enable the Angle checkbox and key in the angle.

4. If you enabled both checkboxes in steps 2 and 3, a dynamic multi-line attaches to the cursor. The first data point places it and restarts the command. If none of the checkboxes were enabled, or only one were enabled, the first data point click starts rubberbanding the multi-line to your cursor, and you are prompted for the next vertex.

5. Continue entering data points to define the other vertices of the multi-line until you've specified the location for the last vertex.
6. Click the Reset button to create the element and restart the command.

Place Stream Line String

This tool creates a line string without clicking data points for its vertices. It is often used when digitizing maps to create an irregular line quickly, such as a coastal line, by simply tracing over it.

The tool examines cursor movement and converts it to data points based on the values of options in the Tool Settings window. A description of each of the tool's options follows:

Delta: The incremental distance, when exceeded, that causes the cursor location to be examined.

Tolerance: The maximum distance between vertices of the line string created.

Angle: The angle, when exceeded, that causes the last cursor location examined to be entered as a line string vertex.

Area: The area, when exceeded, that causes the last cursor location examined to be entered as a line string vertex.

To use the tool:

1. Click its icon. You are prompted to enter the first point.
2. Click a data point at the location you wish to start the line string.
3. Move the cursor to automatically place a stream of data points, based on the settings discussed above, that follow your cursor.
4. Click the Reset button to complete the creation of the line string.

You might recall that a line string is limited to 101 vertices. Because this tool can place data points very rapidly, you can easily exceed this limit. When the limit is exceeded, rather than drawing a line string, the tool creates a complex chain.

Place Point or Stream Curve

A point curve is the simplest of the curve types supported by MicroStation. The other curves—*conical*, *helical*, and *spiral*—can be found under the B-spline Curves tool frame under the Tools menu.

Use this tool to create a smooth curve that passes through supplied data points. Or, use it to create a stream curve—helpful during digitization of irregular lines often found on maps.

To use the tool:

1. Click its icon. The Tool Settings window displays the Method option button and the status bar prompts for the first point on the curve.
2. Select Points as the method to enter data points, or, select Stream to have data points generated as you move the cursor.

   If you select Stream as the method, the Tool Settings window adjusts to display additional options: Delta, Tolerance, Angle, Area. See the Place Stream Line String tool for a description of these options.
3. Click a data point to identify the beginning of the curve.
4. If drawing a point curve, click a second data point to identify a location for the first curve segment to pass through and follow this with a third data point to place the first segment.

   If drawing a stream curve, simply move the cursor to place a stream of data points that follow your cursor.
5. If drawing a point curve, enter additional data points, as needed, to add segments to the curve.
6. Click the Reset button to complete the creation of the curve.

Construct Angle Bisector

This tool constructs a line that divides the angle formed by three data points. This tool has no options. The figure below shows the sequence of data points the tool needs to bisect an angle.

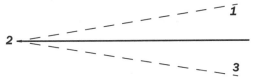

The line drawn divides the angle between data points 1, 2, and 3.

To use the tool:

1. Click the icon. You are prompted for an angle leg's end point.
2. Click a data point to identify one end point of the angle to be bisected. You are prompted to enter the vertex of the angle.
3. Click a data point to identify the angle vertex. You are prompted to enter the other angle leg's end point
4. Click a data point to identify the second end point of the angle. A new line that bisects the angle formed by the three data points, as shown in the above figure, is drawn.

The length of the line drawn is the average of the distances between the points 1-2 and 2-3.

Construct Minimum Distance Line

As its name suggests, this tool computes the minimum distance between two elements and draws a line along it. This tool has no options.

To use the tool:

1. Click the icon. You are prompted for the first element.
2. Click a data point to identify an element. The element highlights. You are prompted to accept the highlighted element by identifying the second element, or to reject it.
3. To reselect the first element click the Reset button and try again. Otherwise, click a data point to identify the second element. The element highlights, and you are prompted to accept it to initiate the minimum distance calculation.
4. To select another element as the second element, click the Reset button and identify the second element again.
5. Accept the second element with a data point anywhere in the view window. A line along the minimum distance between the two points is drawn.

Other uses for the tool may not be so obvious. For example, this tool simplifies the construction of lines perpendicular to a circle and a line. If done manually on the drafting table, it's a difficult exercise. But this tool makes the exercise simple. Why? Because a minimum distance straight line between a line and a circle is perpendicular to each.

Construct Line at Active Angle

This tool lets you construct a line at the specified angle from another element. While constructing the line you can specify a point on the element to draw the line from. Alternately, you can specify a point in space from which to project a line at the active angle to the element.

The former construct corresponds to the From Point method in the Tool Settings window for the tool. The latter construct corresponds to the To Point method.

Were you to draw such a line using the Place Line tool, you would first have to determine the angle of the existing line, and add to it the desired angle to determine the angle of the new line. This would be a little tedious. The Construct Line at Active Angle simplifies the creation of such constructs.

To construct a line from a point on an element:

1. Click its icon and select From Point from the Method option button in the Tool Settings window. You are prompted to identify an element. Make sure the Active Angle field in the Tool Settings window specifies the angle desired.

2. Click a data point to identify an element at the location from which you want the line drawn. The element highlights and you are prompted to enter the end point for the line being drawn dynamically as you move the cursor.

   If you identify a line, the Active Angle field in the Tool Settings window can't be 0 or 180 degrees—you get an error message otherwise. If you identify an arc, circle, ellipse, or curve, you will create a tangential line if the active angle is 0 or 180 degrees.

3. Click a data point to complete the line. If the Length checkbox in the Tool Settings window is enabled with a value, that value is used for the length of the line constructed.

To construct a line to an element from a point in space:

1. Click its icon and select To Point from the Method option button in the Tool Settings window. You are prompted to select a line segment. Make sure the Active Angle field in the Tool Settings window specifies the angle desired.

Take note of the prompt. This tool only works with line segments, not arcs, circles, ellipses, or curves. Consequently, the Active Angle must not be either 0 or 180 degrees.

2. Click a data point to identify a line or a line segment in a complex element. The element highlights with a dynamically drawn line that maintains the required angle to the highlighted element and is attached to the cursor. You are prompted to enter the point in space where you wish the line to end.

3. Click a data point to complete the line. If the Length checkbox in the Tool Settings window is enabled with a value, that value is used for the length of the line constructed.

Patterns Toolbox

While creating a drawing, you will want to enhance its appearance. You do this by hatching and crosshatching a regular pattern within drawing areas to give them texture. For example, the front elevation of a house may be enhanced by the use of a brick hatch pattern. The cross-section through a steel beam also may be enhanced by using the industry's standard steel hatch pattern.

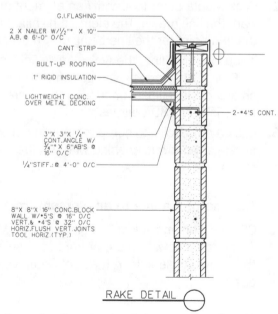

Example of a rake detail that uses hatch patterns.

The Patterns toolbox shown below includes tools to hatch areas and linear elements. It also includes tools to query and match pattern attributes, and to delete patterns.

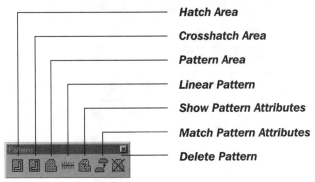

Hatch Area

Crosshatch Area

Pattern Area

Linear Pattern

Show Pattern Attributes

Match Pattern Attributes

Delete Pattern

The Patterns toolbox.

Patterning is the process of copying lines or placing cells repeatedly within an identified area, or along a linear element, at the specified spacing and orientation.

Before discussing each of the patterning tools in the toolbox, you will want to become familiar with their parameters.

When placing patterns, you can make them *associative*, and you can make them *snappable*. When patterns are placed with their associative attribute enabled, changing the element they are associated to changes the pattern automatically. When patterns are placed with their snap attribute enabled, you can snap to individual pattern elements.

The term *spacing*, when used in the Tool Settings window by patterning tools, refers to the distance between each hatch or crosshatch line, or between each row of cells. When using cells, there is *column spacing* that refers to the distance between cell boundaries along a row.

The term *angle*, when used by patterning tools, refers to the angle of the hatch or crosshatch line, or the row of cells.

The term *tolerance*, when used by patterning tools, refers to the accuracy with which to compute the extent of patterns adjacent to curved boundaries. The smaller the tolerance, the longer it takes to pattern an area or linear element.

The first three tools in the Patterns toolbox are used to pattern an area and are called *area patterning* tools. These tools implement the pattern methods listed in the table below.

Pattern Method	Description
Element	Patterns a closed element you identify.
Fence	Patterns the area within an active fence.
Intersection	Patterns the area intersected by two or more closed elements.
Union	Patterns the combined area of two or more closed elements.
Difference	Patterns the area of first element less second intersecting element.
Flood	Patterns the closed area within a group of crossing elements.
Points	Patterns the area enclosed within a polygon you define by clicking data points.

NOTE: The display of patterns can be turned off in a view. Use the Patterns checkbox in the View Attributes dialog box. If you use patterns extensively in your drawing, screen refreshes can become sluggish. For better performance, you can turn off pattern display during editing sessions. To see patterns on hardcopy, you must turn pattern display on before printing.

Hatch Area

Use this tool to hatch an area by specifying the spacing between hatch lines and their angle of orientation. A *hatch* is a series of parallel lines.

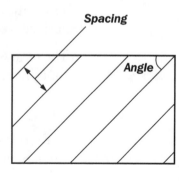

When you invoke the tool, you are prompted to identify a closed element. Before identifying the element, use the Tool Settings window to select the desired parameters. These were discussed earlier.

The adjacent figure shows a hatch pattern and identifies its spacing and angle parameters.

Crosshatch Area

Use this tool to crosshatch an area by specifying the spacing between the two sets of hatch lines and their angle of orientation. A *crosshatch* consists of two independent hatch lines.

When you invoke the tool, you are prompted to identify a closed element to crosshatch. Before identifying the element, use the Tool Settings window to select the desired parameters. These were discussed earlier.

The adjacent figure shows a crosshatch pattern. The spacing and angle of each set of parallel lines can be controlled independently in the Tool Settings window.

Pattern Area

Use this tool to pattern an area with a row and a column of cells.

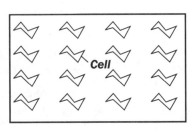

When you invoke the tool, you are prompted to identify a closed element to pattern. Before identifying the element, use the Tool Settings window to select the desired pattern cell from an attached cell library. To control the size of the cell, use the Scale field. Other options for the tool are spacing, angle, and tolerance, discussed earlier.

The adjacent figure shows an area patterned with cells. Because a cell is a custom symbol, the Pattern Area tool can fill an area with any pattern you may need.

MicroStation delivers a sample library of cells, `areapat.cel`, suitable for linear patterning in the `c:\Bentley\Workspace\System\Cell` folder.

Linear Pattern

Use this tool to replace a linear element with a cell placed repeatedly end to end. Unlike the Construct Points Along Element that leaves the element intact, the Linear Pattern tool replaces the element.

Linear Element ——————

Cell

Patterned Element

When you invoke the tool, you are prompted to identify a linear element. Before identifying the element, select the cell and its scale in the Tool Settings window. Cycle is a patterning option unique to this tool. The Tool Settings window displays it as an option button with the following four choices:

- *Truncated*: Last instance of the cell is truncated, if necessary.
- *Complete*: Last instance of the cell must be complete, not truncated. The pattern scale is adjusted if necessary.
- *Single*: A single cell instance replaces each segment of the linear element.
- *Multiple*: Same as Complete, except that each segment in a linear element also ends with a complete cell.

MicroStation delivers a sample library of cells `linepa.cel` suitable for linear patterning in the `c:\Bentley\Workspace\System\Cell` folder.

NOTE: If you turn off the display of patterns in a view, you see the original element instead of the linear pattern.

Show Pattern Attributes

Use this tool to query the angle and spacing of a pattern element. On identifying a pattern with this tool, its pattern attributes appear in the status bar.

Match Pattern Attributes

Use this tool to set your active patterning parameters from an existing pattern element. On invoking the tool, you are prompted to identify an element. On identifying the element, you are prompted to accept or reject the selection. When you click a data point to accept it, your active patterning parameters change to match those used when hatching that element.

Delete Pattern

Use this tool to delete a pattern element previously placed. When you invoke the tool, you are prompted to identify a pattern element. On identifying the element, it appears in the highlight color, and clicking a data point accepts the deletion.

If you accidentally delete a pattern, you can restore it by using the Undo command from the Edit menu, or by using the Ctrl+Z keyboard combination.

Polygons Toolbox

Polygons are closed shapes composed of line segments. The Polygons toolbox offers tools to place polygons in many ways. The following screenshot identifies each available tool.

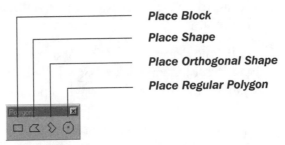

Place Block

Place Shape

Place Orthogonal Shape

Place Regular Polygon

The tools in the Polygon toolbox.

All tools implement the following fill-related options:

- **Area:** Sets the active area parameter to either Solid or Hole.
- **Fill Type:** Sets the active fill type to None, Opaque, or Outlined. When Opaque, the shape is filled with the active color. When Outlined, the shape outline is drawn in the active color, and the shape is filled with the fill color.
- **Fill Color:** Sets the fill color. It can be different from the active color.

Place Block

This tool creates a rectangle from diagonal data points. Its Tool Settings window offers a choice of two methods: Orthogonal or Rotated.

When the default Orthogonal method is chosen, the rectangle is aligned with the view axes. When the Rotated method is chosen, the first two data points define the rotation, and the third data point provides the diagonal point with respect to the first data point.

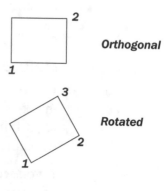

Orthogonal

Rotated

Place Shape

This tool creates a free-form polygon. Its Tool Settings window implements a Close Element button to simplify drawing the last segment of the closed shape. The Length and Angle fields it offers are similar to those discussed for the Place Line tool.

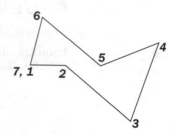

Last data point on first data point indicates closure

Unlike the Place SmartLine tool that waits for a Reset button click to signal the last segment, this tool waits for a data point click at the shape's starting point. Placing the last data point directly on top of the starting point isn't always easy, specially when you're drawing a small shape with closely spaced vertices. The Close Element button in the Tool Settings window simplifies this. Rather than locate and click a data point at the starting point, you can click this button to close the shape.

TIP: If you are having trouble drawing a shape with closely spaced vertices, zoom in for better control.

Place Orthogonal Shape

This tool creates a multi-sided orthogonal shape. The first two data points define the shape's axis. Every subsequent segment is either parallel or perpendicular to this axis. Unlike the Place Shape tool, this tool does not implement the Close Element button.

Because each subsequent shape segment must be perpendicular to the previous segment, MicroStation converts the data point coordinates before passing them to the tool.

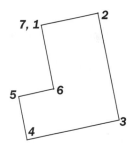

Last data point on first data point indicates closure

Place Regular Polygon

This tool creates regular polygons. All sides in a regular polygon are equal in length. While drawing a regular polygon, you can specify the number of its edges, or sides.

This tool also implements the following three methods:

- **Inscribed:** The polygon is drawn by specifying its center and a vertex. To specify the size of the inscribed circle, use the Radius option.

- **Circumscribed:** The polygon is drawn by specifying its center and the midpoint of a side. You may use the Radius option to specify the size of the circumscribing circle.

- **By Edge:** This method uses the two data points you click to define the size and angle of its edge. The Radius option is unavailable for this method.

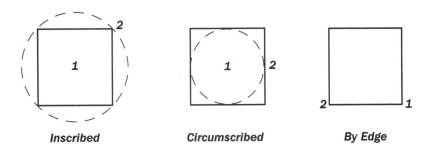

Inscribed   *Circumscribed*   *By Edge*

Arcs Toolbox

The Arcs toolbox contains tools to create circular arcs and elliptical segments. It also contains arc modification tools. The following screenshot identifies each available tool.

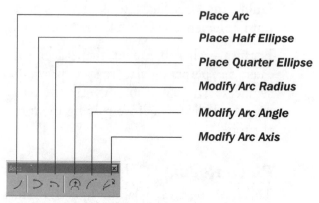

The tools in the Arcs toolbox.

Place Arc

Use this tool to draw a partial circle. When creating an arc, in addition to the center and radius, you must specify the direction of sweep (the *start angle*) and its angle (*sweep angle*). See the figure below.

The Place Arc tool implements the following two methods:

- **Center:** to specify the center and two endpoints.
- **Edge:** to specify three points the arc must pass through.

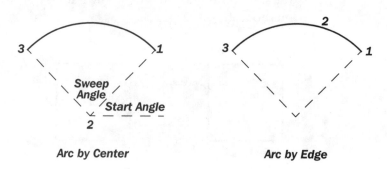

Look at the sequence of data points in the above figure. MicroStation measures angles in a counterclockwise direction. Similarly, arcs are drawn counterclockwise.

When drawing an arc by the Center method, first identify an endpoint, then, the center. These data points determine the arc's start angle. The third data point identifies the arc's other endpoint in the clockwise direction. The earlier figure visually defines the sweep angle.

When drawing an arc by the Edge method, first identify an endpoint, then the point it must pass through, and, the last endpoint.

When using either method, you can enter a value, if known, for any of the three text fields in the Tool Settings window: radius, start angle, and sweep angle.

Place Half Ellipse

Use this tool to draw a half ellipse. This tool has no options. First you are prompted to identify one end of an axis. The ellipse starts from this point. Next, you are prompted for a point it must pass through. Finally, you must specify the other end of the axis. The half ellipse ends on this point.

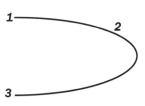

Depending on the location of the second data point, the first and the third data points can define either the major or the minor axis of the ellipse.

Place Quarter Ellipse

Use this tool to draw a quarter ellipse. This tool has no options. First you are prompted to identify one end of the ellipse quarter. The ellipse starts from this point. Next, you are prompted for a point on its axis. Finally, you must specify the other end of the ellipse. The quarter ellipse ends on this point.

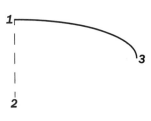

Depending on the location of the third data point, the line between the first two data points defines either the major or the minor axis of the ellipse.

Modify Arc Radius

This tool maintains the endpoints of the selected arc. It lets you designate a new point the arc must pass through. This changes both the existing center of the arc and its radius.

This tool only modifies circular arcs and has no options.

Modify Arc Angle

This tool maintains the center, the radius, and one endpoint of the selected arc. It lets you designate a new point for its other end. This changes the arc's sweep angle. The endpoint closer to the data point you click is modified.

This tool modifies both circular and elliptical arcs, and has no options.

Modify Arc Axis

This tool can modify both circular and elliptical arcs. However, its primary role is to modify elliptical arcs.

When you identify an elliptical arc with this tool, the endpoint further from the data point remains anchored, allowing you to designate a new point for the other endpoint. This tool maintains the direction of both axes, changing only the length of the axis corresponding to the endpoint being moved.

When you identify a circular arc with this tool, you can change it to become an elliptical arc.

Ellipses Toolbox

The Ellipses toolbox contains tools to create circles and ellipses. Being closed shapes, each tool implements Area, Fill Type, and Fill Color options discussed for the Polygons toolbox. The following screenshot identifies each available tool.

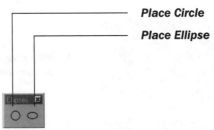

Place Circle

Place Ellipse

The tools in the Ellipses toolbox.

Place Circle

Use this tool to create circles in a variety of ways. The tool implements three methods: Center, Edge, and Diameter.

When either of the first two methods is selected, an additional option button appears. This option button lets you specify a value for either Radius or Diameter for greater flexibility.

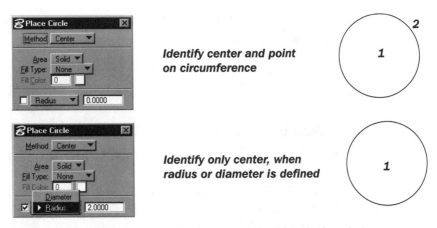

This figure explains the Center method for placing circles.

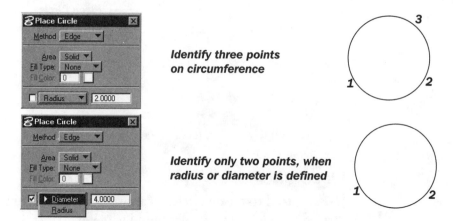

This figure explains the Edge method for placing circles.

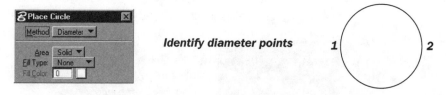

This figure explains the Diameter method for placing circles.

Place Ellipse

The circle and ellipse are geometrically related elements. An ellipse has two perpendicular axes: major and minor. A circle is a special kind of an ellipse. Both its axes are identical. You might recall from chapter 3, MicroStation stores both circles and ellipses as Type 15 elements.

The Tool Settings window for the Place Ellipse tool offers the following three fields:

- Primary: refers to the primary radius (half the primary axis length).
- Secondary: refers to the secondary radius.
- Rotation: refers to the primary axis angle with respect to the X axis, measured counterclockwise.

The following figure identifies these variables.

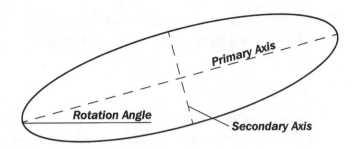

If you know the values of these three variables for the ellipse you need to draw, you only need to identify its center to create it. Similarly, if you fill in the values for any two values, you need to enter two data points to define the missing value.

To create an ellipse by the center method:

1. Click the icon. Select Center for Method in the Tool Settings window if not already selected. You are prompted to identify the ellipse center.

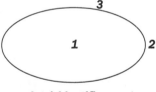

point 1 identifies center

2. Click a data point to identify the center. A temporary marker is placed at that location and a dotted line follows the cursor.

3. Click a data point to identify the primary radius and its rotation. You are prompted for another data point.

4. Click a data point to identify the secondary radius and the ellipse is created.

To create an ellipse by the edge method:

1. Click the icon. Select Edge for Method in the Tool Settings window if not already selected. You are prompted to identify a point on the ellipse.

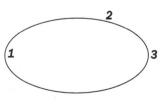

points 1 and 3 define an axis

2. Click a data point. A temporary marker is placed at that location and you are prompted for another data point.

3. Click a data point. A second temporary marker is placed at that location and an ellipse passing through the markers is drawn that moves as you move the cursor. You are prompted for another data point.

4. Click the third data point to create the ellipse.

Text Toolbox

Though graphics is MicroStation's forte, it must work with text. Typical construction drawings include a significant amount of text. You need to label drawing parts with text, add specification notes, create bill of material tables, and document construction procedures—all of which require flexible text annotation tools.

MicroStation's text creation, editing, and query tools reside in the Text toolbox shown in the figure below.

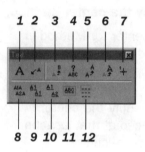

1. **Place Text**
2. **Place Note**
3. **Edit Text**
4. **Display Text Attributes**
5. **Match Text Attributes**
6. **Change Text Attributes**
7. **Place Text Node**
8. **Copy/Increment Text**
9. **Copy Enter Data Field**
10. **Copy/Increment Enter Data Fields**
11. **Fill in Single Enter-Data Field**
12. **Auto Fill in Enter-Data Fields**

The text tools.

Before discussing each of the text tools, you will find an introduction to text parameters helpful. You will encounter many of these in the Tool Settings window as you work with text. These parameters let you control the active font, the size of letters and their spacing, justification, and others.

The text tools are also affected by other non-text parameters. For instance, new text is placed with the active symbology (color, weight, and level). Additionally, the active angle determines the orientation in which text is placed in the drawing.

Some text-specific parameters are located in the Preferences dialog box accessed from the Workspace menu. However, most can be found in the Text dialog box shown in the figure below. This dialog box is invoked from the Element menu.

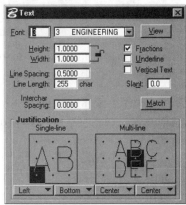

Select Text from the Element menu to activate this dialog box.

The first line in the dialog box is labeled Font. Here you either key in the font number to use, or select it from a drop-down list. You may also set the active font by keying in FT=n, where *n* is a valid font number. Clicking the View button opens the Fonts dialog box to preview available fonts.

It's important you realize that MicroStation doesn't use system fonts, as do word processors and spreadsheets. MicroStation keeps its fonts in a proprietary format optimized for drafting needs and for vector hardware devices, such as plotters. To use TrueType, PostScript Type 1, or other supported fonts, you must import them in MicroStation using the Font Installer accessed by selecting Install Fonts from the Utilities menu.

The Height and Width fields determine the size of text. Both fields can be locked together, so a change in one affects the other. You do this by clicking the lock icon to the right of these fields in the dialog box. When enabled, the icon shows the lock in a closed position.

The Line Spacing field affects multi-line text. It determines the spacing between lines. It also affects text elements placed with the Along Element, Above Element, and Below Element methods. In this case, the line spacing value determines the space between the element and text. *As a rule of thumb, set line spacing to be half of text height.*

The Line Length field only affects multi-line text. It determines the maximum number of characters in a line when typing new text or importing text from an external file.

NOTE: To import text from an external ASCII text file, select Import, then Text from the File menu. Alternatively, use the `INCLUDE filename` key-in, where *filename* is the name of the file to import, including complete directory specification.

The Interchar Spacing field determines the spacing between characters. It also affects text when placed using the Along Element method.

The Fractions checkbox, when enabled, uses stacked characters for numbers separated by a slash. The Underline checkbox, when enabled, underlines text as it is placed. The Vertical Text checkbox, when enabled, places characters one below another, rather than to the right.

T
E
X
T

Example of Vertical Text

The Slant field accepts an angular value between -89° and 89°. Text placement tools slant, or italicize, text by this angle.

The Match button is used to change the active text settings to match those of a text element in the design file. Clicking this button is the same as selecting the Match Text Attributes tool from the Text toolbox.

The Justification groupbox in the Text dialog box lets you control the position of text relative to its placement point, also known as *origin*. Single-line and multi-line text can each be controlled independently. There are nine justification settings for single-line text and fifteen settings for multi-line text. Closely examine the Text dialog box to see these as dots in the Justification groupbox. You specify the justification value by either clicking these dots, or by selecting the horizontal and vertical justification position from the option buttons below the sample text in the dialog box.

Unlike graphical elements that represent a full-scale model, text is different. It is like a symbol, such as the North arrow symbol you see on maps. No matter what the scale, text must typically appear in the same size on the plot. In other words, text size depends on its plot scale.

Let's consider two examples to help you understand this better. When drawing the apartment unit layout in chapter 2, suppose the project specification required drawings to be plotted at 1/8" = 1'-0" scale with a text height of an eighth of an inch. The plot scale corresponds to a scale factor of 96 (=12 x 8), thus text should be drawn with a height of 1 foot (=1/8 x 96 inches).

Let us consider another example in metric units. Suppose project specifications require plots at 1:100 scale with a text height of 2.5 mm on the paper plot. In this case the text you draw in your design file must have a height of 250 mm (=2.5 x 100).

NOTE: If you change the scale you plot drawings in, you will need to change the size of any text already in the drawing. To change text size, you can use the Scale tool in the Manipulate toolbox.

If you like using key-ins, the following table presents several you can add to your treasure chest. Obviously, only text key-ins are listed below. Note that the letters after the '=' symbol are placeholders that must be substituted with desired values.

Key-in	Description
FT=nn	Sets active font to the number specified.
TH=mu:su:pu	Sets the active text height in working units.
TW=mu:su:pu	Sets the active text width in working units.
TX=mu:su:pu	Sets the active text size (both TH and TW to same value) in working units.
LS=mu:su:pu	Sets the active line spacing in working units.
LL=nn	Sets the active line length to the number (not more than 255) of characters specified.

With this background information on text, you are now ready to tackle any single-line or multi-line text placement or editing tool. You will need to understand the concept of *enter data* fields before you use the last five tools in the Text toolbox. This will be explained just before you learn about those tools.

Place Text

Use this tool to place single-line or multi-line text. On activating this tool, a Text Editor window opens in which you compose the text you wish to place in the design file. The Tool Settings window displays several options, most of which were discussed earlier.

> **NOTE:** The Text Editor window is resizable. If you find the window is small and you must scroll horizontally or vertically to keep the text in view, resize it by dragging its corner.

To use this tool:

1. Click its icon.
2. Select the desired options in the Tool Settings window.
3. Enter the desired text in the Text Editor window. If multi-line text is desired, separate the lines by pressing the Return key between them.
4. Click a data point at the location you want the text placed.
5. Click a data point at another location if you wish to place the text again. To clear the text in the Text Editor window, click Reset.

You can edit the text in the Text Editor window by using the common cursor movement and dialog box editing keys. The *Insert* key toggles text insertion status—new text either inserts within, or overwrites existing text. Shift+arrow keys select text. Ctrl+X cuts selected text. Ctrl+C copies selected text. Ctrl+V pastes previously cut or copied text.

The following table lists the text placement methods for the tool.

Method	Description
By Origin	Places text origin at data point.
Fitted	Places text between two data points by adjusting text size and orientation.
View Independent	Same as By Origin, except that once placed, text maintains orientation regardless of view rotation.
Fitted VI	Same as Fitted and View Independent.
Above Element	Places text parallel to and at the Line Spacing distance above a line or segment of a shape, line string, or multi-line.

Method	Description
Below Element	Places text parallel to and at the Line Spacing distance below a line or segment of a shape, line string, or multi-line
On Element	Places text parallel to and inside a line or segment of a shape, line string, or multi-line by clipping the element.
Along Element	Places each letter separately as part of a graphic group at the Line Spacing distance, either above or below (indicated by the second data point), a line, line string, shape, arc, curve, or ellipse.

TIP: If text is oriented at an angle during placement, and you want it aligned to the view axis, do not yet click the data point. Press the Esc key to switch the focus to the Key-in window and key in AA=0 to return the active angle to zero. You may now click the data point to place the text.

Place Note

Use this tool to place a *leadered note*, a term that refers to text that includes a line pointing to an element. Though in the Text toolbox, it is stored in the design file as a dimension element. This distinction is important. To edit the parameters of a single-line leadered note, use the Dimension Settings dialog box accessed from the Element menu, *not* the Text dialog box. Refer to the *Dimension Toolbox* section in this chapter for details.

To place a leadered note:

1. Click its icon. The Text Editor window opens.
2. Compose the text in the Text Editor window.
3. Select single-line or multi-line for Type in the Tool Settings window. Single-line parameters are set in the Dimension Settings dialog box.

   If you select multi-line, additional options become available in the Tool Settings window. These options supplement the parameters in the Dimension Settings dialog box.
4. Click a data point to identify the arrowhead location.
5. Click a data point for the other end of the leader line. Text is also placed at this point if Location in the Dimension Settings dialog box's Placement category is set to Automatic or Semi-automatic. If set to manual, you can add more vertices to the leader line and click Reset to place the text.

The two most important single-line note parameters are: Location and Orientation. Location is set in the Placement category, and Orientation in the Text category of the Dimension Settings dialog box.

The upper row of three notes in the figure to the right illustrates the In Line, Above, and Horizontal orientation when the Location option is set to automatic. The numbers in the figure designate the sequence of data points.

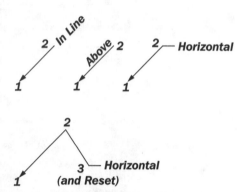

The lower row in the figure illustrates the Horizontal orientation when the Location option is set to manual. In manual mode, you must click Reset to inform the tool that you have specified the last vertex of the leader line.

Edit Text

Use this tool to edit the text in a text element, text node, or dimension element.

On activating this tool, you are prompted to identify an element. On identifying and accepting the element with data points, it is placed in the Text Editor window (if text or text node), or in the Dimension Text dialog box (if dimension element). Here you edit the text and click the Apply button (in Text Editor) or the OK button (in Dimension Text).

NOTE: A computed number in a dimension element appears as an asterisk in the Text field of the Dimension Text dialog box.

Display Text Attributes

Use this tool to display the parameters of a single-line text or multi-line text node element.

On activating this tool you are prompted to identify a text element. On identifying a single-line text element, the status bar displays the text height (TH), text width (TW), level (LV), and font (FT). On identifying a multi-line text element, the status bar displays the node number (NN), line length (LL), line spacing (LS), level (LV), and font (FT). You must identify the multi-line text element again to display its height and width.

Match Text Attributes

Use this tool to set your active text parameters from an existing text element in the design file.

On invoking the tool, you are prompted to identify a text element. On identifying the element, you are prompted to accept or reject the selection. When you click a data point to accept it, your active text parameters change to match those of the element.

Change Text Attributes

Use this tool to change the text parameters of existing text elements in a design file.

On invoking the tool, you are prompted to identify an element. The Tool Settings window displays nearly a dozen text attributes. Enable the checkbox for the parameter you wish to change and set its value. On identifying the element, you are prompted to accept or reject the selection. When you click a data point to accept it, the specified text attributes of the element are changed.

NOTE: You can change the attributes of text elements one at a time by individually identifying them, or in a group by using a fence or selection set.

Place Text Node

Use this tool to place empty text nodes (these have node numbers like multi-line text elements) that can be filled with text later.

Empty text nodes are not visible on screen unless you enable the Text Nodes checkbox in the View Attributes dialog box. Text nodes appear with a small cross and a node number when text node visibility is enabled in a view.

To fill text nodes, use the Place Text tool and enable the Text Node Lock checkbox in the Tool Settings window. Text you compose in the Text Editor window can only be placed when you identify an empty text node.

When text is later filled in a text node, it takes on the attributes of the text node, not the active attributes. You fill text in text nodes with the Place Text tool or the Attach Displayable Attributes tool in the Database toolbox discussed in chapter 10.

On activating the tool, you are prompted to enter the text node origin. The Tool Settings window displays two options: View Independent and Active Angle. These were discussed earlier and have the same meaning. Clicking a data point places the text node in the design file, and the command starts over.

Copy and Increment Text

Use this tool to copy, while incrementing numbers in, a text element. The text element you identify with this tool must be a single-line element containing a number anywhere within it.

This tool is useful when you need to label a series of parts, rooms, or other items with text containing consecutive numbers.

Room A2	Room A3
Room A4	Room A5

On activating the tool, you are prompted to identify an element. If the element you identify is not single-line text, or does not contain a number, the tool will not find the element.

The Tag Increment value in the Tool Settings window is used to compute the next value of the embedded number. The default is the number 1. If the tag increment is 3, the text *Room A2* will increment to *Room A5*, and so on.

Identifying a valid element attaches a copy to the cursor, and you are prompted to accept or reject the selection. You accept the text by clicking a data point at the location you want the incremented copy placed.

After the incremented copy is placed, the tool assumes you wish to place additional incremented instances of the text. It continues to prompt for data points for additional text locations. A Reset button click drops the element from the cursor, and the tool restarts.

Copy Enter Data Field

Before you can use the remaining four tools in the Text toolbox, you must understand the concept of *enter data* fields. An enter data field is a placeholder for text that may change in value. In contrast to an empty text node, an enter data field is defined with a fixed number of characters. Additionally, once you fill a text node with the Place Text tool, you can edit it, but you cannot fill it again. In contrast, you can use the enter data field tools to fill or revise text in enter data fields at any time.

Enter data fields are most commonly used in cells that need to contain editable text. They are also used in standard notes that do not change, except for a word or two, within a text element.

To create an enter data field, simply use the underscore character as the place holder when creating text with the Place Text tool.

Enter Data Fields

Refer to Section __ of Guide.

The figure at right shows an enter data field. When the Data Fields checkbox is enabled in the View Attributes dialog box, the underscore characters are visible. When it is unchecked, you do not see the blank placeholder, just the text entered in them.

Refer to Section 14 of Guide.

Refer to Section 25 of Guide.

Use this tool to copy the contents of one enter data field to another. If the source contains more characters than the destination, the source is truncated.

To use this tool:

1. Click its icon. You are prompted to select the source enter data field.
2. Click the enter data field you wish to copy. The field highlights with a rectangle around it. The value in the field appears in the status bar.
   Should you click the text surrounding the enter data field, but not the field, an error message will appear in the status bar, and you must click again.
3. Click the target enter data field. The contents of the source are copied to the destination.
4. Continue copying the contents to other enter data fields, or click Reset to start over.

Copy and Increment Enter Data Fields

This tool is similar to the Copy and Increment Text tool, except that it works with enter data fields. You first identify the source enter data field, then click data points on one or more target enter data fields. The text in the source field must contain a number; otherwise, the field will refuse to highlight.

Selecting the target enter data field copies the text from the source and increments its value. The default increment value is 1, and it can be changed in the Tag Increment field in the Tool Settings window.

Fill in Single Enter Data Field

Use this tool to fill enter data fields. You select the fields, one at a time, in the sequence you wish to fill them.

This tool requires you to highlight the enter data field before composing text in the Text Editor window. This sequence is the inverse of the Place Text sequence, where you compose text first, then identify a data point. Take a little time getting used to this tool.

To use this tool:

1. Click its icon. You are prompted to identify an element.
2. Identify the enter data field you wish to fill. Be sure to click the text element at the location of the enter data field. The element highlights, and a rectangle appears around the field.
3. Compose the text for the field in the Text Editor window and press the Return key.
4. The text in the Text Editor is placed in the enter data field.

If you enter more characters than will fit in the enter data field, the excess is truncated. Compare this to an empty text node that imposes no restriction on the size of text it can accommodate.

Auto Fill in Enter Data Fields

Use this tool to fill all empty enter data fields in a view without having to find and click on each.

When you activate this tool, you are prompted to identify a view. On clicking a data point anywhere in a view window, the first empty enter data field is highlighted. You compose text for it in the Text Editor window and press the Return key to enter the value, and the next empty enter data field highlights. Continue composing values for the fields and pressing the Return key until all fields are filled.

To leave an enter data field blank, simply press the Return key without entering a data value. The sequence in which enter data fields are highlighted by this tool is the same sequence in which you created them.

Cells Toolbox

Symbols of all sorts are commonly used in drafting. A construction site plan uses the North arrow symbol. A schematic electrical drawing uses resistor and capacitor symbols. A traffic control plan uses symbols for traffic signs and devices. An industrial process drawing uses symbols for pumps, valves, and gates.

MicroStation implements cells and cell libraries for managing the use of symbols in design files. You will learn about the two different types of cells, graphic and point, in chapter 21. You will also learn how to create cells and cell libraries in that chapter.

In this section, you learn about cell placement and query tools in the Cells toolbox.

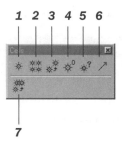

1. **Place Active Cell**

2. **Place Active Cell Matrix**

3. **Select and Place Cell**

4. **Define Cell Origin**

5. **Identify Cell**

6. **Place Active Line Terminator**

7. **Replace Cells**

The tools in the Cells toolbox.

Before discussing the cell tools, you will find an introduction to the Cell Library dialog box helpful. This dialog box lets you *attach* a cell library. It also lets you designate a cell from the library as *active*.

When you invoke a cell placement tool from the Cells toolbox, the active cell, designated in the Cell Library dialog box, is placed. You invoke the Cell Library dialog box from the Element menu.

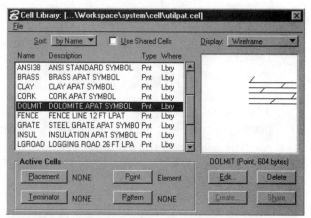

Select Cells from the Element menu to activate this dialog box.

When opened, the Cell Library dialog box displays the contents of the cell library last attached to the active design file. If no cell library was attached, the listbox in the dialog box is empty. To attach a cell library, select Attach from the File menu in the dialog box, not the MicroStation menu bar. The Attach Cell Library dialog box opens. Locate the cell library you wish to use, highlight it, and click the OK button to attach it. Its contents will display in the dialog box.

NOTE: Several cell libraries are delivered with MicroStation. They are located in the `C:\Bentley\Workspace\System\Cell` folder.

The four buttons in the Active Cells groupbox, shown in the screenshot above, let you designate a cell as active for a certain set of tools. To designate a cell as active for the Cells toolbox, highlight the cell name in the listbox and click the Placement button, or the Terminator button when using the Place Active Line Terminator tool. To designate a cell as active for point placement tools, click the Point button. Similarly, for patterning tools, click the Pattern button.

Cells can be of two types: point and graphic, as mentioned earlier. Don't confuse the Point button with the point cell. The Point button designates an active cell as available for use by the tools in the Points toolbox. Both point and graphic cells can be designated for use by point placement tools.

Place Active Cell

Use this tool to place an instance of the *active placement cell* in the design file. You use the Placement button in the Cell Library dialog box for this, as was explained earlier.

When you place a graphic cell in a design file, the cell's symbology and level usage remain unchanged. When you place a point cell, it assumes the active symbology and level. An example will make this clear. When you place a graphic cell with elements drawn on level 5 in yellow color, its elements stay on level 5 and continue to display in yellow—regardless of the active color and level. When you place a point cell, no matter what its original symbology or level structure, all its elements are placed in the design file on the active level with active symbology.

To use this tool:

1. Click its icon. If no cell is active, the status bar displays an error message stating no cell is active. To make a cell active, highlight it in the Cell Library dialog box and click the Placement button. Its name appears in the Active Cell field in the Tool Settings window.

2. Select the desired rotation angle and placement scale in the Tool Settings window. You can disproportionately scale the cell by keying in different values for the X and Y scales. Click the lock icon in the Tool Settings window so it displays an open lock if you wish to scale the cell disproportionately. You are prompted to enter the origin for the cell.

3. Click a data point where you want the cell placed.

4. Continue placing additional instances of the cell with data points, or click the Reset button to terminate the command.

This tool's Tool Settings window also displays two checkboxes: Relative and Interactive.

If the active cell is a graphic cell, and the Relative checkbox is enabled, the lowest level in the cell is placed on the active level, and higher levels are placed relative to the active level. For example, if the active cell has elements on levels 5 and 9, when placed on level 7 with the Relative checkbox enabled, elements on level 5 in the cell will be placed on level 7 in the design file, and elements on level 9 in the cell are placed on level 11 in the design file.

If the Interactive checkbox is enabled, you define the scale and rotation of the cell interactively with additional data points.

Place Active Cell Matrix

Use this tool to place several instances of one cell in a matrix, or a row and column format. The cell is rotated by the active angle, and scaled by the active scale during placement.

In addition to the active cell's name, its Tool Settings window displays four fields: Rows, Columns, Row Spacing, Column Spacing. You specify the number of rows and columns, and their spacing, in these fields.

To use this tool:

1. Click its icon. Make sure a placement cell is active.
2. Key in the desired values in the Tool Settings window for the cell matrix desired. Also, change the active angle and active scale values as needed.
3. Click a data point to locate the lower left corner of the desired cell matrix.

Select and Place Cell

Use this tool to place an additional instance of a cell in the design file.

To use this tool:

1. Click its icon. The Tool Settings window displays the active angle and scale. Change these as needed. If you wish to place a graphic cell *relative* to the active level, enable the Relative checkbox. You are prompted to identify an element.

2. Identify a cell in the design file to copy. The cell highlights and you are prompted to accept or reject it. The scale and rotation of the cell identified are ignored; those in the Tool Settings window are used instead.

3. Click a data point at the desired location to place an instance of the cell identified in step 2. Or, click Reset if you wish to identify another cell without placing it.

4. Continue to place additional instances with data points, if desired. Or, click Reset to restart the command.

Define Cell Origin

This tool is used to define an origin for a cell when creating it. See chapter 21 for details on using this tool.

Identify Cell

Use this tool to display the name and level of a cell in the design file. This tool has no options.

When you activate the tool, you are prompted to identify an element. On identifying a cell, its name and levels are displayed in the status bar.

Place Active Line Terminator

This tool places the active terminator cell at the endpoint of a line, a line string, or an arc. The cell is rotated during placement by an angle equal to the element's orientation. It's commonly used to place an arrowhead cell. Though this tool can be used to create leaders for notes, you will find the Place Note tool more flexible.

To use this tool:

1. Click its icon. The Tool Settings window displays the terminator scale (different from the active scale and can be set with the TS= key-in) and the name of the active terminator cell. This is set in the Cell Library dialog box by highlighting a cell and clicking the Terminator button. You are prompted to identify an element.

2. Identify a line, a line string, or an arc. It highlights, and you are prompted to accept or reject it.

3. Click a data point to accept the element. The active terminator cell rotates to match the orientation of the element and is placed on its endpoint. The tool uses the endpoint closer to the data point.

Replace Cells

Use this tool to update existing cells in a design file with a cell of the same name in the attached cell library. Also, use it to replace existing cells with an active cell. You can perform this update or replacement one at a time, or in a group by using a fence.

Use the Update method in the Tool Settings window to update existing cells with a cell of the same name in the attached cell library. Use the Replace method to specify an active cell.

Dimension Toolbox

The element placement tools you've learned so far will serve nearly all your 2D drawings needs, except dimensioning. The last of the placement toolboxes in the Main tool frame, the Dimension toolbox, complements the detailing tools discussed in the Patterns and Text toolboxes.

Dimensioning refers to annotation that communicates the size of the model. Drafting standards vary by discipline on how to draw such annotation. MicroStation offers the Dimension Settings dialog box to help configure its dimensioning tools to address any standard.

MicroStation's dimensioning tools reside in the Dimension toolbox, shown in the figure below.

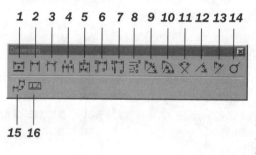

1. Dimension Element
2. Dimension Size with Arrow
3. Dimension Size with Stroke
4. Dimension Location
5. Dimension Location (Stacked)
6. Dimension Size Perp. to Points
7. Dimension Size Perp. to Line
8. Dimension Ordinates
9. Dimension Angle Size
10. Dimension Angle Location
11. Dimension Angle Between
12. Dimension Angle from X
13. Dimension Angle from Y
14. Dimension Radial
15. Update Dimension
16. Geometric Tolerance

The dimensioning tools.

Before we discuss each of the dimensioning tools, you will find an introduction to dimensioning and its settings helpful. You may encounter new terms in the status bar prompts and the Tool Settings window as you work with dimensions. This introduction will help you understand them better.

Dimensioning options are located in the Dimension Settings dialog box shown in the figure below. This dialog box is invoked from the Element menu by selecting Dimensions.

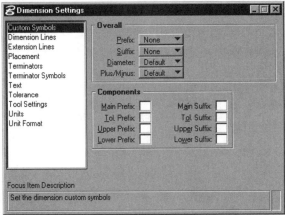

Select Dimensions from the Element menu to activate this dialog box.

This dialog box has a list of categories to the left, and options relevant to the selected category to the right. The settings you select in this dialog box affect all dimensioning tools.

Like multi-line settings, only one set of dimension settings can be active at a given time. To save dimension settings for use later, use the Settings Manager discussed in chapter 14.

A dimension element is made up of extension lines, dimension lines with arrowheads (called terminators), dimension text, tolerance, prefix, suffix, and special symbols. The following figure identifies each dimension element component.

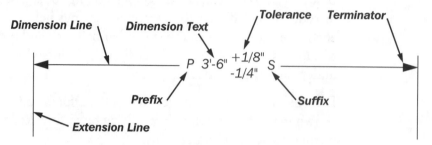

The components of a dimension element.

The *dimension line* defines the boundaries of the distance or angle measured. The *terminators* at its ends can be arrowheads or strokes (short inclined lines).

The *dimension text* displays the value of the distance or angle measured. It can include a prefix, a suffix, or tolerances. Dimension text can be configured to lie in-line with the dimension line, above it, or always stay horizontal.

Extension lines, also called *witness lines* in the drafting world, identify the starting and ending points close to the object being measured. The dimension line runs between them.

Prefixes, suffixes, and symbols enhance dimension text to convey additional information. For example, the diameter symbol as a suffix to dimension text means that the distance shown is the diameter for an arc or circle.

The Dimension Settings dialog box implements eleven categories to help you set up parameters relevant to the format, symbology, and orientation for each of these dimension element components. These categories are listed in the table below.

Dim. Setting Category	Description
Custom Symbols	Set options for prefix, suffix, diameter, and plus/minus symbols.
Dimension Lines	Set dimension line symbology and the stack offset—the distance between dimension lines—when using the stacked dimension tools.

Dim. Setting Category	Description
Extension Lines	Set extension line symbology, and values for extension above dimension lines and offset from data points identifying start and end of a dimension.
Placement	Set dimension placement alignment and location options.
Terminators	Set terminator symbology, arrowhead size and type, and criteria for their adjustment.
Terminator Symbols	Set custom symbols to use in place of the standard arrowhead and stroke symbols.
Text	Set dimension text symbology, orientation, justification, margin, and options for drawing a frame around the text.
Tolerance	Specify whether to display tolerance information and how to format it.
Tool Settings	Set options for each tool, and its method, in the Dimension toolbox.
Units	Set the format (mechanical or AEC) and scale factor for the distance computed by the dimensioning tools.
Unit Format	Set the format for angular and metric measurements, and whether to display leading and trailing zeros for primary and secondary units.

As you select a dimension setting category from the Dimension Settings dialog box, a description of the category displays along its bottom in the Focus Item Description field. When you select an option on the right side of the dialog box, a description of the option is displayed. You will find these descriptions invaluable as you adjust option values for your own needs.

NOTE: If you do not like the standard arrowheads and symbols MicroStation uses, you can use those in font 102. This font contains fourteen symbols, identified with the letters A through N. Select *Symbol* from the option in the Terminator Symbols category of the Dimension Settings dialog box, and key in the character to use from font 102.

With this background information on dimensions, you are now ready to tackle dimensioning.

Dimension Element

This is an intelligent dimensioning tool. It recognizes the element type you select and adjusts its behavior accordingly. You can perform most dimensioning tasks with the tool alone.

When you identify a line segment, clicking the Next button in the Tool Settings window or pressing the space bar cycles the tool through the following tools:

- Dimension Size with Arrow
- Dimension Size with Stroke
- Label Line
- Dimension Size Perpendicular to Line

When you identify an arc segment, clicking the Next button or pressing the space bar cycles the Dimension Element tool through the following tools:

- Dimension Radius
- Dimension Radius (Extended Leader)
- Dimension Arc Size
- Dimension Arc Size (Opposite side)

When you identify a circle, clicking the Next button or pressing the space bar cycles the tool through the following tools:

- Dimension Diameter
- Dimension Diameter (Extended Leader)
- Dimension Diameter Parallel
- Dimension Radius
- Dimension Radius (Extended Leader)

To use this tool:

1. Click its icon. You are prompted to identify an element.
2. Identify the element to dimension with a data point. A temporary dimension element attaches to your cursor for preview.

3. If the dimension format is not what you want, click the Next button in the Tool Settings window or press the space bar to cycle through several dimensioning tools for the element, until the one needed is activated. You are prompted to accept the dimension.

4. Click a data point to place the dimension, or click Reset to start over.

The Tool Settings window also displays a checkbox labeled Association Lock. To associate the dimension with the element it measures, enable this checkbox and locate the element first with a tentative button click, followed by a data point.

> **NOTE:** To create associative dimensions, you must first identify the element with a tentative button before accepting it with a data point. Otherwise, the dimension will not be associative even if the Association Lock checkbox is enabled.

The term *associative dimension* refers to a dimension that updates when you edit the element it measures.

The Alignment option button is the last parameter in the Tool Settings window. This option button is also located in the Dimension Settings dialog box under the Placement category. The following figure explains the four available alignment options: View, Drawing, True, and Arbitrary.

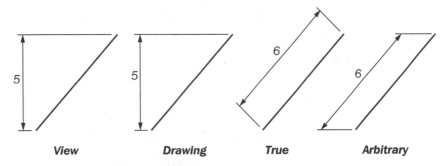

The four Alignment options for placing dimensions.

In the above figure, the View option orients the dimension line along the view axes. The Drawing option orients it along the design plane axes. If a view is unrotated, both View and Drawing alignments result in the same dimension format. The True alignment option aligns the dimension along the element with extension lines perpendicular to the dimension line. The Arbitrary alignment option is the same as True, except that extension lines need not be perpendicular to the dimension line.

Dimension Size with Arrow

Use this tool to dimension linear elements with arrowheads as terminators at the ends of the dimension line. The numbers 1, 2, and 3, in the figure to the right, designate the sequence of data points for the tool.

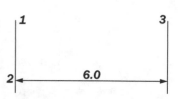

The Alignment and Association Lock options in the Tool Settings window were discussed in the Dimension Element tool.

Dimension Size with Stroke

Use this tool to dimension linear elements with strokes as terminators at the ends of the dimension line. The numbers 1, 2, and 3, in the figure to the right, designate the sequence of data points for the tool.

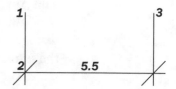

The Alignment and Association Lock options in the Tool Settings window were discussed in the Dimension Element tool.

Dimension Location

Use this tool to dimension linear elements from a common base line. This tool is commonly used in mechanical design. It offers the same Alignment and Association Lock options discussed earlier.

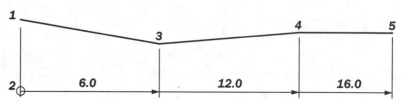

All distances are measured from a common location, or datum.

Dimension Location (Stacked)

Use this tool to dimension linear elements from a common base line. This tool is the same as the Dimension Location tool, except that it stacks dimensions. The numbers 1, 2, 3, 4, and 5, in the figure below, designate the sequence of data points for the tool.

Its Tool Settings window displays the same Alignment and Association Lock options discussed earlier.

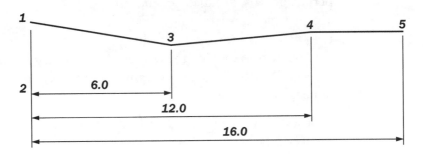

All distances are measured from a common location, or datum.

Dimension Size Perpendicular to Points

Use this tool to dimension the distance between two points, perpendicular to a direction you define. This tool requires three data points. The first data point identifies the first point. The second data point defines the direction and endpoint of the extension line. The third data point identifies the second point.

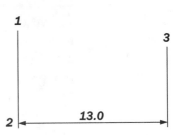

The distance is measured perpendicular to the direction defined by the first two data points.

Its Tool Settings window displays the same Association Lock option discussed earlier.

Dimension Size Perpendicular to Line

Use this tool to dimension a perpendicular distance from a line to a point. When you activate the tool, it prompts for the base of first extension line. Use the tentative button to snap to the endpoint (point 1) of the line you want the perpendicular distance from, and accept it with a data point. You are 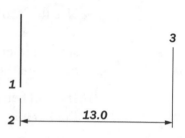 then prompted for the endpoint (point 2) of the extension line. Click a data point to designate the length of the extension line that starts from the line. Finally, you are prompted for the endpoint (point 3) of the dimension element.

Its Tool Settings window displays the same Association Lock option discussed earlier.

Dimension Ordinates

This tool is similar to the Dimension Location tool. You use it to dimension the distance of points from a common datum. It doesn't draw dimension lines or terminators. It places dimension text on extension lines. This is useful when you need to dimension several closely spaced points and do not have the room for dimension lines 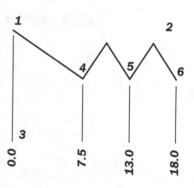 and terminators. Numbers 1 to 6 in the figure show data point sequence.

Dimension Angle Size

Use this tool to dimension an angle. It requires a data point sequence similar to the Dimension Size Arrow tool, except for an additional data point to locate the vertex of the angle. You designate the start point, the extension line location, the angle's vertex, and the endpoint. The numbers 1, 2, 3, and 4 in the figure designate the sequence of data point required by the tool.

Its Tool Settings window displays the same Association Lock option discussed earlier.

Dimension Angle Location

Use this tool to dimension angles from a common baseline or datum. This tool is similar to the Dimension Location tool you learned earlier.

Dimension Angle Between Lines

Use this tool to dimension angles between lines by identifying the lines. This tool is similar to the Dimension Angle Size tool, except that it doesn't prompt for the start, end, and center points. The angle is drawn counterclockwise. Notice that the angle is measured from line 1 to line 2 in the figure to the right.

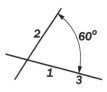

Its Tool Settings window displays the same Association Lock option discussed earlier.

Dimension Angle from X-Axis

Use this tool to dimension the orientation of a line from the X, or the horizontal axis. It requires two data points—one to identify the line, the other to locate the horizontal line.

Its Tool Settings window displays the same Association Lock option discussed earlier.

Dimension Angle from Y-Axis

Use this tool to dimension the orientation of a line from the Y, or the vertical axis. It requires two data points. One to identify the line, the other to locate the vertical line.

Its Tool Settings window displays the same Association Lock option discussed earlier.

Dimension Radial

Use this tool to dimension the radius or diameter of a circle or a circular arc. It can also place a center mark at the center of a circle or arc. When you activate the tool, it offers the following radial dimensioning methods:

- Center Mark
- Radius
- Radius Extended
- Diameter
- Diameter Extended

The following figure explains each of these methods.

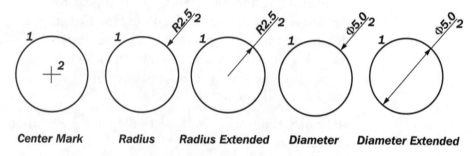

Center Mark   Radius   Radius Extended   Diameter   Diameter Extended

The radial dimension methods.

The Alignment and Association Lock options it displays in the Tool Settings window were discussed earlier.

Update Dimension

This tool invokes the Change Dimension to Active Settings command. Use this tool to change the format of existing dimensions to conform to changes you later make in the Dimension Settings dialog box.

On activating this tool, you are prompted to identify the dimension element to change. On identifying it, the element highlights, and you are prompted to accept it with a data point.

Geometric Tolerance

This tool is used to label mechanical drawings with geometric tolerance symbols. You concatenate geometric tolerance symbols with other text to compose a feature control box that can be placed as text, or as a leadered note.

This tool uses fonts 100 and 101. The former contains the geometric tolerance symbols and enclosing boxes, the latter contains standard ANSI symbols.

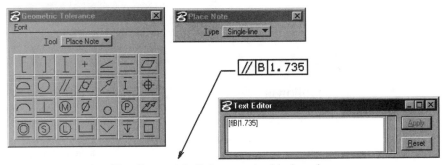

The Geometric Tolerance tool helps place feature control notes on mechanical drawings.

When you invoke the tool, the Geometric Tolerance and the Text Editor dialog boxes open. The former displays geometric tolerance symbols. The latter is used to compose the note. With the focus in the Text Editor window, you click desired symbols in the Geometric Tolerance dialog box to compose the feature control frame. You place it in the drawing as you do any text note.

Element Manipulation Tools

These tools are used to copy, move, scale, rotate, and mirror existing elements in a design file. They are also used to change element attributes or properties. These tools affect the entire element.

MicroStation's element manipulation tools are located in the Manipulate and Change Attributes toolboxes. The following figure identifies the location of these toolboxes in the Main tool frame.

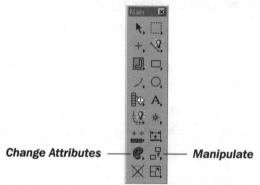

Change Attributes ——— **Manipulate**

The location of manipulation tools in the Main tool frame.

Manipulate Toolbox

The following figure identifies all tools found in the Manipulate toolbox.

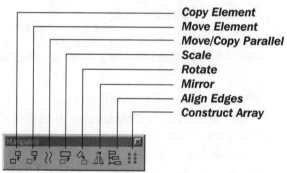

Copy Element
Move Element
Move/Copy Parallel
Scale
Rotate
Mirror
Align Edges
Construct Array

The tools in the Manipulate toolbox.

Each element manipulation tool is discussed below in the same sequence it appears in the Manipulate toolbox.

Copy Element

Use this tool to copy an element. On activating the tool, you are prompted to identify an element. When you click on an element, it highlights, and you are prompted to enter another data point to define the distance and direction. As you move the cursor, a copy of the element attaches and awaits a data point.

The point you click to identify an element also defines the point by which the tool copies it.

A data point places the element in the design file. To place additional copies of the same element, enter additional data points. To release the element, click the Reset button.

> **NOTE:** Instead of clicking data points to define a location in the design file, you can use any of the precision key-ins to define locations accurately.

This tool can also be used with a selection set or a fence. To copy several elements in a single step, group them with the Element Selection tool, the PowerSelector, or a fence. These element grouping tools were discussed in chapter 3.

When a selection set is active and you invoke the Copy Element tool, you are prompted for the first point to use as an origin for the copy. If a fence is active and you wish to use it, enable the Use Fence checkbox in the Tool Settings window.

Move Element

Use this tool to move an element from one location to another. On activating the tool, you are prompted to identify an element. When you click on an element, it highlights, and you are prompted to enter another data point to define the distance and direction. As you move the cursor, the element moves with it.

The point you click to identify an element also defines the point by which the tool moves it.

A data point places the element at its new location in the design file. To continue moving the element, enter additional data points. To release the element, click the Reset button.

This tool can also be used with a selection set or a fence. To move several elements in a single step, group them with the Element Selection tool, the PowerSelector, or a fence. These element grouping tools were discussed in chapter 3.

When a selection set is active and you invoke the Move Element tool, you are prompted for the first point to use as the origin. If a fence is active and you wish to use it, enable the Use Fence checkbox in the Tool Settings window.

Move/Copy Parallel

Use this tool to create an element parallel to an existing element. This tool computes the vertices of the new element such that each segment maintains the same perpendicular distance from its corresponding segment in the source element.

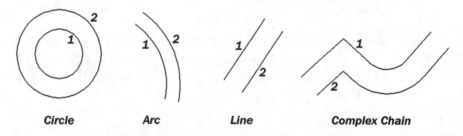

| Circle | Arc | Line | Complex Chain |

The result of the Copy Parallel tool on various elements.

The tool offers two options in the Tool Settings window: Distance and Make Copy. When both checkboxes are unchecked, the tool creates a new element and deletes the original element.

To use the tool:

1. Click its icon. It prompts you to identify an element.
2. Click a data point on an element. It highlights and a new parallel element is attached to the cursor. You are prompted to accept or reject the element.
3. To leave the original element identified in step 2, enable the Make Copy checkbox. If left unchecked, the original element will be deleted when the new element is created.
4. To specify a distance between the original element and the created element, enable the Distance checkbox and enter a value in the corresponding text field. If left unchecked, the distance of the cursor from the original element is used.

5. Move the cursor to the desired location and click a data point to create the new element. If a distance was supplied in step 4, the data point defines the side from the original element the new element is created on.

6. Click the Reset button to release the element from the cursor. The tool restarts.

This tool consolidates the function of four separate commands. Notice the command name in the status bar as you select options in the Tool Settings window. When both checkboxes are unchecked, the status bar displays the command name as Move Parallel by Distance. When the Make Copy checkbox is enabled, the Copy Parallel by Distance command name displays. When the Distance checkbox is enabled, the command names change to Move Parallel by Key-in and Copy Parallel by Key-in.

The more complex the source element, and greater the distance value used by the tool, the more likely the created element will have fewer segments than the source element.

Scale

Use this tool to increase or decrease the size of an element. The default method for this tool is Active Scale as shown in the figure to the right. The active scale consists of three values corresponding to each of the three coordinate axes, X, Y, and Z. The Z Scale only applies to 3D design files.

The lock icon to the right of the scale components determines whether to keep the scale same across all axes. To scale an element disproportionately, open the lock by clicking the icon and key in different values for each scale component.

A scale factor of 1 keeps the element the same size. A scale factor of 0.5 reduces the element to half its original size. A scale factor of 2 doubles the element.

TIP: To have the tool perform simple arithmetic when changing the active scale factor, use the Key-in window. Keying in AS=*6 multiplies each of the active scale components by 6.

Like the Move Parallel tool the Scale Element tool deletes the element you identify by default. It scales the original element. To scale a copy of the original element, enable the Make Copy checkbox.

When scaling multi-lines, the distance between multi-line components are maintained in their original values. To have the scale factor applied to these distances as well, enable the Scale Multi-line Offsets checkbox.

This tool can also be used with a selection set or a fence. To scale several elements in a single step, group them with the Element Selection tool, the PowerSelector, or a fence. These element grouping tools were discussed in chapter 3.

When a selection set is active and you invoke the Scale tool, you are prompted for the first point to use as the origin. If a fence is active and you wish to use it, enable the Use Fence checkbox in the Tool Settings window.

Another method of scaling is by *3 points*. When you select this method in the Tool Settings window, the active scale component fields disappear. They are replaced with a new checkbox labeled Proportional. This method is a different means of defining the scale factor. The first data point identifies the scale origin. The second data point identifies a reference point. The third data point identifies a new location for the reference point. The distance and direction between the first and second, and the first and third data points are used to compute the scale factor.

To use the tool:

1. Click its icon. You are prompted to identify an element. If a selection set is active, or a fence is enabled for use, you are prompted for the scale origin.
2. To scale a copy of the original element, enable the Make Copy checkbox. To scale multi-line offsets, enable the Scale Multi-line Offsets checkbox. Specify the desired active scale components when using the Active Scale method.
3. Click a data point to identify the element to scale, and you are prompted to identify the scale origin.

   If using a fence or selection set, this data point defines the scale origin, and the element is scaled.

4. If a selection set or a fence were not in use, click a data point to identify the scale origin, and the element is scaled.

5. Click the Reset button to release the element from the cursor.

As you move the cursor, just before identifying the scale origin, you will see a scaled copy of the element move. Contrary to what you might expect, this dynamic copy does not necessarily pass through the scale origin you are about to identify. This is because, in addition to the element, the tool scales the distance from the original element to the cursor.

The purpose of this seemingly incomprehensible behavior is to maintain a spatial relationship between the scaled element and the original element. Should you identify the scale origin at a vertex of a shape, the scale element will share that vertex. Should you identify the scale origin at the midpoint of a segment, the scaled element segment's midpoint will pass through that point. Should you identify the scale origin at the centroid of a shape, the scaled element's centroid will pass through that point. There is method to this madness!

Rotate

Use this tool to rotate an element by a specified angle. The default method for this tool is Active Angle, as shown in the figure to the right. This is the same active angle you've encountered when using other placement tools, such as Place Text and Place Active Cell.

Angular rotation is measured counterclockwise. You can specify the active angle by keying in a value in the Tool Settings window. You can also use the **AA=** key-in to define it.

Like the Scale Element tool the Rotate tool deletes the element you identify by default. It rotates the original element. To rotate a copy of the original element, enable the Make Copy checkbox.

This tool can also be used with a selection set or a fence. To rotate several elements in a single step, group them with the Element Selection tool, the PowerSelector, or a fence. These element grouping tools were discussed in chapter 3.

When a selection set is active and you invoke the Rotate tool, you are prompted for the point to rotate about, called the *pivot point*. If a fence is active and you wish to use it, enable the Use Fence checkbox in the Tool Settings window.

Other methods of rotating are by *2 points* and *3 points*.

When you select 2 points, the active angle field is disabled. You are prompted to first identify the pivot point, then the amount of rotation. The rotation angle is computed as the angle between the X-axis and the line from the pivot point to the data point that defined the rotation.

When you select the 3 points method, again, the active angle field is disabled. You are prompted to identify the pivot point, a second point to define the start of rotation, and a third point to define the amount of rotation. The angle or rotation is computed as the angle between the first and second, and the first and third data points.

To use the tool:

1. Click its icon. You are prompted to identify an element. If a selection set is active, or a fence is enabled for use, you are prompted for the pivot point.
2. To rotate a copy of the original element, enable the Make Copy checkbox. Specify the desired active angle when using the Active Angle method.
3. Click a data point to identify the element to rotate and you are prompted to identify the pivot point.

   If using a fence or selection set, you do not identify the element; the data point defines the pivot point, and the element rotates.
4. If a selection set or a fence were not in use, click a data point to identify the pivot point, and the element rotates.
5. Click the Reset button to release the element from the cursor.

The above steps assume the Active Angle method. If using another method, additional data points are required, as discussed earlier.

Mirror

Use this tool to create mirror images of elements. You can mirror an element using any of three methods: Vertical, Horizontal, and Line. Other available options include checkboxes for Make Copy, Mirror Text, Mirror Multi-line Offsets, and Use Fence.

The option button labeled Mirror About in the Tool Settings window defines the axis about which to mirror the element. To mirror an element about the X-axis, use the Horizontal option. To mirror it about the Y-axis, use the Vertical option. To define an arbitrary axis, use the Line option. The following figure illustrates each of the three methods.

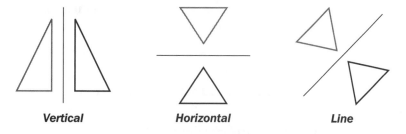

Vertical	Horizontal	Line

The Mirror tool methods.

Like the Rotate tool, by default, the Mirror tool deletes the element you identify. It mirrors the original element. To mirror a copy of the original element, enable the Make Copy checkbox.

When mirroring a text element, to keep the text readable, the tool only mirrors its location, but the text still reads from left to right. To mirror the text as well, enable the Mirror Text checkbox.

When mirroring multi-lines, the tool retains their format and mirrors the vertex locations. To mirror the multi-line offsets as well, enable the Mirror Multi-line Offset checkbox.

This tool can also be used with a selection set or a fence. To mirror several elements in a single step, group them with the Element Selection tool, the PowerSelector, or a fence. These element grouping tools were discussed in chapter 3.

When a selection set is active and you invoke the Mirror tool, you are not prompted to identify elements.

Align Edges

Use this tool to align an edge of an element to the corresponding edge of another element. To perform its task, this tool moves the elements you wish to align. You can align elements along any of seven edge options:

- **Top:** Aligns the top of the element being manipulated to the top edge of another element.

- **Bottom:** Aligns the bottom edge of the element being manipulated to the bottom edge of another element.

- **Left:** Aligns the left edge of the element being manipulated to the left edge of another element.

- **Right:** Aligns the right edge of the element being manipulated to the right edge of another element.

- **Horiz Center:** Aligns the center of the element being manipulated to a horizontal line passing through the center of another element.

- **Vert Center:** Aligns the center of the element being manipulated to a vertical line passing through the center of another element.

- **Both Centers:** Aligns the center of the element being manipulated to the center of another element.

This tool can also be used with a selection set or a fence. To align the bounding rectangle around several elements to an edge of another element, referred as the *base element*, group them with the Element Selection tool, the PowerSelector, or a fence. These element grouping tools were discussed in chapter 3.

On activating this tool, when no selection set or fence is active, you are prompted to identify a base element for alignment. Identify the base element; not the element that will be manipulated. On identifying it, the element highlights. If the element is not rectangular, a dashed bounding rectangle is drawn around it. The edges of this rectangle will be used for alignment purposes. Next, you are prompted to select the element to align. On identifying it, the element moves to align with the base element. The tool continues asking for additional elements to align. Click the Reset button to restart the tool.

Construct Array

Use this tool to copy an element, or a group of elements in a selection set or fence, to construct a rectangular or polar array. In the Tool Settings window, you can select Rectangular or Polar from the Array Type option button. The two array methods are illustrated in the figure below.

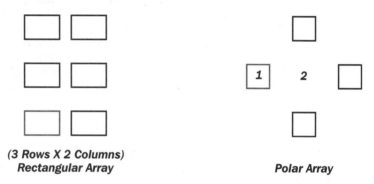

(3 Rows X 2 Columns)
Rectangular Array

Polar Array

The Rectangular and Polar arrays constructed from an element shown gray.

When the Rectangular option is selected, you can specify the active angle. The tool uses this angle to rotate the array axes. However, the elements retain their original orientation—they are not rotated. The other fields you need to specify values for, before using the tool, define the number of rows, columns, and their spacings. In the above figure, the active angle was set to 0, rows to three, and columns to two.

When the Polar option is selected, you specify the number of items the circular array is to contain, the angle of rotation of the array axis while placing each element, and whether to rotate the elements during placement. In the above figure, the number of items was set to four, and the delta angle to 90°. Notice that the element to manipulate was identified with a tentative button followed by a data point, to locate its center (point 1), and then the center of rotation (point 2) was identified. It is important to identify the element you need to manipulate at a carefully chosen location. Otherwise, the results may not be what you expect. Finally, notice that the elements placed around the circular array retain their original orientation. If you wish to rotate each element in the circular array, you must enable the Rotate Items checkbox.

Change Attributes Toolbox

The following figure identifies all tools found in the Change Attributes toolbox.

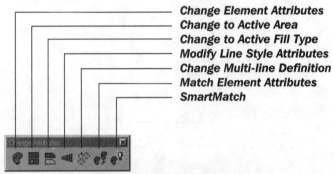

The tools in the Change Attributes toolbox.

Each tool is discussed below in the same sequence it appears in the Change Attributes toolbox.

Change Element Attributes

Use this tool to change the level, color, line style, line weight, or class of an element. You can also use a selection set or a fence with this tool. The Tool Settings window displays checkboxes for the attributes you can change.

To change an attribute, enable its checkbox. Its text edit field becomes available. Assign the needed value to the attribute. You are prompted to identify an element. Click a data point on the element and accept it with another data point to change its attributes.

Change Element to Active Area

Use this tool to change the area attribute, Solid or Hole, of a closed element.

To change the area attribute, select the desired value, Solid or Hole, from the Tool Settings window. You are prompted to identify an element. Click a data point on the element and accept it with another data point. Its attribute changes. This tool works with only closed elements.

Change Element to Active Fill Type

Use this tool to change the fill attribute of closed elements.

To change the fill attribute, select the desired value, None, Opaque, or Outlined, from the Tool Settings window. These were discussed earlier under the *Element Placement Tools* section. You are prompted to identify an element. Click a data point on the element, and accept it with another data point. Its attribute changes. This tool works with only closed elements.

Modify Line Style Attributes

Use this tool to change the line style attributes of custom line styles. Lines that use the standard eight line codes are not affected by this tool.

To change the attributes of elements that use custom line styles, select the attribute to change: Width, Start Width, End Width, Scale, Dash Scale, Gap Scale, and Shift. These custom line style attributes are discussed in chapter 20. You are prompted to identify an element. On selecting the element, it highlights. As you move the cursor, the element's attribute changes dynamically. Click a data point to accept the attribute as displayed.

Change Multi-line to Active Definition

Use this tool to change multi-line attributes after it's been placed.

To change the attributes of multi-lines, define the desired attributes in the Multi-lines dialog box accessed from the Element menu. Invoke the tool. You are prompted to identify an element. On selecting the multi-line, it highlights. Click a data point to accept it. Its attribute changes.

Match Element Attributes

Use this tool to set the active level, color, line style, and line weight from an existing element. On activating the tool, you are prompted to identify an element. In the Tool Settings window, enable checkboxes for the attributes you wish to match. On clicking an element, it highlights. Click a data point to accept it. Active attributes identified in the Tool Settings window change to match those of the element.

SmartMatch (Match All Element Settings)

The Match Element Attributes tool works with the basic attributes: level, color, line style, and line weight. This tool works with the basic attributes and other attributes specific to elements, such as multi-lines, dimensions, and patterns. Use it in the same way as you'd use Match Element Attributes: identify an element and accept it.

Element Modification Tools

These tools are used to modify components of elements. The manipulation tools discussed earlier work on elements globally. These tools modify endpoints, create new vertices in, delete vertices from, and add segments to existing elements.

MicroStation's element modification tools are located in the Modify toolbox. The following figure identifies the location of this toolbox in the Main tool frame. The section also discusses the Delete Element tool.

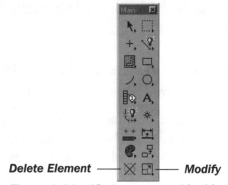

Delete Element —— **Modify**

The tools identified are covered in this section.

Delete Element

Use this tool to delete elements. To activate this tool, click its icon or key in DELETE in the Key-in window. You are prompted to identify an element. On selecting it with a data point, it highlights. You are prompted to accept the deletion. Click a data point to delete the element, or click the Reset button if the highlighted element is not the one you want deleted.

When elements are close together, and you click the Reset button, MicroStation releases the selected element and highlights another element close to the data point. Clicking a data point deletes the highlighted element.

The Delete Element tool also works with selection sets. If you invoke the tool when a selection set is active, the selected elements are deleted immediately and the default tool, usually the Element Selection tool, is activated. You can also delete elements in a selection set by pressing the Delete key.

If you need to delete many elements, you will find it easier to first select them with the Element Selection tool, or PowerSelector. You can also use the Delete Fence Contents tool discussed in chapter 3.

To restore an element or a group of elements in a selection set, that were inadvertently deleted, use the Undo command from the Edit menu.

 NOTE: As your experience with MicroStation grows, you will begin to make better use of data points you click to accept actions on highlighted elements. Rather than click these data points away from all elements, you will use them to identify the next element to be processed by the tool.

Modify Toolbox

The following figure identifies all tools found in the Modify toolbox.

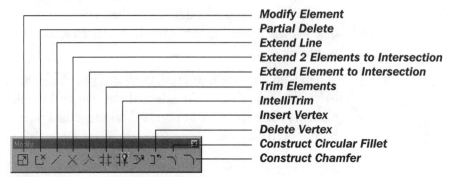

The tools in the Modify toolbox.

Each tool is discussed below in the same sequence it appears in the Modify toolbox.

Modify Element

This is one of the *smart* tools—it changes for each supported element type. Use it to move an element's vertices and segments, change a circle's radius, move dimension text, and other tasks.

Depending on where you identify an element, the tool selects its vertex, segment, or axis for modification.

To modify an element, activate the tool. Click the element on its vertex, segment, or axis. The element highlights, and a preview of the modification displays onscreen. Move the cursor until you achieve the desired modification. Click a data point to accept it, or click Reset to start over.

Partial Delete

Use this tool to delete a part of an element. It works with open and closed elements.

To delete a part of an element, activate the tool. Click the element at one end of the part to delete. For open elements, click the other end that defines the deleted segment. For closed elements, click a data point to define the direction, followed by a data point that defines the deleted segment.

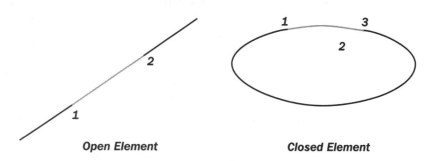

Open Element   *Closed Element*

Deleting parts of open and closed elements.

Extend Line

Use this tool to lengthen or shorten a line, or a line segment at the end of a line string or multi-line. This tool maintains the orientation of the line or line segment, and moves its endpoint.

How do you specify the endpoint to move? Identify the element close to that endpoint.

To specify a distance by which to move a line's endpoint, use the Distance field in the Tool Settings window. To lengthen an element, use a positive distance. To shorten an element, use a negative distance.

Extend Two Elements to Intersection

Use this tool to lengthen or shorten two elements to their intersection. The tool can work with lines, line strings, and arcs, or any combination of these.

When lengthening both elements to their intersection, where you identify them isn't important. When shortening elements that extend past their intersection, you must select them on the side you wish to keep. The following figure illustrates this.

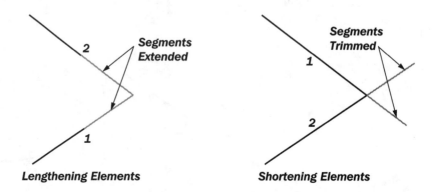

Extending two elements to their intersection.

Extend Element to Intersection

This tool is similar to the Extend Two Elements to Intersection tool. The difference being that it lengthens or shortens only the first element, the second element is left intact. Again, remember to identify the element being shortened on the side you wish to keep.

First select the element to lengthen or shorten, then select the element that stays unchanged. When selecting the intersecting element—the element that remains unchanged—click the side you wish the first element to extend to, if it has more than one intersection points with the first element.

Trim Element

Use this tool to trim elements at their intersection with other elements. You designate elements to trim, and elements to use as cutting edges.

The tool can work with lines, line strings, circles, ellipses, arcs, curves, B-spline curves, shapes, complex chains, and complex shapes. These elements can be cutting edges, and they can also be trimmed.

This tool is more efficient in the number of clicks used, when compared to the Extend Element to Intersection tool, when trimming multiple elements against a single cutting element. This is illustrated in the figure below.

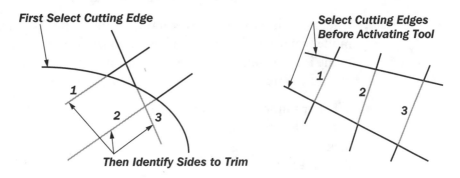

Using the Trim Element tool.

On activating the tool, you are prompted to select a cutting element. You can only select one element in this mode. On selecting the cutting element, you are prompted to identify an element to trim. The sides of intersecting elements you identify are trimmed. This process is illustrated in the left half of the above figure.

Another not-so-obvious way of using the tool is to trim segments from intersecting elements between several cutting elements. This is accomplished by first selecting the cutting elements with the Element Selection tool (hold the Ctrl key down when adding elements to the selection set), then activating the Trim Element tool, followed by identifying the segments to trim. This is illustrated in the right half of the above figure.

IntelliTrim

The Trim Element tool trims or cuts elements that cross other elements you designate as cutting edges. IntelliTrim goes a step further. It trims, cuts, and extends elements against cutting elements.

Elements it can work with include lines, line strings, circles, ellipses, arcs, curves, B-spline curves, shapes, complex chains, complex shapes, text nodes, and cells. However, B-spline curves can't be cutting edges, but can be trimmed; and text nodes and cells can be cutting edges, but can't be trimmed. Lines, line strings, elements that end in line strings, and B-spline curves are the only ones the tool can extend.

IntelliTrim has two operating modes: Quick and Advanced. In quick mode, you can select any of three actions: Trim, Extend, and Cut. This mode is called *quick* because it needs only three data points to trim or extend any number of elements, and two data points to cut them.

When trimming or extending elements, the first data point highlights the cutting element. The remaining two data points draw a temporary line to identify all crossing elements as trim elements. The following figure illustrates this.

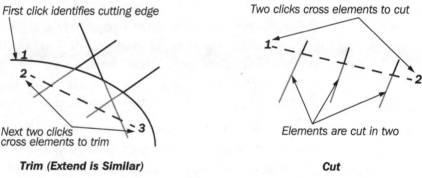

First click identifies cutting edge

Two clicks cross elements to cut

Next two clicks cross elements to trim

Elements are cut in two

Trim (Extend is Similar)

Cut

IntelliTrim needs only two or three clicks in quick mode.

Advanced mode does not cut. It trims and extends. In this mode, IntelliTrim adds two radio buttons to the Tool Settings window: Select Elements to Trim, and Select Cutting Elements.

In advanced mode, you can pick more than one cutting edge. Choose the Select Cutting Elements radio button and identify each cutting element in turn. Then, click Reset and IntelliTrim switches to selecting elements to trim. After you have selected all elements you wish to trim, click the Reset button to see the result in highlight color. Click Reset to accept, or click data points on element sides you wish to keep, and click Reset.

Insert Vertex

Use this tool to insert a vertex in a line, line string, multi-line, shape, or B-spline control polygon. When you identify a line or line string at an endpoint, this tool attaches a new segment to that endpoint. You can also use this tool to add an extension line to a dimension element.

The first data point inserts a vertex at the location identified with a data point on the element. The second data point locates the new vertex.

Delete Vertex

Use this tool to delete existing vertices from a line string, multi-line, shape, or B-spline control polygon. You can also use this tool to delete an extension line from a dimension element.

The first data point identifies the vertex or extension line to delete. The second data point accepts the deletion.

Of course, the tool will refuse to work when an element type has reached its minimum configuration. You can't delete the vertex from a two-node line string, or from a triangular shape. If you try to do this, the status bar displays the message: Minimum Element Size.

When you delete a vertex on a line, it becomes a zero-length line, also referred to as a point.

Construct Circular Fillet

Use this tool to create a tangential arc, called a *fillet*, between two elements. The tool requires you to specify a radius for the fillet. It also offers three choices on what to do with element segments past the tangential fillet points. The choices are listed in the Tool Settings window as None, Both, or First in an option button labeled Truncate. The following figure illustrates these choices.

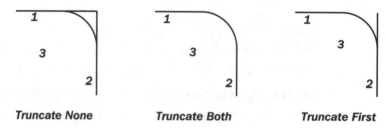

Truncate None   **Truncate Both**   **Truncate First**

The Truncate choices for the Fillet tool; numbers designate data points.

This tool can place a fillet between arcs, circles, and lines. When placing the fillet between closed shapes, such as circles, the Truncate options are ineffective. The fillet is placed without modifying the elements.

Construct Chamfer

Use this tool to create an inclined line, called a *chamfer*, between two intersecting lines, or adjacent line segments in line strings and shapes. The tool requires you to specify two distances from the intersection to define vertices for the chamfer. The following figure illustrates how these distances are used by the tool.

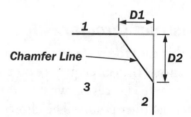

D1 and D2 designate chamfer distances; numbers designate data points.

The distances are usually equal, and define a 45° chamfer between perpendicular lines. By using an unequal distance along each line, you can create a chamfer with any orientation.

Like the Fillet tool, Chamfer requires three data points. The first two identify the lines between which to create the chamfer. The third data point accepts the chamfer preview displayed on the screen.

Exercises

This chapter introduced you to nearly a hundred of MicroStation's 2D drafting tools. However, it takes more than an introduction to really learn how the tools work.

The remainder of this chapter is devoted to exercises that help you practice what you've learned.

We start by practicing concepts, such as precision key-ins and element selection, that you can use with any tool. Then, we practice the use of tools with exercise files on the CD-ROM. The files you need to copy on your computer are identified at the beginning of every exercise.

Exercise: Using Precision Key-ins

This exercise uses the DL and DI precision key-ins to create a pentagon. Each side of the pentagon will be 5 units long. Remember, the enclosed angle of a pentagon is 72° (= 360/5), and MicroStation measures angles in a counterclockwise direction. The following figure illustrates the exercise.

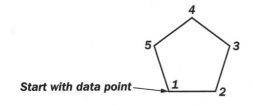

Point 2 is DL=5,0 from 1
Point 3 is DI=5,72 from 2
Point 4 is DI=5,144 from 3
Point 5 is DI=5,216 from 4
Point 1 is DI=5,288 from 5

Start with data point

DL and DI key-ins are used to locate the next data point.

Use the following steps as a guide for this exercise:

1. Start MicroStation with a blank 2D design file.
2. Invoke the Place Line tool.
3. Click a data point in the lower left corner of the view window. This is the starting point for the pentagon. This is the only data point you will supply with a mouse. The remaining data points are supplied with a precision key-in.

4. Key in **DL=5,0** to locate point 2, as shown in the above figure. The DL key-in specifies the X and Y distances relative to the previous data point. Key-ins are typed in the Key-in Window. If necessary, open the Key-in window by selecting Key-in from the Utilities menu.

5. Key in **DI=5,72** to locate point 3. The DI key-in specifies the radial distance and the angle relative to the previous data point. The number 5 before the comma designates the distance. The number 72 defines the counterclockwise angle measured from the X-axis.

6. Key in **DI=5,144** to locate point 4.

7. Key in **DI=5,216** to locate point 5.

8. Key in **DI=5,288** to locate point 1. This draws the last line to close the pentagon.

9. Click the Reset button to release the rubberbanding line from the cursor.

10. Depending on the working units in your drawing, the pentagon drawn may be too large or too small for the view window. Click the Fit View icon from the window's view control bar. The view magnification will change to fit the pentagon.

Any time MicroStation expects a data point, you can define its location by clicking the left button on a mouse, or you can use the keyboard to type a precision key-in.

Exercise: Snapping to Elements

This exercise uses several snap modes to draw line segments by snapping to keypoints on existing elements. You will use the design file **snaps.dgn** in the **\Exercise\Ch05** folder on the CD-ROM. Copy this file on your computer's hard drive. Once copied, clear its read-only attribute using Windows Explorer. This is important. Otherwise, you won't be able to write to the file.

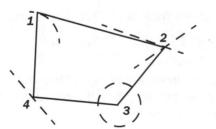

Point 1 is tangent to arc
Point 2 is intersection of lines
Point 3 is center of circle
Point 4 is midpoint of line
Point 1 is endpoint of line

You will draw the solid lines shown by using various snap modes.

Use the following steps as a guide for this exercise:

1. Start MicroStation with a copy of the `snaps.dgn` file. Your screen will display—in a dashed line style—an arc, two intersecting lines, a circle, and a line, arranged as shown in the figure above.

2. Invoke the Place Line tool. You will start a line tangential to the arc from the number 1. Numbers referred to in the exercise are shown in the above figure; they do not appear in the design file on your screen.

3. Click the active snap icon in the status bar to open the Snaps menu. Select Tangent to use this snap mode for the next tentative button click.

4. Identify the arc in the upper left corner of the screen with a tentative point, and accept it with a data point. A line that is always tangent to the arc attaches to the cursor.

5. Make the Intersection snap active. Select Intersection from the Snaps menu that is activated by clicking the active snap icon on the status bar.

6. Identify the first intersecting line with a tentative point, then the second intersecting line with another tentative point. The cursor jumps to point 2, shown in the above figure. Accept this point with a data point. You've drawn the first line segment from point 1 to 2.

7. Make the Center snap active. See step 5 if you need help on invoking the Snaps menu to select this mode from.

8. Identify the circle anywhere on its perimeter with a tentative point, the cursor snaps to the center of the circle. Accept it with a data point. You've drawn the second line segment from point 2 to 3.

9. Make the Midpoint snap active.

10. Identify the line on the lower left with a tentative point, the cursor jumps to the middle of the line. Accept it with a data point. You've drawn the third line segment from point 3 to 4.

11. The active snap returns to the default Keypoint mode after every snap. We could use the Endpoint snap for the next step, but the default Keypoint snap mode will work as well. Leave the snap mode to Keypoint.

12. Identify with a tentative point the first line segment you had drawn, close to its endpoint designated with the number 1. If the cursor snaps to the endpoint of the arc, or another undesired location, move the cursor closer to point 1 and click the tentative button again till it jumps to the endpoint of the line. When the tentative cursor finds the endpoint, accept it with a data point.

13. Click the Reset button to release the rubberbanding line from the cursor.

Any time you need to place a data point on an element, select an appropriate snap mode, click the tentative button to locate the desired point with the tentative cursor, and accept it with a data point.

Exercise: Using a Selection Set

This exercise demonstrates how to use PowerSelector to move several elements in a single step. You will use the Move Element tool after adding several elements to the selection set with PowerSelector. This exercise uses the design file `moveset.dgn` in the `\Exercise\Ch05` folder on the CD-ROM. Copy this file on your computer's hard drive. Once copied, clear its read-only attribute using Windows Explorer. This is important. Otherwise, you won't be able to write to the file.

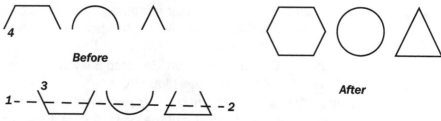

Select elements with PowerSelector (1 and 2); then move from 3 to 4.

Use the following steps as a guide for this exercise:

1. Start MicroStation with a copy of the `moveset.dgn` file. Your screen should show separated halves of a hexagon, a circle and a triangle, as shown in the above figure. You will join the halves in this exercise.

2. Make a selection set from the lower halves. Activate PowerSelector and click data points at locations identified as 1 and 2. The elements highlight.

3. Invoke the Move Element tool. Because a selection set is active, you are prompted for the first point. Identify endpoint 3 with the tentative button, followed by a data point. The selection set (the lower halves) attach to the cursor, and you are prompted to define distance and direction.

4. Identify the endpoint 4 with the tentative button, followed by a data point. The elements become whole and the lower halves remain attached to the cursor.

5. Click the Reset button to release the elements from the cursor. The lower halves are still in the selection set and remain highlighted. PowerSelector terminates, and the Element Selection tool becomes active.

6. Click a data point in an empty space to release the selection set.

PowerSelector makes the selection of several elements a simple two-click process.

Exercise: Stretching Elements in a Fence

This exercise demonstrates the use of a fence. You will place a fence around several elements and use the Fence Stretch command to stretch elements that cross its boundaries. This exercise uses the design file fence.dgn in the \Exercise\Ch05 folder on the CD-ROM. Copy this file on your computer's hard drive. Once copied, clear its read-only attribute using Windows Explorer. This is important. Otherwise, you won't be able to write to the file.

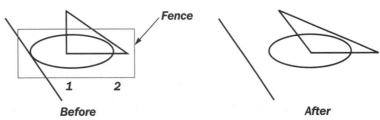

Before   *After*

Stretch fence contents from point 1 to 2.

Use the following steps as a guide for this exercise:

1. Start MicroStation with a copy of the fence.dgn file. Your screen displays a line, an ellipse, and a triangle, as shown in the left half of the above figure.

2. Place a Fence around the elements as shown above. Use Block as the type of fence in the Tool Settings window. The fence should completely enclose the ellipse, cross over a part of the line, and leave out the top vertex of the triangle.

3. Activate the Manipulate Fence Contents tool from the Fence toolbox. It is the third icon in the toolbox. If the tool does not activate, you probably lost the fence from your view. Place the fence, and try again.

4. Select Stretch from the Operation option button in the Tool Settings window. Leave Inside as the active fence mode. You are prompted to define the origin.

5. Click a data point close to the point 1 shown in the figure above. The exact location is not important for this step. Anywhere close to point 1 will suffice.

6. The fence moves with your cursor, and you are prompted to define the distance.

7. Click a data point to the right of point 1. This is shown above as point 2. Again, the exact location is not important so long as you click a data point to the right of the previous data point. Fence contents are manipulated.

8. Click Reset to release the fence from the cursor.

9. Activate the Place Fence tool again to remove the fence from the view.

Take a moment to examine how the Fence Stretch command manipulated the elements. The line remains unchanged because its vertices were outside the fence. The ellipse moves, but otherwise remains unchanged, because it was completely inside the fence. The triangle stretches because some of its vertices were inside, and some were outside, the fence. The triangle vertex outside the fence remains at its original location, the triangle vertices inside the fence move.

Exercise: Manipulating Element Handles

This exercise demonstrates the use of handles around selected elements to manipulate them. You will move an element by dragging it. You will also change an element's shape by dragging its handle. This exercise uses the design file `handles.dgn` in the `\Exercise\Ch05` folder on the CD-ROM. Copy this file on your computer's hard drive. Once copied, clear its read-only attribute using Windows Explorer. This is important. Otherwise, you won't be able to write to the file.

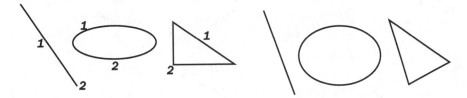

Dragging from Point 1 moves elements; dragging their handles at Point 2 changes element shapes.

Use the following steps as a guide for this exercise:

1. Start MicroStation with a copy of the `handles.dgn` file. Your screen displays a line, an ellipse, and a triangle, as shown in the left half of the above figure.
2. Identify the line with the Element Selection tool. Handles appear at its endpoints.
3. Drag the element from the location marked as Point 1 above. The element moves. Release the mouse button and drag the handle at its endpoint marked at Point 2. The vertex moves and the element changes shape.
4. Repeat step 3 for the ellipse.
5. Repeat step 3 for the triangle.
6. Your screen will show the three elements similar to the right half of the above figure.

Black square dots that appear around selected elements are called *handles*. Moving a handle changes the shape of the element. Dragging the element from anywhere other than its handles keeps its shape unchanged and simply moves it.

Element manipulation by handles isn't recommended for elements that must be manipulated with precision. It's helpful for moving annotation elements whose placement is usually determined by visual appeal.

Exercise: Using Grids

This exercise demonstrates the use of the grid to quickly draw dimensionally accurate elements. You will turn on the grid, enable the grid lock, and draw a shape. This exercise uses the design file `grids.dgn` in the \Exercise\ch05 folder on the CD-ROM. Copy this file on your computer's hard drive. Once copied, clear its read-only attribute using Windows Explorer. This is important. Otherwise, you won't be able to write to the file.

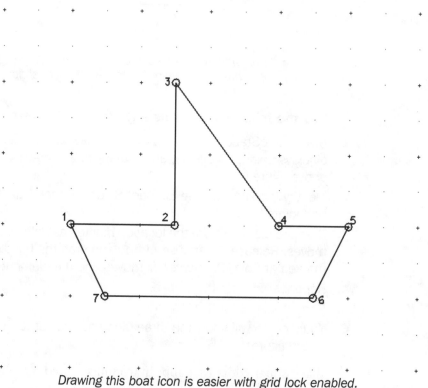

Drawing this boat icon is easier with grid lock enabled.

Use the following steps as a guide for this exercise:

1. Start MicroStation with a copy of the `grids.dgn` file. Your screen displays numbers 1 to 7 and tiny circles identifying their location. You will draw a boat icon as an irregular polygon by connecting the dots. The dots are placed directly on top of grid points. Enabling grid lock will simplify this task and eliminate the constant snapping to the center of the dots.

2. Enable grid display. Enable the Grid checkbox in the View Attributes dialog box accessed from the Settings menu, and click the Apply button. Close the View Attributes dialog box.

3. Enable the grid lock. Click the lock icon on the status bar and select Grid from the pop-up menu that appears. This restricts the cursor movement to grid points visible on screen.

4. Activate the Place Shape tool. It is the second icon in the Polygons toolbox. You are prompted for a first point.

5. With the cursor constrained to move on the grid points, locating each of the dots on screen is simplified as each dot lies on a grid point. Identify each of the dots labeled 1 to 7 in turn, and close the shape by identifying point 1 again. The shape closes to complete the boat icon.

When vertices of a shape you wish to draw can be located on grid points, using the grid will simplify its creation greatly.

Exercise: Changing Element Symbology

This exercise demonstrates the use of the Change Element Attributes tool, and the Primary toolbox, to change symbology (color, level, line style, and line weight) of elements. This exercise uses the design file **attrib.dgn** in the **\Exercise\Ch05** folder on the CD-ROM. Copy this file on your computer's hard drive. Once copied, clear its read-only attribute using Windows Explorer. This is important. Otherwise, you won't be able to write to the file.

This exercises uses Change Element Attributes and Primary Tools.

Use the following steps as a guide for this exercise:

1. Start MicroStation with a copy of the **attrib.dgn** file. Your screen displays two elements. You will change the color, style, and weight of one with the Change Element Attributes tool. You will change the color and weight of the other with the Primary toolbox.

2. Activate the Change Element Attributes tool. It is the first icon in the Change Attributes toolbox.

3. In the Tool Settings window, enable the Color, Style, and Weight checkboxes and fill in numbers 3, 2, and 3 in their text fields. You are prompted to identify an element.

4. Click the star-shaped element to identify it. It highlights. Click another data point anywhere in the view to accept the change in symbology.

5. You will now use the Primary toolbox. Activate the Element Selection tool and select the text element. Handles appear around it.

6. From the color picker in the Primary toolbox, select the color green (color 2 for the default color table). The element changes in color and remains selected.

7. From the Weight option button in the Primary toolbox, select weight 4. The element thickness changes.

8. Click in a blank area in the view window. The element is released from the selection set.

The Change Element Attributes tool lets you change several attributes before identifying the element. When using the Primary toolbox, you first select the element, then change its attributes one at a time.

Exercise: Partially Deleting Elements

This exercise demonstrates the use of the Partial Delete tool. You will break a segment from a line element and from an ellipse. This exercise uses the design file **partial.dgn** in the **\Exercise\Ch05** folder on the CD-ROM. Copy this file on your computer's hard drive. Once copied, clear its read-only attribute using Windows Explorer. This is important. Otherwise, you won't be able to write to the file.

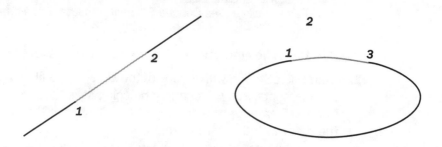

This exercise helps you delete parts of a line and an ellipse.

Use the following steps as a guide for this exercise:

1. Start MicroStation with a copy of the `partial.dgn` file. Your screen displays a line and an ellipse.

2. Activate the Partial Delete tool. It is the second icon in the Modify toolbox. You are prompted to select the starting point for partial delete.

3. Identify the line at Point 1 shown above. The line breaks open at that point and the opening grows bigger as you move the cursor toward Point 2.

4. Click a data point at Point 2 shown above. The line segment between Points 1 and 2 is deleted. The tool restarts and prompts you to select the starting point for partial delete.

5. Identify the ellipse at Point 1 shown above. The element highlights, and you are prompted to select the direction of partial delete. The tool behaves differently when selecting closed elements because closed elements have two sides for the same two points. The direction you specify determines which side is deleted.

6. Click a data point at Point 2 located to the right of and above Point 1. The element breaks open at Point 1, and the opening widens as you move the cursor to Point 3.

7. Click a data point at Point 3 shown in the figure above. The segment of the ellipse between Points 1 and 3 is deleted.

The Partial Delete tool requires two data points for open elements, and three data points for closed elements.

Exercise: Group Hole for Patterns and Fill

This exercise demonstrates the use of the Group Hole tool introduced in chapter 3. You will discover how to create holes in solid shapes with the tool. You will pattern one group hole element and fill another. This exercise uses the design file `holefill.dgn` in the `\Exercise\Ch05` folder on the CD-ROM. Copy this file on your computer's hard drive. Once copied, clear its read-only attribute using Windows Explorer. This is important. Otherwise, you won't be able to write to the file.

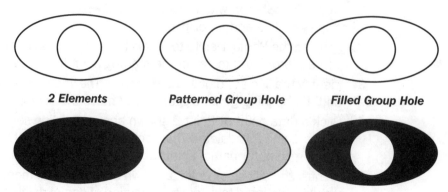

2 Elements   **Patterned Group Hole**   **Filled Group Hole**

Filling the ellipse obscures the circle, unless a group hole is created.

Use the following steps as a guide for this exercise:

1. Start MicroStation with a copy of the `holefill.dgn` file. Your screen displays three copies of two elements, a circle inside an ellipse, as shown along the top row of the figure above. When created, each of these elements was designated as solid with no fill.

2. Invoke the Change Element to Active Fill Type tool. It is the third icon in the Change Attributes toolbox.

3. In the Tool Settings window, select Opaque for Fill Type and 3 (color red for default color table) for Fill Color. You are prompted to identify an element.

4. Identify the first ellipse to the left and accept it. The ellipse fills and obscures the circle inside. If you wanted to fill only the difference area between these elements, this is unacceptable. To solve this problem, you will need to group the two separate elements into a single element with a hole. Use the Group Hole tool for this.

5. Activate the Group Hole tool. It is the last icon in the Groups toolbox. You are prompted to identify the solid element. This is the outside element within which you wish to create a hole.

6. Click a data point on the ellipse in the center. It highlights, and you are prompted to identify the hole element. This is the inside element that will create the hole.

7. Click a data point on the circle inside the ellipse in the center. It highlights. You are prompted to accept the hole.

8. Click a data point in an empty area to accept the hole.

9. Click the Reset button to release the highlight and create a single element with a hole from the two elements. The tool restarts.

10. Repeat steps 6 through 9 for the ellipse and circle to the right. You now have two solid elements with holes. You will pattern one, and fill the other.

11. Activate the Hatch Area tool. It is the first icon in the Patterns toolbox. In the Tool Settings window, enter the number 2 for Spacing and 45 for Angle. You are prompted to identify an element.

12. Identify the element in the center and accept it with another data point. The element is hatched and the hole is left unhatched, as desired.

13. Activate the Change Element to Active Fill Type tool, the third icon in the Change Attributes toolbox. Ensure fill type is Opaque with 3 for fill color. You are prompted to identify an element.

14. Identify the element to the right and accept it with another data point. The element is filled with color and the hole is left open, as desired.

When hatching or filling areas, the Group Hole tool can help create holes in solid elements so they fill properly.

Beyond Basics

After you become familiar with, and can proficiently use the tools discussed in this chapter, you graduate from being a beginner to an experienced user.

The remaining chapters in Part 1 help you explore many advanced topics, including:

- Workgroup collaboration with reference files
- Dimension-driven modeling
- Nongraphic data links to graphical elements
- Web integration tools
- Engineering configurations

Chapter 6
Referencing External Files
Coordinating Workgroups

It's a small world! You've probably heard this phrase many times. It's easier today, more than ever before, to collaborate on projects with geographically distant partners. Electronic communication technology, especially computer networks and the Internet, make this possible.

When computer networks weren't as ubiquitous, everyone worked on their isolated desktop computers. Coordinating drawing effort between designers within the same office was possible, but difficult.

In a networked computer environment, reference files address the need for collaboration among project team members.

Reference files permit designers to display as background, or use as a part of their own drawing, the ongoing work of other designers. When other designers update their work, your reference of it also changes.

If you've previously worked with CAD software that doesn't support reference files, you might have copied the contents of another needed drawing for such collaboration. Though this approach works, there are significant advantages to using reference files, as you will discover shortly.

This chapter introduces you to reference files, and the tools you use with them. The chapter organization is listed below.

- **Understanding Reference Files** discusses situations best suited to the use of reference files, their advantages and disadvantages. There is also a discussion of raster images as reference files.

- **Working with Reference Files** introduces you to the tools you use to attach, detach, and work with reference files. The Reference Files dialog box and the Reference Files toolbox are discussed. You will also read about the Image Manager.

- **Using Reference Files** puts your knowledge of reference files to use in step-by-step exercises.

New MicroStation users should read the whole chapter, and work through the exercises. The introductory material will help you identify situations where you might use reference files. The exercises will help reinforce your understanding of available tools in a guided environment.

Experienced MicroStation users can skim through this chapter, paying particular attention to raster reference files, and the discussion on uses of reference files. If you find an area new to you, locate the exercise relevant to this feature and work through it.

Understanding Reference Files

A *reference file* is a MicroStation design file (`.dgn`), or a raster image in a supported format, attached as a background, i.e. reference, to an active design file. Think of reference files as background files.

You can see, locate, and snap to elements in a reference file, but you can't edit them. You can also selectively display, or change the display attributes of elements in reference files. Elements in reference files remain unchanged; however, you can configure their display attributes in the active design file. More on this later.

As their name suggests, reference files are references to external files. You *attach* external files as references to active design files. Previous MicroStation versions were limited to attaching no more than 32 reference files. Since the release of MicroStation 95, this limit has been increased to 255. For compatibility with older versions and to conserve computer memory, you may wish to reduce this number in the Preferences dialog box.

NOTE: To change the number of reference files your design files can support, open the Preferences dialog box from the Workspace menu. Click Reference File in the Preference category list to display its options. Change the number in the *Max.Ref. Files* field in the dialog box.

Reference files you attach can be moved, rotated, scaled, and clipped with respect to your active design file. Again, reference file contents remain unchanged; you merely change what is displayed in the active design file. You can even modify the appearance of reference file elements on plots through resymbolization, discussed in chapter 7.

Why Use Reference Files?

This section discusses the benefits of using design files as reference files. Raster images as reference files are discussed in a later section.

Each of the reasons for using reference files, discussed in the following pages, is an example of how you might use them.

Workgroup Collaboration

Reference files, used across a computer network, promote collaboration among project team members. Proper planning and implementation—where to store reference files and how to name them—can help team members stay coordinated, despite changes, as a project progresses.

This is best explained with an example. Let's suppose that you're working on the plumbing drawing for a building. You must coordinate your drawings with others working on its architectural, structural, and HVAC drawings.

To avoid re-creating the architectural wall layout in which to draw the plumbing, you attach the wall layout of the building created by the architect. Without duplication, the architect's building plan becomes a background for your drawing—a background that updates when the architect makes changes.

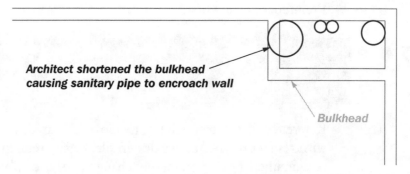

Architect shortened the bulkhead causing sanitary pipe to encroach wall

Bulkhead

A change to the referenced wall layout is obvious in this drawing.

Of course, such use of reference files presupposes a computer network. If reference files are large, the network bandwidth must be high enough to keep the system responsive.

For your building's plumbing drawing, you could have copied the contents of the architect's wall layout drawing into yours, and organized your work on a separate level. When the architect changes the layout, you must be notified of the change so you can replace the old copy with the revised version—an error-prone process that is the disadvantage of this approach.

With reference files, no notification is necessary. Attached reference files can be updated at will to check for conflicts. Following are the two most significant benefits of reference files, when used for workgroup collaboration.

- **Efficiency:** Team members save time because the work of others is not redrawn, it is referenced.
- **Accuracy:** Team members stay coordinated because they see the work of others and modify their own work accordingly.

Consistent Project Border

Workgroup collaboration through the use of reference files requires a computer network. However, you don't need a network to use reference files. You can attach design files, such as border files on the local hard drive, to several drawings that share the same border layout.

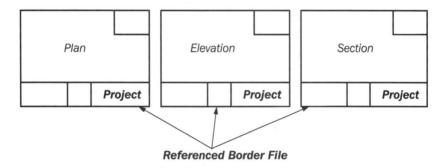

Referenced Border File

Updating a referenced border affects all drawings that use it.

Such a use of reference files ensures that borders used by all project drawings are consistent. Should you edit the border, it will update in all drawings because it is attached as a reference.

Composing Several Drawings from One Model

Roadway design applications, such as InRoads and GEOPAK, use this feature extensively. Using COGO program modules, these applications gather survey data and help you create a full-scale three-dimensional model.

Once the model is ready, they use detailing modules to automatically generate dozens of roadway sections, plans, and elevations. Because the design drawings are created from the same model, they represent the project consistently and accurately.

The concept of composing several drawings from the same model need not be restricted to design applications or to three-dimensional models. When working on the first floor plan of a shopping mall, you could create a separate design file that contains the entire floor plan, even if it would never be plotted on one sheet. At drawing production, you would reference desired parts of the floor plan to detail drawings, to the appropriate scale.

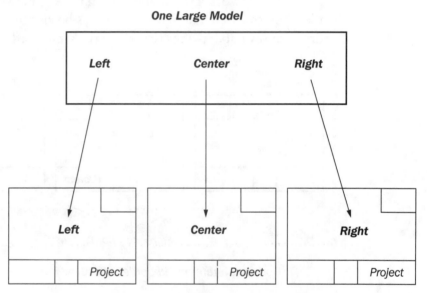

Parts of one model referenced in separate drawings.

To help you compose drawings, or sheet files, from three-dimensional models, MicroStation includes the Drawing Composition utility. Select Drawing Composition from the File menu to open the Drawing Composition dialog box. This utility uses standard views or saved views in the model file, and attaches them to sheet files.

In the *Working with Reference Files* section later in this chapter, you will learn the tools needed to help you attach reference files, manipulate them, and control their display symbology. You need not rely on design applications or the Drawing Composition utility to create multiple drawings from one model. The reference file tools you learn will help you do this.

Self-Referencing Larger-Scale Details

We've discussed the attachment of external files as reference files. I'd be remiss, were I not to mention MicroStation's ability to attach a file as a reference to itself. That's right; you can attach a design file to itself as a reference.

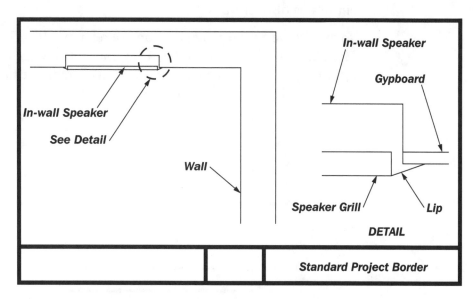

The detail on the right is referenced from the same drawing.

When details of construction appear too small on a plan, they are difficult to annotate. The area to be annotated, such as the in-wall speaker to wall connection shown above, could be clipped and referenced at another location in the same drawing to a larger scale, where it can be more easily annotated.

Because the detail is referenced, you make changes in the plan, and the detail updates.

Rather than clipping and referencing, you could have clipped and copied by using the Clip fence mode. You now have a plan and a detail not linked in any way. The disadvantage of this approach is that changes made to the detail will also need to be made to the plan—increasing workload and coordination effort. Of course, new details that are not scaled versions of geometry elsewhere are created independently without referencing.

Multiple References Extend Design Plane

As you learned in chapter 3, the MicroStation design plane is finite. Of course, you can adjust working unit components to accommodate virtually any project. But there are times, especially in mapping, when you need to work with large geographic areas with high precision. In such cases, the desired working unit precision may not accommodate the entire area of interest.

To extend the design plane, you can use reference files. Because MicroStation allows you to assign any coordinate value to the design plane origin, with proper planning you can tile multiple files into a single composite drawing with the desired accuracy.

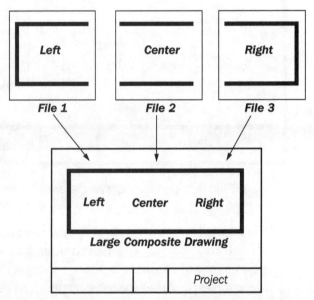

You match edges of adjacent reference files by shifting design plane origin.

The design plane origin is set, by default, to its center. All element coordinates are stored in the design file with respect to this origin. To change the origin of a design file, use the GO= key-in. Later, an exercise illustrates its use. It is important you realize that the actual design plane origin remains unchanged. The Global Origin key-in (GO=) merely assigns an arbitrary coordinate value, for coordinate transformation purposes as shown here, to a location—monument point—you specify.

Raster Reference Files

In addition to using design files as reference files, MicroStation supports the use of *raster*, or bit-map, files as reference files. The file formats supported for this use are listed below.

Filename Extension	Description of Raster Format
.a	X-Windows RGB format (UNIX)
.bmp	Microsoft Windows bitmap
.cit	Intergraph's highly compressed format for engineering drawings
.cot	Intergraph's monochrome or grey scale image format
.eps	Adobe's encapsulated PostScript
.gif	CompuServe's compressed 256-color format
.jpg	Joint Photographic Experts Group for photographs (highly compressed, but *lossy*)
.p	X-Windows palette format (UNIX)
.pct	Apple Macintosh PICT format
.pcx	ZSoft's PC Paintbrush format
.rgb	Intergraph's RGB format for full-color images
.rle	Intergraph's older run-length encoding format
.rs	Sun Microsystems' raster format
.tga	TrueVision's popular TARGA format
.tif	Tag Image File Format popular for desktop publishing
.wpg	WordPerfect graphics format

MicroStation supports the use of raster images at many levels. You can insert images as elements, attach them as a view background for rendering, and of course, attach them as raster reference files that maintain their position with respect to the design plane. This section discusses raster reference files in relation to these other uses.

Compared to Raster Elements

When you import raster images in the design file, they are stored as raster elements. Consequently, the size of the design file increases. Raster reference files, on the other hand, only marginally affect the design file size. Only the name, location, and other information about the file is stored, not the image itself.

To import a raster image:

1. Select Import, then Image from the File menu. The Select Image File dialog box opens.
2. Locate the image file desired, and click the OK button. You are prompted to identify a location for the image.
3. Click a data point to identify a corner. You are prompted for the opposite corner.
4. Click a data point to define the size of the image file being imported. Its aspect ratio is maintained. The image is copied into the design file.

Compared to Raster View Backgrounds

The default MicroStation view window is black. You can change it to white, as I've done to create the screenshots for this book, by enabling the Black Background to White checkbox in the View Windows category of the Preferences dialog box you access from the Workspace menu.

When you create 3D models, you want them shown against a more interesting background than plain black or white. For this purpose, MicroStation allows you to display an image, such as the sky or the sunset, as a background to a view window.

View backgrounds are not saved in the design file as are imported images. In this regard they are similar to raster reference files. However, there are significant differences in how they behave.

A view background is attached as an unchanging background between the borders of a view window. Whether you zoom or pan, the background image stays stationary. Raster reference files and imported images, on the other hand, will pan and increase in magnification when you use view controls.

When importing or attaching images, their aspect ratio is maintained. View backgrounds, in contrast, resize to fill the borders of the view window.

To attach a raster image as a view background:

1. Click the View category in the Design File Settings dialog box accessed from the Settings menu. Its options display.
2. Click the Background Image button and select the desired background image in the Display Image File dialog box that opens.
3. Enable the Background checkbox to enable its display. You can also do this from the View Attributes dialog box.
4. Click OK to close the Design File Settings dialog box. The selected raster image displays. You can turn its display off by unchecking the Background checkbox in the View Attributes dialog box.

Image Manager

Bentley bundles Image Manager with MicroStation. Image Manager is based on technology developed by HMR for its MicroStation Reprography line of products. It is not installed automatically when you install MicroStation. To install and use Image Manager, you must enable its checkbox in the MicroStation Utilities Selection dialog box as shown in the installation options figure in chapter 1.

Image Manager lets you control the display and plot of images within design files. Each view can be configured to display one or more images independent of another. Consequently, because MicroStation supports eight views, you can maintain information about eight sets of image files.

Information about image files, and their relationship to the design file and other images, is maintained in the design file. To use image file groups from one design file to another, Image Manager also supports the use of `.prj` project files that are stored separately.

The Image Manager dialog box is the control center for all its image attachment and manipulation tools. To open the Image Manager dialog box, select Image Manager from the File menu.

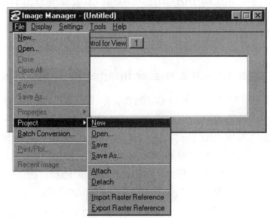

The Image Manager dialog box.

Image Manager plays the same role as raster reference files. However, it offers more advanced features and is scalable to even more capable raster file management applications from HMR.

You can have Image Manager take over control of raster reference files by choosing Import Raster Reference from its Project submenu. This detaches the raster reference and attaches it again under Image Manager's control. You can switch back control of raster files to MicroStation by choosing Export Raster Reference from Image Manager's Project submenu that is accessed from the dialog box's File menu.

Working with Reference Files

To manage reference files, MicroStation consolidates all functions in the Reference Files dialog box. Many of the frequently used commands are also available from the Reference Files toolbox invoked from the Tools menu.

Personally, I rarely use the Reference Files toolbox. Instead, I access all commands from the Reference Files dialog box.

You are introduced to the Reference Files dialog box and the Reference Files toolbox in the next several pages.

Reference Files Dialog Box

As the primary tool for managing and manipulating all reference files, the Reference Files dialog box supports two modes: Design and Raster. The former mode works with design files, the latter mode works with raster images.

Select Reference from the File menu to open the Reference Files dialog box, as shown in the figure below. Notice that the dialog box title bar contains the words *Design Files*. This indicates Design mode. To switch to Raster mode, select Raster from the Display menu.

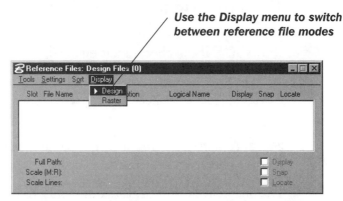

Use the Display menu to switch between reference file modes

The Reference Files dialog box in Design mode.

In the dialog box above, there are no reference files. Consequently, many choices in its menu bar are disabled. When reference files are attached, selecting one from the listbox enables all menu choices. Also, information fields in the dialog box display the selected file's settings.

Design File Reference Mode

In Design mode, a listbox occupies most of the space on the dialog box. This listbox has several columns, three checkboxes, and three information display fields described below.

Slot: Every reference file you attach is assigned a unique slot number.

File Name: The name of the design file that is attached as a reference.

Description: An optional description you assign a reference file just before attaching it.

Logical Name: An optional short name you assign a reference file just before attaching it. When you attach the same reference file several times, this field becomes mandatory. A different logical name for each attachment helps you correctly select the desired attachment.

Most users keep logical names just a few characters long. They may standardize letters for function, such as P1 for plan 1, E1 for elevation 1, and so on. They may use relative location of the reference files, such as UL for upper left, UC for upper center, LR for lower right, and so on. The purpose is to quickly recognize the reference file used.

Display: Associated with the Display checkbox below the listbox, it shows an X if the checkbox is enabled.

The Display checkbox toggles the display of the selected reference file in all views. Use it to check the contents of a reference file by toggling its display without detaching it.

Snap: Associated with the Snap checkbox below the listbox, it shows an X if the checkbox is enabled.

The Snap checkbox toggles your ability to use the tentative button to snap to visible elements in the selected reference file. If you need to use geometry in the reference file as a basis for starting new geometry in the active design file, enable the checkbox.

Locate: Associated with the Locate checkbox below the listbox, it shows an X if the checkbox is enabled.

The Locate checkbox toggles your ability to identify elements in the design file with the data button for copying to the active design file. You can use fence manipulation commands to copy elements in a group. If you don't want to copy any elements from the reference file to the active design file, uncheck the checkbox.

Full Path: Displays the complete directory specification for the reference file selected in the listbox.

Scale (M:R): Displays the attachment scale, in master units, as a ratio between the master file (active design file) to the reference file. This is set when you attach a reference file. It can be modified after attachment.

Scale Lines: Displays the status, On or Off, whether custom line styles are scaled for display using the Scale (M:R) setting above. This is set in the checkbox labeled Scale Line Styles when attaching reference files.

To work with reference files, the dialog box implements a menu bar. Use the Tools menu to invoke commands and access dialog boxes that help you work with reference files. The choices in the Tools menu are listed in the following table.

Tools Menu Choices	Description of Tool
Attach	Attaches a reference file.
Attach URL	Opens the Select Remote Design File to Attach dialog box.
Detach	Detaches the selected reference file.
Detach All	Detaches all references files currently attached.
Reload	Refreshes copy of reference file in memory from source file.
Ref Agent	Opens the Reference File Agent dialog box to manage local copies of remote reference files.
Exchange	Closes the active design file and opens the selected reference file as the active design file.
Move	Moves the location of the selected reference file.
Scale	Scales the size of the selected reference file.
Rotate	Changes the orientation of the selected reference file.
Copy Attachment	Copies reference file attachment a specified number of times to slots. Logical name is changed for each copy.
Merge Into Master	Copies contents of the selected reference file into the active design file, and detaches the reference file.
Mirror Horizontal	Mirrors the display of the selected reference file about the horizontal axis.
Mirror Vertical	Mirrors the display of the selected reference file about the vertical axis.

Tools Menu Choices	Description of Tool
Clip Boundary	Uses the active fence to clip the selected reference file so that only portions inside the fence display.
Clip Mask	Uses the active fence to clip the selected reference file so that portions inside the fence don't display.
Clip Mask Delete	Deletes the reference file mask defined by a previous Clip Mask.
Clip Front	Only valid in 3D files. Sets the front clipping plane for the selected reference file.
Clip Back	Only valid in 3D files. Sets the back clipping plane for the selected reference file.

The functions from the Tools menu you are likely to perform most often include Attach, Detach, Move, Scale, Clip Boundary, and Clip Mask.

To attach reference files, select Attach from the Tools menu. The Preview Reference dialog box opens. This is a standard file navigation dialog box. In it, you can preview the contents of a `.dgn` file by clicking the Preview button after selecting the file. Once you've selected the file you wish to attach, click the OK button. The dialog box closes and the Attach Reference File dialog box opens, as shown below.

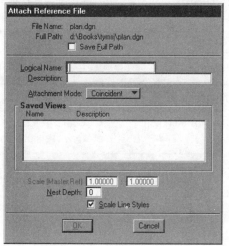

The Attach Reference File dialog box.

If you wish to save the directory path of the reference file in the active design file—not just the name of the file—enable the Save Full Path checkbox.

The logical name is optional. If the same file is attached more than once, it is required. The description field is optional, but using it will help you recognize files because file names can be difficult to decipher.

When attaching, you have the choice of bringing the reference file coincidentally so design planes match exactly, regardless of working units. To attach a reference file to a scale, or a part clipped, the reference file must have saved views. If no saved views exist, the Saved View choice on the Attachment Mode option button is disabled, and no saved views display in the listbox. If saved views exist, select the desired view and enter the desired scale in the Scale fields below the listbox.

The Scales (Master:Ref) fields under the listbox accept a ratio between the master units of the active design file (the master file) and the master units of the reference file. Master units, regardless of the sub and positional unit settings, are used for this scale.

You can also specify the nesting depth for the reference file, and whether to scale custom line styles in the reference file by the above scale.

Clicking the OK button attaches the reference file to the active design file and it appears in the Reference Files dialog box. If you don't see the contents of the reference file in your view window, click the Fit View tool in the view control bar and make sure All is selected for Files in the Tool Settings window.

Other common reference file functions, such as Move, Scale, and Detach, available in the Tools menu, are easy to use. You invoke them from the Tools menu and click a data point or two, as prompted. You will use them in the exercises later.

NOTE: You can access the Tools menu choices by clicking the right mouse button on a reference file in the Reference Files listbox. A pop-up menu appears at the cursor location.

In addition to functions in the Tools menu that let you attach and manipulate reference files, the Reference Files dialog box offers the Settings menu to control attachment settings, as listed in the table below.

Settings Menu Choices	Description of Item
Attachments	Permits editing of attachment information.
Levels	Permits selective display of reference file levels.
Level Symbology	Permits change to reference file level symbology. Yellow elements in reference file can be made to display in red.
Update Sequence	Permits change to sequence in which reference files update.
View Reference	Opens a window displaying the reference file contents.

The Sort menu in the Reference Files dialog box is used to sort reference files. It offers the following four choices:

- **By Slot:** sorts files by the slot number
- **By File Name:** sorts files alphabetically by their name
- **Description:** sorts files alphabetically by their description
- **By Logical Name:** sorts files by their logical name

As explained earlier, reference files are attachments, or references. You cannot edit contents of reference files.

You can, however, copy their contents to the active design file, if Locate is on. If Snap is on, you can use reference file elements as a basis of creating new elements using the element snaps. You can also plot reference files as if they are a part of your design file.

Raster File Reference Mode

When you select Raster from the Display menu, the Reference Files dialog box changes to accommodate options relevant to working with raster files, and its title bar contains the words *Raster Files* to indicate Raster mode. The dialog box is shown below.

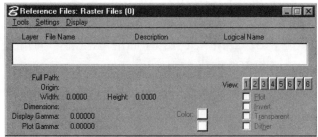

The Reference Files dialog box in Raster mode.

In the dialog box above, there are no reference files. Consequently, many choices in its menu bar are disabled. When reference files are attached, selecting one in the listbox enables all menu choices. Also, information fields in the dialog box display the selected file's settings.

In Raster mode, the listbox of reference files is smaller, and there are many more information fields. The listbox has four columns, four checkboxes, seven information fields, and other items described below.

Layer: Every raster reference file you attach is assigned a unique layer number.

File Name: The name of the design file that is attached as a reference.

Description: An optional description you assign a reference file before attaching it.

Logical Name: An optional short name you assign a reference file just before attaching it. When you attach the same reference file several times, a different logical name for each attachment helps you correctly select the desired attachment.

Full Path: Displays the complete directory specification for the reference file selected in the listbox.

Origin: Displays the location, in working units, of the data point where you inserted the reference file during attachment.

Width/Height: Displays the size, in working units, of the raster reference file when attached to the design file.

Dimensions: Displays the size, in pixels, of the source image that is attached as a reference.

Display Gamma: Adjusts the darkness of images for display on screen that may appear too dark or too light.

Plot Gamma: Adjusts the darkness of images for hardcopy that may plot too dark or too light.

Color Pickers: Display the colors assigned as an overall tint for the image, and the color to treat as transparent.

View: Displays eight buttons, corresponding to each of the eight views MicroStation supports. A raster reference file can be designated as visible in a specific view. The buttons appear enabled for views where the reference file will be visible.

Plot: When enabled, includes the raster image in the plot.

Invert: When enabled, it inverts the raster image; similar to making a negative from a photograph.

Transparent: When enabled, it permits the creation of mosaics that display design elements through the raster image. The color to be made transparent is set during attachment.

Dither: When enabled, it performs half-toning to simulate colors. It is used when colors in images are more than the number supported on your display hardware.

To work with raster reference files, the dialog box implements a menu bar. Use the Tools menu to invoke commands and access dialog boxes that help you work with reference files. The choices in the Tools menu are listed in the following table.

Tools Menu Choices	Description of Tool
Attach: Interactive/Fixed	Attaches a raster reference file. Interactive option asks for data points. Fixed option is valid for only Intergraph format raster files that save an attachment location within them.
Attach URL	Opens the Select Remote Design File to Attach dialog box. See chapter 12 for additional details.
Preview: Interactive/Fixed	Invokes the Attach Reference File dialog box. See Attach above.
Detach	Detaches the selected reference file.

Tools Menu Choices	Description of Tool
Detach All	Detaches all references files currently attached.
Reload	Refreshes copy of reference file in memory from source file.
Ref Agent	Opens the Reference File Agent dialog box to manage local copies of remote reference files.
Save As	Allows you to save an attached raster file in another format.
Move	Moves the location of the selected reference file.
Modify	Modifies the size of the selected reference file. Maintains aspect ratio.
Rotate: 90/180/270	Changes the orientation of the selected reference file by the amount specified.
Mirror Horizontal	Mirrors the display of the selected reference file about the horizontal axis.
Mirror Vertical	Mirrors the display of the selected reference file about the vertical axis.
Clip Boundary	Uses the active fence to clip the selected reference file so that only portions inside the fence display.
Clip Mask	Uses the active fence to clip the selected reference file so that portions inside the fence don't display.

The Tools menu functions you are likely to perform most often include: attach, detach, move, and scale reference files.

The Settings menu in the Reference Files dialog box is used to modify attachment settings of reference files in the listbox. It offers the following choices:

- **Attachment:** Opens the Attachment Settings dialog box to let you edit attachment setting of the attached raster reference file.
- **Update Sequence:** Opens the Update Sequence dialog box to let you edit the sequence in which reference files update in the design file.

As explained earlier, reference files are attachments, or references. You cannot edit contents of images you attach. You can attach them as spatially related images. Raster images, such as aerial photographs, are used in civil engineering and GIS projects.

Reference Files Toolbox

The most commonly used functions from the Reference Files dialog box menus are available in the Reference Files toolbox, shown in the figure below. The toolbox is invoked by selecting Reference Files from the Tools menu on the MicroStation menu bar (*not* the Reference Files dialog box).

1. *Attach Reference File*
2. *Clip Reference File*
3. *Mask Reference File*
4. *Delete Clip Mask*
5. *Set Back Clipping Plane*
6. *Set Front Clipping Plane*
7. *Reload Reference File*
8. *Move Reference File*
9. *Scale Reference File*
10. *Rotate Reference File*
11. *Mirror Ref. File Horizontal*
12. *Mirror Ref. File Vertical*
13. *Detach Reference File*

The Reference Files toolbox.

All of these tools were discussed under the Tools menu of the Reference Files dialog box. As you might have guessed by reading the tool names, many of them invoke commands specific to design reference files.

Using Reference Files

Now you're ready to work with reference files and their tools. The following exercises use several files on the CD-ROM. The table below lists the files you need to copy to your local hard drive. Files copied from a CD-ROM retain their read-only attribute. Turn this attribute off because you'll be writing to the files.

File Name	Description
aptunit.dgn	An apartment unit layout to be used as the active design file to which you will attach reference files.

File Name	Description
plat.dgn	A survey plat design file to be attached as a reference.
owners.jpg	Raster image of apartment unit owners to be attached as a reference.
border.dgn	Project border to be attached as a reference.

You'll be attaching a property line survey drawing, and a border file to the apartment unit drawing. You'll then attach a raster reference file. The composite drawing is shown in the figure below. Each of the files that forms the composite is also identified.

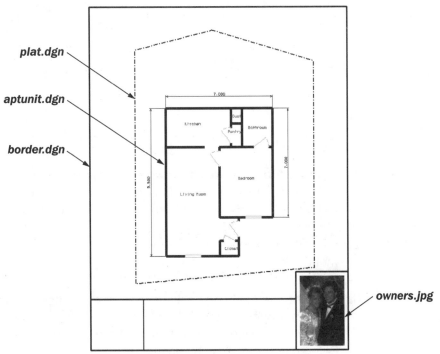

The files used in the following exercises.

After completing the following exercises, your project will look like the figure shown above.

Exercise: Attaching the Property Survey

As an architect, you contracted a survey of the property line within which the unit you designed is to be placed. The owners requested that the project be conducted in metric units. Your standards call for the following working unit set up for the `aptunit.dgn` and the `border.dgn` files.

`working units (mu:su:pu): m: 1000 mm: 100 pu`

The surveyor also conducted the project in metric units, but his working units are different than yours. Surveyors typically will use different working units than architects. The master units are the same (both are meters), but the subunit and its relationship to positional units can be different. The surveyor's working units for the `plat.dgn` file are:

`working units (mu:su:pu): m: 10 dm: 1000 pu`

Notice that a meter is represented by 100,000 positional units in the architectural drawings, and by 10,000 positional units in the survey drawing. That amounts to a difference of 10 x factor.

With this background information about the three reference files, you are ready to start the exercise.

To attach the survey file to the plan drawing:

1. Start MicroStation with the design file `aptunit.dgn`. You copied this file from the CD-ROM to your computer. Make sure the read-only attribute of the file is off. Files copied from a CD-ROM usually have this attribute enabled. It must be turned off before you can edit the file.

2. Open the Reference Files dialog box by selecting Reference from the File menu. Make sure it's in design file mode; otherwise, use the Display menu to switch its mode.

3. From the File menu of the dialog box, select Attach. The Preview Reference dialog box opens. Locate the file `plat.dgn` you copied before starting this exercise, and click the OK button. The dialog box closes, and the Attach Reference File dialog box opens.

4. Enter PLAT in the Logical Name field, and Property Line Survey in the Description field. Because the survey file doesn't have any saved views, the only attachment mode available is Coincident. In this mode, design planes of both files are placed coincidentally, regardless of working units.

5. Click the OK button. The dialog box closes, and the filename appears in the Reference Files dialog box. Note the Scale information field states the Master to Reference ratio is 10, as shown in the figure below.

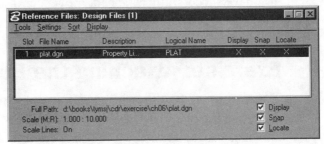

This was to be expected, given the difference in the working units between the two files. This means the survey drawing will appear 10 times smaller than plan drawing.

6. Activate the Fit View tool in the view control bar. The display adjusts and you will see the survey drawing appear in the upper right side of the view window. Typically, an architect will draw a plan with the lower left corner set to the center of the design plane, an arbitrary decision. A surveyor, on the other hand, will use the accepted state plane coordinates when drawing property lines. That is why the survey drawing appears so far away from the building plan. It's your job to superimpose the property line drawing on the plan drawing. You must scale the reference file and move it.

7. Right-click the reference file in the dialog box. The Tools menu appears. Select Move. You are prompted to enter the point to move the reference file from. Identify the reference file with a data point. You are prompted for the point to move it to. Identify the center of the building plan. The reference file moves.

8. Activate the Fit View tool again. The display adjusts and you see the survey inside the building. The reference file must be scaled. Because both use a meter as their master unit, you must restore the scale to 1. Remember, the scale on the Reference File dialog box is based on master units. It's currently for a coincidentally attached file, regardless of working units.

9. Again, right-click the file name in the dialog box. The Tools menu appears. Select Scale. In the Tool Settings window, set the scale to 1:1 to match the master units of both files. You are prompted to enter a point about which to scale the reference file. Identify the center of the survey drawing. The reference file scales to surround the plan.

10. Activate the Zoom Out tool from the view control menu. The display adjusts to let you work more easily with the drawings. Move the survey reference file again, if necessary, so it surrounds the plan with space all around.

You have successfully attached, moved, and scaled the survey reference file to your plan drawing.

Exercise: Attaching the Border

The working units of both the plan and the border files are the same. Also, like the plan file, the lower left corner of the border was arbitrarily drawn at coordinates (0, 0), the center of the design plane. On attaching the border, you can expect it to come in at the same size, when coincidentally attached, as the plan drawing, and share the lower left corner with the apartment unit plan.

To attach the border file to the plan drawing:

1. Start MicroStation with the design file `aptunit.dgn`, if its not already open.
2. Open the Reference Files dialog box by selecting Reference from the File menu. Make sure it's in design file mode; otherwise, use the Display menu to switch its mode.
3. From the File menu of the dialog box, select Attach. The Preview Reference dialog box opens. Select the file `border.dgn` you copied before starting this exercise, and click the OK button. The dialog box closes, and the Attach Reference File dialog box opens.
4. Enter BDR in the Logical Name field, and Border in the Description field. Because the border file doesn't have any saved views, the only attachment mode available is Coincident.
5. Click the OK button. The dialog box closes, and the filename appears in the Reference Files dialog box. Note the Scale information field states the Master to Reference ratio is 1. As expected, the border file shares its lower left corner with the building.
6. Move the border to surround the building and the survey. If you need help, see step 7 in the previous exercise.

Your screen should now look similar to the figure shown in the introduction to the exercise files. The only thing remaining is to attach the photograph of the apartment unit owners. This is done in the next exercise.

Exercise: Attaching a Raster Image

To complete the project, you need to attach the raster image of the unit owners you were given in the JPEG (`.jpg`) format. MicroStation supports this file format for reference file attachments.

To attach the raster image of the owners to the plan drawing:

1. Start MicroStation with the design file `aptunit.dgn`, if not already open.
2. Open the Reference Files dialog box by selecting Reference from the File menu. Switch the dialog box to raster mode by selecting Raster from the Display menu.
3. From the File menu of the dialog box, select Attach, then Interactive. The Attach Raster Reference File dialog box opens. Select the file `owners.jpg` that you copied before starting this exercise so that its name appears in the Files field. Accept the default Layer 1 assigned to this image. Enter PHOTO for the logical name, and Photograph of Owners in the Description field, and click the OK button. The dialog box closes, and you are prompted for an origin for the image.
4. Click a location inside the rectangular area reserved for the photograph in the lower right hand corner of the border. A dashed rectangle tracks the cursor maintaining the image's aspect ration.
5. Click the upper right hand corner for the image. The image is attached and appears in the border. Its name also appears in the dialog box.
6. Close the Reference Files dialog box.

This completes our exercises, and your introduction to reference files.

Chapter 7

Generating Output
Printing, Plotting, and Exporting Your Creations

No matter how good the electronic model you create, if it can't be delivered in a format the client needs, your effort would be wasted. In keeping with the flexibility it offers in model creation, MicroStation supports an extensive list of output devices and formats.

In the early to mid-1980s, pen plotters were a common fixture at most engineering companies using CAD. They are now obsolete. Ink-jet, electrostatic, and laser devices are now the norm.

Printers and plotters are electromechanical devices that require electronics to control its mechanical motion that moves and applies ink or toner to paper. The printer and plotter electronics, in turn, must receive instructions on how to move and where to apply the ink. Vendors created printer control languages for this. When software creates output, it generates an electronic file containing instructions to control the printer or plotter's electronics in the language its vendor created.

The immense popularity of plotters and laser printers from Hewlett-Packard has made its printer control languages a de facto standard. You may recognize the acronyms HPGL and PCL. The former stands for Hewlett-Packard Graphics Language, a vector graphics language used by all the company's plotters. The latter stands for Printer Control Language, a raster graphics language, and is the standard for Hewlett-Packard's laser printers—many of which also support HPGL.

These two languages are very popular and supported by competing printer and plotter manufacturers. Consequently, if your particular plotting device is not directly supported, you can likely use it with HPGL or PCL.

MicroStation supports these two output languages and many others standards, such as Adobe PostScript. MicroStation uses driver files to create output compatible with printers, plotters, and other devices and applications.

MicroStation processes the CAD model through the driver file to create the electronic file the output device needs. Depending on the type of output file you need, you select the appropriate driver file. A driver file interfaces with the system printer that Windows uses. Scores of driver files interface with many other printers.

Native Windows drivers are generic and written for mainstream applications. MicroStation's drivers are more efficient in how they process and control the output device from CAD models. These drivers are more easily configurable for special CAD needs, such as line weights and styles. MicroStation also lets you *resymbolize* plots, meaning, you can create output so solid lines in the model appear dashed on the plot.

In this chapter, you are introduced to the following topics.

- How to print and plot with MicroStation.
- How to configure driver files.
- How to resymbolize plots.
- How to plot several files in a batch.
- How to create images from your CAD models that are compatible with other applications.

Printing and Plotting

We discussed printers and plotters as devices you can use to create output on paper. When pen plotters were still common, a clear distinction existed between these two devices. One was vector (the plotter), the other was raster (the printer).

Vector devices draw each element, such as a line or a circle, individually. To print the element on paper, they make the pen travel from one place to another, panning and scrolling the paper accordingly. Consequently, plot times could be large, upwards of an hour.

Raster devices, on the other hand, don't individually imprint each element. They pre-process the image to the device's print resolution, usually measured in dpi (dots per inch), and imprint the paper with tiny dots that go across the paper as it travels forward at constant speed. The paper only moves once in a single direction and the print is complete. Print times on these devices are significantly reduced.

With the advent of ink-jet and electrostatic plotters, this distinction is no longer valid. Both printers and plotters are raster devices. Perhaps the only distinguishing feature between them is the size of paper each can accommodate. For this reason, the words *print* and *plot* are used interchangeably in the rest of the chapter.

Gone are the days when printers had to be moved to the computer that needed to plot. In offices big and small virtually all printers are networked. This means the output devices can stay in one protected place and everyone in the office can print to them.

Large format printers, such as the Hewlett-Packard DesignJet, can plot on paper varying in size from letter-size to large poster-size, even 10 feet or 3 meters long—when using roll-fed paper.

Plotting is not restricted to regular copying paper, called *bond media*. You can plot on mylar and vellum. These are translucent, durable papers used by ammonia-based blueline machines for duplication.

When drawings were created by hand, durability of the drafting medium was important. Often linen was used so the original drawing would last the life of the asset, bridge or building, it would document. With CAD, because plots can be generated from the electronic model at any time, media durability is not so much an issue. Plots on bond paper are fairly routine. However, one other related issue has gained significance within the architectural and engineering design community—modifications to plots without making changes to the CAD model that generated the plots.

NOTE: If you make changes on the plot, make the same changes to the CAD model too. When you create plots from CAD later, this will ensure the new plots reflect the changes. This will avoid confusion later, after the project has been designed. Lack of such coordination has been known to result in litigation.

Many clients demand electronic CAD files in addition to traditional paper drawings. This raises the issue of client modifications without the consent of the designer who created the original work.

To flag modifications to files after they've been delivered, MicroStation supports digital signatures. One can seal drawings with a digital signature unique to the designer to establish identity. A digital signature also reveals if files in an archive were changed.

MicroStation's digital signature capability is located in the Archive utility, discussed in chapter 16. You open the Archive dialog box from the Utilities menu.

How to Print

CAD models are created full-scale on a large design plane. The paper you plot them on is limited in size. Printing the model on paper, therefore, requires that the model be scaled.

You can plot the CAD model to fit the selected paper size automatically. You can create plots scaled to an industry standard scale.

Printing from MicroStation involves the following steps in sequence:

- Identify area of design file to plot.
- Select the driver that supports your printer.
- Configure plot options.
- Send generated plot to your hardcopy device.

Of course, elements in the CAD model are not scaled during plot. They remain the same. The image on the paper is a scaled representation of the model.

Identify Plot Area

Before you can plot, you must identify the area in the model you wish to document on paper. One way of doing this is to arrange the plot area in a view window, as was done in chapter 2. Another way is to place a fence around the area.

If you wish to define precisely the extent of the model to plot and its scale, you must use a fence.

Project drawings invariably include a title block area and border corresponding to the paper you'll be plotting them on. A rectangular fence is usually placed around the plot area by snapping to predefined points (zero length lines) in a border, or to the diagonal corners of a border.

Printers use a small width of the paper edge, called the hardware clip limit, to grab and move it through toners. Printers, therefore, can't plot on the entire paper area—hardware clip limits are off limits! Consequently, borders are drawn smaller than actual page sizes to accommodate the hardware clip limits.

NOTE: View attributes of the view you plot from determine what prints on paper. It's a good idea to check the view attributes carefully before sending the plot. For example, if you have construction lines, turn their display off in the view so they don't plot.

What you can see in the view window you plot from, you will get on the hardcopy as well. If a level were off during plot generation, turning it on later when plotting another copy of the drawing might result in a different drawing.

You can track manually what levels need to be turned on or off during plot generation by drawing a level map outside the border. But this takes time and is error-prone. You can also automate this process by writing macros, scripts, or applications. My upcoming book, *75 BASIC Macros for MicroStation/J*, includes a macro that processes multiple design files in batch mode. It creates a separate text file documenting level usage for such purposes.

With the preliminaries behind us, you are ready to invoke the print dialog box that lets you control the printing process.

Select Driver and Other Options

Select Print/Plot from the File menu, or use the keyboard shortcut Ctrl+P, to open the Plot dialog box shown below.

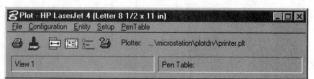

The Plot dialog box lets you control all printing options.

In addition to the menu bar and the row of icons, this dialog box displays three important information fields. To the lower left it displays *View 1*, the view that will be plotted. Were the plot being generated from a fence in View 5, the field would have displayed the message *Fence (View 5)*. You use the Entity menu to select what to plot: fence or view. To select a fence, a fence must already be active. If a fence is active when the dialog box is opened, the Fence choice under Entity is automatically selected.

To the lower right is the pen table information field. No pen table was active when the Plot dialog box was invoked in the above figure. Consequently, the words Pen Table are not followed by any information.

The third field displays the name of the plotter driver in the dialog box. It reads *Plotter: ...\microstation\plotdrv\printer.plt* in the figure above. The *printer.plt* driver, a special MicroStation plotter driver, interfaces with the printer(s) set up in the operating system.

To select a different driver, click the Plotter Driver icon (the icon with a question mark next to a printer), or select Driver from the dialog box's Setup menu. The Select Plotter Driver File dialog box opens to let you select available plotter drivers from the default plotter driver directory `c:\bentley\program\microstation\plotdrv`. This directory may be different if you are on a network with centralized control of plotter drives on a server. The directory is pointed to by the MS_PLTR configuration variable. You will learn about configuration variables in chapter 17.

Some of the available drivers are shown in the following table.

Plotter Driver File Name	Description
cal907.plt	Plots on Calcomp or compatible devices that use its plotting language.
cgm.plt	Creates output in CGM format.
epscripm.plt	Creates output in monochrome PostScript format.
emf.plt	Creates output in Enhanced Windows Meta File format.
hpdjet.plt	Plots on H-P DesignJet and compatible plotters.
hppcl5.plt	Plots on H-P LaserJet and compatible laser printers that support the PCL 5 language.
imgen.plt	Image Manager plotter driver for raster plots on the Windows system printer.
imrtl.plt	Image Manager plotter driver for raster plots on H-P DesignJet.
svfhires.plt	Creates output in Simple Vector Format in high resolution.
tiff.plt	Creates output in the TIFF file format.
wmf.plt	Creates output in the Windows Meta File format.

These drivers are text files that can be edited to configure the output to meet your needs. Editing driver files is discussed later.

Once the correct driver is selected, you must check other available plotting options. This is done from dialog boxes invoked by clicking the three icons to the left of the Plotter Driver icon, or by selecting choices from the Setup menu in the Plot dialog box.

To specify the paper size, select Page from the Setup menu or click the Page Setup icon. The Page Setup dialog box opens, as shown below. If the system printer is selected, the operating system's Print Setup dialog box opens instead of the Page Setup dialog box.

The Page Setup dialog box lets you pick paper size and orientation.

In addition to selecting page size, you can specify the rotation for the page. The Rotate 90° checkbox is similar to the Portrait/Landscape radio button you've seen on printer options in other applications. On roll-fed media plotters, enabling rotation may help you plot more economically. For example, when plotting C-size drawings on 36"-wide rolls, a lengthwise plot created by enabling the 90° rotation saves paper.

To specify page margins, plot scale, and location, select Layout from the Setup menu or click the Plot Layout icon. The Plot Layout dialog box opens, as shown below.

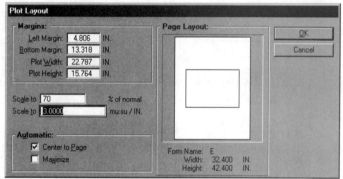

Use the Plot Layout dialog box to set the plot scale and margins.

You can set the scale for plots in two ways. Either key in the scale as a percentage of normal size, or specify working units per plotter units.

When creating scaled plots, you will use the Scale field the most. It lets you specify working units per plotter unit.

The two scale factor fields and the four margin fields in the dialog box are linked. Changing one updates others. Should you key in a scale or another value larger than the paper size can accommodate, MicroStation beeps and doesn't accept the value.

If the border you snap to and the selected paper size are coordinated to a standard scale, it's quicker to enable the Maximize checkbox than to tinker with the scale field values.

The dialog box also implements the Center to Page checkbox. Enable it to center the plot vertically and horizontally.

To see plot-related view attributes for the view you are plotting from, select Options from the Setup menu or click the Plot Options icon. The Plot Options dialog box opens, as shown below.

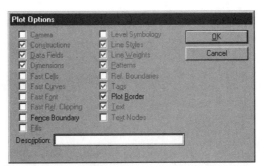

Use View Attributes to change plot related view attributes shown in the Plot Options dialog box.

Most of the view attributes shown in Plot Options are for information only—that's why they are gray. To modify these options, use the View Attributes dialog box.

The Fence Boundary checkbox, when enabled, draws the fence boundary on the plot. The Plot Border checkbox, when enabled, draws a rectangle around the plot extents and places descriptive text, such as file name and plot time just outside the border, if the plotter driver is so configured.

Use the Description field to enter up to a 50-character message to be plotted just outside the border. For this, Plot Border must be enabled.

Plot Preview

To preview the plot on the screen before it's sent to the printer, select Preview from the Plot menu or click the Preview Refresh icon. The Plot dialog box grows to display a preview of the plot, as shown below.

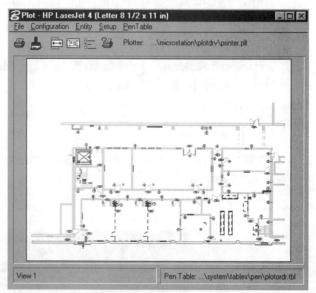

The Preview mode of the Plot dialog box.

To collapse the dialog box, drag its bottom edge upward with the mouse.

Plot Preview provides an accurate representation of plots. MicroStation uses the plotter driver selected to process the plot, and displays it onscreen in the Plot dialog box.

Using plot preview helps to verify plot settings, such as orientation and element attributes, before sending the output to paper. For example, when using a monochrome plotter, if Plot Preview displays the plot in color, you are immediately alerted to a configuration option that must be adjusted.

Having selected the plotter driver appropriate for your printer, and enabled the desired plot choices, you are ready to print the design file.

Send Output to Printer

After identifying the plot area, and selecting desired options, click the Plot button, or select Plot from the File menu to start plotting. Whether the plot is sent to a file or printer port is determined by the plotter driver file. Once MicroStation completes processing the file, it displays the message *Finished Creating Plot* on the status bar.

The system printer is usually configured to send output directly to the printer. Most MicroStation plotter drivers are configured to create plot files. Plot filename extension is configured to use .000 by default. If necessary, the default filename extension can be changed easily in the plotter driver file. This is explained later.

The directory where MicroStation saves plot files is pointed to by the configuration variable MS_PLTFILES. See chapter 17 for a discussion on configuration variables.

In an office network environment, logical ports are usually defined for various plotters you have access to. For instance, the logical port for the color H-P DesignJet 650C plotter may be LPT3, and for the half-size monochrome laser plotter, it might be LPT4. If you create plot files, you can send them to the plotter's logical port assignment by using the following command:

```
copy /b directory\plotfilename lpt3
```

from the system's command prompt.

As stated earlier, logical ports are typically assigned by your network administrator. However, savvy users may want to know how logical ports are set up. In a Windows NT Server network environment, you can use the command prompt to assign logical ports to shared printer resources. The following table lists some of the common network resource access commands.

Command as Typed	Description
net use lpt3 \\server\printer	Assigns logical port LTP3 to *printer* on *server*. Words in italics are names you supply.
net view *server*	Display available shared resources on *server*.
net help	Display online help for the *net* series of commands.

Configuration Files

Design is an iterative process that gets refined over time. A design file you create will need to be plotted many times during the course of its completion.

Though the design file may change, the plotting parameters you use the first time will likely be used for all later plots. To help you generate such plots quickly, MicroStation supports the use of plotter configuration files. These files have the extension `.ini` and are saved in the files `C:\Bentley\Workspace\System\Data` folder.

Use the Configuration menu on the Plot dialog box to create new configuration files, open previously saved configurations, and save changes you may make after opening a configuration file. All active plot settings in the Plot dialog box are saved in a configuration file.

To create a plot configuration file, set up all plot parameters in the Plot dialog box and select New from the Configuration menu. The Plot Configuration File dialog box opens. In it, key in the name for the new configuration file and click the OK button. Once saved, you can open this configuration by selecting Open from the Configuration menu on the Plot dialog box.

A plot configuration file saves the following plot parameters:

- Plot area, whether view or fence.
- Page size and orientation.
- Plot layout, margins, and scale.
- Plot options, such as element attributes and fence boundaries.
- Pen table information, if used.

When you use a configuration file, the Configuration option under the Entity is enabled, and so are element attributes in the Plot Options dialog box. Another benefit of plot configuration files is quicker plot generation without interactively setting plot. To generate a plot without invoking the Plot dialog box, in the Key-in window, type:

`PLOT configfilename plotfilename`

where `configfilename` is the name of the configuration file, and `plotfilename` is the name of the plot file to generate.

Batch Plotting

MicroStation's BatchPlot is a utility to plot several design files in a single step. It uses *plot specifications* to define how to plot the files. It uses *job sets* to identify the files to plot.

In a plot specification, you define how the utility is to identify the printer to use, the plot area, the paper layout, and element attributes to override during plot. Plot specifications are saved in external files so they can be shared across job sets.

To invoke BatchPlot, select Batch Print/Plot from MicroStation's File menu. The BatchPlot dialog box opens, as shown below.

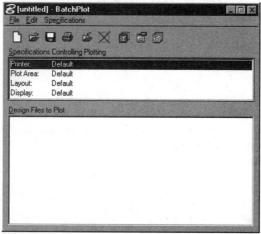

Plot specifications appear in the upper listbox, and design files in the job set appear in the lower listbox.

The Edit menu in the dialog box lets you work with design files to plot—the lower listbox. The Specifications menu offers commands that work with plot specifications—the upper listbox. The File menu lets you work with job sets.

To use BatchPlot at the simplest level, choose Add Files from the Edit menu to select design files. Then select Print from the File menu to batch plot the selected files.

For greater control over the batch plotting process, double-click the plot specification component: Printer, Plot Area, Layout, or Display. Its default properties dialog box opens. Change the options as desired.

To select from available plot specifications for a specific component, highlight it and choose Select from the Specifications menu. A dialog box that lists available specifications opens. To create new specifications for later use, highlight the component and choose Manage from the Specifications menu. The BatchPlot Specification Manager dialog box opens. This dialog box offers choices to edit, create, copy, rename, or delete specifications.

Configuring Plotter Drivers

Plotter driver files are ASCII text files that contain plotter configuration records. A driver file can also contain blank lines and comments. Comments start with a semicolon (;) and continue to the end of the line.

A plotter driver file can contain scores of different record types. Some records are mandatory, some are optional. If a mandatory record type is missing or incorrectly entered the plotter driver file will not work properly.

NOTE: In MicroStation version 5 and earlier releases, plotter driver files used to be called plotter configuration files. The name change was necessary because MicroStation now supports resymbolization that uses what it calls configuration files.

To get the most from plotting, treat the driver files that come with MicroStation as a starting point and configure them for your specific network and other plotting needs.

Following is a listing of the `example.plt` file delivered with MicroStation. Examining it will help you identify records and the syntax used in plotter driver files.

```
; Example Plotter Configuration file

num_pens=8; Must be first record
change_pen=color; either "color" or "weight"

size=(6.2,9.6)/num=0/off=(-3.1,-4.8)/name=a
size=(14.0,9.0)/num=0/off=(-7.0,-4.5)/name=b
size=(14.0,20.0)/num=0/off=(-7.0,-10.0)/name=c
```

```
size=(31.0,20.0)/num=0/off=(-15.5,-10)/name=d
size=(42.00,32.0)/num=0/off=(-21,-16.0)/name=e

resolution(IN)=(0.000984252,0.000984252); specifies both res and units
stroke_tolerance=4.5; unitless num0 < tol <10

pattern_len(1)=1; set pattern length 1
pattern_len(2)=1; set pattern length 2
pattern_len(3)=1; set pattern length 3
pattern_len(4)=1; set pattern length 4
pattern_len(5)=1; set pattern length 5
pattern_len(6)=1; set pattern length 6

pen(1) = (0, 8,16,24,32)/speed=40; set mapping for element
pen(2) = (1, 9,17,25,33);   color to pen numbers
pen(3) = (2,10,18,26,34)
pen(4) = (3,11,19,27,35)
pen(5) = (4,12,20,28,36)
pen(6) = (5,13,21,29,37)
pen(7) = (6,14,22,30,38)
pen(8) = (7,15,23,31,39-128)

pen_width(1) = 10; width of pen =
pen_width(2) = 10;   10 * .000984 IN
pen_width(3) = 10
pen_width(4) = 10
pen_width(5) = 10
pen_width(6) = 10
pen_width(7) = 10
pen_width(8) = 10

;   set up mapping for line weights to number of strokes,
;weight 0=1 stroke, weight 1=1 stroke, weight 2=2 strokes
weight_strokes = (1,1,2,2,3,3,4,4,5,5,6,6,7,7,8,8)

start_plot = pause; stop at beginning of plot
end_plot = eject; eject page after plot
pen_change = pause; pause between pen changes

autocenter; automatically center plot
rotate = none; enable/disable automatic rotation to
; maximize plots: cw = rotate clockwise,
; ccw = rotate counter-clockwise,
; none = disable

communication=(handshake=0, eol1=13, eol2=0, port=2, baud=9600)
communication=(parity=none, stopbits=1, databits=8)

; Use the following config to plot using the Calcomp's if you want to
; run autocad on the same system as MicroStation. Remember to set the
; plotter to match these parameters.
;
; communication=(handshake=2, port=2, baud=9600, parity=even, data=7, stop=2)
; communication=(syncval=22, munsync=2, eom=13, recordsize=128, checksum)
```

```
border/pen=1/filename; leave this out for no border
model=7585b; plotter model number
driver=hpgl; MDL driver to use
default_extension/auto_incExt = '000'; default extension for plotfiles
;
; To configure a default output file name comment out the default_extension
; line above and uncomment this line.  "lpt1" may be substituted with any
; desired filename - e.g. "$(MS_PLTFILES)plotfile.000"
;
;default_outFile/auto_overwrite = "lpt1"

; Substitute the name of a pentable file to be loaded when this driver is
selected
;pentable=\dir\file.tbl
```

The above example plotter driver file is well commented. A careful examination will help you understand its syntax and intent. The `size` record defines supported sheet sizes. The `pen()` record specifies which plotter pen is to plot which element colors in the design file.

For a detailed description of each plotter driver record and its meaning, refer to MicroStation's documentation.

Resymbolizing Plots

Resymbolization means the creation of different looking plots from a design file, without editing it. This feature has been implemented in server-based CAD plotting solutions for many years. MicroStation implements it with pen tables.

Of what use is resymbolization? An example will help answer this question. As an architect, you may prefer the walls in a plan layout plotted thicker than an engineer who needs to focus on the lighting wiring diagram. The engineer would rather plot the walls thinner and show the wiring schematic thicker.

By using one pen table, you can plot the walls thicker. By using another on the same design file, you can plot the walls thinner and the wiring thicker.

Pen tables are stored with the filename extension `.tbl` in the folder `C:\Bentley\Workspace\System\Tables\Pen`. Pen table files are ASCII text files you can examine with a text editor. They contain many sections that define resymbolization parameters. You can even incorporate

MicroStation BASIC macros for advanced plot resymbolization requirements. When you load a pen table before generating a plot, the resymbolization parameters defined in it are applied to design file elements just before they are plotted.

NOTE: When resymbolizing, design file elements do not change. The plotting utility applies changes to elements on-the-fly as they are plotted.

Use resymbolization to:

- Change the appearance of elements as they plot.
- Control the plotting sequence of the active design file and its attached reference files.
- Substitute text strings in the design file.

MicroStation delivers two example pen tables: `plotordr.tbl` and `cellsub.tbl`. The first demonstrates how to control the relative plotting order of elements in a design file. The latter demonstrates how to use MicroStation BASIC macros in pen tables to substitute cells.

To create or modify pen tables:

1. Open the Plot dialog box. You will find it helpful to resize the Plot dialog box to Plot Preview mode.
2. Select New from the PenTable menu to create pen tables. Select Modify to edit the loaded pen table, or to edit an existing pen table if none is loaded. Specify a new pen table file name if creating one. Select an existing pen table file if editing it.
3. The Modify Pen Table dialog box opens. Edit the fields in the Element Criteria and Output Actions sections of the dialog box as desired.
4. Click the Preview Refresh button in the Plot dialog box to see the effect of pen table changes you made. Make edits, as necessary, to the pen table definition until the definition is finished.

To use pen tables, load the desired table before plotting. To load a pen table, select Load from the PenTable menu in the Plot dialog box. To unload a pen table, select Unload from the PenTable menu.

Exporting to Other Formats

In addition to generating hardcopy output, MicroStation lets you export design files in a variety of formats. To see the vector formats you can export design files to, select Export from the File menu, as shown below.

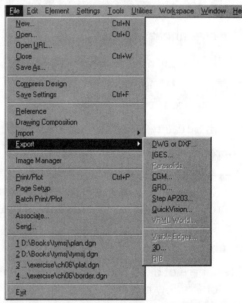

Use the Export menu to create output in other file formats.

Translation of design files to AutoCAD .dwg and .dxf formats is covered in chapter 18.

NOTE: The Export choice on the File menu lets you change the design file dimensional status, from 2D to 3D, or from 3D to 2D.

To translate a design file to another vector file format:

1. Select the desired file format from the Export submenu in the File menu. A dialog box opens.
2. Type a name for the new file and select options relevant to the export.
3. Click the Export button to generate the file.

In addition to translating design files into a different vector file format, you can render them in a large number of raster formats. The rendering of design files to raster format isn't restricted to 3D design files. You can save images of 2D design files in `.tif`, `.jpg`, or other supported formats.

The raster file formats supported for export are the same as raster reference file formats discussed in chapter 6.

To create raster images from design files:

1. Arrange the design file in a view window as you would like it imaged.
2. Select Save from the Image submenu in the Utilities menu. The Save Image dialog box opens, as shown below.

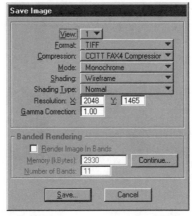

Use the Save Image dialog box to create raster images from design files.

3. Select the view number you used in step 1.
4. Select the desired file format, its resolution, and other options.
5. Click the Save button. The Save Image As dialog box opens.
6. Enter a file name and click the OK button. MicroStation processes the selected view and creates its image in the designated file.

The generated image file is saved as a default in the following directory.

`c:\Bentley\Workspace\Project\Examples\Generic\Out`

This folder is identified by the configuration variable MS_IMAGEOUT. To change the default image output directory, change the value of this configuration variable in the Configuration Variables dialog box accessed from the Workspace menu.

You can also generate output in other file formats from MicroStation's Plot dialog box. By selecting a plotter driver file, such as TIFF or WMF, you can create a plot file. To create a plot file, make sure the driver file isn't configured to send the plot directly to a port. When you plot in this mode, a dialog box will prompt you for a file name.

To create a vector output in HPGL, a format used by many word processors for importing graphics, use an H-P pen plotter drive file.

Chapter 8

Mastering AccuDraw
The Intelligent Drafting Assistant

Though introduced in an earlier MicroStation version, AccuDraw is perhaps not as widely used as it should. You're in for a treat if you never learned it. AccuDraw helps you create geometry quickly by minimizing the effort spent on cursor control and precision key-ins.

A significant portion of the time you spend in MicroStation is used to identify design plane coordinates by clicking data points, and to constrain the cursor in relation to the previous data point. For example, to draw a vertical line, you must first enable axis lock before clicking data points. To enter precision key-ins, you must switch focus to the Key-in window before entering a keyword designating the type of key-in followed by coordinate values.

With AccuDraw, you need not invoke axis lock to draw vertical lines, nor switch focus to the Key-in window to enter design plane coordinates. Like an old friend, AccuDraw is there to help control the cursor or to accept coordinate data values.

AccuDraw is based on the premise that the previous data point is important. It constantly tracks cursor position. Depending on its relationship to the previous data point, AccuDraw nudges the cursor or offers onscreen hints to accomplish what it thinks you want to do next more easily.

Many of MicroStation's element placement and modification tools check to see if AccuDraw is in use. Behind the scenes, they send AccuDraw messages to help it guess your next move. This makes AccuDraw the intelligent drafting assistant you'll want to learn and use at every opportunity.

This chapter introduces you to AccuDraw. I assume here that you have no previous knowledge of the utility. You'll learn to recognize where it can reduce effort, and how to control AccuDraw to do your bidding. You'll learn about its compass, input fields, and its settings. The chapter also presents several exercises to help you master AccuDraw.

This chapter is organized in the following sections:

- **Introducing AccuDraw** shows you how to activate and close the utility, discusses its interface, shortcuts, and onscreen hints. After reading this section, you will recognize terms describing its various features and actions.

- **Understanding AccuDraw** discusses how the cursor control utility works in conjunction with element placement and editing tools. Exercises are presented to help you better understand AccuDraw, including its ability to compute new values from cursor coordinates.

- **Customizing AccuDraw** explores the AccuDraw Settings dialog boxes and how they can be used to modify the utility's behavior. You also learn how to edit, create, and delete AccuDraw shortcuts.

If you're new to AccuDraw, I suggest you read the entire chapter in sequence and work through each exercise. The concepts and practical examples will help you use the utility effectively.

If you're familiar with AccuDraw, but don't recognize where it can be useful, read the exercises. Reading them and mentally following the steps needed to solve the problem may help you recognize situations you may have overlooked where AccuDraw could come in handy.

Introducing AccuDraw

The AccuDraw utility consists of five interfaces. The *AccuDraw window* accepts keystrokes and displays distances and angles. The *compass* displays axis orientation and coordinate input mode. *Shortcuts* are used to send commands that control AccuDraw and MicroStation. Onscreen *hints* are visual cues AccuDraw displays to communicate with you as you move the cursor. Finally, two *AccuDraw settings* dialog boxes are used to configure the utility.

The first four interfaces are introduced in the rest of this section. The AccuDraw settings dialog boxes are covered in a separate section toward the end.

To start the AccuDraw utility, click the Start AccuDraw icon in the Primary toolbox. A small window with AccuDraw in its title bar appears. AccuDraw is now active and watching your cursor movements. By default, AccuDraw is turned off when you start MicroStation. To use this utility, you must start it.

When you are placing or editing elements, AccuDraw's normally helpful behavior may get in the way. At such times, you can close AccuDraw with a single keystroke. To close AccuDraw when it has the focus, press the letter **Q** on the keyboard or close the AccuDraw window.

The AccuDraw Window

On starting AccuDraw a small window opens. This window contains two data input fields and corresponding checkboxes that lock data values. It's shown in the figure below.

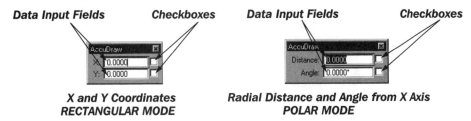

Data Input Fields   Checkboxes   Data Input Fields   Checkboxes

X and Y Coordinates
RECTANGULAR MODE

Radial Distance and Angle from X Axis
POLAR MODE

The two modes of the AccuDraw window.

The AccuDraw window has two modes: rectangular and polar. In *rectangular* mode, it accepts X and Y distances in a Cartesian coordinate system. In *polar* mode, it accepts a radial distance and angle.

You can toggle between the two modes by pressing the space bar when the AccuDraw window has the focus.

The input focus in data fields of most dialog boxes remains unchanged when you move the cursor. The AccuDraw window differs in this respect. When in rectangular mode, the input focus in its data fields depends on the location of the cursor with respect to its origin.

When you move the cursor upward, the input focus shifts to the Y data field. When you move the cursor sideways, the input focus shifts to the X data field. Such cursor awareness is a part of what makes AccuDraw the intelligent drafting assistant.

You can also switch the input focus between fields by using the tab key or the comma. The comma is used to switch between data fields because it is the data separator character in precision key-ins.

The AccuDraw Compass

When AccuDraw controls coordinate input, a compass appears at the last data point clicked. The compass is a square in rectangular mode, and a circle in polar mode. It is shown in the figure below.

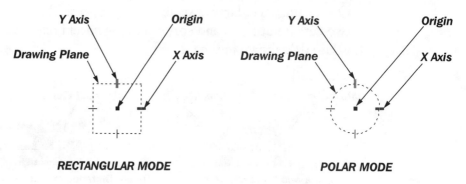

The two modes of the AccuDraw window.

The center of the compass is known as the *origin* point. Values in the AccuDraw window data fields relate to this origin point. The AccuDraw window and the compass go hand in hand. The former accepts values, and the latter controls the origin of measurement.

By default, the last data point entered is the origin point. However, you can move the origin to any location desired if this is more convenient.

The dashed square or circle that surrounds the origin point is the *drawing plane indicator*. The plane in which the dashed square or circle lies, determines the direction of AccuDraw's axes. It also determines the plane in which AccuDraw will place data points.

In 2D design files, there is only one plane, the XY plane. The drawing plane indicator always resides in this plane. In 3D design files, there are three planes: the XY plane, the XZ plane, and the YZ plane. The drawing plane indicator can be oriented to lie in any of the three planes. AccuDraw's ability to restrict the cursor to lie in the plane defined by its compass makes it particularly valuable for 3D modeling.

The colored tick marks at right angles to each other on the compass perimeter are its axes. The default color of the tick mark representing the positive X direction is red, while it's green for the positive Y direction. These colors are customizable in the AccuDraw Settings dialog box.

When the compass initially appears, its axes are aligned to the view axes. However, when using tools that send messages to AccuDraw, the axis rotates so that its X-axis is defined by the direction of the last two data points.

Shortcuts

You've already seen two AccuDraw keyboard shortcuts. We used the space bar to switch coordinate input mode between rectangular and polar. We also used the letter **Q** to close AccuDraw.

Shortcuts are one- or two-letter keystrokes used to communicate with AccuDraw. The utility supports scores of shortcuts for a variety of tasks. To list available shortcuts, press the **?** key. The AccuDraw Shortcuts dialog box opens, as shown below.

*Press the **?** key to display the AccuDraw Shortcuts dialog box.*

Because AccuDraw sets its compass at the last data point, many beginners assume you can't control its location. To move the AccuDraw compass to the tentative cursor location, press the **O** key. Another shortcut you will appreciate is the letter **V**. Pressing it aligns the AccuDraw axes, if they are rotated, with view axes.

The following table lists shortcuts you are likely to use most often.

AccuDraw Shortcut	Action Performed by Shortcut
Enter	Turns on checkbox that has focus in AccuDraw window.
Space	Toggles input between rectangular and polar modes.
A	Locks the angle field in the AccuDraw window. (Polar)
C	Makes center snap mode active.
D	Locks the distance field in the AccuDraw window. (Polar)
N	Makes Nearest snap mode active.
O	Moves compass origin to tentative cursor location.
RQ	Interrupts AccuDraw to rotate compass.
V	Rotates compass to align with view axes.
X	Locks the X data field in the AccuDraw window. (Rectangular)

Onscreen Hints

To signal that the cursor is within its target range, AccuDraw displays onscreen hints. When the cursor is within the tolerance range of AccuDraw's X- or Y-axes, a thick line appears from the AccuDraw compass origin, and the cursor is drawn toward the axis. This is the *axis alignment hint*. It indicates that clicking a data point, while the hint displays on screen, will place it along the axis. When the cursor is aligned to an AccuDraw axis, and its distance from the origin is the same as when the last data point was clicked, AccuDraw displays a small tick at the end of the axis alignment hint. Clicking a data point, while this hint displays on the screen, makes the distance between the data point and the origin the same as the previous distance. These hints are illustrated in the figure below.

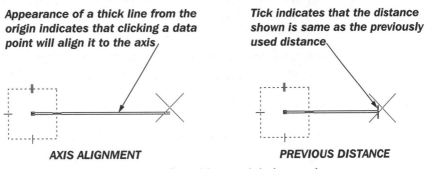

Common AccuDraw hints and their meanings.

In addition to the two hints discussed, AccuDraw displays dashed lines perpendicular to its axes when a checkbox in the AccuDraw window constrains a distance.

This brief introduction to AccuDraw, and the ways in which it communicates during cursor movement, is the first step in using AccuDraw effectively. The next section focuses on the contexts in which the interfaces you've learned, apply. Several exercises demonstrate this intelligent drafting assistant.

Understanding AccuDraw

AccuDraw adjusts its behavior depending on cursor location and the tool it's working with. It has the ability to receive hints from tools, and many of MicroStation's tools are written to communicate their needs with it.

AccuDraw's ability to communicate with other tools and make adjustments to its mode of operation based on a tool's needs is called *context sensitivity*.

The following bulleted list explains what AccuDraw does when working with some tools.

- Compass rotates as cursor moves from point to point during element placement.
- Coordinate mode changes from rectangular to polar when the Place Circle or Place Arc tools are activated. Also, when you switch the segment mode from lines to arcs in Place SmartLine, the compass switches from rectangular to polar mode.
- Compass remains at center, instead of moving to the data point identifying its primary axis, and locks a field when placing an ellipse by the center method.
- Compass rotates but remains at first data point when placing a rotated block.
- Compass snaps to the center and switches to polar mode when you identify a circle with the Modify Element tool.
- Compass snaps to a vertex, or to a point on a segment, depending where you identify it, and switches to rectangular mode when you identify a shape with the Modify Element tool.
- Compass rotates to match an element's orientation when you identify it with the Copy Parallel tool.
- Compass snaps to the other endpoint and rotates to match its orientation when you identify a line with the Extend Line tool.

Other examples of AccuDraw's approach to managing cursor position are discussed in the following paragraphs.

For element placement tools that require more than one data point, such as the Place Line tool, a data point must be entered before AccuDraw will display its compass. For tools that need only one data point, such as the Place Text and the Place Cell tools, the compass appears at the previously entered data point.

When working in 3D files without AccuDraw, text and cell placement tools create elements on a plane defined by the view. For example, a cell placed in the Top view is placed in the top plane. When AccuDraw is active, no matter what view you create the element in, it orients to AccuDraw's drawing plane.

For tasks such as fence placement and dimensioning, where its compass would get in the way, AccuDraw turns it off.

Let's now practice what you've learned about AccuDraw. The exercises are carefully chosen to demonstrate concepts, some not yet discussed, and to increase your understanding of AccuDraw.

Exercise: Entering Coordinate Data

This exercise uses AccuDraw in conjunction with several element placement tools. It demonstrates AccuDraw's context sensitivity and coordinate input capabilities. This exercise uses the design file **coord.dgn** in the **\Exercise\Ch08** folder on the CD-ROM. Copy this file to your computer's hard drive. Once copied, clear its read-only attribute. This is important. Otherwise, you won't be able to write to the file.

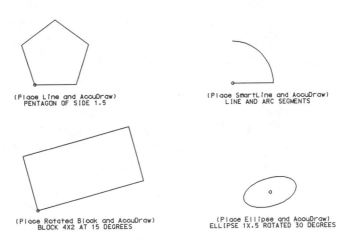

(Place Line and AccuDraw)
PENTAGON OF SIDE 1.5

(Place SmartLine and AccuDraw)
LINE AND ARC SEGMENTS

(Place Rotated Block and AccuDraw)
BLOCK 4X2 AT 15 DEGREES

(Place Ellipse and AccuDraw)
ELLIPSE 1X.5 ROTATED 30 DEGREES

The four tasks you will complete in this exercise.

Use the following steps to complete this exercise:

1. Start MicroStation with a copy of the `coord.dgn` file. You will see four text titles in each quadrant of the screen with a small circle designating the starting point for each tool.

2. Start AccuDraw. If it comes up in polar mode, switch it to rectangular mode by pressing the space bar. You will draw a pentagon in the top left quadrant of the screen. Use the Place Line tool in conjunction with AccuDraw.

3. Invoke the Place Line tool. Change the active snap mode to Center. Snap to the center of the small circle by using a tentative button click. The tentative cursor appears. Accept it with a data point. The AccuDraw compass appears. Move the cursor upward and notice that the focus in the AccuDraw window is in the Y field. Move the cursor to the right and notice the focus shifts to the X field. Keep moving the cursor until AccuDraw nudges the cursor to align with the X-axis. This is called *axis indexing*.

4. While AccuDraw restrains the cursor along the X-axis, key in `1.5`. The number is entered in the X field of the AccuDraw window and its checkbox is enabled. The length of the line is now constrained to be 1.5 units long in the X direction. Verify this by moving the cursor. A thin dashed vertical line appears on the screen to confirm this. Bring back the cursor until the line indexes to the X-axis, and click a data point. The compass jumps to the data point just entered.

5. Switch AccuDraw to polar mode by pressing the space bar. It will be easier to draw the rest of the pentagon in the polar mode, as its distance cue and rotation capabilities will help you draw the shape more quickly.

6. Press the comma to switch focus to the Angle field and type `72`. The cursor moves along the angle defined. Move it slowly until the *previous distance tick* appears at the cursor. Click a data point to draw the second segment of the pentagon. If the previous distance doesn't appear, you can switch to the Distance field and press the Page Down key to recall, or type 1.5 as the distance value. The compass jumps to the data point just accepted.

7. Repeat step 6 for each of the other vertices of the pentagon to complete the shape.

8. Press Reset to release the line from the cursor. The AccuDraw compass disappears.

Once you are comfortable using AccuDraw, you'll appreciate the quick flow of steps in this exercise compared to the *Using Precision Key-ins* exercise in chapter 5.

Let's move to the next phase of this exercise in the upper right segment of your screen, which demonstrates AccuDraw with SmartLine.

9. Invoke the Place SmartLine tool. Check to see that Segment Type is Lines and Vertex Type is Sharp in the Tool Setting window. Change the active snap mode to Center. Snap to the center of the small circle designating the start point for the tool by using a tentative button click. The tentative cursor appears. Notice that the focus switched from the Tool Settings window to AccuDraw. Accept the tentative cursor location with a data point. The AccuDraw compass appears. It remains in the previously used polar mode. Press the space bar to switch it to rectangular mode.

10. Move the cursor to the right until it indexes to the X-axis and the previous distance tick appears. The X field will display the number 1.5. Click a data point to accept this position. The compass jumps to this location.

11. Press the tilde key (it's to the left of the number 1 key on your keyboard; you can press this key without holding down the shift key) to *bump* the Tool Settings window option from Lines to Arcs. SmartLine prompts you for the center of the arc.

12. Move the cursor to the starting point until the cursor indexes to the X-axis and the distance tick appears. Click a data point to accept the starting point as the center of the arc you are about to draw. The compass automatically switches to polar mode at the request of SmartLine.

13. Swing the cursor counterclockwise until it indexes to the Y-axis to show a quarter arc. Accept the location with a data point.

14. Click Reset to complete the element.

This exercise demonstrated how to bump tool settings. Notice how AccuDraw switches the mode to polar when Arcs is selected as Segment Type in SmartLine.

Let's move to the next phase of this exercise in the lower left quadrant of your screen.

15. Invoke the Place Block tool. Change the Method in the Tool Settings window to Rotated. Change the active snap mode to Center. Snap to the center of the small circle designating the start point for the tool by using a tentative button click. The tentative cursor appears. Notice that the focus switched from the Tool Settings window to AccuDraw. Accept the tentative cursor location with a data point. The AccuDraw compass appears.

16. Switch AccuDraw to polar mode, if it's in rectangular mode. Press the space bar to do this.

17. With focus in the Distance field, type `4,15`. This enters a value of 4 for distance, switches focus to Angle, and enters a value of 15. Both checkboxes are enabled, i.e., the cursor is fully constrained and defines the endpoint completely. Click a data point to accept the data entered.

18. Compass remains at its starting location but rotates. Also, it switches to rectangular mode with a value of 4 for X that is locked.

19. Move the cursor upward and the focus is in the Y field. Enter a value of 2 and accept it with a data point.

20. Click Reset and the compass disappears.

    The purpose of this exercise was to demonstrate AccuDraw's behavior when used with the Place Rotated Block tool.

    On to the next phase of this exercise in the lower right quadrant of your screen.

21. Invoke the Place Ellipse tool. Change the Method to Center, if it not already. Change the active snap mode to Center. Snap to the center of the small circle designating the start point for the tool by clicking it with the tentative button. The tentative cursor snaps to the center and the focus shifts to AccuDraw. Accept it with a data point. The AccuDraw compass appears.

22. Switch AccuDraw to polar mode, if it is in rectangular mode.

23. With focus in the Distance field, key in `1,30` to enter 1 for distance and 30 for angle. Click a data point to accept the values entered.

24. Compass remains at the center of the ellipse and rotates to match the primary axis rotation. Also, it locks the angle to 90°.

25. Press `,` (comma) to switch focus to Distance and key in `.5`. Click a data point to accept and complete the ellipse.

26. Click Reset, and the compass disappears.

This exercise demonstrated the use of AccuDraw for coordinate input with four tools. It also showed how some tools modify AccuDraw's behavior to simplify data input.

Exercise: Locking Cursor

This exercise uses AccuDraw to lock the cursor to be perpendicular to a line segment while its vertex is determined by snapping to another element's endpoint. For this exercise, you will use the design file `curlock.dgn` in the `\Exercise\Ch08` folder on the CD-ROM. Copy this file to your computer's hard drive. Once copied, clear its read-only attribute. This is important. Otherwise, you won't be able to write to the file.

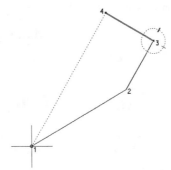

Pressing Enter locks the cursor direction, letting you snap to another point for length.

Use the following steps to complete this exercise:

1. Start MicroStation with a copy of the `curlock.dgn` file. You will see the numbers 1 through 4, as shown in the figure above. A small circle designates the starting point next to the number 1.

2. Start AccuDraw. If it comes up in rectangular mode, switch it to polar mode by pressing the space bar. You will draw a line 4 units long at a 30° incline, from 1 to 2.

3. Invoke the Place SmartLine tool. Change the active snap mode to Center. Snap to the center of the small circle next to the number 1 by using a tentative button click. The tentative cursor appears at the center of the circle. Accept it with a data point. The AccuDraw compass appears.

4. With focus in the Distance field, type 4,30. This enters a value of 4 for distance, switches focus to Angle, and enters a value of 30. Both checkboxes are enabled, i.e., the cursor is fully constrained and defines the endpoint completely. Click a data point to accept the data entered.

5. With focus in the Angle field, type 30,2 to enter a value of 30 for angle and 2 for distance. Accept the location with a data point. The compass moves to the location designated by the number 3.

6. Move the cursor toward point 4 until the cursor aligns with the Y-axis of the compass. Press Enter to lock the direction of the cursor along this axis. This frees the cursor so you can move it outside the tolerance range and still keep it aligned with the axis.

7. Snap the cursor to the starting point 1 with the tentative button. This action is shown in the figure above. You have now determined the length of the segment between points 3 and 4 by snapping to point 1. Accept the data point.

8. Click Reset to finish the line string.

This exercise demonstrated the use of the Enter key to lock the cursor to move along an axis.

Exercise: Rotating and Moving Origin

This exercise rotates and moves the AccuDraw origin to more conveniently draw a line from one point in the direction of another. For this exercise, you will use the design file **mvorigin.dgn** in the **\Exercise\Ch08** folder on the CD-ROM. Copy this file to your computer's hard drive. Once copied, clear its read-only attribute using Windows Explorer. This is important. Otherwise, you won't be able to write to the file.

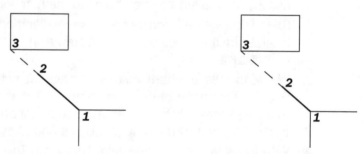

Draw line from 1 to 2, along 3, where distance 1 to 2 is 3 units   *Draw line from 1 to 2, along 3, where distance 2 to 3 is 3 units*

AccuDraw makes these tasks easy, without drawing construction lines.

Use the following steps to complete this exercise:

1. Start MicroStation with a copy of the **mvorigin.dgn** file. You'll see two copies of a block and line string. You are to draw lines starting from 1 along the direction to 3. Length of the proposed lines is explained in the figure above.

2. Start AccuDraw. If it comes up in rectangular mode, switch it to polar mode by pressing the space bar. You will work on the left half of the screen where the proposed line is 3 units long.

3. Invoke the Place Line tool. Snap to the line string vertex, designated as point 1, by using the tentative button. Accept it with a data point. The AccuDraw compass appears with its axes aligned with the view. You must now rotate the compass to align its X-axis in the direction of point 3.

4. Press the key **R** followed by the key **Q** to initiate AccuDraw's Rotate Quick command. Snap to point 3 with a tentative click and accept it with a data button. The compass aligns as desired.

5. Place cursor between points 1 and 3 so it indexes with the X-axis of the compass, and key in 3 in the Distance field. Accept this location with a data point to complete the first line.

6. Click Reset to restart the Place Line tool. You will now work on the right half of the screen, where the proposed line's endpoint is 3 units away from the point 3.

7. The Place Line tool should be still active, if not, activate it. Snap to the line string vertex, designated as point 1, by using the tentative button. Accept it with a data point. The AccuDraw compass appears with its axes aligned with the view. You must now move the compass to point 3 and align its X-axis in the direction of point 1. This will allow you to easily locate the desired point 2.

8. Do not click Reset. Snap to point 3, the desired location for the compass, with the tentative button and press the key **O** to initiate AccuDraw's Move Origin command. The compass moves to point 3. You must now rotate its X-axis in the direction of point 1.

9. Press the key **R** followed by the key **Q** to initiate AccuDraw's Rotate Quick command. Snap to point 1 with a tentative click and accept it with a data button. The compass aligns as desired.

10. Place cursor between points 1 and 3 so it indexes with the X axis of the compass and key in 3 in the Distance field. Accept this location with a data point to complete the proposed line.

11. Click Reset.

This exercise demonstrated the added flexibility gained by being able to rotate and move the AccuDraw origin.

Exercise: Dividing Distance

This exercise showcases the efficiency gained by using AccuDraw's ability to accept mathematical operators. For this exercise, you will use the design file `copyblk.dgn` in the `\Exercise\Ch08` folder on the CD-ROM. Copy this file to your computer's hard drive. Once copied, clear its read-only attribute. This is important. Otherwise, you won't be able to write to the file.

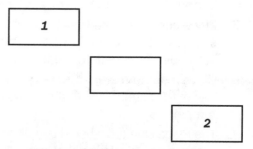

Copy block 1 and place it midway between identical blocks 1 and 2

AccuDraw makes this possible with two data points.

Use the following steps to complete this exercise:

1. Start MicroStation with a copy of the `copyblk.dgn` file. You'll see two identical blocks designated as 1 and 2 in the figure above. It is your task to make a copy of block of 1 and place it exactly midway between the two blocks.

   Before you continue, I invite you to think how you might accomplish this without AccuDraw. One possible way is to draw a construction line between the centers of the two blocks. Then use the Copy Element tool to pick a copy of block 1 from its center, and snap it to the center of the construction line. Delete the construction line.

   AccuDraw offers a quicker way without any construction lines. Here's how.

2. Start AccuDraw. If it comes up in rectangular mode, switch it to polar mode by pressing the space bar.

3. Invoke the Copy Element tool. Snap to the center of block 1. The default snap mode was saved as Center in the exercise file, so click on the block with the tentative button to snap to its center. The block highlights. Accept it with a data point—the first data point. A copy of the block attaches to the cursor.

4. Snap to the center of block 2 with the tentative button. Do not accept this position yet. With the focus in the Distance field, press /2 to divide the distance between the two blocks by 2.

5. The copy of the block moves to the desired location. Click a data point—the second data point—to accept it.

6. Click Reset to release the copy of the block from the cursor.

If the above instructions went by too quickly, read them again and do the exercise another time or two. Its simplicity is indeed amazing. Without AccuDraw, you would doubtlessly go through many more steps using temporary construction lines.

Customizing AccuDraw

Many aspects of AccuDraw are customizable. How it behaves, and the shortcuts it understands, are configured in the following two dialog boxes:

- AccuDraw Setting
- More AccuDraw Settings

So far in the chapter, we've used the default settings for the colors of its axis ticks in the compass, its context sensitivity, the movement of its origin from one data point to another, and other aspects of its behavior.

In this section you learn how to customize these aspects of AccuDraw.

AccuDraw Settings

To specify default AccuDraw settings or to change them, select AccuDraw from the Settings menu. Or, while AccuDraw has the focus, press the letter **G**, followed by **S**. The AccuDraw Settings dialog box opens, as shown below.

The AccuDraw Settings dialog box.

This dialog box is *nonmodal*, i.e., it can be left open while you work in MicroStation. It organizes its settings in the following four categories.

Unit Roundoff

When the **Distance** checkbox is enabled, AccuDraw forces the cursor to move in increments of the value specified. Similarly, when the **Angle** checkbox is enabled, AccuDraw constrains rotation by increments of the value specified. The checkboxes are unchecked by default, and distances and angles are not rounded off.

This feature provides benefits similar to grid lock. Isometric drawings are easier to create when you enable the Angle checkbox and use 30° as value for increment.

You can override the round-off values at any time by keying in desired values for distance or angle in the AccuDraw window.

Coordinate System

There are shortcuts for choices you can make from option buttons in this category. The **Rotation** option button offers the choices: Top, Front, Side, View, Auxiliary, and Context.

The first four choices correspond to the **T, F, S,** and **V** shortcuts that rotate the drawing plane indicator to the standard planes. The Auxiliary option aligns the drawing plane to the active Auxiliary Coordinate System. The Context option aligns the drawing plane for the duration of a single command.

The **Type** option button offers two choices: Rectangular and Polar. These are the two coordinate modes discussed earlier.

Operation

The checkboxes in this category control how AccuDraw influences the cursor.

The **Floating Origin** checkbox is enabled by default. It causes the compass to follow your last data point. When off, the compass remains stationary.

The **Context Sensitivity** checkbox is enabled by default. AccuDraw accepts hints from tools designed to communicate with it. See the bulleted list of examples of AccuDraw's context sensitive behavior under the *Understanding AccuDraw* section. To disable the context sensitive behavior of AccuDraw, turn off the Context Sensitivity checkbox in the AccuDraw Settings dialog box.

The **Smart Key-ins** checkbox is enabled by default. It causes the focus to shift from the X to the Y data field, depending on cursor location. Also, a numerical value is treated as either positive or negative, depending on cursor position. To explicitly specify positive or negative numbers, turn this checkbox off.

The **Auto Point Placement** checkbox is unchecked by default. When enabled, it automatically places a data point when the cursor is fully constrained. Otherwise, you must click a data point to accept the constrained cursor position.

Display

Click the **X axis** or the **Y axis** buttons to change the color of the positive axis tick marks on the drawing plane indicator. When you click either button, the Modify Axis Color dialog box opens. You can pick one of the standard colors, or use slider bars to mix a custom color.

Clicking the **Coordinate Readout** button opens a dialog box to let you change the display accuracy and format of distances and angles. It affects the coordinate readout in all of MicroStation and is the same as the Coordinate Readout category in the Design File Settings dialog box discussed in chapter 3.

Clicking the **Shortcut Key-ins** button opens the AccuDraw Shortcuts window. This is the same window that opens when you press the **?** key while the AccuDraw window has the focus. This window is discussed in detail later.

More AccuDraw Settings

For added flexibility, AccuDraw provides access to more settings you can customize. From the AccuDraw Settings dialog box, click the More button. Or, while AccuDraw has the focus, press the letter **G**, followed by **M**. The More AccuDraw Settings dialog box opens, as shown below.

The More AccuDraw Settings dialog box.

Like the AccuDraw Settings dialog box, it is nonmodal. It organizes its settings in the following three categories.

Indexing

The term *indexing* refers to AccuDraw's cursor control hints. When the axis alignment hint appears, the cursor is said to *index* to the axis.

When the **Axis** checkbox is enabled, AccuDraw forces the cursor to lie along an axis when it is within the specified tolerance. To free the cursor from aligning with the compass axes, turn this checkbox off.

When the **Distance** checkbox is enabled, AccuDraw displays a tick mark at the cursor when its distance from the compass origin is the same (within tolerance limits) as a previously used distance. To force it not to track previous distances for indexing, turn this checkbox off.

The Tolerance field accepts an integer that specifies the number of pixel for tolerance. AccuDraw performs indexing when the cursor is within this tolerance value specified here.

Display

The **Hilite** button lets you change the color of the indexing line and origin point. The **Frame** button lets you change the color of the drawing plane indicator. Clicking either button opens the Modify Axis Color dialog box that displays when you change the axis colors.

When the **Delayed Update** checkbox is enabled, the distance and angle fields in the AccuDraw window update their values after a perceptible delay. It is off by default.

When the **Show Negative Angles** checkbox is enabled—the default— angles greater than 180° are displayed as negative numbers.

When the **Shortcut Popups** checkbox is enabled—the default— commands activated by pressing shortcuts are confirmed with a pop-up message on the AccuDraw window.

Operation

This section of the dialog box offers a single option button labeled **Default Origin**. Of the three choices—View center on active Z, Global origin, and Global origin on active Z—the first is the default. The choice you make determines AccuDraw's default origin.

Working with Shortcuts

AccuDraw anticipates your next move and changes its mode to accept input in the way you wanted. Sometimes, however, you want to direct its actions through *shortcuts*.

A shortcut is a quicker way of invoking an action. Shortcuts are of two types: those that control AccuDraw and those that invoke other MicroStation tools or commands. All actions invoked by AccuDraw's shortcuts are key-ins you can type in the Key-in window.

When AccuDraw has the focus, pressing a shortcut invokes an action. Many actions associated with shortcuts were discussed earlier. Shortcuts can be one or two-letter sequences. You can also edit existing shortcuts or create your own.

To edit an existing shortcut:

1. Open the AccuDraw Shortcuts window.

    Do this by pressing **?** when AccuDraw has the focus. Alternatively, click the Shortcut Key-ins button in the AccuDraw Settings dialog box.

2. Scroll through the shortcuts listed in the window and highlight the one you wish to edit.

3. Click the Edit button. The Edit Shortcut dialog box opens. It displays three fields: Shortcut, Description, and Command. *Shortcut* is the letter you press to 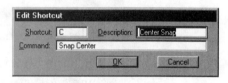 activate the key-in listed in the *Command* field. Text in the *Description* field appears next to the shortcut letter in the AccuDraw Shortcuts window. It also helps you remember what the shortcut does.

4. Change the desired field(s) in the dialog box.

5. To accept the changes, click the OK button. The dialog box closes. To close the dialog box without making the changes, click the Cancel button.

To create a new shortcut:

1. Open the AccuDraw Shortcuts window.

    Do this by pressing **?** when AccuDraw has the focus. Or, click the Shortcut Key-ins button in the AccuDraw Settings dialog box.

2. Click the New button. The New Shortcut dialog box opens. It displays the same three fields found in the Edit Shortcut dialog box: Shortcut, Description, and Command.

3. Enter up to two letters for the new shortcut in the Shortcut field. Enter a description and a valid MicroStation key-in for the shortcut in the appropriate fields.

4. To save the shortcut, click the OK button. The dialog box closes. To close the dialog box without saving the new shortcut, click the Cancel button.

As you've probably noticed, the AccuDraw Shortcuts dialog box doesn't include a Delete button. You can either edit existing shortcuts or create new ones in the dialog box interface. There is, however, a way to delete shortcuts you may no longer want.

To delete a shortcut:

1. Locate the file `shortcut.txt`.

This file resides in the `c:\Bentley\Workspace\System\Data` folder for a default MicroStation installation. AccuDraw reads this file to load shortcuts, their descriptions, and commands.

2. Open the file in a text editor, such as Windows Notepad.

3. Delete the line corresponding to the shortcut you wish to delete.

4. Save the edited file.

Exercise: Creating a Shortcut for Loading RS Tools LE

RS Tools LE is an MDL application that automates many common drafting tasks. See chapter 25 for a description of each tool in the application. You will create an AccuDraw shortcut to load this application.

As this exercise demonstrates, AccuDraw shortcuts need not be related to cursor control or coordinate data input. Any valid MicroStation key-in can be assigned a shortcut.

For this exercise, from the CD-ROM, copy the file `rstools.ma` to the `C:\Bentley\Workspace\Standards\MDLapps\IntelNT` folder on your computer's hard drive. The file is located in the `\MDLapps` folder on the CD-ROM.

To create RS as a shortcut that loads RS Tools LE:

1. Open the AccuDraw Shortcuts window. Do this by pressing **?** when AccuDraw has the focus. Or, click the Shortcut Key-ins button in the AccuDraw Settings dialog box.

2. Click the New button. The New Shortcut dialog box opens.

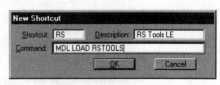

3. In the Shortcut field, type `RS`. In the Description field, type `Load RS Tools LE`. In the Command field, type `MDL LOAD RSTOOLS`.

4. Click the OK button. The shortcut definition is saved and the New Shortcut dialog box closes.

5. To load RS Tools LE, while AccuDraw has the focus, press the letter R, followed by the letter S. The RS Tools LE toolbox opens.

This concludes the exercise and this chapter. In the next chapter, you learn about MicroStation's dimension-driven design capabilities.

Chapter 9

Dimension-Driven Design

Creating Variational Geometry

When you use the Dimension Element tool, MicroStation determines the type of element identified and computes its size from the geometric data stored in the design file. You can also enable the association lock when placing dimensions. Should you modify an element to which an associative dimension is attached, the dimension updates to reflect the new element size.

When you create geometry with dimension-driven design tools, modifications to dimensions update geometry. In this respect, such geometry is the opposite of associative dimensioning.

In one, you associate a dimension with a geometric element. In the other, you associate geometry with dimensions—and other constraints discussed later—to create a *profile* that usually serves as a basis for creating part families.

Other common industry terms for dimension-driven design are variational geometry and parametric design.

Dimension-driven design technology trickled into MicroStation as a result of Modeler's development at Bentley. MicroStation Modeler is the mechanical engineering configuration for the manufacturing industry. Many of the terms you will learn in this chapter are used by mechanical designers who use parametric modeling software.

Though this technology has obvious uses in the manufacturing industry, you too can benefit from it for tasks unrelated to mechanical design. Examples of its use in other disciplines are covered in exercises later.

A list of chapter sections and their brief descriptions follows:

- **Basic DD Design Concepts** describes dimension-driven design and introduces associated terminology. Here you read about possible uses for this feature.
- **The DD Design Tool Frame** introduces MicroStation's DD Design tool frame and the tools it contains for creating dimension-driven geometry.
- **Creating Variational Geometry** helps you practice the tools in step-by-step exercises.

If you're new to variational geometry, I suggest you read all sections in sequence. For those of you who have worked with other variational geometry systems, skimming the first section will relate the terms you know to the context of how MicroStation uses them. You'll want to work through the exercises to learn how to use MicroStation's dimension-driven design tools.

If you've been using MicroStation for years, but haven't worked with dimension-driven design, you're not alone. Many perceive this topic as difficult and leave its benefits unexplored. Granted that a certain level of comfort with MicroStation's basic drafting features is a prerequisite, the topic isn't all that difficult.

Dimension-driven design is a power user's essential tool because of its many uses. New users may want to come back to this chapter after gaining experience with basic drawing and dimensioning tools. Experienced users, on the other hand, may dive right in to explore the possibilities!

Basic DD Design Concepts

MicroStation uses the acronym DD Design to refer to dimension-driven design. Its purpose is to help you create profiles that consist of geometric elements with attributes defining relationships between them. Such profiles behave intelligently. If you manipulate its defining parameters, usually dimensions, the profile responds by changing its geometry in such a way that all relationships are maintained.

Geometric elements are the basic CAD entities such as lines, arcs, circles, ellipses, B-spline curves, and dimensions. What, then, are the relationships you can define between them?

With dimension-driven design tools, you can define the following distinct types of relationships among geometric elements:

- **Geometric**. When you constrain a line to be always parallel or perpendicular to another, you are defining a *geometric* relationship between them.

- **Locational**. When you constrain an element's endpoint to lie always at the midpoint or intersection of another, you are defining a *locational* relationship. Locational constraints can also anchor an element to a specific design plane coordinate.

- **Dimensional**. When you attach a dimension to a geometric element in such a way that changing the dimension text will update the geometry, you are defining a *dimensional constraint*, or relationship. Dimensional constraints can be assigned names, called *dimensional variables*, such as radius, width, height, and others.

- **Algebraic**. When you define mathematical equations to relate dimensional variables, you create *algebraic* relationships among geometric elements.

In addition to the above terms, you will encounter others that may not be familiar. These are defined in the following paragraphs.

A *construction* is a geometric element drawn with the construction class attribute. Consequently, you can turn its display on or off by toggling the Constructions checkbox in the View Attributes dialog box. Constructions are used to create the skeleton for a profile.

A *constraint* is a relationship between geometric elements. MicroStation displays constraints as graphical symbols whose size is determined by the active text height. The four types of constraints supported by dimension-driven design tools are listed in bullet form above. A profile must have enough constraints so it is well-defined.

Any time you add an element to a profile, you add movements that must be constrained to unambiguously define it. The number of unconstrained movements in a profile determines its *degrees of freedom*, or DOF. A well-defined profile has zero degrees of freedom.

The following table lists common geometric elements used as constructions, and the degrees of freedom each adds.

Geometric Element	Associated Degrees of Freedom
Point	2 (location on X-axis, location on Y-axis)
Circle	3 (location of center on X-axis, location of center on Y-axis, and radius)
Line	4 (starting point's location on X-axis, on Y-axis, length of line, orientation or angle of line)
Ellipse	5 (location of center on X-axis, on Y-axis, length of primary axis, length of secondary axis, and rotation of primary axis)

A profile that has unconstrained movements, or degrees of freedom, is called *under-constrained*. It can have many solutions. Additional constraints must be applied to it before it will be ready to use as a profile. A *well-constrained* profile has zero degrees of freedom and is in a state you want it to be. An *over-constrained* profile has redundant constraints that may conflict with other constraints. Usually, you'll want to remove constraints from such profiles because they don't add value to existing relationships. In fact, they may add inconsistencies.

NOTE: Until a profile is well-constrained, constructions created by dimension-driven design tools appear yellow with a dashed line style. After a profile has been well-constrained, the constructions appear white.

You can create dimension-driven profiles in one of two ways: manual or automatic.

In the *manual method*, you draw geometry, not necessarily at the final location or of the exact size, and add geometric, locational, dimensional, and algebraic constraints. Then you check its degrees of freedom. If the profile is not yet well-constrained, you edit, add, or delete constraints until the constructions are unambiguously defined.

In the *automatic method*, you draw geometry with the Sketch Profile tool and have it generate reasonable geometric constraints automatically. Or, you take geometry that is as close to the final profile dimensions as possible, and use the Convert Element to Profile tool to have it create necessary constructions and geometric constraints. To this you add desired dimensional constraints and check its degrees of freedom. If the profile is not yet well-constrained, you edit, add, or delete constraints until the constructions are unambiguously defined.

Once defined, profiles are commonly added to cell libraries for use as dimension-driven cells.

Dimension-driven design concepts have long been used by mechanical designers in the manufacturing industry. Everyday parts, such as door knobs, towel hangers, camera body, speaker cabinets, and others, are designed as parametric models. Such modeling empowers a designer to change the model's shape by editing its key parameters.

Parametric modeling leads to manufacturing efficiency because parts evolve over several iterations to satisfy both aesthetic and functional needs. The initial effort needed to create parametric parts is more than compensated by the efficiencies gained in editing because components are related. Changes to parameters propagate throughout the part so as to maintain component relationships.

The following paragraphs discuss several examples not related to mechanical design to showcase the general usefulness of dimension-driven design.

Civil engineers use underground manholes for servicing utility pipes. The manhole geometry for various jurisdictions is usually well-defined and changes only dimensionally, typically by depth. A dimension-driven cell that incorporates the manhole depth as a variable parameter could automate the drawing of manholes.

Bridge designers draw details to show the bearing length and size of pads at the ends of beams. Rather than redrawing details for the various sizes, a dimension-driven cell can prove useful. Upon placement in the design file, the cell can prompt the designer for the desired bearing length, and on receiving this input, can modify itself dimensionally.

Architects draw wall details that use standard building components, such as bricks and drywall, except they might have varying distances between them for different wall thicknesses. Rather than redrawing such wall details, a dimension-driven cell can adjust distances during placement.

I'm sure you can think of many other scenarios. If you often create variations to geometry that is essentially similar in definition, you should consider developing dimension-driven cells for them.

The DD Design Tool Frame

All tools you need to create and edit dimension-driven geometry are located in the DD Design tool frame. To open the tool frame, select DD Design from the DD Design submenu on the Tools menu. This tool frame is home to six toolboxes, as shown in the figure below.

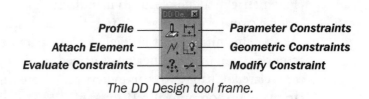

The DD Design tool frame.

Whether you need to apply a geometric, dimensional, or locational constraint to an element; create a profile from existing geometry; verify the degrees of freedom in a construction; or write algebraic equations to relate various dimensional variables, you will find the tools in this tool frame.

Profile Toolbox

This toolbox contains the tools for a somewhat automated creation of constraints in a profile. With one, you sketch geometry and constraints are created as you draw elements. With the other, you process existing geometry to have constraints generated.

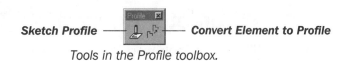

Sketch Profile ———— Convert Element to Profile

Tools in the Profile toolbox.

Sketch Profile

Use this tool to apply geometric constraints automatically as you draw profile geometry. The Geometric Constraints checkbox in the Tool Settings window must be enabled if the tool is to create constraints. With this tool you can sketch lines, arcs by center, arcs by edge, and curves.

This tool works like the Place SmartLine tool and supports variations in vertex type. As you sketch the profile, the vertices may be sharp, rounded, chamfered, or tangential.

On clicking the Settings button in the Tool Settings window, it displays options that control its actions. You can have the tool set the text size for constraint symbols and dimensions automatically. You can also have the tool set tolerances automatically. The Distance Tolerance determines the distance within which points are processed for applying constraints. The Angle Tolerance determines angles within which elements are processed to determine perpendicular or parallel relationships. There are also checkboxes for geometric constraint types you want applied by the tool, based on tolerance values. To close the settings section of the Tool Settings window, click the Settings button.

Convert Element to Profile

Use this tool to automatically create constraints on existing geometry to convert it to a profile. On activating the tool you are prompted to identify an element to convert. You can identify a single element, such as a line string, shape, complex chain, or complex shape. You can also gather several elements in a selection set before invoking the tool. On identifying the element to convert, you are prompted to accept the selection. Clicking a data point initiates the conversion.

The Tool Settings window options for this tool are the same as were available for the Sketch Profile tool.

Parameter Constraints Toolbox

This set of tools works with dimension elements. Use it to assign constants or variables to dimensional constraints, create algebraic constraints, or convert associative dimension elements to constraints.

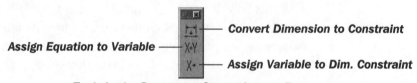

Assign Equation to Variable —— Convert Dimension to Constraint

Assign Variable to Dim. Constraint

Tools in the Parameter Constraints toolbox.

Convert Dimension to Constraint

This tool requires dimension elements it converts to be associative. It attempts to convert nonassociative dimensions by first making them associative. However, you may run into problems if the associativity assumptions it makes weren't what you intended. For this reason, you will always want to create associative dimensions for elements you want converted to constraints.

To convert a dimension element to a dimensional constraint, activate the tool. You are prompted to identify a dimension element. Identify and accept it. The Choose Parameter Name dialog box opens. Type a name for the constraint in the Variable field of the dialog box and click the OK button. The variable name with its assigned value appears in the dimension as it is converted to a constraint.

Assign Equation to Variable

Algebraic equations are placed in the design file with the standard Place Text tool. Similarly, to edit equations, use the Edit Text tool.

To create equations, use well-known algebraic rules. Equations may include constants, variable names that have been assigned to dimensional constraints, trigonometric functions, and the constant "pi."

To assign an equation to a variable, first create the equation with the Place Text tool. Then activate this tool. You are prompted to identify the equation. Identify the text element that defines the equation, then identify an element that uses one of the variables in its dimensional constraints.

Upon successful assignment of the equation to a variable, a degree of freedom is removed from the profile.

Assign Variable to Dimensional Constraint

Variable names are placed in a design file as text elements, much like equations. You can edit them with the Edit Text tool. To assign a variable name that has already been placed in the design file, activate the Assign Variable tool and identify the text element, then identify a dimensional constraint.

Upon successful assignment of a variable to a dimensional constraint, the dimension's value is replaced with the variable and a degree of freedom is added to the profile.

Attach Element Toolbox

This set of tools works with existing construction and constraints. Use it to attach line strings, arcs, shapes, or ellipses to constructions. When solving profiles, the size or shape of elements and their locations are modified to maintain the attachments.

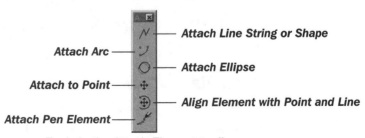

Tools in the Attach Element toolbox.

Attach Line String or Shape

Use this tool to create a line string or a shape that has its vertices attached to constraints, construction points, or centers of construction circles.

To create an attached line string or shape, activate the tool and identify the constraints, points, or centers of circles where you want the vertices attached. To create a shape, enter a data point at the starting point.

Attach Arc

Use this tool to attach an arc to an existing construction ellipse or circle. After activating the tool, you first identify an existing construction ellipse, then a constraint to define the starting angle, followed by another constraint to define the counterclockwise sweep angle for the arc.

The attached arc shares the perimeter of the construction ellipse with the start and sweep angles defined by other constructions or constraints.

Attach Ellipse

Use this tool to attach an ellipse or a circle to an existing construction ellipse or circle.

After activating the tool, identify the construction circle or ellipse, and accept it. The attached ellipse lies directly on top of the construction ellipse.

Attach to Point

Use this tool to attach an element to a constraint or construction point. The starting point of the element, or its center, if the element is an ellipse, is attached to the constraint identified.

After activating the tool, identify the element, then the constraint. On accepting it, the element moves to complete the attachment.

Align Element with Point and Line

Use this tool to attach an element to a constraint and define its orientation along a construction line. The starting point of the element, or its center, if the element is an ellipse, is attached to the constraint.

After activating the tool, identify the element, then the constraint, followed by a construction line. On accepting it, the element moves to lie on the constraint and rotates to take the orientation of the construction line.

Attach Pen Element

Use this tool to attach an element to a constraint so the attached element becomes a *pen* leaving a trail on the screen. The tool is used for *range of motion* or interference studies.

After activating the tool, you identify the element to be used as a pen, then the constraint to which to attach it. On accepting it, the pen element moves to complete the attachment.

When you re-solve a profile, as the constraint moves, the pen element leaves a trail you can examine. The trail created by temporary graphics, vanishes when you update the view.

Geometric Constraints Toolbox

Use this set of tools to create geometric constraints.

Tools in the Geometric Constraints toolbox.

Smart Constrain Elements

Use this tool to constrain a line or ellipse to be tangent, perpendicular, or parallel to another element. With it, you can also fix the angle of an element to be horizontal or vertical.

Make Construction Invariant

Use this tool to convert a variable to a constant value, or to make a construction invariant so it does not change when the profile is modified or re-solved.

Constrain Point on Construction

Use this tool to constrain a point, or the center of an ellipse or circle, to lie on a construction. It can also be used to have a construction pass through a point.

Constrain Point at Intersection

Use this tool to make two constructions intersect and have their point of intersection pass through a specified point or the center of a circle. The first two data points identify the constructions, and the third data point identifies the point of intersection. If you click Reset before identifying a point of intersection, a constraint is created at their current intersection point.

Constrain Points Coincident

This tool works with points, circles, or ellipses. On identifying two elements and accepting them, they are constrained to be concentric or coincident.

Fix Point at Location

Use this tool to constrain a point, or the center of a circle or ellipse, to be fixed at the specified point in the design plane.

Equate Constructions

Use this tool to have two constructions share an endpoint. Or, use it to make two lines colinear. When making elements share an endpoint, click data points near the endpoints when identifying them. To make two lines colinear, identify the lines away from their endpoints.

Evaluate Constraints Toolbox

Use this set of tools to determine the degrees of freedom still left to be constrained in a profile, to reapply constraints after a profile has been edited with MicroStation's element manipulation commands, and to evaluate relationships between constraints.

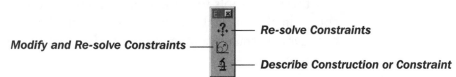

Tools in the Evaluate Constraints toolbox.

Re-solve Constraints

After a profile has been edited with MicroStation's element modification tools, the relationships created with DD Design tools can be compromised. This tool reapplies dimensional and other constraints to geometry and reports the number of movements, or degrees of freedom (DOF), still left unconstrained.

After activating the tool, identify an element in the profile and accept it. The status bar reports the number of unconstrained movements still left in the profile. Additionally, each vertex that has remaining degrees of freedom displays a question mark symbol.

Modify and Re-solve Constraints

While creating a profile, it is helpful to see what types of movements are still possible. This lets you determine the types of constraints you need to apply. Use this tool to drag a construction or constraint and observe the profile move.

After activating the tool, click and hold the left mouse button on a construction or constraint, and move the mouse. If still not well-constrained, the profile moves.

Describe Construction or Constraint

Use this tool to identify relationships between constructions and constraints in a profile.

After activating the tool, identify a construction or constraint and accept it. Its name, and the names of other constructions it is attached to, appear.

Modify Constraint Toolbox

Use this set of tools to work with geometry that has already been constrained. You can break or trim constrained geometry, add fillet or chamfer constraints, and modify values of variables or dimensional constraints.

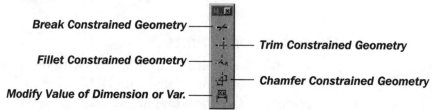

Break Constrained Geometry

Fillet Constrained Geometry

Modify Value of Dimension or Var.

Trim Constrained Geometry

Chamfer Constrained Geometry

Tools in the Modify Constraint toolbox.

Break Constrained Geometry

Use this tool to insert a break in a construction between constraints. This is useful when you want to modify a profile by inserting new geometry and additional constraints at the location of the break. It works on lines, line strings, arcs, or shapes.

After activating the tool, identify the element to break, then the cutting element or a point on the element where the break is to be inserted. An unconstrained node is added at the break.

Trim Constrained Geometry

Use this tool to trim two intersecting constructions.

After activating the tool, identify the two constructions and they are trimmed so as to meet at a common intersecting point. This action normally reduces the number of movements in a profile.

Fillet Constrained Elements

Use this tool to insert a fillet constraint between two constructions.

After activating the tool, in the Tool Settings window, specify a radius for the fillet and whether to create a dimensional constraint for it. Then identify the two construction. A circular fillet is inserted. If a radial dimension was requested, the Choose Parameter Name dialog box opens where you can type a variable name for it.

Chamfer Constrained Elements

Use this tool to insert a chamfer between two constraints.

After activating the tool, select the desired method in the Tool Settings window. You can place the chamfer with two distances, with a distance and an angle, or with a chamfer length. Depending on the method selected, enter the distance or angle values to be used. Then, identify the constructions. To have dimensional constraints created for the chamfer, enable the Create Dimensions checkbox in the Tool Settings window.

If dimensions were requested, the Choose Parameter Name dialog box opens where you can assign variable names for the constraints.

Modify Value of Dimension or Variable

Use this tool to edit the value of a dimensional constraint or the name of a variable.

After activating the tool, identify the variable. On accepting it, you are prompted to enter a value in the Tool Settings window. Enter a value and press Enter. The constructions change to reflect the new value.

Creating Variational Geometry

With the introduction to concepts and tools behind us, you are now ready to explore the world of variational geometry. MicroStation delivers an example design file with the name `cnstrn.dgn` in the folder `C:\Bentley\Workspace\Projects\Examples\Generic\Dgn`. This file shows a variety of geometric, dimensional, and equation constraints. It also includes several examples of constructions. I suggest you study it.

The rest of this section is devoted to exercises that familiarize you with DD Design tools and show you how to create your own dimension-driven designs.

Exercise: Sketch Constructions Freehand

In this exercise you create a freehand sketch of constructions you will use to create a dimension-driven profile. For this exercise, you'll use the design file `jar1.dgn` in the `\Exercise\Ch09` folder on the CD-ROM. Copy this file on your computer's hard drive. Once copied, clear its read-only attribute. This is important. Otherwise, you won't be able to write to the file.

To complete this exercise, follow along with these steps:

1. Start MicroStation with a copy of the `jar1.dgn` file. The view window will come up empty, as this is a blank design file.

2. Use the Place Line and the Place Circle tools to create the sketch shown below in the center of view window 1. The dimensions and the exact alignment of the elements is not important for this exercise. As long as the sketch looks similar to that shown below, the geometry will serve its purpose.

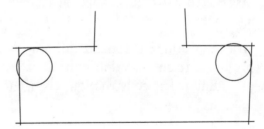

Use Place Line and Place Circle to create such a freehand sketch.

3. Use the Save As command from the File menu to save this file under the name `jar2.dgn` on your hard disk. You will convert this freehand sketch to constructions by applying geometric constraints in the next exercise.

Exercise: Apply Geometric Constraints

This exercise demonstrates the use of geometric constraints to establish relationships between constructions. For this exercise, you will use the design file `jar2.dgn` you saved in the previous exercise. If you didn't work through that exercise, you may copy it from the `\Exercise\Ch09` folder on the CD-ROM to your computer's hard drive. Once copied, clear its read-only attribute. This is important. Otherwise, you won't be able to write to the file.

To complete this exercise, follow along with these steps:

1. Start MicroStation with a copy of the design file `jar2.dgn`. It contains the freehand sketch you drew in the previous exercise.

2. Invoke the Smart Constrain Elements tool. In the Tool Settings window, select the last method: Fix Angle of Line or Ellipse, select Horizontal from the Angle Lock option button, and after clicking the Settings button, enable the Convert to Constructions checkbox and disable the Join Ends at Junctions checkbox. You are prompted to identify a line or ellipse.

3. Highlight and accept the line designated as **1** in the following figure. The line becomes horizontal, its color changes to yellow, its line style becomes dashed, and a geometric constraint symbol appears at its endpoint.

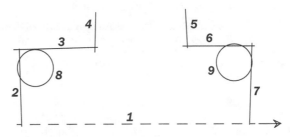

Constrain Line 1 to be horizontal.

4. With the Smart Constrain Elements tool still active, in the Tool Settings window select the method: Constrain Two Lines to be Perpendicular.

5. Identify line **1**, and it highlights. Then identify line **2**, and it highlights. Accept the selections with a data point. The line you identified second becomes perpendicular to the first and a geometric constraint symbol appears at the intersection of the two lines to designate perpendicularity.

6. With the Smart Constrain Elements tool still active, in the Tool Settings window select the method: Constrain Two Lines to be Parallel.

7. Identify line **3**, and it highlights. Then identify line **1**, and it highlights. Accept the selections with a data point. The line you identified first becomes parallel to the second, and a geometric constraint symbol appears at the endpoint of the line highlighted first.

8. Repeat steps 6 and 7 to make lines 4, 5, and 7 parallel to line 2.

9. With the Smart Constrain Elements tool still active, in the Tool Settings window select the method: Constrain Two Constructions to be Tangent. You want to make circle 8 tangential to lines 2 and 3.

10. Identify circle **8**, and it highlights. Then identify line **2**, and it highlights. Accept the selections with a data point. The circle moves to become tangential to the line and a geometric constraint symbol appears at the point of tangency.

11. Repeat steps 9 and 10 to make circle **8** tangent to line **3**, and circle **9** tangent to lines **6** and **7**.

12. The only element that doesn't have a geometric constraint is line 6. We could have made it parallel to line 1, as we did line 3. But this would mean that lines 3 and 6 could move independently of each other. Because the intent is that both lines stay colinear, we need to create points on each line that can be so constrained.

13. Invoke the Constrain Point at Intersection tool. Identify line **3**, then **2** and accept it. Then click Reset to create a point at their intersection. A geometric constraint symbol appears.

14. Repeat step 13 for creating a point at the intersection of lines 3 and 4, lines 5 and 6, and lines 6 and 7.

15. Invoke the Equate Constructions tool from the Geometric Constraints toolbox.

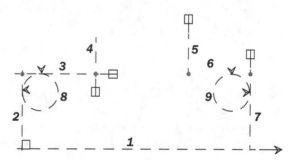

Constructions after all geometric constraints have been applied.

16. Identify lines 3 and 4 at locations close to their midpoints, and accept them with a data point. The lines are made colinear. Your screen should look similar to that shown above.

17. Use the Save As command from the File menu to save this file under the name `jar3.dgn` on your hard disk. Next, you'll determine its degrees of freedom and remove them to make it a well-constrained construction.

Exercise: Determining DOF

This exercise demonstrates the use of the Re-solve Constraints and Modify and Re-solve Constraints tools. For this exercise, you will use the design file `jar3.dgn` you saved in the previous exercise. If you did not do the exercise, you may copy the file from the `\Exercise\Ch09` folder on the CD-ROM. Once copied, clear its read-only attribute. This is important. Otherwise, you won't be able to write to the file.

To complete this exercise, follow along with these steps:

1. Start MicroStation with a copy of the design file `jar3.dgn`. It contains the geometrically constrained sketch you developed in the previous exercise.

2. Invoke the Re-solve Constraints tool from the Evaluate Constraints toolbox.

3. Identify any element on the construction and accept it.

4. The status bar reports DOF=8. This means that our construction can move in eight independent ways. It is your goal to remove these degrees of freedom.

Can you visualize the degrees of freedom? The next step identifies the tool you can use to help identify these independent movements.

5. Invoke the Modify and Re-solve Constraints tool. Identify line 1 (see the figure on the previous page) and move the cursor up and down. The construction line moves with it. This is the first DOF. Click Reset to leave the construction and its constraints undisturbed.

6. Identify line 2 and move the cursor sideways. This is the second DOF. Click Reset.

7. Similarly identify lines 3, 4, 5, and 7 to visualize four more degrees of freedom. Click Reset after each selection, as before.

8. Identify circle 8 and move the cursor. The changing radius is the seventh degree of freedom. Click Reset.

9. Similarly, the circle 9 radius represents the last degree of freedom. Click Reset.

Exercise: Making Construction Well-Constrained

As you've seen in the last exercise, your construction has eight degrees of freedom that must be removed to make it well-constrained. Having applied geometric constraints to all constructions, you must use the remaining constraint types: Locational, Dimensional, and Algebraic.

For this exercise, you'll use the design file jar3.dgn you saved in an earlier exercise. If you didn't do that exercise, you may copy to your hard drive the design file from the \Exercise\Ch09 folder on the CD-ROM. Once copied, clear its read-only attribute. This is important. Otherwise, you won't be able to write to the file.

To complete this exercise, follow these steps:

1. Start MicroStation with a copy of the design file jar3.dgn. It contains the geometrically constrained sketch you'd developed earlier. You will apply a locational constraint to anchor a point.

2. Invoke the Fix Point at Location tool from the Geometric Constraints toolbox. Identify the point at the intersection of lines 2 and 3, and accept it. Notice that the point and lines 2 and 3 turn white and the status bar displays the message that only 6 more degrees of freedom remain to be constrained. You will use dimensional constraints for these.

3. Invoke the Dimension Size with Arrow tool from the Dimension toolbox. In the Tool Settings window, select Drawing from the Alignment option button, and enable Association Lock. Snap to the endpoint of line 2 close to its intersection with line 1 and accept it with a data point. Click a data point directly below for the length of the extension line. Snap to the endpoint of line 7 close to its intersection with line 1 and accept it. Line 7 turns white and the status bar displays that DOFs are down to 5.

4. Continue using Dimension Size with Arrow to dimension the distance between lines 1 and 3 along line 2; the distance between lines 2 and 4 along line 3; the distance between lines 4 and 5 along the top. As you successively place these dimensions, a line turns white and a DOF reduces. After placing these three additional dimensions, the DOF should be down to 2. To complete the exercise, you'll need to constrain the diameter of the two circles.

5. Invoke the Dimension Radial tool from the Dimension toolbox. In the Tool Settings window, select Diameter for mode, Drawing for Alignment, and enable Association Lock. Snap to the circles and accept them in turn to place the dimension elements. Unlike the tool that dimensions linear distances, this tool doesn't recognize a construction element and must be manually converted to a dimensional constraint.

6. Invoke the Convert Dimension to Constraint tool from the Parameter Constraints toolbox. Identify the radial dimension for circle 8 and accept it. The Choose Parameter Name dialog box opens. Enter the letter **r** for the radial constraint variable name and click OK. The circle turns white and the parameter name appears under the dimension. One DOF is removed.

7. Repeat step 6 for the radial dimension for circle 9. In the Choose Parameter Name dialog box, double-click the previously entered constraint variable name **r** and click OK. The circle changes in size to match the size of circle 8 and turns white. The status bar displays DOF=0.

8. You now have a well-constrained construction—the goal when creating dimension-driven designs.

9. Use the Save As command from the File menu to save this file under the name `jar4.dgn` on your hard disk.

What you have created so far is a construction, or the skeleton for a profile. You must attach profile elements to this, as shown in the next exercise.

Exercise: Adding Profile Geometry to Constructions

A well-constrained construction is the foundation for a dimension-driven profile. In this exercise you will attach profile elements to the construction. Because element attachment tools only attach elements to points or constraints, you will need to create additional points on the construction.

For this exercise, you'll use the design file `jar4.dgn` you saved in the previous exercise. If you didn't do that exercise, you may copy to your hard drive the design file from the `\Exercise\Ch09` folder on the CD-ROM. Once copied, clear its read-only attribute. This is important. Otherwise, you won't be able to write to the file.

To complete this exercise, follow these steps:

1. Start MicroStation with a copy of the design file `jar4.dgn`. It contains the fully constrained construction you developed earlier. Before proceeding, let's create points at the ends of line 1 where it intersects lines 2 and 7.

2. Invoke the Constrain Point at Intersection tool. Identify line 1, then 2, and accept it. Click Reset to create a point at the intersection of lines 1 and 2.

3. Repeat step 2 for lines 1 and 7 to create another point.

4. Invoke the Attach Line String or Shape tool. Click the top tangent constraint for circle 8, then the top tangent constraint for circle 9, followed by a Reset to attach the first line.

5. Continue with the tool and attach a line string from the left tangent of circle 8 to the intersection point between lines 1 and 2, then to the intersection point between lines 1 and 7, then to the right tangent of circle 9. Click Reset to attach the second element, a line string. Your screen should look similar to the figure below.

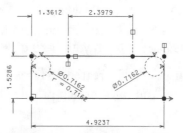

The construction after adding two profile elements.

6. Invoke the Attach Arc tool. Identify circle 8, then its top tangent constraint, followed by its left tangent constraint. An arc is attached to the construction.

7. Repeat step 6 to attach an arc to circle 9. Remember, angles are measured counterclockwise, so be sure to identify the right tangent constraint first, then the top tangent constraint. This completes the profile.

8. Use the Save As command from the File menu to save this file under the name `jar5.dgn` on your hard disk.

To vary the profile geometry, use the Modify Value of Dimension or Variable tool. Identify line 1's dimension and accept it. In the Tool Settings window, type 5 and press Enter. The profile changes. Try changing the radial dimension and see how both arcs update. To reuse DD geometry, add it to a cell library. This concludes the chapter.

Chapter 10

Linking Nongraphic Data to Elements

Tag Data and External Databases

You've probably heard the term *intelligent drawing*. It refers to an electronic model that incorporates nongraphic data. Many add-on applications that cater to specific engineering design tasks use nongraphic data links extensively. The data structure and its use is determined by the application or the MicroStation user.

The core data set stored in a design file describes geometric elements *graphically*. The data set consists of attributes that define an element's appearance (color, line style, line weight), shape, or size. This is *graphic data*, and you can't infer much more from it. *Nongraphic data*, on the other hand, is similar to a database. You can structure it for any purpose.

MicroStation has long supported the attachment of nongraphic data to its elements. You may attach nongraphic data as tags or external database links. Both are discussed in this chapter.

Facilities Management (FM) and Geographic Information Systems (GIS) are two prominent application examples that extend CAD to perform database-dependent queries. The former refers to the task of managing a building or industrial plant's various inventories, such as furniture and equipment, in a visual CAD environment. The latter refers to the task of managing inventories, such as underground utilities and land parcels, in a spatial, i.e., geographical context.

You don't, however, need these add-on applications to benefit from nongraphic data attributes. With a little planning, you can create applications that add *intelligence* (nongraphic data) to drawings. A few examples of what you might accomplish with these links are listed below:

- **Door and Window Schedules in Architectural Drawings:** You can attach nongraphic data, such as type, model number, color, and material, to each door and window as it is placed. Later, using MicroStation's tag reporting capability, you can create a tabular schedule including this information.

- **Furniture Inventory Management on Office Plan Drawings:** You can attach data, such as the user's name, room location, cost, and model number to every piece of furniture in an office layout drawing. This facilitates inventory management by keeping data next to its visual representation.

- **Drawing Management with Title Block Information:** You can use *tags*, defined later, when placing drawing information, such as project number, submittal date, and drawing type, in a title block. This data can be exported later to keep track of drawings.

The complexity of your needs will determine whether tags or external database links are more suitable for your project. Tags are simpler to set up and offer limited queries. They are also self-contained—no additional software is necessary. External database links use data from an external database. They are more difficult to set up, but offer powerful query capabilities you expect of databases.

If you haven't used nongraphic data linkages before, start with tags. Using them will help you learn their benefits. You might decide that they serve all your nongraphic data needs in MicroStation.

If you're an experienced database user and have data that adds value to drawings, you might skip tags and explore database links instead.

Working with Element Tags

In this section you learn how to create, manage, and use element tags. You learn about tags as members of tag sets, how to attach tags to elements, and how to write templates for tag reports. You also learn how to select elements based on tag values in a query.

A *tag* is a nongraphic data field you can attach to an element. You decide the name, content, and format for tags. They can be numeric or string—like database fields. MicroStation organizes tags into *tag sets*. Before you can create a tag, you must create a tag set.

If you're familiar with databases, think of a tag set as a database table; and of tags as data fields in the table. A tag can exist only in the context of a tag set. You can create multiple tag sets in a design file.

Let's learn how to create tags, also called *tag data*.

Exercise: Creating Tags

Before creating tags, you must define tag sets. You create tag sets by invoking the Tag Sets dialog box. From the Tags submenu on the Element menu, select Define. The Tag Sets dialog box opens, shown in the figure below.

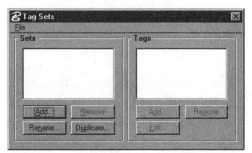

Select Tags, then Define, from the Element menu to open the Tag Sets dialog box.

To follow the steps explained below, you'll want to copy the file **tagoffc1.dgn** from the **\Exercise\ch10** folder on the CD-ROM to your hard disk. Once copied, remove its read-only attribute and change its name to **tagoffce.dgn**.

> **NOTE:** You may use another design file for this exercise. The file you use is not as important as understanding the tools.

Defining Tag Sets

In this exercise you are the facilities manager for an office building. The design file shows an office plan layout. It's your responsibility to maintain information about personnel and furniture. Therefore, you will create two tag sets: Personnel and Furniture.

To create the tag sets:

1. Open the Tag Sets dialog box, as shown above, from the Element menu. The dialog box has two sections: Sets and Tags, both empty. All buttons in the Tags section are disabled because no tag sets exist.
2. Click the Add button in the Sets section. The Tag Set Name dialog box opens.
3. Key in Personnel in the Name field, and click OK. The tag set appears in the list box.
4. Repeat steps 2 and 3 to create the Furniture tag set.

Adding Tags to Tag Sets

After defining tag sets, you can add tags. For Personnel, you need:

- *Name*: the last name and the first initial;
- *Room*: the room number assigned;
- *Phone*: the phone number.

For Furniture, you need:

- *Type*: whether table or chair;
- *Manufacturer*: who makes it;
- *Room*: the room number assigned;
- *Price*: the price.

All the above tags will be of the string type. The tag *price* will be an integer. Let's first define the Personnel tags:

5. Select Personnel in the Sets listbox and click the Add button in the Tags section. The Define Tag dialog box opens.

6. Key in `Name` in the Tag Name field and `Enter Name as: Last, F.I.` in the Prompt field. Select Character for Type, enable the Variable and Display Tag checkboxes. Leave the other checkboxes unchecked.

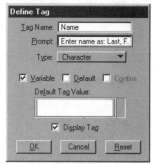

The Define Tag dialog box.

NOTE: Text in the Prompt field is optional and is used as a prompt in the Attach Tags dialog box when attaching tags. If you don't type a prompt, the default prompt *Value?* appears. The Type option button is used to define a data type: Character, Integer, or Real. Use the Display Tag checkbox to display or hide the tag value, once the tag's been attached to an element.

7. Click OK to add the tag.

8. Repeat steps 5 through 7 to add the Room and Phone tags. For the Room tag, in the Prompt field, enter `What's the Room No.?` and enable the Variable checkbox. Uncheck the Display Tag checkbox. For the Phone tag, in the Prompt field, enter `What's the Phone No.?` and enable the Variable checkbox. Uncheck the Display Tag checkbox.

To edit or remove an existing tag definition from a tag set, highlight the tag and click the appropriate button.

9. Select Furniture in the Sets listbox and click the Add button in the Tags section. The Define Tag dialog box opens.

10. Add the four tags, identified earlier, for the Furniture tag set. For the Type tag, in the Prompt field enter `Is it a table or chair?` and enable the Variable and Default checkboxes. In the Default Value field, type `table`. Uncheck the Display Tag checkbox.

11. For the Manufacturer tag, in the Prompt field enter `HON is authorized vendor!` and enable the Variable and Default checkboxes. In the Default Value field, type `HON`. Uncheck the Display Tag checkbox.

12. For the Room tag, in the Prompt field enter `What's the Room No.?` and enable the Variable checkbox. Uncheck the Display Tag checkbox.

13. For the Price tag, in the Prompt field enter `How much was paid?` and enable the Variable, Default, and Confirm checkboxes. Enter a value of 100 as the default. Uncheck the Display Tag checkbox.

The meanings of two checkboxes in the Define Tag dialog box may not have been very clear in the above exercise. The tag value in the Default Tag Value field isn't used until you enable the Default checkbox. When the Default checkbox is enabled, the Confirm checkbox becomes available. On attaching a tag that will use a default value, the Attach Tags dialog box doesn't open. To have the Attach Tags dialog box open, enable the Confirm checkbox.

The File menu in the Tag Sets dialog box provides access to *tag set libraries*. You can export tag sets to libraries, or import tag sets from them. Tag set libraries have the filename extension of `.tlb`. They let you share tag sets across design files. Tag sets can also be imported from or exported to an external database, if you've set one up.

This completes the tag definitions. Let's now attach them to graphical elements. Tags can be attached to any graphic element in a design file: line, cell, text, or other.

Exercise: Tagging Elements

Tools for attaching, editing, reviewing, and changing tags are located in the Tags toolbox, located in the Main tool frame.

Use these tools to attach tags to elements and to edit and review tag values.

The Tags tool box is shown in the figure below.

1. **Attach Tags**
2. **Edit Tags**

3. **Review Tags**
4. **Change Tags**

1 2 3 4

The Tags toolbox.

Tools in the Tags toolbox attach and manipulate tag values. To edit tag definitions, use the Tag Sets dialog box.

To follow the steps explained below, use the design file `tagoffce.dgn` you worked on in the previous exercise. If you didn't do that exercise, you may copy the design file `tagoffc2.dgn` to your hard disk from the `\Exercise\Ch10` folder on the CD-ROM. Once copied, remove its read-only attribute and change its name to `tagoffce.dgn`.

In this exercise you'll attach the Personnel tag set to each of the room number labels. Though all three tags in the tag set will be attached, only the name tag value will display. You might recall, while defining tags, we had unchecked the Display Tag checkbox for all tags, except Name.

To attach tags to room labels:

1. Invoke the Attach Tags tool. The Tool Settings window displays the furniture and personnel tag sets in a listbox. Highlight the personnel tag set, identify the room label 101, and accept it. The Attach Tags dialog box opens.

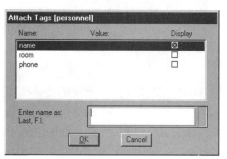

Use the Attach Tags dialog box to assign values to tags.

2. Highlight the Name tag and enter `smith, T` in the tag value field. Do not click OK yet. Highlight the Room tag and enter `101` in the tag value field. Similarly, assign the value `x 31` to the Phone tag.

3. Click OK. The displayable tag value attaches to the cursor.

4. Click a location in the room for the tag value. The tag is attached to the element. The Attach Tags command restarts.

5. With the Personnel tag set still highlighted, identify the room label 102 and accept it. The Attach Tags dialog box appears.

6. In the dialog box, highlight the Name tag and enter Dyke, V in the tag value field. Similarly, assign the values 102, and x 32 to the Room and Phone tags.

7. Click OK. The displayable tag value attaches to the cursor.

8. Click a location in the room for the tag value. The tag is attached to the element. The Attach Tags command restarts.

9. Repeat steps 5 through 8 for room labels 103 to 112 in the office layout drawing. Use any name and phone number as values for the tags.

10. Repeat the exercise for all tables in rooms 101 to 112. Notice that values for only the room tag in the furniture tag set are empty. All other tags have a default value. You need only enter a room number for each table. This speeds up data entry for the furniture tag set.

Displayable tags appear as text elements on the screen. However, you can't use the Edit Text tool to change their value. Use the Edit Tag tool instead.

You can use the Move Element tool to change the location of a displayable tag. When you move the location of tag values, the elements they are attached to remain in their original position. However, when you move an element with a tag, the tag moves to maintain the relative position to the element. Note that if you copy an element that has a tag attached, the tag is copied. If you delete an element with an attached tag, the tag is deleted as well.

Editing and Reviewing Tags

The Edit Tags and Review Tags tools allow you to edit and review tags that have already been attached to elements. After activating the tool, identify an element with tags. A dialog box opens to display the list of attached tags in the tag set.

The Edit Tags dialog box is shown in the figure below.

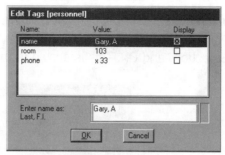

The Edit Tags dialog box.

NOTE: A tag can be attached only once to an element. If you try to attach the same tag set, MicroStation will refuse to highlight the element.

To delete a tag attached to an element, simply remove it with the Delete Element tool.

To remove a tag set definition along with all instances of its tags from a design file, in the Tag Sets dialog box, highlight the tag set and click the Remove button. An Alert dialog box opens. Click the OK button to confirm the deletion.

Exercise: Using Tag Values to Select Elements

One of the benefits of attaching tags to elements is that you can use tag values to select elements for manipulation.

To follow the steps below, use the design file `tagoffce.dgn` you worked on, in the previous exercise. If you didn't do that exercise, you may copy the design file `tagoffc3.dgn` to your hard disk from the `\Exercise\Ch10` folder on the CD-ROM. Once copied, remove its read-only attribute and change its name to `tagoffce.dgn`.

In this exercise you'll use the Select By Attributes dialog box to select tables in rooms along the south wing of the building. As you might see in the design file, the room numbers assigned to these rooms are greater than 106. The query you execute on tags will use this expression.

To select all tables in rooms along the south building wing:

1. Invoke the Select By Attributes dialog box from the Edit menu.
2. Verify that the option buttons in the Mode section are set to Inclusive, Selection, and On. This is shown in the figure below.

3. Click the Tags button. The Select By Tags dialog box opens.
4. Select *furniture.room* in the Tags field and *greater than* in the Operator field. Type 106 in the Expression field.
5. Click the Insert button to make the criteria active, as shown in the figure below. You may now close the Select By Tags dialog box.

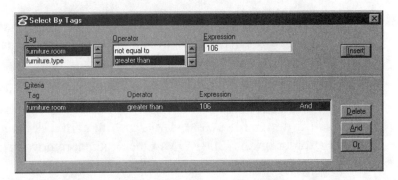

6. Click the Execute button on the Select By Attributes dialog box. All tables in rooms along the south wing of the building are selected.

Once elements are selected, you can manipulate them in any way, as you would a selection set.

Creating Tag Reports

In addition to selecting elements based on tag values, you can generate reports that include tag data. Creating reports requires two steps. First, you define a report template. Next, you initiate report extraction. Both tasks are accomplished from the Tags submenu on the Element menu.

Defining a Template

To define a template for use by the tag report generator, select Generate Templates from the Edit menu's Tags submenu. The Generate Templates dialog box opens, as shown below.

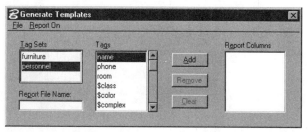

In the Generate Templates dialog box, select tags to include in report.

The Generate Templates dialog box provides a point-and-click interface for selecting tags to include in a report. Select a tag set, its tags appear in the Tags list box. Select the desired tag, and click Add to include the tag as a column heading in the report.

The Report On menu option in the dialog box offers two choices: Tagged Elements, or All Elements. Make the appropriate choice. After you've selected the tags desired, enter a name for the report file to be generated in the Report File Name field. Then select Save As from the File menu on the dialog box. The Save Template As dialog box opens.

Use the .tmp filename extension for template files. MicroStation looks for this extension when generating reports. Generated report files use the .rpt filename extension as a default.

The `c:\Bentley\Workspace\Projects\Examples\Generic\Out` folder is used to save template and report files for the default workspace. You can create as many template files as you wish. Template files are used by the Generate Reports dialog box, discussed next.

Generating a Report

To generate reports, select Generate Reports from the Element menu's Tags submenu. The Generate Reports dialog box opens, as shown below.

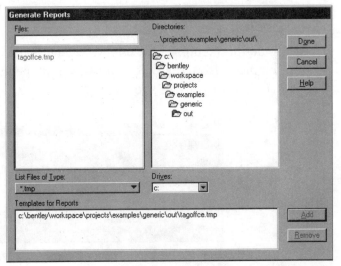

In the Generate Reports dialog box, add the templates to process.

Template files you created earlier are used as input in this dialog box. Select the template to process, and click the Add button. The template is added to the Templates for Reports listbox. You can process more than one template at a time. The name of the generated report file was specified on the Report File Name field of the Generate Templates dialog box.

After selecting the templates to process, click the Done button. This initiates report generation. When reports are generated, the dialog box closes. If you selected multiple templates, each report is saved in its own report file. Reports are saved in a comma-delimited ASCII file format. This format is compatible with most spreadsheet and database programs, where it can be further processed, if needed.

Report files can also be imported in MicroStation as text. From the Import submenu on the File menu, select Text to open the Include Text File dialog box. Locate the report file and click OK to import the text as a multi-line text element.

You can also use the *Table* macro to import the text in a tabular format. The report file may have to be edited in format to make it compatible with the Table macro. Select Macros from the Utilities menu. The Macros dialog box opens. Scroll until the Table macro appears. Highlight it and click Run. The Table Input File dialog box opens. Locate the report file, specify table symbology options, and click OK to place it in the design file.

In summary, element data tagging imparts intelligence to your drawings. It offers query and reporting capabilities that extend your model's usefulness. You can select elements based on their tag attribute values, and you can also generate useful reports.

Working with Databases

Earlier, you learned how to link nongraphic data tags to elements, and how to use their values to select elements. Tags and graphic elements are both stored in a design file. No additional files are needed when sharing files with others. Tags, however, have limited query capabilities. The operators supported in the Select By Tags dialog box are simple.

If your nongraphic data application needs are more sophisticated, you'll want to explore MicroStation's ability to link with external databases. Imagine being able to highlight elements based on information stored in external relational database software containing construction, schedule, maintenance, or manufacturer data.

Relational database principles will not be taught here. It's assumed you are familiar with databases. In the remainder of this chapter, you'll learn how to:

- configure a database for use in MicroStation.
- link graphical elements to external database records.
- display and edit database records from within MicroStation.

Though database software will let you harness the full power of external database links, if you don't have database software, you can still use external database links. MicroStation includes interfaces that let you work with several external database file formats and create files for them. You can also add to and edit records in those files. Of course, having database simplifies these tasks. A Microsoft Access database is used as an example in what follows.

The power of relational databases lies in their ability to relate information between different tables through a common field. For example, a table with information about street lights in a county can be related to a vendor table through a common vendor ID field to track warranties. The key is to minimize data redundancy by normalizing table structure.

To provide access to data in a vendor-neutral environment, Microsoft developed the ODBC (Open DataBase Connectivity) interface that uses a language based on the SQL standard. Depending on the format of the database file you wish to access, you configure its ODBC driver. Though there are other ways to interface with external databases, in the Windows world, ODBC is a standard. It will be our focus in the remainder of this chapter.

Support for external databases is optional. If you selected a typical installation, database support wasn't installed. See the *Installing MicroStation* section in chapter 1 for screenshots of dialog boxes and the checkboxes you must enable to install database drivers.

If the folder `c:\Bentley\Program\MicroStation\Database` on your computer is empty, database support was not installed. To install it, rerun the Setup program and enable the Databases checkbox in the MicroStation/J Installation dialog box.

Database Configuration

The folder `c:\Bentley\Program\MicroStation\Config\Database` contains several `.cfg` files that configure MicroStation to use databases. These are ASCII files you can examine in a text editor. From the Workspace menu, select Configuration to open the Configuration dialog box. Select Database from the Category list in the dialog box. The list of configuration variables related to database support displays on the right. For ODBC support, the variable MS_SERVER is assigned a value *odblddlm*, and the variable MS_LINKTYPE is assigned a value of *ODBC*.

A database you wish to connect to from MicroStation must include a table with the name MSCATALOG. This table is a catalog of database tables. It includes a row for each table you intend to access. The structure of the table, from the file `mscat.sql` delivered with MicroStation, is listed below.

```
create table mscatalog

    (

    tablename char(32) not null,

    entitynum int not null,

    screenform char(64) null,

    reporttable char(32) null,

    dastable char(32) null,

    sqlreview char(240) null,

    fencefilter char(240) null,

    formtable char(64) null

    )

create unique index mscat_entitynum on mscatalog (entitynum)

go
```

This is an SQL command file you can run in the SQL Window that opens when you enter SQL in the Key-in window. This command file creates the *mscatalog* table with the various columns it must include. Of all the fields in this table, the two that must be filled with values are *tablename* and *entitynum*. The former is the name of the table in the database MicroStation will access. The latter is a unique integer you assign to the table.

The first requirement to configuring a database for access from MicroStation is that the database contain the *mscatalog* table with fields as listed earlier. The second requirement is that the database table you will access include the *mslink* (type integer) field with unique values for each record.

When you use its database tools, MicroStation attaches *entitynum* and *mslink* values to elements. By looking up the *tablename* value corresponding to *entitynum* in *mscatalog*, MicroStation knows the table an element is linked to. By looking up the *mslink* value, MicroStation knows the record in the table the element needs to link to.

Exercise: Creating ODBC System DSN for Database

Included on the CD-ROM is the database file `tymsj.mdb` in the `\Exercise\Ch10` folder. It was created in Microsoft Access 97 and contains several tables, including the mandatory *mscatalog* table. Open it in Microsoft Access and examine the structure of the tables it contains. As you'll notice, it recreates data from the tag data exercises you worked on earlier. Copy the database file to your computer's hard disk. Also copy the `dboffice.dgn` file from the CD-ROM to the same folder.

To make the database visible in MicroStation, you must configure it.

To create a system DSN:

1. Double-click the ODBC icon in the Windows Control Panel. The ODBC Data Source Administrator opens. The User DSN tab is active because it's the default.
2. Click the System DSN tab to activate it.
   The acronym DSN stands for Data Source Name. A user DSN is only visible to the user creating it. A system DSN, is visible to all users of that computer. You'll set up the database as a system DSN.
3. Click the Add button, the Create New Data Source dialog box opens. Select Microsoft Access Driver in the listbox and click the Finish Button. The ODBC Microsoft Access 97 Setup dialog box opens, as shown below.

Enter data in the dialog box and click OK to create a system DSN.

4. In the Data Source Name field, enter `TYMSJ`. In the Description field, enter `Chapter 10 exercise`. Click the Select button and navigate to locate the `tymsj.mdb` file you copied from the CD-ROM. Click OK to close the file navigation dialog box. The filename appears above the Select button.

5. Click OK to close the ODBC Microsoft Access 97 Setup dialog box. The system DSN is added to the ODBC Data Source Administrator dialog box. It can now be used in MicroStation. You may now close this dialog box and the Control Panel.

Once a properly structured database is made available as a system DSN, its records can be linked to MicroStation elements.

To use the database in MicroStation, you must connect to it. Start MicroStation. From its Settings menu, select Database, then Connect to open the Connect to Database dialog box, shown below.

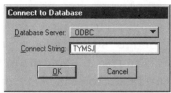

Select ODBC for server, and enter TYMSJ as connect string to connect to the system DSN declared earlier.

Enter information as shown in the figure below and click the OK button. MicroStation connects to the database and the status bar displays the message *Database: TYMSJ*.

Linking Records to Elements

Linking records in a database to MicroStation elements is a two-step process. First, you make the desired record active, and then you invoke the Attach Active Entity tool. When you make a database record active, MicroStation creates a temporary *active entity* table in memory. This table contains a copy of the active database record. When you attach the record to an element, the active entity table is cleared.

Before we attach database records to elements, let's familiarize ourselves with some of MicroStation's database-related dialog boxes.

From the Settings menu, select Database, then Setup. The MSCATALOG dialog box opens. This dialog box displays seven data fields where you can enter information, as shown in the figure below.

This dialog box lets you manage the mscatalog *table in MicroStation.*

Instead of managing the *mscatalog* table in the database software, such as Microsoft Access, you can use this dialog box to maintain names of tables you need to attach to elements. The data fields in this dialog box correspond to the field names listed in the `mscat.sql` SQL command file listed earlier. Use its Table menu to add or delete existing tables from the *mscatalog* table. You can also create new tables from this menu.

From the Settings menu, select Database, then Dialog to open the Database dialog box, shown below. This dialog box controls the database linkage mode and a few other parameters.

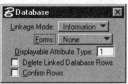

Use this dialog box to control database linkage mode.

The following table explains the four linkage modes available.

Linkage Mode	Description
None	In this mode, no records can be linked to elements.
New	In this mode, the active entity is appended as a new row in the table with a new *mslink* value. Use it to ensure every link to an element has a unique row in the database.

Linkage Mode	Description
Duplicate	In this mode, the active entity is linked to the element. No new records are created in the table. Many elements can be linked to the same active entity.
Information	This mode is identical to the Duplicate mode except that a special flag is saved with the link. Add-on applications can use this flag while processing linkages.

The Forms option button in the Database dialog box should remain None. This causes the SQL Window to open to display database records when you query linkages. If you create screen forms in a database table language, you can select Text Screen to use that form instead. MicroStation determines the name of the form to use from the *mscatalog* table.

The design file `dboffice.dgn` on the CD-ROM in the `\Exercise\Ch10` folder contains links to records in the *rooms* table contained in the `tymsj.mdb` database in the same folder. Feel free to copy it to your computer's hard drive and work with it. Because creating links can be a little tedious, I've already created them. However, you may wish to delete all links and recreate them. To delete links, use the Detach Database Linkage tool from the Database toolbox accessed from the Tools menu. Identify each room label in the design file and accept it to delete links.

To create links:

1. Start MicroStation with a copy of the `dboffice.dgn` file.
2. Connect to the TYMSJ database. This can be done from the Connect to Database dialog box, as discussed earlier.
3. Set the linkage mode to Information in the Database dialog box. This was discussed earlier. You don't want new records created for each link.
4. Make the record with `room_id=101` in the *rooms* table active. Do this by typing `fi=select * from rooms where room_id = '101'` in the Key-in window. This key-in is patterned after the SQL database language. It finds the record and makes it active. The status bar displays the message *Database operation complete*.
5. (This step is optional.) In the Key-in window, type `ae=$`. The SQL Window opens to display the contents of the active database record.

6. Invoke the Attach Active Entity tool from the Database toolbox accessed from the Tools menu. You are prompted to identify an element to link the record to. Select the text label for room 101.

7. Repeat steps 4 through 6 for each of the remaining `room_ids`, attaching them to corresponding room labels in the design file.

Displaying Linked Records

You can display the contents of records attached to elements by using the Review Database Attributes of Element tool from the Database toolbox. On activating the tool, you are prompted to identify an element. When you accept an element that has an attached link, the SQL Window opens to display the record.

To display and check all the database links in the design file, you can use the *dbcheck* utility. In the Key-in window, type MDL LOAD DBCHECK. The Database Verification Utility dialog box opens. Review the checkboxes, and change them if desired. Click the Go button. An Alert box opens asking if you wish to view the text file. Click the OK button. The text file is displayed on screen, as shown in the figure below.

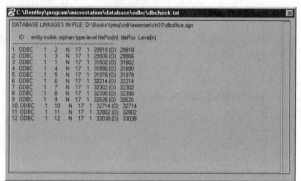

Report generated by the dbcheck *utility.*

If the dbcheck utility is already loaded, but its dialog box is closed, you can reopen it by typing DBCHECK in the Key-in window.

This concludes our introduction to database links in MicroStation. I hope you feel more comfortable with database links and will be able to tackle more advanced texts you encounter on the topic.

Chapter 11

3D Modeling and Rendering

Visualizing Concepts through Modeling

The rendered image on this book's cover depicts a three-dimensional (3D) model of downtown Philadelphia. Bentley helped develop the model in MicroStation. The rich details captured in the image showcase the power and flexibility MicroStation offers when it comes to three-dimensional modeling and rendering.

The tools and techniques implemented in MicroStation for this purpose are varied, and deserve a book of their own. I can't hope to teach everything there is to know about them in a chapter. However, I do have room to introduce the fundamental concepts and tools you need to know as you venture into 3D modeling.

After you read this chapter, you will have learned how to create basic 3D models, assign material to their surfaces, and how to render them for creating photo-realistic images.

The differences between 2D and 3D modeling are best explained by comparing a drawing created on the drafting table to a clay model you might sculpt to represent an object. A 2D modeling environment, just like a paper drawing, requires multiple views of an object, such as plan, side, and elevation, to describe its many facets. A 3D modeling environment, on the other hand, captures the object's many facets by using basic building blocks that have depth—the third dimension.

Because the computer screen you view a 3D model on has a 2D surface, acquiring 3D computer modeling skills takes some effort. Unlike the sculptor who can reach out to any part of the model to mold it, you must become comfortable with concepts of active depth and multiple views to model successfully in 3D.

As you venture into the world of three-dimensional modeling, be prepared for moments of frustration when you can't seem to draw an object that seems easy. 3D modeling is inherently more difficult. With practice, you'll surely master it.

Following is a series of models many of you gave me to include in this book as examples of your 3D modeling work in MicroStation. Credits for images are noted in their captions. To contribute examples to showcase in future editions of this book, I invite you to e-mail me. You'll find my e-mail address in the *Acknowledgments* section of the book, just before the *Contents*.

A plug valve. (Courtesy of CH2M Hill, Inc.)

Section through a proposed wastewater treatment facility building.
(Courtesy of CH2M Hill, Inc.)

The two models from CH2M Hill, Inc., an international engineering firm, are drawn from their environmental projects related to the design of wastewater treatment facilities. They have an industrial look, governed strictly by functional and engineering needs. The next was created for fun by Charles Wood of HLM Design, who loves fast cars!

Rendered model of the Nebula GNX car. (Courtesy of Charles Wood. Logo on wheels used with permission of The Goodyear Tire & Rubber Company.)

White Flint Place. (Courtesy of HLM Design.)

This image from HLM Design, an architectural firm that also creates 3D computer models, shows the level of aesthetic detail you can add to make models more lifelike.

Obviously, the images showcased on these pages took effort to create and to render. All the tools to create such masterpieces are available to you in MicroStation.

Information in this chapter is organized as follows:

- **Understanding the 3D Environment** discusses coordinate axes, use of views, active depth, display depth, and other concepts.

- **Basic 3D Modeling** discusses the various ways in which you can create 3D elements. It also demonstrates several modeling tools.

- **Introduction to Rendering** discusses basic lighting and material assignment issues. It also demonstrates rendering tools.

Understanding the 3D Environment

When you create design files, MicroStation requires a seed file as a basis for the new file. Files you created in earlier chapters were 2D because they used a 2D seed file such as SEED2D.DGN, that is delivered with MicroStation. To create 3D files, you must choose a 3D seed file.

To create a new 3D design file, select New from the File menu. The Create Design File dialog box opens, as shown in the figure below. Check the name of the seed file along the bottom of the dialog box. If it's not 3D, click the Select button and pick one. Type a name for the new design file, and click the OK button to create it.

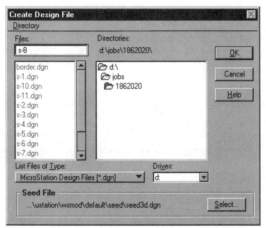

Specify a 3D seed file when creating new 3D design files.

In chapter 3 you were introduced to the MicroStation design plane, a square of over 4 billion positional units along each side. In 3D, it's called a design cube. MicroStation's 3D modeling environment is defined in terms of standard cartesian coordinate axes: X, Y, and Z. Each side of the cube is over 4 billion positional units long.

In 2D, you can only draw on one plane—the design plane. You define coordinates in terms of X and Y axes. Z coordinate values are assumed zero for all points. When you display the design file on the screen, no matter how you rotate the view, its Z-axis is always perpendicular to the monitor plane, with the positive Z direction coming from the screen toward you.

In 3D, you can draw on six planes—the surfaces of the design cube, as shown in the figure below.

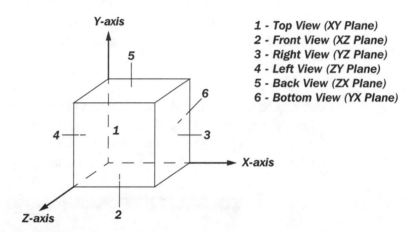

1 - Top View (XY Plane)
2 - Front View (XZ Plane)
3 - Right View (YZ Plane)
4 - Left View (ZY Plane)
5 - Back View (ZX Plane)
6 - Bottom View (YX Plane)

The design cube's six faces, and their relationship to the X, Y, and Z axes.

The default view in 3D is the *top view*, and its positive Z direction points toward you as you stare at the screen. The plane of the monitor is referred to as the *view plane*. If you think of all drawing plane rotations in reference to the view plane, it'll help keep your bearings straight.

A 2D drawing plane is always parallel to the view plane, with the positive Z-axis pointing toward you. When you orient the top view in a 3D model to be parallel to the view plane, the direction of its positive Z-axis also points toward you as you stare at the screen. This is why the default 3D view is the top view.

As you rotate a view, the design plane and element coordinates remain invariant—they are measured from the design cube's origin. It's the position of the model that moves with respect to your screen—the view plane.

View rotation in 2D design files is simple because rotation can only take place about the Z-axis. In 3D design files, things get more complicated. Views may be rotated about any of the three axes. With all the rotations possible, it's easy to lose track of the positive directions of the various axes. MicroStation adheres to the same *right-hand rule* you may have learned in your coordinate geometry class.

Hold your right hand in front, palm facing you, and the thumb pointing to the right. Extend the forefinger to point upward, and turn the three remaining fingers toward you, as shown in the figure below.

The right-hand rule for coordinate axis orientation.

When positioned this way, the thumb points in the positive X-axis direction, the forefinger points in the positive Y-axis direction, and the remaining fingers point in the positive Z-axis direction.

To determine the positive direction of rotation for an axis, again, use your right hand. Hold your right hand such that its thumb points toward the positive direction of an axis. The direction of curl of your fingers determine the positive direction of rotation for that axis.

Let's see how this rule applies to angular rotations in 2D design files. As you've learned, the positive direction of the Z-axis comes toward you from the screen. If you point your right hand thumb toward you, the curl of the fingers—counterclockwise—determines the positive direction of rotation. That's why MicroStation measures angles counterclockwise.

Using Views in 3D

In chapter 4, you learned how to use multiple views to simplify tasks that span great distances. Use of multiple views is far more important in 3D modeling than it is in 2D. By keeping the top, front, and side views open concurrently, you can more easily visualize your models as you create them. Experienced 3D modelers routinely open multiple views that show different parts of their model.

If you find working with multiple views confusing, and wish to minimize the number of views you keep open, at least open two adjacent views. What are adjacent views? *Adjacent views* are perpendicular to each other. If you're working in the Top view, the four adjacent views would be Left, Right, Front, and Back. By keeping any of these views open, in addition to the top view you're working in, you'll find it easier to specify a value for depth.

Rotating Views

To help you orient views, MicroStation includes the six design cube planes and isometric views as standard views. Click the Rotate View icon on the View Control Bar, while in a 3D design file. The Tool Settings window displays the following methods:

- Dynamic
- 3 Points
- Top
- Front
- Right
- Isometric
- Bottom
- Back
- Left
- Right Isometric

Selecting any of the last eight choices rotates the view to correspond to that standard view. Refer to the figure that shows a design cube's six faces for the orientation of the standard views.

To rotate a view dynamically, select the Dynamic option and enable the Dynamic Display checkbox. Click a data point. As you move the cursor, the view will rotate depending on the cursor's position relative to the data point clicked.

Each view window on your screen can be rotated independently. Click the Rotate View icon in the view's window to manipulate its view orientation. Alternatively, you can use the **VI=** key-in to rotate a view to assume one of the standard orientations. For example, to rotate a view to the standard top view orientation, in the Key-in window, type **VI=TOP** and click a data point in the view.

MicroStation provides one other way to rotate its views: the View Rotation dialog box. This dialog box is accessed from the 3D View Control toolbox. From the Tools menu, select View Control, then 3D. The 3D View Control toolbox opens. On this toolbox, click the Change View Rotation icon. The View Rotation dialog box opens, as shown in the figure below.

The 3D View Control toolbox is used to open the View Rotation dialog box.

To rotate a view with this dialog box, click next to the axis you wish to rotate in the right half of the dialog box. The left side displays the design cube rotation. You can rotate the cube along any of the axes. Once you've rotated the cube in the dialog box as necessary, select the view number to rotate, and click the Apply button. The selected view rotates.

Notice the option button labeled Axis in the dialog box. It offers two choices: View and Drawing. When View is selected, the cube in the left half of the dialog box rotates around the view axes. Thus, if you click the Z-axis in the right half of the dialog box, the cube rotates about the axis that pierces the screen. When Drawing is selected, the cube rotates about the drawing axes. Thus, if you click the Z-axis in the right half of the dialog box, the cube rotates about the axis that pierces its Top plane— the drawing's Z-axis, regardless of how the view is rotated.

The Active Depth

When you click a data point in a 3D design file, it's placed on a plane parallel to the screen, also called the *view plane*. The location of the data point with respect to the axis passing through the design plane's origin and perpendicular to the view plane, is determined by the *active depth* value.

If you click a data point in the top view, and the active depth is 4, the data point is located in a plane parallel to the top view located 4 units away from the design plane origin along the drawing's positive Z-axis. Similarly, if the data point were clicked in the front view, it would be placed on a plane parallel to the front view located 4 units away from the design plane origin along the drawing's positive Y-axis.

If the above paragraph sounds confusing, you'll find it helpful to refer to an earlier figure that shows the design cube's six faces and their associated axes.

To set a view's active depth:

1. Open the 3D View Control toolbox. Select View Control, then 3D from the Tools menu.
2. Activate the Set Active Depth tool by clicking its icon on the 3D View Control toolbox. You are prompted to select a view.
3. Identify the view where you wish to set the active depth for by clicking a data point in it. You are prompted to enter an active depth point.
4. Move the cursor to an adjacent view so you can specify a depth. A plane parallel to the view identified earlier attaches to the cursor and moves with it.
5. Click a data point at the desired depth, or use a precision key-in. The active depth for the view is set.

To complement the Set Active Depth tool, MicroStation provides the Display Active Depth tool. This tool is also located on the 3D View Control toolbox. On activating the tool, you are prompted to identify a view. Click a data point in a view, and its active depth value is displayed on the Status Bar.

Exercise: Understanding Active Depth

The concept of active depth is fundamental to understanding where MicroStation places elements when you click data points in a view. In this exercise, you'll set the active depth of a view. Then, you'll invoke an element placement tool to see how active depth affects the tool.

Copy to your computer's hard disk, the 3D design file cube.dgn, included on the CD-ROM in the \Exercise\Ch11 folder. Files copied from a CD-ROM retain their read-only status. Because you'll be writing to this file, after copying, clear its read-only attribute.

Use the following steps for this exercise:

1. Start MicroStation with the design file cube.dgn. An annotated cube displays in four views on the screen.
2. Activate the Set Active Depth tool from the 3D View Control toolbox. You're prompted to select a view.
3. Click a data point in window 3, the front view. Then, move the cursor to an adjacent view: window 4, the right view. A plane attaches to and moves with the cursor. The moving plane can be seen more clearly in the isometric view, as shown in the figure below.

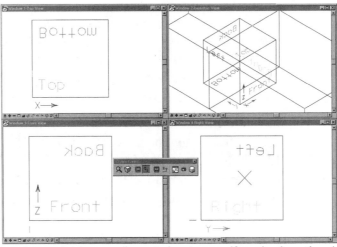

Click a data point in an adjacent view to specify a view's active depth.

4. In the status bar, MicroStation prompts you to enter an active depth point. Click when the cursor in the right view is on the right edge of the square.

5. The active depth for the front view is set so that data points in the view will lie on the back plane of the cube. To see for yourself the validity of this statement, activate the Place Circle tool and select Center for method in the Tool Settings window. You're prompted to identify a center point.

6. Click in the front view close to the center of the square, and watch the isometric view as you move the cursor. The circle is drawn on the back plane of the cube. It appears as a line in the top and right views, and as an oval in the isometric view.

7. Place a circle in the isometric view. Note that it appears as a circle in the isometric view, and as identical ovals in the other three views. This is because an isometric view has the same 60° orientation to other views.

NOTE: You can use the AZ= key-in to set the active depth instead of the Set Active Depth tool. The active depth value you specify is measured from the design file's global origin.

The Display Depth

MicroStation's standard views are orthogonal; they have no perception of depth. For example, when you draw a line in the top view, it looks identical, no matter what its distance along the view's Z-axis. Consequently, it becomes difficult to distinguish between elements on the top face from those on the bottom face.

To help you focus on elements within a depth range, MicroStation implements *display depth*. When you define the display depth for a view, you are telling MicroStation to hide from view any elements that lie outside the range specified.

So, if your model spans between 10 and 15 meters along an axis, and you wish to focus only on elements that are within 0.5 meter of its center (12.5 along the axis), you'd specify the display depth to lie between 12.25 and 12.75 meters. Only elements that lie within this range will display, and others will be out of range for all element manipulation and modification tasks.

To set a view's display depth:

1. Open the 3D View Control toolbox by selecting View Control, then 3D from the Tools menu.

2. Activate the Set Display Depth tool. To do this, click its icon on the 3D View Control toolbox. You are prompted to select a view.

3. Identify the view where you wish to set the display depth for by clicking a data point in it. You are prompted to define the front clipping plane.

4. Move the cursor to an adjacent view so you can specify a depth. A plane parallel to the view identified earlier attaches to the cursor and moves with it. Click a data point to define the starting point for the display depth. You are prompted to define the back clipping plane.

5. Click a data point at the ending point along the view axis for the display depth. The display depth is set for the view.

To complement the Set Display Depth tool, MicroStation provides the Show Display Depth tool, also located on the 3D View Control toolbox. On activating the tool, you are prompted to identify a view. Click a data point in a view, and its display depth is displayed on the Status Bar. The display depth is a pair of numbers (minimum, maximum) separated by a comma.

NOTE: You can use the DP= key-in to set the display depth instead of the Set Display Depth tool. The display depth value pair is specified with a comma separating them. For example, the key-in DP=-50,50 will apply a display depth from -50 to 50 to the view you identify. Yet another display depth key-in is DD=. It stands for delta depth and adds the specified depth values to the existing values.

It's important to remember that the display depth clipping planes are parallel to the view plane. It's possible to set the display depth in an isometric view so that only the corners of a model display! Try it in the cube.dgn file you worked on earlier. Set the display depth in the isometric view.

While you're learning how to create 3D models, you'll want to do all element placement in the standard views. It's best to use the isometric view for visualizing the model as it takes shape. Additionally, using AccuDraw will help you bypass MicroStation's default view plane and active depth behavior.

Using Fence and Boresite Lock

Using a fence in 3D is no different than using one in 2D. However, there's one significant difference. The elements a fence processes depend on the view's display depth. When a fence is active, only the elements you can see are processed. If the display depth is set so that only a part of the model is visible, fence manipulation commands will only process the part that's visible.

As you learned, clicking a data point in a view places it on a plane parallel to the view plane, at a location defined by the active depth. The active depth affects data points used for element placement. However, when you edit or manipulate elements, a data point can identify elements at any depth. This is controlled by the *boresite lock*.

As a default, the boresite lock is enabled, allowing element editing commands to *bore* through any depth. To restrict element identification to active depth, turn boresite off in the Locks menu, accessed by clicking the lock icon on the status bar.

If you wish to restrict element identification to elements located at the active depth from the view plane, you must disable the boresite lock. When the boresite lock is off, and you click elements visible in a view, only those at the active depth will highlight.

Do take note that this behavior differs from that exhibited by fence commands that process all visible elements.

Fit View Changes Clipping Planes

Working in 3D can be a challenge, especially for beginners. If you have modified the active and display depths in so that you're lost, Fit View come to the rescue.

The Fit View tool determines the limits of the model and extends the clipping planes in all directions to match them. The entire model becomes visible. Also, it sets the active depth to the center of the display depth.

Tentative Points and AccuDraw Override Active Depth

When you click data points in a 3D design file, they are placed at the active depth. However, when you snap to elements by clicking the tentative button and accept its location with a data point, the active depth is ignored. The data point is placed at the location snapped.

You learned earlier that data points fall on a plane parallel to the view plane at a location determined by the view's active depth. This maxim doesn't hold true when you use AccuDraw. The drawing plane indicator in AccuDraw, which you can rotate at will, determines the plane for data points, regardless of the view you click in.

Your facility in using AccuDraw can help you place data points where you need to, regardless of the view or the active depth. This is a significant issue. Examine the screenshot below.

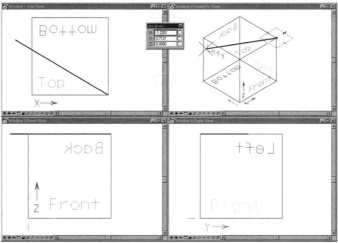

AccuDraw is shown constraining the cursor to the top plane in the isometric view.

After activating AccuDraw, the starting point of a line was located by snapping to the top right corner of the cube in the isometric view. The AccuDraw compass appeared, with the drawing plane parallel to the view plane. Pressing the letter т rotated the drawing plane indicator to align with the drawing's top plane. All cursor movements in the isometric view are now constrained to the top plane, as is evident by looking at the three other views.

Because an isometric view shows several planes of a model, it is commonly left open on the screen. However, the view is rarely used to place elements, as data points are typically needed along cube planes. With the help of AccuDraw, you can release the cursor from the view plane and create complete models in isometric view.

In addition to tentative points and AccuDraw, MicroStation provides one more means to release the cursor from the active depth when placing points. This is implemented as 3D tentative and data point clicks.

The *3D data point* is accessed by clicking the data point button while holding the Alt key down. The *3D tentative point* is accessed by clicking the tentative button while holding the Alt key down.

On clicking a 3D tentative or data point, a dashed line, called the *bore line*, appears in adjacent views. You then move the cursor to an adjacent view and identify the location along the bore line with another 3D tentative or data point.

Basic 3D Modeling

The previous pages introduced you to the terminology and concepts used when creating 3D models in MicroStation. This section completes the rest of the picture. Here, you're introduced to the various element placement techniques used in modeling. Information on the following pages is organized as shown below.

- **Placing and Projecting Planar Elements** discusses the use of familiar 2D tools, such as Place Line and Place Circle, in a 3D environment. Its focus is on showing how to extrude and rotate planar elements, called profiles, along an axis or center of rotation to create 3D surfaces.
- **3D Elements** introduces the Surface Modeling and 3D Main tool frames. Becoming familiar with the tools you find in these tool frames will help you construct even the most sophisticated models.

Placing and Projecting Planar Elements

Planar elements, as their name implies, are those that can only lie in a 2D plane. When you place planar elements (found in the Main tool frame) on a standard view, they appear as lines in adjacent views.

Planar elements are useful in 3D modeling in their own right. Most man-made surfaces around us are planar: walls, equipment faces, tables, and others.

In a 2D environment, you can modify or manipulate planar elements such that they remain in their original plane. In a 3D environment, you can manipulate planar elements in a unique way—you can project them onto a third dimension to create surfaces.

When you project a straight line along another straight line, you get a plane surface. When you project an arc, circle, or ellipse along a straight line, you get a simple curved surface. When you project an arc along another arc, you get a complex surface, such as a horse's saddle.

Projecting Elements to Surfaces

To project planar elements to surfaces, MicroStation provides the Extrude tool. This tool, like other 3D modeling tools, is found in the 3D Main tool frame. To open this tool frame, from the Tools menu, select 3D Main, followed by another 3D Main. The tool frame is dockable along the screen edge, as are other toolboxes and tool frames.

The upper right toolbox in the 3D Main tool frame is named 3D Construct. The Extrude tool is invoked by clicking its first icon, as shown in the figure below.

Use the Extrude tool to project planar elements to surfaces.

Before using the tool, create a planar element and open a few adjacent views. Keeping an isometric view open will help you visualize the model better as you create it. To use the tool, identify the planar element, followed by a data point, to specify its height of projection. It's easiest to specify the height in an adjacent view.

It's an easy tool to use and a great way of projecting plan views to take on an appealing 3D look. The following exercise demonstrates its use by projecting the apartment unit layout you created in chapter 2.

Exercise: Adding Depth to a Plan

Before starting the exercise, copy to your computer's hard disk the design file apt3d.dgn, included on the CD-ROM in the \Exercise\Ch11 folder. Files copied from a CD-ROM retain their read-only status. Because you'll be writing to this file, after copying, clear its read-only attribute.

This exercise file is derived from the apartment unit layout you created in chapter 2. I converted the file to 3D by using the Export option on the File menu, and selecting 3D. After converting the file's dimensional status, I opened two adjacent views, an isometric view, and tiled all the windows.

Use the following steps for this exercise:

1. Start MicroStation with the design file apt3d.dgn. An apartment unit layout displays in four views on the screen, as shown below.

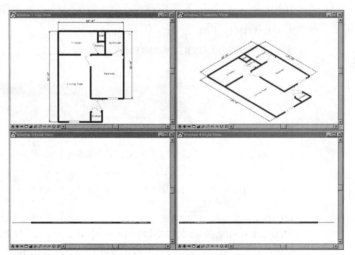

2. Activate the Extrude tool from the 3D Construct toolbox. You're prompted to identify a profile. The Orthogonal checkbox should remain enabled—the default. Ensure Surface is selected on the Type option button in the Tool Settings window.

3. Identify the left exterior wall in the top view. This is the view window on the upper left of the screen. You're prompted to define a distance for the extrusion. Because the extrusion is orthogonal, or perpendicular, to the profile view, it's easiest to define the height for the extrusion in the front or right views.

4. Move the cursor to the front view and you'll see the wall extruded to the height defined by the cursor location in the right and isometric views. Click a data point at the height you desire.

5. Repeat steps 3 and 4 for all the remaining walls in the apartment layout. By snapping to the top of the first wall you placed, you'll ensure all walls have the same height. After extruding the walls, your screen should look similar to the screenshot below.

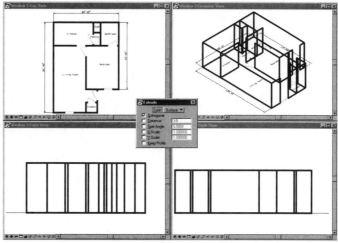

The apartment layout with extruded walls.

In this exercise, the Extrude tool took the element you identified and projected it along an orthogonal axis while keeping the element size the same at the top and the bottom.

If the Orthogonal checkbox were unchecked, you would have a hard time visualizing the direction in which the wall would extrude. Try it! Place a line in the top view and extrude it with the Orthogonal checkbox off. In this case, the only reliable way to identify extrusion height is with a precision key-in, such as DL=0,0,10, or AccuDraw.

The Angle and Scale fields in the Tool Settings window control the rotation and size of the top of the surface when compared to the original profile element. If you select 0.5 for Scale, the top of the extrusion is half the size of the base profile element. The Angle field is used to rotate the profile as it extrudes.

When you select Solid for Type in the Tool Settings window, the Extrude tool still creates surfaces from closed profiles, such as a circle, only the ends of the surface elements are capped. Notice the message on the status bar as you switch the option button between surface and solid. It displays the status of *capped surface placement*.

Revolving Elements to Surfaces

In addition to projecting elements along a linear path with the Extrude tool, you can revolve them around an axis to create yet another variety of surfaces. To revolve profiles, MicroStation provides the Construct Revolution tool. This tool is located next to the Extrude tool you used earlier, on the 3D Construct toolbox. The tool and its Tool Settings window are shown in the figure below.

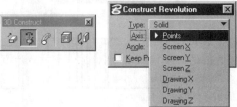

Use the Extrude tool to project planar elements to surfaces.

Before using the tool, create a planar profile, keeping in mind its intended axis of rotation. For instance, if you want to create a top—the toy children spin—sketch only the profile that's symmetrical about the axis of rotation, as shown below.

Rotating by 360° the profile on the left, you get the surface on the right.

To create the above surface of revolution, sketch in the front view the profile shown using the Place SmartLine tool. Then, invoke the Construct Revolution tool. In the Tool Settings window, select Screen Y for axis, because you will revolve the profile about the center line along the view plane's Y-axis. Identify the profile again while the cursor is in the front view. Then, snap to the center line representing the axis of rotation, and accept it with a data point.

If you wish to practice this, you can use the profile already drawn in the design file `toprevlv.dgn` on the CD-ROM in the folder `\Exercise\Ch11`.

3D Elements

When you extrude a profile, the path of extrusion determines whether surface edges are created from line strings or arcs. Similarly, the shape of the profile and the axis of rotation determines the type of edges created.

Surfaces are like closed shapes you encountered in 2D. In addition to vertex coordinates and other similar information, they have an area. You determine the area enclosed by their surface edges by using the Measure Area tool in the Measure toolbox.

Extruding or revolving profiles is one of the easier methods of creating surfaces. You are not restricted to creating surfaces this way. MicroStation includes many other surface modeling tools.

Surface Modeling Tool Frame

The Surface Modeling tool frame can be accessed from the Tools menu. This tool frame consists of four toolboxes as shown in the figure below.

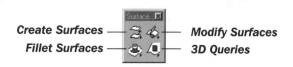

The Surface Modeling tool frame.

To create free-form surfaces, construct them by defining edges and sections, or to offset existing surfaces a certain distance away, use the tools in the Create Surfaces toolbox.

The tool frame provides many other tools and methods to manipulate and modify surfaces. Experiment with them and observe the prompts they display on the status bar. This is a good strategy for learning the tools.

3D Main Tool Frame

Just as the Main tool frame is indispensable in 2D design work, the 3D Main tool frame offers a valuable selection of modeling tools. This tool frame is also accessed from the Tools menu. It consists of four toolboxes, as shown in the figure below.

The 3D Main tool frame.

The 3D Primitives toolbox provides a tool to create a rectangular 3D shape, called a *slab*. Think of it as a 2D block with depth. It also provides tools to create spheres, cylinders, cones, tori, and wedges (shaped like the slice of a pie).

Earlier, you learned a couple of tools for projecting and revolving profiles from the 3D Construct toolbox. It contains many additional tools. You can project profiles along a path defined by another profile by using the Extrude Along Path tool. You can also shell a solid to become hollow, or thicken a surface to become a solid.

The tools in the 3D Modify toolbox allow you to extend the height of solids, remove faces from them, construct Boolean operations (Union, Intersection, and Difference), cut, fillet, and chamfer edges.

The 3D Utility toolbox offers tools to align faces of solids, change the display of SmartSolids, extract the geometry from the face of a solid, or intersect a solid or surface with a curve.

The most significant change in this version of MicroStation is the incorporation of the Parasolids solid-modeling kernel. Previously, to create true solids (not surfaces that have caps at their open ends) you had to rely on a MicroStation add-on, such as Modeler. True solids that are based on the Parasolids kernel are called *SmartSolids*.

To perform feature-based solid modeling, you still need to enhance MicroStation with Modeler (now an engineering configuration available at no charge to those who license new copies of MicroStation/J).

From an end-user's perspective, solid modeling in MicroStation is far more capable as it includes new tools such as Shell Solid. The following exercise demonstrates how easily you can create solids made of thin materials. If solids in MicroStation were capped surfaces, such operations wouldn't be possible.

Exercise: Thin Shelling

Before starting the exercise, copy the file `thincyl.dgn`, included on the CD-ROM, to your computer's hard disk from the `\Exercise\Ch11` folder. Files copied from a CD-ROM retain their read-only status. Because you'll be writing to this file, after copying, clear its read-only attribute.

In this exercise you start with a cylinder created with the Place Cylinder tool in the 3D Primitives toolbox. This is a Type 23 cone element, a capped surface—not a true solid. You then use the Shell Solid tool to make it hollow. Because surfaces are elements with no thickness, the cone element is converted to a SmartSolid, and then it's carved—all behind the scenes, transparent to the user.

Use the following steps for this exercise:

1. Start MicroStation with the design file `thincyl.dgn`. A cylinder displays in four views on the screen.
2. Invoke the Shell Solid tool from the 3D Construct toolbox. You're prompted to identify the target solid.
3. Enter a value of `0.5` in the Shell Thickness field in the Tool Settings window. Leave the Shell Outward checkbox unchecked.
4. Identify the cylinder in any view. It highlights. You are prompted to identify a face to open. We'll open the top face of the cylinder.

5. Move the cursor to the top view. As the cursor approaches the cylinder, its top face highlights. Look in the isometric view to confirm this. Click a data point to accept the face.

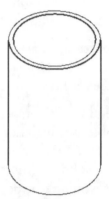

A cylinder carved with the Shell Solid tool.

6. The cylinder is converted to a SmartSolid and is shelled to the thickness desired, as shown in the figure above.

With the 3D modeling basics you've learned in this chapter, you can go a long way in creating impressive models. Of course, the more you practice, the more comfortable you'll feel with the tools, and 3D modeling will become easier.

To complement its sophisticated modeling capabilities, MicroStation includes a rich set of rendering tools that can display your models at their very best. The rest of this chapter introduces you to MicroStation's rendering environment and tools.

Introduction to Rendering

Rendering refers to the creation of a more realistic display of 3D models for visualization. Photo-realistic renderings have obvious aesthetic appeal. However, aesthetics isn't all they're good for. Renderings help solve interference and other modeling problems that are otherwise difficult to spot.

Take another look at the front view window in the screen shot accompanying the exercise titled *Adding Depth to a Plan*. Can you make sense of all the vertical lines and their relationship to each other? Probably not! Only if you look at the top view as you visually project the vertical lines will you relate what each vertical line represents. It's as if all walls were transparent. This isn't how objects appear in real life.

The simplest way to visualize models better so that objects no longer appear in *wireframe*—a term used to describe the display of models as if they were made from wires—is to render them in *hidden line* mode. In this mode, hidden lines are removed from the display. So, objects that are hidden behind others aren't visible.

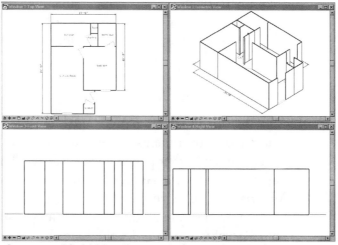

Compare this hidden line rendering to the wireframe display accompanying the Adding Depth to a Plan *exercise.*

If you could only create hidden line displays, you wouldn't achieve the photograph-like quality rendering software strives for. There needs to be a way to attach materials and textures to surfaces. For rendering purposes, you can assign bitmap images of real objects to surfaces so they appear to be made from that material.

By taking a photographic image of a sheet of roof shingles and assigning it to the surface that represents a roof in your model, you can make the roof look lifelike when rendered. Let's see what types of materials come with MicroStation, and how you assign them to model surfaces.

Assigning Materials to Model Surfaces

Before learning material assignment, you need to be aware of two types of bitmap images that can define a material—pattern maps and bump maps. A *pattern map* refers to a bitmap image that drapes a surface. When you assign a material containing a pattern map, the default color and fill of the element is replaced with the image. MicroStation stores pattern maps in the `c:\Bentley\Workspace\System\Materials\Pattern` folder. Over two hundred pattern maps in `.jpg` and `.tif` format are included with MicroStation.

To further enhance the quality of pattern maps, MicroStation supports *bump maps*. Pattern maps, like photographs, are flat. Despite the realism they add to renderings, surfaces rendered with pattern maps can still appear flat. To create the appearance of a rough surface texture, MicroStation uses an additional bitmap image—the bump map—slightly offset from the pattern map. MicroStation includes over two dozen bump images in the `c:\Bentley\Workspace\System\Materials\Bump` folder in the `.jpg` file format.

MicroStation organizes pattern and bump maps into material palettes. A material palette contains material definitions that include names of image files and other parameters. Over two dozen material palettes are delivered in the `c:\Bentley\Workspace\System\Materials` folder. Material palettes have the filename extension `.pal` and are ASCII files you can open in a text editor. A sampling of material palettes delivered with MicroStation includes the following:

- `BACKYARD.PAL` various fences and mulch for backyards of houses
- `CARPET.PAL` different types of carpets for interior floors
- `DOOR_WIN.PAL` door and window styles for building exteriors
- `FLORA.PAL` contains material definitions for trees and bushes
- `GLASS.PAL` contains material definitions for transparent materials
- `VEHICLE.PAL` various types of cars and other vehicles

A wireframe display shows elements as see-through stick figures. When you render models, all surfaces become opaque. However, transparent materials do exist. To simulate glass, water, and other transparent objects, MicroStation supports the definition of transparent materials.

You can define your own materials and store them in material palettes by using the Define Materials dialog. From the Settings menu, select Rendering, then Define Materials. The Map groupbox in the Define Materials dialog box provides access to pattern and bump maps you might want to include in a material definition.

If you wish to practice the steps given below, copy the file `apt3dmat.dgn` from the `\Exercise\ch11` folder on the CD-ROM to your computer's hard disk.

To assign materials to a surface:

1. Invoke the Assign Materials dialog box. From the Settings menu, select Rendering, then Assign Materials. The dialog box opens.

    Notice the title bar of the dialog box. A material assignment file with the same name as the design file, but with the `.mat` extension was automatically created. Materials you assign to surfaces will be stored in it. Like material palettes, this too is an ASCII file you may open in a text editor.

2. From the File menu on the dialog box, select Open Palette. The Open Palette File dialog box opens. Pick `masonry.pal` and click OK to display the materials defined in the selected material palette in the Palette listbox on the Assign Materials dialog box.

3. Select the desired material, say *Brick - rose*, from the material list. The preview pane in the dialog box updates to show how the material will look when assigned to a surface, as shown in the figure below.

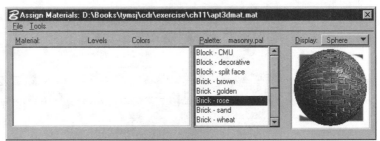

The Assign Materials dialog box.

You now need to assign the material to a surface. Materials are typically assigned by a combination of level and color. The walls in the exercise file are on level 4 and have color 0.

4. From the Tools menu on the dialog box, select Assign. The Assign Material dialog box opens. Enter **4** and **0** in the Level and Colors fields, and click OK.

5. Continue with other material assignments as desired. After completing material assignments, close the dialog box and save the material assignment file when prompted.

6. To see the isometric view rendered with the material assignments just completed, from the Utilities menu, select Render, then Smooth. Click a data point in the isometric view to see the rendering.

To further improve the quality of the rendering, you'll need to learn more about camera angle, lights, perspective, ray tracing, and other rendering options.

Setting Up the View

Rendering as an art form is like photography. In the hands of an artist the model can come to life. Every aspect of a rendering—its background, distance from view plane, light intensity, material selection, color scheme, and direction of shadows—can be controlled, and how each is set up determines its overall appeal.

I can't promise to develop the artist in you. However, I certainly can introduce you to rendering tools and options, and make you aware of their presence. You can control most aspects of rendering in the tabbed Rendering Setup dialog box. From the Settings menu, select Rendering, followed by Setup to open the dialog box, as shown below.

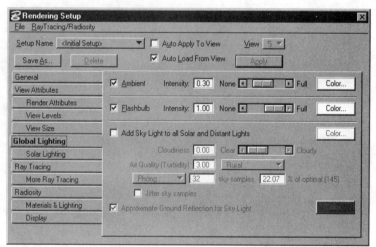

Control most aspects of rendering in this tabbed dialog box.

As with photography, the presence, location, and type of light makes the most significant difference to the overall look of a rendering. You can position the following types of lights around your models:

Global Lighting: The term *global lighting* refers to light sources that are global. In other words, the intensity of these light sources does not fade over a distance. There are three types of global light sources. They are listed in bullet form below.

- *Ambient*: Control the intensity of this light in the Global Lighting tab of the above dialog box. It affects the brightness of all objects in a view. It has a default value of ten percent, or 0.1. When turned off, and no other light source exists, objects appear black. It is a flat light source and does not cast shadows.

- *Flashbulb*: Control its intensity in the Global Lighting tab of the above dialog box. It is a directional light source emanating from and perpendicular to the view plane. A surface's orientation to the light source (the view) determines its brightness. Its intensity can vary from zero to one. Lower values produce darker shades of color. This light source does not cast shadows.

- *Solar*: Control its intensity and direction in the Solar Lighting tab of the above dialog box. It is a directional light source whose direction can be controlled by longitude, latitude, and time zone. You can specify the values of these geographical parameters by opening a global map projection by clicking the Maps button on the dialog box. This is the only global light source that casts shadows, and you'll want to use it.

For better quality rendering, don't turn on all three global light sources together. Usually, a combination of solar light with one other will work better.

Shadows provide realism to any rendering. You'll want to include either solar, or source lighting—discussed next—in your renderings. Each can cast a shadow. To see shadows in a rendered image, you must use the Phong mode. Also, the Shadows checkbox must be enabled for the view in its Rendering View Attributes dialog box.

Source Lighting: The term *source lighting* refers to light sources that cover a finite distance range. This light can cast shadows and is of four types, as listed in bullet form below.

- *Distant*: Like solar light, it is directional and equally bright over its range of action. It can cast shadows.

- *Point*: Like an incandescent light bulb, this shines light in all directions. Surfaces that directly face the light appear bright. This light source does not cast shadows.

- *Spot*: Like a spotlight, it radiates a conical beam of light. You can define the angle of the cone of light, and the distance over which the light falls off. It can cast shadows.

- *Area*: The other three source lights are placed in a view by clicking a location for them. This light source requires you to identify an area element to convert to an area light. This light source simulates fluorescent light enclosed in boxes on office ceilings.

To place and set up source lighting, invoke the Source Lighting dialog box. From the Settings menu, select Rendering, then Source Lighting. The dialog box opens, as shown below.

Use this dialog box to place and set up source lighting in a view.

The Tools menu in the dialog box provides access to light placement, editing, and manipulation commands. Before placing the light, select its type from the Type option button, and specify its properties.

Source lights are placed as cells with the construction class attribute. When rendering, turn off the display of construction class elements from the view so that source light cells aren't visible.

Rendering Toolbox: MicroStation implements the Rendering toolbox to provide easier access to many of its rendering tools. From the Tools menu, select Visualization Tools, then Rendering Tools to open the toolbox. The toolbox implements eight tools, listed below.

- *Define Light*: Creates new or modifies existing light sources.
- *Define Camera*: Places and controls camera position, orientation, and focal length.
- *Apply Material*: Another tool to create material assignments for surfaces.
- *Render*: Initiates rendering. See a description of the rendering methods below.
- *Query Radiosity*: After solving radiosity (render in radiosity mode) you can use this tool to determine light level at a point.
- *Facet Smoothing*: Lets you attach or detach facet smoothing linkages.
- *Photomatch*: Lets you calibrate a view camera to match a photograph's perspective so a model and photograph can be superimposed.
- View Size: Lets you control the size of a view window.

Despite proper light sources and material assignments, if your rendering doesn't cast shadows or display transparent materials properly, check the rendering attributes of the view in the Rendering View Attributes dialog box (accessed from the Rendering submenu on the Settings menu).

Rendering Methods

After you've created your model, set up material assignments, and the view, you're ready to initiate rendering. To render a model, from the Utilities menu, select Render, then one of the rendering modes. You are prompted to identify a view. Click the desired view, and it's rendered in the selected mode.

The following paragraphs explain the various rendering modes.

- *Wireframe*: You have used this default stick-line mode to create models before. Use this mode to switch a view that's been set up to render its contents at all times by using the Display option button in the Rendering View Attributes dialog box (accessed by selecting View Attributes from the Rendering submenu in the Settings menu).
- *Wire Mesh*: In a busy model, distinguishing between plane and curved surfaces can be difficult sometimes. This mode drapes a wire mesh over curved surfaces so that you can distinguish them more readily.

- *Hidden Line*: This is an efficient rendering mode as it processes quickly. You'll use it often to visualize the model. It treats every surface as white opaque and hides surfaces hidden behind others.

- *Filled Hidden Line*: This is the same as hidden line, except that each surface is filled with its color, and edges between surfaces are displayed in white.

- *Constant*: Use this to render models quickly for checking light sources and other parameters. It produces a coarse image with plane facets for curved surfaces and a constant color within a facet.

- *Smooth*: This mode still facets curved surfaces but averages the shade between facets at their edges, thus providing a smooth transition between surface colors.

- *Phong*: Rather than computing the shading for a surface—as is done in constant and smooth modes—this mode calculates the shade of each pixel depending on the material properties and its distance from light sources. It results in excellent renderings, and takes significantly more time than the previous modes.

- *Phong Stereo*: This is a variation of the Phong mode discussed earlier. It renders two phong images in different colors and is suitable for viewing through specially colored glasses for a stereo effect.

- *Phong Antialias*: This is another variation of the Phong mode. It blends sharp edges of an object by blurring them. It improves quality of images generated at lower resolutions.

- *Ray Trace*: All previous rendering modes disregard reflection of light from surfaces. In ray trace mode, MicroStation traces the path of light rays even after they hit a surface. Such rendering imparts a hue on surfaces adjacent to colored surfaces. It is the most realistic rendering mode and uses computer processing power the most. To ray trace only a portion of the image, place a fence around the area, and type RENDER FENCE in the Key-in window.

- *Radiosity*: This is an advanced lighting engineering feature. When rendered in this mode, MicroStation solves the radiosity of a view and keeps it in memory so you can query the light level in lumens at any point in the view.

Saving Rendered Images

In addition to displaying rendered images on the screen, MicroStation provides the ability to save them to electronic files in a variety of image formats.

A typical video display has a 75 dpi (dots per inch) resolution. Laser printers typically offer 600 dpi resolution. Imaging hardware that converts electronic files to camera-ready film for printing purposes requires even higher resolutions. MicroStation's Save Image dialog box lets you save images to any desired resolution. From the Utilities menu, select Image, then Save. The dialog box opens, as shown below.

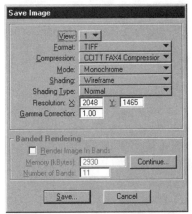

The Save Image dialog box.

Before you invoke this dialog box to save rendered images, prepare a view for rendering with camera, lighting, and other parameters as needed.

Most of the fields in this dialog box are obvious to you. The View field specifies the view you have set up for rendering. The Format field specifies the image format desired. Supported file formats are listed in the *Raster Reference Files* section in chapter 6. The Compression field specifies the compression format you wish to use for the file type selected. The Mode field determines the color depth (monochrome to 24-bit color). Shading type specifies whether to use antialiasing or stereo imaging. The Resolution field lets you control the image size in pixels. The aspect ratio between the X and Y resolution is determined by width and height of the view window you are rendering. The Gamma Correction field is used to adjust and lighten the middle tones of an image without affecting the dark and light regions. If the rendering is for print media, not projections on a screen with light, a larger value is recommended.

After you've selected the desired options in the Save Image dialog box, click the Save button to generate the rendered image file. Depending on the color depth, the resolution, and mode of rendering, this process can take a long time—even overnight!

This concludes your introduction to 3D modeling and rendering.

Chapter 12

Using Web Links and Tools

Exploiting the Internet and the Intranet

It's hard to imagine an office without a network. I might add that it's even harder to find one that doesn't have access to the Internet—the network of networks.

The Internet started two decades ago as a means of connecting government and educational institutions for collaboration on research projects. Today, anyone with a computer and a local Internet Service Provider (ISP)—practically the entire civilized world—can connect to the Internet. On the Internet, you can access, send, and receive *any* information in electronic form.

Its electronic data connectivity and wealth of available information is such a potent combination that project managers are using it to foster better communication among team members that include owners, contractors, and consultants.

The Internet is revolutionizing how teams across continents collaborate on architectural and engineering projects. It's common for the larger project to host a site on the World Wide Web (commonly referred to as the Web) to serve as a clearinghouse for technical specifications and administrative transmittal log information.

MicroStation incorporates several tools that use your connection to the Web or a local intranet to enhance a project's work flow. This chapter introduces you to those tools and concepts.

Following is a list of chapter sections and what they cover.

- **MicroStation Is Web-aware:** You can link URLs to MicroStation elements. When identified with another tool, such elements invoke your Web browser and open the page identified by the URL (Uniform Resource Locator). MicroStation is also web-aware in other respects.

- **MicroStation's HTML Authoring Tools:** With tools MicroStation provides, you can publish HTML pages from cell libraries, saved views in a design file, MicroStation BASIC macros, and file snapshots.

Bentley uses the term *Engineering Links* to describe its Web-enabled tools that create content in Web-supported formats and use it from within MicroStation. As you'll see, MicroStation's support for Web technologies goes beyond exporting design files as images in a format compatible with Web browsers.

MicroStation Is Web-aware

Of its various services, Internet e-mail is perhaps the most widely used. By attaching files to e-mail messages, you can easily transmit them from one computer to another.

MicroStation simplifies sending a copy of the active design file by implementing the Send option under its File menu. Without having to close or switch focus from MicroStation, you can start your e-mail client software and attach a copy of the active design file with a menu selection. Of course, you must have Internet access, an e-mail account and e-mail client software, such as Windows Messaging, Lotus cc:mail, Novell GroupWise, or Microsoft Outlook, installed and configured on your computer for this feature to work.

To attach a design file to an e-mail message:

1. If the file you wish to send is not already open in MicroStation, open it.
2. From the File menu, select Send. MicroStation connects to your e-mail software and invokes its dialog box used to compose new messages. The screenshot below shows Microsoft Outlook.

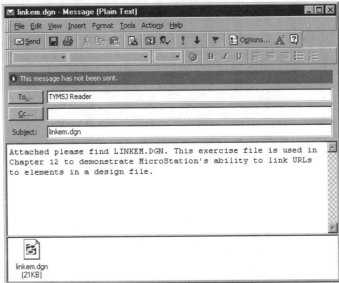

Selecting Send from the File menu opens your e-mail software.

MicroStation attaches a copy of the active design file to the message. It also enters the name of the design file in the Subject field.

3. Enter the recipient's e-mail address, compose text for the message, revise the subject line as desired, and click the e-mail software's Send button to send it.

Look at the File menu again. Notice the option Open URL—it's directly under Open. Open lets you access design files from the network or from your computer's hard disk. Open URL lets you open design files located anywhere on the Internet by specifying its URL.

To open a remote design file, select Open URL. The Select Remote Design File dialog box opens, as shown below.

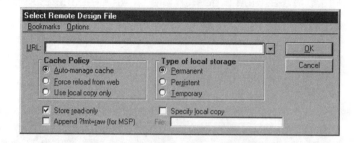

If your browser is connected to the site you want to open the file from, MicroStation enters the server's URL in the dialog box automatically.

A similar dialog box opens when you do either of the following:

- Choose Open URL from the File menu on the Select Settings dialog box (select Manage from the Settings menu).

- Choose Open URL from the File menu on the Archive dialog box (select Archive from the Utilities menu).

- Choose Attach URL from the Tools menu on the Reference Files dialog box (select Reference from the File menu).

- Choose Load Remote Cell Library from the File menu on the Cell Selector dialog box (select Cell Selector from the Utilities menu and select a cell library).

The Bookmarks menu on the dialog box is used to set and edit bookmarks for sites you visit often. The Options menu is used to clear temporary browser history files.

The Cache Policy options on the dialog box let you specify whether to always download a new copy, use a local copy, or download only if the local copy is older than the one at the URL.

The Type of Local Storage options on the dialog box let you specify when to delete the local copy: never (Permanent); when temporary cache size exceeds limit (Persistent); when you exit MicroStation (Temporary).

The *Append ?fmt=raw (for MSP)* option is specific to Web sites running Model Server Publisher. Enable it when connecting to such a site. The *Specify Local Copy* option lets you override the default location for downloaded files. On enabling the checkbox, you can enter a location and name for a local copy of the file.

Configuration variables that control various aspects of MicroStation's Web-enabled environment are located in the Configuration dialog box opened by selecting Configuration from the Workspace menu. Highlight the Engineering Links category in the dialog box to display the variables, as shown in the figure below.

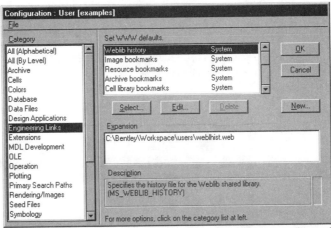

Select Engineering Links in the Configuration dialog box to edit configuration variables that control aspects of MicroStation's Web-enabled environment.

In chapter 6, you learned about reference files and how they can be used for collaboration among team members on a network. Recognizing the role Internet plays in extending a network beyond office boundaries, MicroStation implements the Reference File Agent.

Well-managed large projects make extensive use of reference files. When such collaboration extends beyond an office network, reference files are shared regularly at project meetings between different offices. Many managers set up project Web sites and notify various offices when shared files are updated so team members can download the current versions.

MicroStation's Reference File Agent eliminates such change notification. It helps users manage local copies of remote reference files so they are always current.

To manage remote reference files:

1. Start MicroStation with the design file that is to use remote reference files.
2. Attach remote reference files.

   To attach remote reference files, select Attach URL from the Tools menu in the Reference Files: Design Files dialog box. (Select Reference from MicroStation's File menu to open the Reference Files dialog box.)
3. From now on you can check the status of these files at the remote location by using the Reference File Agent dialog box. To open the dialog box, type **MDL LOAD REFAGENT** in the Key-in window or click the Load RefAgent tool in the E-Links toolbox, accessed by selecting Engineering Links from the Tools menu. Remote reference files attached to the active design file appear in the dialog box, as shown below.

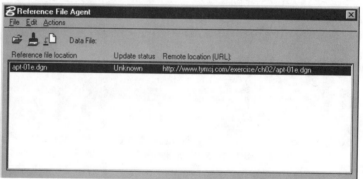

Use the Reference File Agent dialog box to manage remote reference files.

4. Check the column labeled *Update status* in the dialog box. Let's review the choices. N/A is used if the remote file has no associated URL; Current, if the reference file has the same date and time as the remote file; Unknown, if you're not connected to the Internet or the remote site couldn't be located; Out of Date, if the reference file is older than the version on the remote site.
5. To update out-of-date reference files, use the choices in the Actions menu in the dialog box. Actions available are: Update Out-of-date Files, Update All Files, and Update Selected Files.

When you select Refresh from the File menu in the Reference File Agent dialog box, all reference files attached to the active design file are checked against a data file to determine files that have an associated URL. You can choose a data file by selecting Open from the dialog box's File menu. For remote reference files, a request is sent to the Internet to check the date and time of the remote file against the local copy of the reference file. This check determines what appears in the *Update status* column.

If the URL of a remote file changes, or it will no longer be maintained remotely, use the Edit menu on the dialog box to edit or clear it.

In addition to sending active design files as e-mail attachments, opening several file types using URLs, and managing remote reference files, MicroStation lets you attach URLs to elements. Clicking the element opens the attached URL in your default Web browser.

To attach a URL to an element:

1. Select Engineering Links from the Tools menu. Click the Attach Engineering Link tool in the E-Links toolbox. The Tool Settings window displays two fields: URL and Title.

2. Enter a URL and a description for its content. Look at the figure below. If your Web browser were open and MicroStation were connected to it the URL field is automatically filled. You are prompted to identify an element.

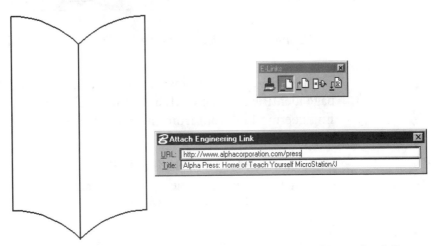

The Attach Engineering Link tool is shown attaching a URL to a book figure.

3. Click an element to identify it, and click again to accept it. The URL is attached to the element.

MicroStation uses an element tag set named Internet that contains tags *URL* and *Title* to attach what it calls *engineering links* to elements. To display elements in the design file that have URLs attached to them, click the Show Engineering Links tool, the first icon in the E-Links toolbox. Elements tagged with a URL display in the view window with a different symbology. Click the Show Engineering Links tool again to return tagged elements to their original display symbology.

To edit the URL for an element already tagged, click the Edit Tags tool in the Tags toolbox (Main tool frame), as shown in the figure below.

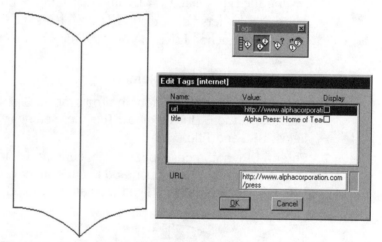

Clicking the book figure with the Edit Tags tool opened this dialog box.

To open a Web browser installed on your system and display the Web page identified by the URL linked to an element, invoke the Follow Engineering Link tool from the E-Links toolbox and identify the element.

You can attach URLs to flags and other symbols in a drawing. On clicking the symbol, a reviewer can read attached notes on a project Web site. You can also attach links to equipment symbols so a click can lead the user to a Web page containing specifications for its use. You'll discover many other uses for these links.

MicroStation's HTML Authoring Tools

To publish information on the Internet or an intranet you must have access to a computer set up to publish Web pages. When an Internet Service Provider gives you space on their servers to host your Web site, the computer you'll place your pages on is set up with Web server software.

Netscape Enterprise Server, Microsoft Internet Information Server (IIS), and Apache Web Server are just a few of the many Web server software packages available.

This section assumes you have access to such a server and are familiar with basic Web page design and publishing concepts. If you need help on how to design Web pages, how to use FTP software to access disk space an ISP has made available for your Web pages, and how to set up links between different pages, you'll find many good books on the market.

Web browsers are equipped to read pages written in HTML (Hypertext Markup Language) with embedded images in JPEG or GIF format. In chapter 7 and chapter 11 you learned how to export design files and rendered models in several file formats, including those supported by Web browsers.

You can use Export options under the File menu, the Save Image dialog box, or plotter drivers that print to a file to create images from design files in browser-compatible formats such as JPEG (Joint Photographic Experts Group), VRML (Virtual Reality Modeling Language), SVF (Simple Vector Format), and CGM (Computer Graphics Metafile). Some of these formats require browser plug-ins.

MicroStation also provides an HTML authoring tool for creating pages that contain embedded graphics ready for publishing on a Web server. This tool creates Web pages from cell libraries, MicroStation BASIC macros, saved views in a design file, or a snapshot of the active design file.

To invoke MicroStation's Web authoring tool from the Utilities menu select HTML Author. The HTML Author dialog box opens, as shown in the figure below.

MicroStation's Web authoring tool creates HTML pages.

The following bulleted list explains each of the radio buttons in the dialog box.

- When you process a cell library, the Web page generated contains a picture of each cell in a tabular format. MicroStation creates an image from every cell and places it in an HTML table on the page it designs.

- When you process saved views in a design file, the generated page contains an image of the saved view.

- When you process macros, the Web page contains a list of all macros in the MicroStation BASIC macros directory.

- When you process the active design file's snapshot, the generated HTML page simulates the view on your screen. If you have four tiled view windows open, it'll generate four images to match the views and pieces them together in the same manner to simulate the screen.

If you are an experienced Web developer familiar with HTML form design, you'll be interested in the *ustnkeyin* and *ustnform* protocols that enable HTML pages to send commands to MicroStation. For syntax details on these protocols, search for the term *Control of MicroStation from HTML Documents* in online Help.

If you're responsible for creating project Web sites and need to make MicroStation design files available on them, you might be interested in ModelServer Publisher, a Web server add-on software from Bentley. This software enhances Netscape Enterprise Server so it can publish MicroStation `.dgn` files on demand over the Internet in formats compatible with any Web browser.

In closing, I'd like to mention that ProjectBank, when available for component modeling applications, will be able to exploit Web technologies even more. It will be able to enforce transaction management and component design rules across the Internet.

Chapter 13

The Engineering Configurations
GeoGraphics, TriForma, and Modeler

Bentley uses the term *engineering configurations* to refer to its add-on applications that extend MicroStation for discipline-specific needs. Using these applications can increase your productivity significantly. This isn't a marketing claim. It's a fact. An accounting template helps you balance books more efficiently than manually using a spreadsheet. Similarly, an engineering configuration reduces effort on projects it is designed for.

Design applications can cost as much as a MicroStation license, if not more. To encourage their use, Bentley offers an engineering configuration at no cost to those who upgrade to MicroStation/J or license a new copy. As of this writing, three configurations are available, with a fourth in the works. Several others are expected to become available in 1999.

In this chapter you learn about GeoGraphics, the GIS configuration; TriForma, the building configuration; and Modeler, the mechanical modeling configuration. CivilPAK, the civil site design add-on is not yet available as a configuration. These applications are mature and industry-proven because they've been available for many years. They are still available as extra cost add-ons to previous MicroStation versions.

Each of these configurations uses MicroStation's CAD engine to display and manipulate graphical elements. It also attaches nongraphic data to elements to enhance their functionality. In TriForma, graphical elements behave as building components. In GeoGraphics, they are spatially aware with data linkages such that database queries manipulate maps. In Modeler, they behave as solids that know their dimensions and relationships to adjoining components so they can be resized by editing parameters.

This chapter is organized in the following sections:

- **GeoGraphics for GIS** introduces the capabilities of GeoGraphics for developing decision support and spatial inventory applications.

- **TriForma for Building Engineering** introduces TriForma's basic features for designing commercial and industrial building projects.

- **Modeler for Mechanical Modeling** introduces Modeler's parametric, feature-based modeling system that supports assemblies.

This chapter assumes you're familiar with basic MicroStation concepts and terms. If you're new to MicroStation, I recommend reading the *Introduction* and chapters 1 through 7 first. For GeoGraphics, I also recommend chapter 10 on nongraphic data linkages. For Modeler and TriForma, I also recommend chapter 11 on 3D modeling. Additionally, I recommend chapter 9 on dimension-driven design for Modeler users.

If you simply need to decide which configuration to request from Bentley, this chapter has no prerequisites. It provides enough introductory information to help you make that decision.

Each engineering configuration is a complex application deserving a separate book to help you explore all its features. This chapter can only introduce you to application functionality and basic concepts so you start off on the right foot. Here, you'll learn the purpose of the configuration, its interface, and steps for basic functions.

GeoGraphics for GIS

GeoGraphics is the engineering configuration for GIS (Geographic Information System) projects. It's a map-based decision support and inventory management system.

It links map features in design files with nongraphic attributes in a relational database. Once a project is set up with such links, map features can turn off, change their color, or modify their graphical appearance in other ways based on data attribute queries.

Following is a list of project types where GeoGraphics can be used:

- *Traffic Signal Inventory*: By linking symbols representing traffic signals on maps to inventory and maintenance records in relational databases, transportation agencies can display query results on maps. Common questions include: Which signals use energy-efficient fixtures? Which signals are over five years old?

- *Emergency Response System*: When a call comes in, the location of the originating phone number can be displayed on a map, along with the best travel route for the emergency response crew.

- *Retail Mall Planning*: Maps linked to demographic data are used by retailers to identify the best location for a mall or shopping center based on population density, spending patterns, property values, and convenient access.

- *Map-based Statistical Studies*: Demographic statistical results can be presented in thematic maps using a different color for each number range, thus revealing patterns that might not otherwise be visible.

- *School Planning*: By linking property boundaries to assessed home values and child population data, local jurisdictions can assess tax revenues for school location planning purposes.

- *Utility Management*: Telephone, electric, gas, and water lines span large geographic distances to serve residents and businesses. Linking these map features to utility inventory and resident databases can help municipalities create mailing labels for affected residents to inform them of proposed utility work. Additionally, new development can be used to predict service needs and plan future infrastructure upgrades.

The above list is not comprehensive. It merely introduces you to types of projects GIS has been used for successfully.

You'll need to know a few concepts and terms before using or creating GeoGraphics projects. These terms are defined below.

Features are graphic elements representing geographic data. They can be lines representing rivers, roads, utilities, or other linear elements. They can be symbols or text representing light poles, houses, traffic signal heads, lot numbers, or other point elements. They can also be closed shapes representing lots, lakes, state or municipal boundaries, or other areas. Features have two components: *graphic* and *attribute*—both stored in different tables in your project database. A single graphical element can be tagged as more than one coincident feature. For example, a single line may represent a road edge and a property boundary.

Maps are design files containing graphical elements tagged with feature attributes. By convention, maps in a category share the same filename extension. (Design files need not use the default .dgn extension.) Maps are stored in the project's DGN folder. In addition to maps, GeoGraphics supports index maps. An *index map* contains outlines on a unique level for maps in a category. Each category uses a separate index map. A *key map* is a visual catalog of all map files in a project. Index maps and the key map are stored in the project's IDX folder.

Categories are a hierarchical collection of similar features. In addition to features, a category definition incorporates an index map and design files that contain the graphical elements corresponding to the features. A feature and a map can belong to only one category. A category can contain many maps and features.

Before creating a GeoGraphics project, you'll want to create maps for the area. You'll also want to set up tables in a database to capture data that must be queried and related to elements on a map.

To use GeoGraphics, you must connect to a relational database as discussed in chapter 10. Connecting to a Microsoft Access file is the simplest. The process is discussed in the following pages.

NOTE: You may explore many features of GeoGraphics without a database connection by using an export file (.exp) that can create database tables in the computer's memory. This is described later.

Because GeoGraphics uses MicroStation's database interface, it requires that an *mscatalog* table exist. It also requires that user-attribute tables include the *mslink* field. Other required tables include *category*, *feature*, *maps*, and other tables, collectively called *system tables*. When you create a new project, GeoGraphics creates all required system tables.

Spatial analysis is an advanced GIS feature. It allows you to build spatial relationships between different features and analyze them. GeoGraphics includes this feature. Spatial analysis isn't covered in this chapter.

The next section explains the menus and toolboxes GeoGraphics adds to MicroStation.

The GeoGraphics Interface

During installation, GeoGraphics prompts for MicroStation's location and installs files in the `c:\Bentley\Program\GeoGraphics` folder by default. A minimum installation copies only the necessary program files. To install all files, including the sample MyTown project that accompanies the software, you must choose complete installation. Upon installation, an icon to invoke GeoGraphics is added to the MicroStation_J submenu on the Start button.

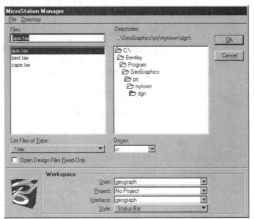

Select the geograph workspace and interface in the MicroStation Manager dialog box to start GeoGraphics.

To start GeoGraphics, select its icon from the MicroStation_J submenu from the Programs menu on the Start button. Notice that GeoGraphics uses *geograph* as the workspace user and interface in the MicroStation Manager dialog box, as shown in the figure above.

On opening a design file, the most obvious interface changes you'll notice are a simpler Main tool frame and two new selections on the menu bar: Project and Database.

Main Tool Frame

The seventeen toolboxes and one tool in the two-column MicroStation Main tool frame are replaced by GeoGraphics with ten toolboxes and three tools in a single column layout, as shown below.

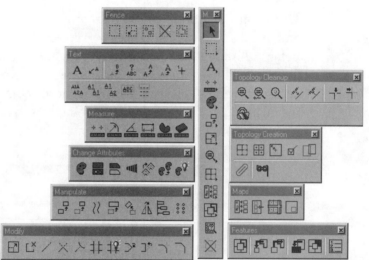

Toolboxes shown to the right of the tool frame are specific to GeoGraphics.

The four new GeoGraphics toolboxes are listed below.

The *Topology Cleanup* toolbox contains tools to find duplicate, similar, and fragmented linework; to delete or add vertices to linework; to close gaps or delete extensions at intersections; and to use rainbow masking for visual display of attribute ranges.

The *Topology Creation* toolbox contains shape and centroid creation tools, the Associate Linkages tool, and tools to validate topology.

The *Maps* toolbox contains tools to attach map files as reference files to a work file by selecting them from a key map and using buttons on the Map Manager; to make a map containing the designated element the master map; to update features in a fence by Map ID; and to display the project key map.

The *Features* toolbox contains tools to select, attach, and detach an active feature; to synchronize an element with its attached feature definition; to make a feature an element's highest priority; and to display a list of features attached to an element.

Project and Database Menus

GIS projects are set up as a collection of categories containing features and maps. Because a category contains several features and maps, GeoGraphics uses project directories to organize them. The Project menu offers choices to set up, open and close projects, and to invoke the Project Setup Wizard. A project also needs to connect to a database with several tables.

The Database menu provides access to several dialog boxes that query the connected project database for resymbolization, annotation, and updates.

Most GIS projects, like databases, are meant to be designed once and used by many to run queries and generate reports. Because the number of tools and menu options in MicroStation can overwhelm a user, GeoGraphics pares down the options it lets MicroStation display on its menus. As you'll notice, the File, Edit, Settings, Tools, and Utilities menus offer far fewer choices than MicroStation. An experienced MicroStation user continues to have access to all of MicroStation's tools via key-ins. The menus also display choices specific to GeoGraphics. Several menu choices will be introduced when discussing steps to access GeoGraphics features.

Creating a GeoGraphics Project

Before you can create a GeoGraphics project, you must set up an external database file with the necessary system tables to accept attribute data. This database file is created outside the GeoGraphics environment.

Once the blank database file is ready, you can use the Project Setup dialog box to populate the database file with required system tables. The following steps are applicable for using the Microsoft ODBC drivers to create an .mdb database file in the project directory tymsjgeo.

To create a project database:

1. Double-click the ODBC icon in the Windows Control Panel. The ODBC Data Source Administrator opens. The User DSN tab is active. It is the default.
2. Click the System DSN tab to activate it. You'll create a system DSN (data source name) so it's visible to all users who log on to the computer.
3. Click the Add button. The Create New Data Source dialog box opens. Select Microsoft Access Driver in the listbox and click the Finish Button. The ODBC Microsoft Access 97 Setup dialog box opens, as shown below.

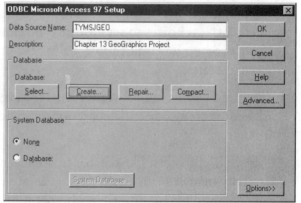

First click Create to create a database file, then OK to create the system DSN.

4. In the Data Source Name field, enter TYMSJGEO. In the Description field, enter Chapter 13 GeoGraphics Project. Click the Create button, the New Database dialog box opens.
5. Navigate to the project's directory and type tymsjgeo.mdb in the database name field. Click OK to create the file and another OK in the message dialog box that reports the successful creation of the file. The database name appears above the Create button.
6. Click OK to close the ODBC Microsoft Access 97 Setup dialog box. The system DSN is added to the ODBC Data Source Administrator dialog box. GeoGraphics can now create required system tables. You may now close this and the Control Panel dialog boxes.
7. Start GeoGraphics with any design file.

8. From the Project menu select Setup. The Project Setup dialog box opens.

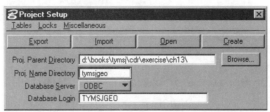

Use the Project Setup dialog box to open or create project tables.

9. Enter the project's root directory in the Parent Directory field. Enter the project's name, for example, `tymsjgeo`, in the Name Directory field. Select ODBC from the Database Server option button. (If using another database server, select that instead.) Enter the system DSN name, for example, `tymsjgeo`, in the Database Login field.

10. Click Create. GeoGraphics creates a directory structure for the project and all required system tables.

If your ODBC driver fails to create the tables, you can use the database file `tymsjgeo.mdb` in the `\Exercise\Ch13\TymsjGeo` folder on the CD-ROM to seed your project database. Rename the file to your project's name and place it in the project folder. Rather than create a new database, click the Select button to select the copied file.

Another way to create the project database is to use Access and manually create the required tables by following the structure of the tables in the `cretable.sql` script file in the `c:\Bentley\Program\GeoGraphics\Setup` folder. A GeoGraphics project directory structure is shown in the figure below.

GeoGraphics project directory structure.

The `dgn` folder is used for maps; `fea` for features and feature groups; `idx` for index and key maps; `imp` for import files; `seed` for seed files; and `sql` for saved SQL queries and scripts used in the project.

After creating a project database, you must create categories and features in the Feature Setup dialog box.

To create categories and features:

1. Start GeoGraphics with any design file.
2. From the Project menu, select Setup. The Project Setup dialog box opens.
3. Enter the project's root directory in the Parent Directory field. Enter the project's name, for example `tymsjgeo`, in the Name Directory field. Select ODBC from the Database Server option button. (If using another database server, select that instead.) Enter the system DSN name, for example `tymsjgeo`, in the Database Login field.
4. Click Open. The status bar reports that it successfully connected to the project database. If GeoGraphics fails to connect, verify that your project database is set up correctly.
5. From the Tables menu on the Project Setup dialog box, select Feature Setup. The Feature Setup dialog box opens, as shown below.

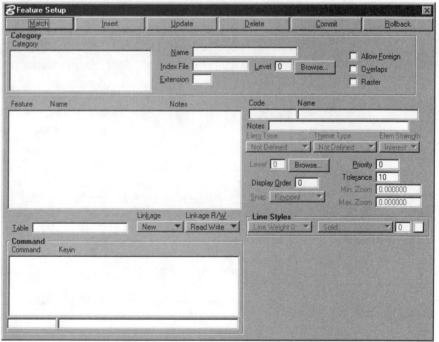

Use this dialog box to define categories and features.

6. Fill data fields in the Category groupbox. Name is a category name. Index File is the name of the map index design file. Level is the design file level containing the map index shape. Extension is the three-letter filename extension for maps in the category. Allow Foreign checkbox, when enabled, permits the category to incorporate features from other categories. Overlaps checkbox, when enabled, allows map index shapes to overlap.

7. Click the Insert button. The category is created and added to Category listbox.

8. Click the Commit button to write the category definition to the database.

9. Fill data fields in the section just below the Category groupbox. Refer to GeoGraphics online help for description of Feature definition fields.

10. Click the Insert button. The feature is added to the Feature listbox.

11. Click Commit to write the feature definition to the database.

The Update and Delete buttons in the dialog box are used to edit and delete category and feature definitions. The Rollback button is used to reverse commits to the database. The Match button is used to copy the feature definition from an existing feature by identifying it.

The Command groupbox under the Feature listbox is used to associate MicroStation key-ins (including UCMs, macros, and MDL commands) with command names project users will need. Commands you may implement for a feature might include DRAW (associated with the Place Line tool), and REMOVE (associated with the Delete Element tool).

After creating a project database, categories, and features, you must create maps containing graphical elements that are to be associated with features in the database.

To create and add maps to the project:

1. Create a design file in the project's dgn folder and draw elements that represent features such as street edges and property boundaries.

2. Draw a map shape using Place Block or Place Shape. A *map shape* is a closed shape representing the map boundary. It is copied to the map index file for visual display of map extents in the key map file.

3. From the Miscellaneous menu on the Project Setup dialog box, select Register Map, then Design File. You are prompted for the map shape element. Identify it, then click a data point to accept it.

4. The map shape is copied to the index map file, and a row is added to the MAPS table in the project database.

5. Finally, create a design file in the project's `idx` folder with the name `vicinity.dgn`. Draw a key map—one per project—using simple shapes displaying a visual catalog of all maps in the project. This map is displayed in the Key Map window (view window 8) and serves as the starting point for attaching maps to a view.

This completes a GeoGraphics project setup. The data input phase follows, when you add tables to the project database for nongraphic data attributes and link them to elements.

The next section uses the sample MyTown project delivered with GeoGraphics to show how a GIS project is used.

Using a GeoGraphics Project

To use the MyTown project, create a System DSN called `MYTOWN` for the project database `mytown.mdb` in the GeoGraphics `prj\mytown` folder. Refer to the steps listed earlier for creating a project database. Start GeoGraphics with any design file. From the Project menu, select Open. The Project Open dialog box opens, as shown below.

Fill the dialog box as shown and click OK to open the sample project.

Clicking OK after entering data in the dialog box opens the project and displays the project key map in view window 8, the lower right view.

If you don't have ODBC drivers or don't wish to connect to a database you can still explore many features in GeoGraphics. Rather than enable the checkboxes in the Database groupbox, select the `mytown.exp` file in the Export File field. This export file contains data from the project database in a neutral export file format. GeoGraphics loads it in memory and performs many actions from this memory image of the database.

To attach maps from the map index to a view:

1. Open the project as described above. The key map displays in view 8, titled Key View.
2. Click the Attach Maps tool from the Maps toolbox. The Map Manager dialog box opens. From the Tool Settings window, select All from the Mode option button and click a point in the Key View. All map shapes in the project highlight in the key map. All map file names are entered in the Map Manager dialog box with the Attach status next to them.
3. Keep the Attach status for the three `*.tax` maps. Highlight the remaining map files and click the Detach button to change their status.
4. Click the Apply button in the Map Manager to attach the files selected as reference files in Window 1, the work view. The status of the attached map files changes to Reference.
5. Invoke the Fit View tool from Window 1's view control bar. The view zooms to fit the three maps. You can close the Map Manager.

Once the desired maps are attached to a view, you can control what features to display from the maps.

To control the display of features:

1. Window 1 displays the three maps in the Tax Map category from the MyTown project. To see the features in this category, open the Display Manager from the Settings menu, as shown below.

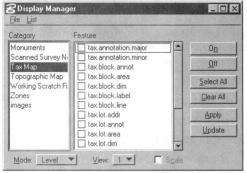

Click the Tax Maps category to see its features.

2. Click Select All, then Off to clear the checkboxes for all features. Then click Apply. All features in the maps are turned off and window 1 is blank.

3. Click Clear All. Highlight the `tax.block.line` feature, click On, then Apply. The blue tax lot lines appear in window 1.

The controls in the Display Manager let you turn features on or off in a view. You can select the view to apply actions to. You can also select the display mode by level or by feature. When the level mode is selected, the level assigned to the feature is toggled. When the feature mode is selected, the feature display is affected regardless of its level or symbology definition.

To annotate maps based on feature data attributes, use the Annotation dialog box. To build SQL statements to query tables in the project database, use the SQL Query Builder dialog box. To create thematic maps, use the Thematic Resymbolization dialog box. These dialog boxes, shown below, are accessed from the Database menu.

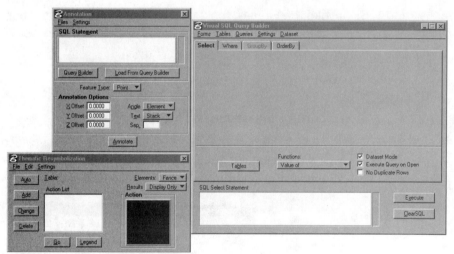

Access these dialog boxes from the Database menu.

For software developers who wish to create custom interfaces for projects or extend the software's functionality, GeoGraphics offers APIs (Application Programming Interfaces) in MDL and JMDL languages. For examples and API libraries, see the `mdl` and `jmdl` folders in the `C:\Bentley\Program\GeoGraphics` directory.

TriForma for Building Engineering

TriForma is the engineering configuration for building design. It will appeal to architects and engineers who design buildings for commercial and industrial markets.

It creates three-dimensional models from volume elements called *forms*. By themselves, forms are 3D geometric elements without intelligence. During placement, forms can be attached to parts. *Parts* are data attributes that impart intelligence to forms. A form attached to a part knows it's a wall, slab, or roof. Parts contain two types of data attributes: drafting (symbology, patterning, and other) and material. TriForma uses the drafting data attribute when extracting 2D representations (plan, elevation, section) from its models. It uses the material data attribute, called *component*, when computing quantities and extracting specifications.

The *tri* in TriForma refers to its three core competencies:

- It creates three-dimensional form-based models.
- It extracts two-dimensional drawings from models.
- It extracts quantities and specifications from models.

TriForma's basic building block is a form. There are tools to create fixed and variable height forms. To create variable height forms, extrude them against intersecting shapes or other during placement. You can move, copy, extend, and otherwise modify or manipulate forms. You can also create openings in forms for doors and windows.

Form attribute data is organized into parts and part families. A *part family* is a named group of similar parts. During conceptual design, when material and construction methods are undecided, you'll want to assign forms to empty parts in part families. As the design progresses and you finalize material and construction methods, you can add parts to part families and revise the form's part assignment.

Parts and part families are customizable and can be defined to meet project needs. Example part and part families are included with TriForma to get you started. Names for part families might be exterior walls, interior walls, concrete, floors, foundations, and others. A part family, such as exterior walls, might contain exterior brick wall and exterior siding wall as parts.

The nongraphic material component data included in a part definition is organized into components and component families. A *component family* is a named group of similar components. For example, the structural steel component family might include Grade 36 steel, Grade 50 steel, and galvanized steel as components. Components and component families can be customized for projects and for conformance to standards. Several components and component families are delivered with TriForma.

A component defines a material, its unit cost, and the filename of a word processor document containing material specification text. When including a component in a part definition, you must also specify the formula to compute component quantity from the form. For example, a wall paint component would include a surface area formula to compute paint quantity. A concrete wall component would include a form volume formula to compute concrete quantity. Obviously, different formulas (inside surface area or volume) from the same form may be required by different components, and component definitions accommodate that.

Parts and part families are defined in the Parts Manager dialog box. Components and component families are defined in the Component Manager dialog box.

In addition to part and component definitions attached to forms, TriForma models contain section definition lines. These lines define the location where sections are to be cut and their orientation. Drawing extraction tools use section definition lines along with part drafting attributes (line style, weight, pattern, fill) to create 2D drawings—plan, section, and elevation—from the model.

TriForma includes report-generation tools to create bill of material and cost reports, and to compile all specification text word processor files for the project. Reports can be exported to spreadsheet programs for further processing.

The next section discusses the menus and toolboxes TriForma adds to MicroStation.

The TriForma Interface

During installation, TriForma prompts for MicroStation's location and installs files in the `c:\Bentley\Program\TriForma` folder by default. A minimum installation copies only program files. To install all files, including example files in metric and English units, you must choose complete installation. Upon installation, a TriFormaJ program folder is added to the Programs menu on the Start button. This folder contains several icons, including one to invoke TriForma.

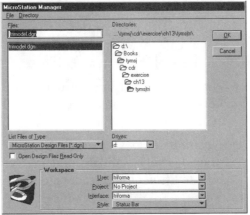

Select the triforma *workspace and interface in the MicroStation Manager dialog box to start TriForma.*

To start TriForma, select its icon from the TriFormaJ submenu from the Programs menu on the Start button. Notice that Modeler uses *triforma* as the workspace user and interface in the MicroStation Manager dialog box, as shown in the figure above.

On opening a 3D design file, the interface changes you'll notice are a significantly bigger Main tool frame, additional controls on the Primary toolbox, a new TriForma item on the menu bar, and a floating TriForma menu window. The TriForma menu choices are listed below.

TriForma Menu Options

- *Catalogs* are one way to organize parts and other commonly used tools or commands in a hierarchical menu structure for easy access. For example, parts may be organized in a catalog that follows industry standard specification sections. Catalog menu choices and their commands are defined in text files with the `.cmf` extension. They are located in a directory defined by the configuration variable TFCAT_DIR. Several catalog menu files are delivered with TriForma for you to customize.

- *Libraries* offer choices for reviewing, creating, importing, exporting, and editing libraries of parts, compound parts, and components. It lets you access the Presets dialog box to include project cost items that don't have associated graphical elements. It also calls up the Variants dialog box to substitute materials assigned to forms for comparative project cost studies.

- The *Main Toolbox* option opens the enhanced Main tool frame if it's not already open on the screen. The tools in 2D files differ from tools on the tool frame in a 3D file.

- *Keynotes Toolbox* opens the Keynotes toolbox used to place and edit keynote symbols in a model. Many TriForma tools work with keynote symbols.

- *Notation Toolbox* opens the Notation toolbox for annotating drawings with standard drafting symbols such as north arrow, match line, revision cloud, leaders, detail symbols, and others.

- *Backup* offers choices to backup the active design file or to invoke the MicroStation TriForma Backup dialog box to select all project design and data files.

- *Setup* opens the TriForma Setup dialog box to select the language used on menus and checkboxes for autoload and log files.

- *Preferences* opens the Preferences dialog box to set the number of successive backups, to compress design files when backing them up, to remember open dialog boxes between sessions, to toggle the TriForma menu window, to set font height and width for auto dimensions, and to specify an increment for openings.

- *Configuration* opens the Edit TriForma Configuration Variables dialog box to define locations for various TriForma part, component, catalog menu, and other data files.

- *Scale Factors* opens the Scale Factors dialog box to specify the scale factors for keynotes, notations, and compound cells placed from catalogs.

Enhanced Main Tool Frame

TriForma adds many toolboxes to the Main tool frame. These toolboxes contain tools for creating and editing forms, generating drawings, compiling specifications, and computing quantities and costs. TriForma-specific toolboxes in the Main tool frame are shown below.

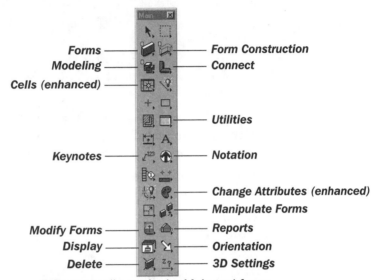

TriForma toolboxes in the Main tool frame.

- *Forms* contains tools to place linear and shape forms, structural steel forms, and generic solid elements.
- *Form Construction* has tools to extrude elements to forms and shapes to solids.
- *Modeling* contains tools to construct solids from other solids. It also offers tools to cut, protrude, chamfer, and stretch solids.
- *Connect* has tools to clean up form intersections and to extend top surfaces of forms to connect with other shapes or forms.
- *Cells* is an enhanced version of the standard toolbox that includes tools to place, manipulate, edit and manage compound cells. A tool invokes the Compound Cell Manager. It also includes tools to place parametric shapes for stairs, trusses, and frames.
- *Utilities* has tools to display and place grids and to create dimensions at intersection points between elements and an intersecting line.

- *Keynotes* has tools to create and edit keynote symbols in a model.
- *Notation* contains drafting annotation tools to place the north arrow symbol, section markers, match lines, and others.
- *Change Attributes* is an enhanced version that includes tools to change and match form attributes, and to change a form's part assignment.
- *Manipulate Forms* contains tools from the MicroStation Manipulate toolbox and those specific to forms, including tools to move and copy openings in forms.
- *Modify Forms* contains tools to modify the height, base, width, and length of forms. It also has tools to modify a form's base, direction, and orientation.
- *Reports* has tools to add section lines in the model using the Section Manager dialog box for 2D drawing production. It also has tools to generate quantities and compile specifications.
- *Display* combines tools from the 3D View Control and Rendering Tools toolboxes and adds a few display tools.
- *Orientation* contains tools to change a view's orientation to the many more standard views TriForma implements, such as Back Left Iso and Back Right Iso views.
- *Delete* contains tools to delete forms and form openings.
- *3D Settings* contains tools to query and set the active depth.

When you have a 2D section drawing open in TriForma, the Main tool frame contains fewer TriForma-specific toolboxes. The individual toolboxes in the 2D main toolbox are listed below:

- *Utilities* has tools to display and place grids and to create dimensions at intersection points between elements and an intersecting line.
- *Display* contains tools to update, pan, and rotate views.
- *Info* is a collection of tools TriForma adds to the Change Attributes toolbox.
- *Document Navigation* contains tools to navigate between the TriForma model and the generated section drawings or to a specific area in the model file.

Defining Parts and Components

Many data files contribute to TriForma's design environment. A general-purpose set of data files is delivered with the software. These data files define parts, components, catalogs, structural steel shapes, and other attributes you attach to forms. As you become more proficient in using TriForma, you'll modify these data files and perhaps create new ones from scratch. Each will be suitable for a different type of project.

TriForma lets you maintain multiple data sets. To use a different data set, edit variables in the Edit TriForma Configuration Variables dialog box. You may access it from the TriForma menu, as shown below.

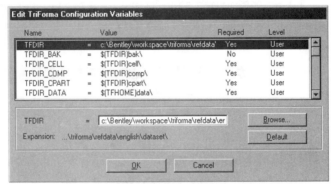

You can switch between data sets from this dialog box.

Parts and part families are created in the Part Manager dialog box. From the TriForma menu, select Libraries, then Parts to open it.

Parts are data attributes that link to forms to make them "intelligent." A part belongs to a part family. To create a part, first define or select its part family. A part family definition requires two data fields: Name and Description. A part requires four categories of information to define it: Definition, Attributes, Section Patterning, Auto Dimensions, and Components.

You can name part families any way you wish. Names of major building components, such as footings and walls, might be one example. The sample TriForma data defines them in common specification divisions.

To create parts:

1. Select the part's family in the Parts Manager, or create one by clicking the New button. Then click the Add button. The Add Part dialog box opens, as shown below.

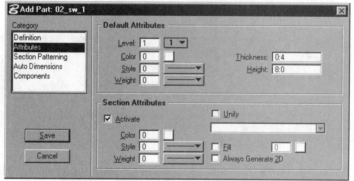

Create parts in the Add Part dialog box.

2. The Definition category is initially highlighted in the dialog box. From the Family list, select one for the part. In the Part field, enter a part name.
3. Select Attributes in the Category listbox and define its symbology in the Default and Section Attributes groupboxes.
4. Select Section Patterning in the Category listbox and define hatching attributes for section drawings generated from the 3D model.
5. Select Auto Dimensions in the Category listbox and define the four types of dimensions TriForma is to generate for forms linked to this part.
6. Select Components in the Category listbox to add components and define formulas for quantity computations.
7. Click Save.

TriForma supports compound part definitions. A *compound part* is a collection of parts that represents a composite building element, such as a cavity wall. A compound part is organized in compound part families, as are parts. Define a compound part by specifying a horizontal and vertical offset distance between its component parts. Compound parts are defined in the Compound Parts dialog box, shown in the figure below. Open it from the TriForma menu by selecting Compound Parts in the Libraries submenu.

Manage compound parts in this dialog box.

To create compound parts:

1. From the Compound Parts dialog box, select its compound part family. If no suitable family exists, create one by clicking the New button, and then highlight it. Then click the Add button to open the Add Compound Part dialog box.
2. In the Sub Parts groupbox of the dialog box, select the desired part and its family, and fill values for the horizontal offset, thickness, vertical offset, and height. Click Insert to add the part to the Sub Parts listbox.
3. Repeat step 2 until all needed parts are inserted in the compound part.
4. Click Save.

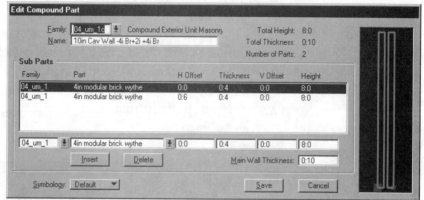

The Edit Compound Part dialog box, opened by clicking Edit on the Compound Parts dialog box, is identical to the Add Compound Part dialog box.

A part definition is incomplete without an assigned component. Material lists and project specification compilation aren't possible if a part definition doesn't incorporate a component. A component definition includes, in addition to a component family and the component's name, material properties (unit of measure, density, thermal characteristics, and price), specification section, and name of specification text document. Components are defined in the Component Manager dialog box, shown in the figure below. Open it from the TriForma menu by selecting Components in the Libraries submenu.

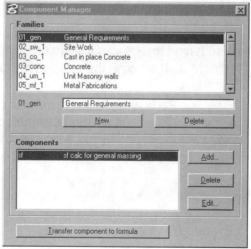

Use this dialog box to create, edit, and delete components.

To create components:

1. From the Component Manager dialog box, select the new component's family. If no suitable family exists, create one by clicking the New button, and then highlight it. Click the Add button to open the Edit Component dialog box, shown below. It's the same dialog box that opens on clicking the Edit button. The selected family appears in the Family list.

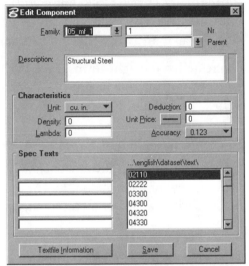

Define a component in this dialog box.

2. Enter a number for the component in the Nr field.
3. If defining components in a hierarchical structure, select a parent component. Otherwise, leave it blank.
4. Enter a description for the component.
5. In the Characteristics groupbox, select or fill in material data. There are controls for Unit of measure, Density to calculate form weight, Lambda to calculate thermal loss, Deduction for minimum opening size to deduct when calculating quantities, Unit Price (can vary with quantity), and Accuracy for decimal places to use in reports.
6. In the Spec Texts groupbox, enter up to five specification documents. When this component is used in a project, the specification documents specified will be compiled. To enter a specification document, click a specification text field, then double-click the document filename in the listbox to the right. The Textfile Information button is used to add specification files, as no samples are delivered with TriForma.
7. Click Save.

Creating Models and Documents

TriForma building models are made of geometric forms linked to parts. When placing forms, the active part definition in the Tool Settings window is linked to the form. If the active definition is a compound part, the form placement tool creates multiple forms.

Forms can be of two types: linear and shape. Linear forms are created like lines and have a base line and direction. Shape forms are extruded from closed planar areas and have no base line or direction.

To create fixed height forms, specify the height in the Tool Settings window. For variable height forms, extend them to other forms or shapes.

To create fixed height forms:

1. Start TriForma with a 3D model file, if it's not already open.
2. Activate any form placement tool from the Forms toolbox. In the Tool Settings window, select a part family and a part.

Select Fixed Height from the Top option button to create fixed height forms.

3. From the Top option button, select Fixed Height and enter a value in the Height field.
4. Click a start point.
5. Click an endpoint for the first segment. Click data points for additional segments if desired.
6. Reset to complete the form.

The Forms toolbox provides tools to place linear, segmented, arc, curved, slab, and free forms. You can also place structural steel forms. Forms may be placed parallel, perpendicular, or between other forms.

To create variable height forms:

1. Start TriForma with a 3D model file, if it's not already open.
2. Activate any form placement tool from the Forms toolbox. In the Tool Settings window, select a part family and a part.

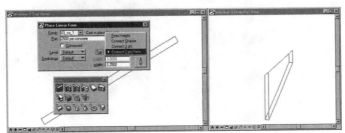

Select one of the Connect choices from the Top option button.

3. From the Top option button, select Connect Shapes to connect the form's top surface to existing shapes. Choose Connect 3 Points to connect the form's top surface to the plane defined by three points. Select Connect 2 Points to connect the form's top surface to a line defined by two points.
4. Select shapes, or click points to define the variable height.
5. Click a start point.
6. Click an endpoint for the first segment. Click data points for additional segments if desired.
7. Reset to complete the form.

In addition to forms, TriForma provides tools to create parametric components such as stairs, trusses, and frames with toolboxes identified earlier.

To extract two-dimensional drawings from models, you first define section planes, specify seed and reference files, and define front and rear views in the Section Manager dialog box. Then you click the Calculate button to generate the drawings. Section Manager can save definitions for use in other models.

To generate 2D drawings:

1. Start TriForma with a 3D model file, if it's not already open.
2. Invoke the Section Manager dialog box from the Reports toolbox.
3. Click the Add button. The Edit Section Definition dialog box opens, as shown below.

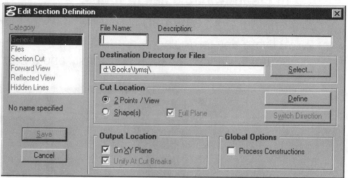

Define section planes in the Edit Section Definition dialog box.

4. In the Filename field enter a name for the file to be generated. In the Description field enter a drawing description. Select 2 Points or Shape(s) and click the Define button to define the section plane by entering two points or identifying a shape. The Category listbox is enabled.

5. Make other desired selections in the dialog box and click the Save button. The Edit Section Definition dialog box closes, and the Section Manager dialog box opens.

6. Click the Calculate All button to generate the 2D drawings.

To extract a bill of materials and compile project specification documents, make appropriate choices in the Quantify dialog box. Then, click the Start button to export or compile desired information.

To generate quantities and compile specifications:

1. Start TriForma with a 3D model file, if it's not already open.
2. Invoke the Quantify dialog box from the Reports toolbox.
3. In the Reports groupbox, enable Detailed to generate a detailed quantity report; enable Summary to generate a summary quantity report. Enable Spec Texts to compile specification documents for the project. Click the layout button to customize report layout.

NOTE: Part definitions *must* contain components for the Quantify dialog box to calculate quantities and compile specifications. It must also include a quantity computation formula, such as SA for surface area.

4. In the Quantified Levels groupbox, turn off levels you don't want to process. Forms in levels that are turned off won't be used in quantity reports. To select active levels from a view, click the Set From button.

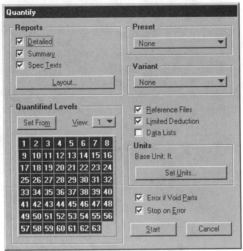

Generate quantities and compile specifications from the Quantify dialog box.

5. Select presets you defined earlier in the Presets dialog box accessed from TriForma's Library submenu. Presets are used to include costs, such as mobilization and demobilization, that don't have associated graphics.

6. Select variants you defined earlier in the Variants dialog box accessed from TriForma's Library submenu. Variants are used to compare alternative construction materials without changing part assignments to forms.

7. Enable the Reference Files checkbox to include quantities from attached reference files. Enable the Limited Deduction checkbox to ignore form openings smaller than the size specified in part definition. Enable the Data Lists checkbox to generate a data list that can be used to transfer part data from one model to another.

8. Click the Set Units button to define the base unit for generated quantities.

9. Enable the Error if Void Parts and the Stop on Error checkboxes to abort quantity and specification generation if an error is encountered.

10. Click Start. Selected quantity reports and specifications are generated.

This concludes the introduction to TriForma. For software developers TriForma offers information and creation APIs in the MDL language to query or create forms. See the `c:\Bentley\Program\TriForma\MDL` folder for examples and API libraries.

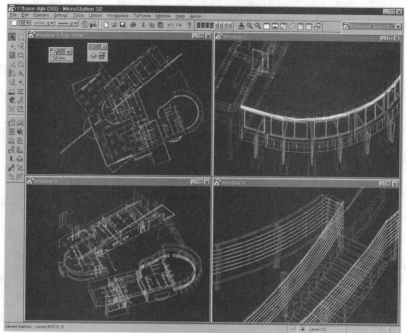

The River Mountains Water Treatment Facility was modeled in MicroStation TriForma. (Courtesy of SNWA and MW/Hill.)

Modeler for Mechanical Modeling

Modeler is the engineering configuration for mechanical design. It implements feature-based parametric solid modeling and will appeal to designers in manufacturing industries. You can design hearing aids, cameras, automobiles, boats, airplanes, and other everyday devices.

The term *feature-based* refers to a design environment where models keep track of changes, called *features*, applied to them. Follow this example in designing a camera body. Take a slab, fillet its edges, and sculpt its gripping surface. The edge fillets and surface sculpting operations are called features applied to the base slab. In feature-based modeling, the base part remembers modifications and their sequence.

Features are stored as attribute data in models. This makes solid models intelligent. For example, if you change the length of the base slab, the fillets and the sculpted surface remain attached to the base slab.

Three-dimensional models created in MicroStation are geometric. To edit them, you change vertex coordinates. Modeler solids are defined in terms of parameters, not coordinates.

In chapter 9, *Dimension-Driven Design*, you learned about profiles and how to develop them so they obeyed dimensional, locational, and geometric constraints. Modeler solids behave the same way and are called *parametric*. To modify the solid, you edit its defining parameters and all associated features adjust to maintain the model logic. You make such changes in the Tool Settings window or in the Feature Manager.

In Modeler, you can take several models and combine them into assemblies by defining how they are attached and in what position. Assemblies let you create exploded views, similar to those that accompany assemble-it-yourself appliances or furniture.

Modeler provides tools to create 2D representations from solid models. It also maintains a *bidirectional association* between the model and its 2D representation. Here's an example. Should you change the model, the drawing will update automatically. Should you change the drawing, the model will also update.

Bentley has incorporated the solid modeling technology of Parasolid in Modeler. You can use finite element analysis software and exchange data with other solid modeling packages or add-ons, such as sheet metal folding or CNC machining that support the Parasolid standard.

The next section discusses the menus and toolboxes Modeler adds to MicroStation.

The Modeler Interface

During installation, Modeler prompts for MicroStation's location and installs files in the `c:\Bentley\Program\Modeler` folder by default. You can choose to install only the program files or also include examples and MDL development libraries.

To start Modeler, select its icon from the MicroStation_J submenu from the Programs menu on the Start button. Notice tha Modeler uses *modeler* as the workspace user and *mech3d* as the interface in the MicroStation Manager dialog box, as shown in the figure below.

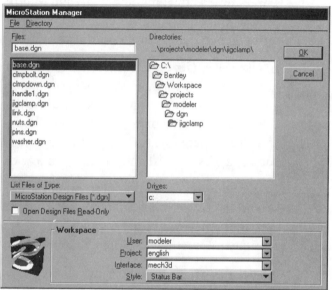

Select the modeler *workspace and* mech3d *interface in the MicroStation Manager dialog box to start Modeler.*

When you open a design file, the most obvious interface changes you'll notice are revised Primary and Standard toolboxes, a smaller Main tool frame, new Modeler and Sheet Detailer tool frames, and modifications to File, Element, and Tools menus. Though Modeler retains all of MicroStation's functionality, it has little use for the bulk of 2D tools in the Main tool frame. Consequently, those tools are hidden and accessible via key-ins.

Menubar Changes

Modeler adds several solid modeling-specific filters in its Import and Export submenus under the File menu. Supported file formats include SAT, IGES, Parasolid, Step AP203, VersaCAD, VRML, and Adams ADM. The File menu also includes choices to synchronize models and parts that may have been opened or edited in MicroStation without loading Modeler.

The STL (Stereo Lithography) format is a standard data exchange mechanism between CAD and numeric control (NC) devices used in manufacturing. Modeler can export its solids in that format.

The Modeler submenu under the Element menu provides access to the Modeler Solids, Modeler Part Manager, and Modeler Feature Manager dialog boxes. The purposes of these dialog boxes are explained below.

- Use the Modeler Solids dialog box to suppress feature display and to specify element types to use when storing parametric solids.
- Use the Modeler Part Manager to manage parts in assemblies. It's especially helpful when assemblies are large and parts span across files.
- Use the Modeler Feature Manager to display and edit a feature tree for the selected solid model. Modeler's ability to modify a solid by editing its construction steps (features) in the feature tree showcases the power of feature-based solid modeling.

The Tools menu provides access to Modeler's tool frames and the toolboxes contained in them. These are discussed next.

Modeler's Tool Frames

Modeler's parametric solid creation, feature creation, manipulation, and modification, and assembly tools are invoked from the tool boxes in the Modeler tool frame.

Modeler's drawing sheet creation, dimensioning, and detailing tools are invoked from the Sheet Detailer tool frame.

Both tool frames and their toolboxes are illustrated below.

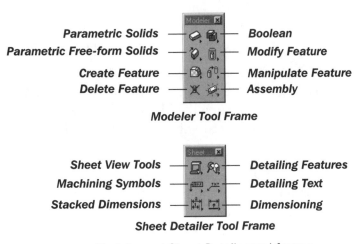

Modeler and Sheet Detailer tool frames.

Modeling Solids

When you create a solid model or part, you're likely to start with a basic solid shape, such as a slab, sphere, or cone, which you'll refine with features to give it the final form. For example, to model a vase, you'd start with a cylinder and refine its shape with a thin shell feature.

Modeler implements many features, such as fillet, chamfer, hole (through, counterbore, countersunk), boss, cut, protrusion, and rib, needed to create solid models from basic solid shapes.

The solid model shown in the figure below was created from a parametric slab modified with rounded edge and counterbore hole features.

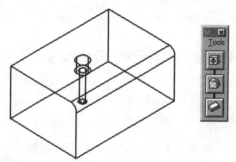

The slab was modified with rounded edge and counterbore hole features.

Each of the three features that make up the solid model above—the slab, the rounded edge, and the counterbore hole—is parametric. The slab knows its height, width, and length. The hole knows all variables that define it. The rounded edge knows the two faces it fillets and the fillet radius.

The feature tree shown next to the solid model in the figure above was invoked by clicking the Modeler Feature Manager icon on the Primary toolbox and identifying the solid model. It displays the three features that make up the solid.

When creating solid models in Modeler, use parametric solids whenever possible. You can edit parametric solids much more easily than geometric surfaces or solids.

The following steps describe how to create the parametric feature-based solid model shown in the figure above. It is included on the CD-ROM in the folder \Exercise\Ch13 and is in the file feature.dgn.

To create the solid model:

1. Start Modeler by selecting its icon from the Start button.

2. Create a new design file for the solid model by using one of the seed files that come with Modeler. Open the design file.

3. Activate the Place Slab tool from the Parametric Solids toolbox. In the Tool Settings window, select Parametric Solid from the Type option button. Enter values for its length, width, and height parameters, or leave them blank to define them with data points.

4. If you entered parameter values in the Tool Settings window, keep clicking data points in the Top view in response to prompts on the status bar for the start point and the parameters. If you decided to define dimensions with data points, click the first three data points to define the start point, length, and width in the Top view, then define the height in the Front view and accept the model shown with a data point. You may find it easier to use AccuDraw.

5. Activate the Round Edges or Faces tool from the Create Feature toolbox. In the Tool Settings window, select Face Face (Yes, that's two Faces!) from the Round option button. Enter a value for the fillet radius.

6. Identify the solid. A dashed outline highlights the slab's face. Move the cursor and the highlight moves to another face. Accept with a data button when the desired face highlights.

7. Continue moving the cursor to highlight the next adjoining face and accept it with the data point. A preview of the fillet displays.

8. Accept it with a data point.

9. Activate the Create Hole tool from the Create Feature toolbox. In the Tool Settings window, select Counterbore from the Hole Type option button; Blind from the Drill option button; Face Normal from the Direction option button, and enter values for the hole and counterbore diameters and depths.

10. Identify the solid. A counterbore hole moves along the solid surface as you move the cursor. Enter a data point to define its location.

11. Accept it with a data point.

The above steps outlined the general procedure for creating feature-based solids. You start with a primitive parametric solid. You can also start with a dimension-driven profile (see chapter 9) and extrude or revolve it to serve as a basis for more complex solids. Then, you add features such as fillets, holes, and cuts to complete your model.

NOTE: MicroStation Modeler includes many dimension-driven cells in the cell library `modeler.cel`.

You could have created the above model in MicroStation without Modeler. Why use Modeler? The answer becomes obvious when you edit the model. Changing the counterbore hole would be tedious in MicroStation as the diameter and height of the two holes would have to be manipulated individually. In Modeler, you identify the counterbore feature, enter new values in a dialog box, and the feature updates to maintain its normal relationship to the surface it drills through.

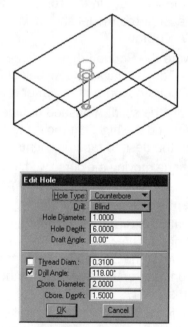

Editing parametric solids is as easy as entering new parameter values in a dialog box.

Consider another example. When you increase the height of a feature-based solid with a through hole, the hole length automatically increases.

To revise a solid model:

1. Activate the Modify Parametric Solid or Feature tool from the Modify Feature toolbox. You are prompted to identify a feature.
2. Click the feature you wish to edit. The feature highlights.
3. Accept the feature with a data point. A dialog box opens to display the feature's editable parameters.
4. Enter new values for parameters you wish to change.
5. Click OK. Modeler revises the feature geometry and makes other changes that may be required to keep the solid consistent with dependent feature definitions.

Creating Assemblies

When working on a project, you're likely to create several solids that might be assembled in some way. For example, a fountain pen model might consist of several solids: barrel, nib, and cap.

The term *assembly* in Modeler is defined as a collection of several parametric feature-based solids attached with a specific type of joint that defines permissible movements between them. Before you can assemble solids, you must transform them into attachable parts by using the Create Part tool in the Assembly toolbox. When making a part from a solid, you define an origin and give it a name. Next use the Assemble Part tool to specify how the parts are attached.

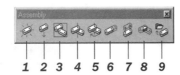

1. Create Part	4. Constrain Part	7. Explode Part
2. Place Part	5. Drag Part	8. Check Part
3. Assemble Part	6. Modify Part	9. Export Part

Use the Assembly toolbox to create assemblies.

To create a part, place an instance of a part in the active design file, assemble part instances, constrain parts, drag a part consistent with its degrees of freedom, modify it in the context of the assembly, set up an exploded view, check the interference of a part with others in the assembly, and to export parts to external design files, use the tools in the Assembly toolbox.

To create an assembly:

1. Create parametric feature-based solids for components that will make up an assembly.
2. Activate the Create Part tool in the Assembly toolbox. To keep part definitions in the active design file, select Active Design File from the Destination option button in the Tool Settings window. Otherwise, select External Design File. You are prompted to identify an element.
3. Identify a solid. It highlights, and you are prompted to accept it with an origin point.
4. Click a point or snap to a location on the part that is to serve as the part's origin. The Create Part dialog box opens, as shown below.

5. Enter a name, description, and density for the part. Click OK. The solid becomes a part. Should you examine the solid's feature tree, you'll see the Create Part action appear as a feature instance.
6. Make parts of other assembly components.
7. Place part instances in the active design file using the Place Part tool.
8. Use the Assemble Part tool to collect together all parts that will form the assembly. The parts identified will appear in the Feature Manager as components on an assembly.

9. Use the Constrain Part tool to attach assembly components together. Select the desired mode of attachment from the Tool Settings window.

   If you wish to practice creating an assembly, you may use the design file `assembly.dgn` in the `\Exercise\Ch13` folder on the CD-ROM. It contains a base part and a shaft, as shown below. Assemble them so the shaft attaches in the center of the counterbore hole.

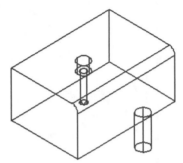

You may use this `assembly.dgn` *file on the CD-ROM to practice part assembly.*

Creating Drawings

Modeler offers the Sheet View Tools toolbox in the Sheet Detailer tool frame to help you compose drawing sheets from models. When you use the Create New Drawing Sheet tool, it creates a special view, called the *sheet view*, in which to place standard view groups (front, top, side).

Modeler creates the sheet view in Window 8 of the same design file that contains the solid model. This is done by self-referencing the design file's various views.

Self-referencing the model file to create the drawing sheet means that the drawing and the model maintain bidirectional associativity. When you edit the solid model, the drawing sheet changes. When you edit the drawing sheet, the model changes.

To create a drawing sheet:

1. Activate the Create New Drawing Sheet tool from the Sheet View Tools toolbox. The Tool Settings window displays two buttons: Create and Settings.

2. Click the Settings button. The Tool Settings window enlarges to display sheet composition options.

3. Make changes to the default sheet composition options as desired. Notice that View 8 is the default sheet view and it uses level 62 for annotations and level 63 for dimensions, as shown in the figure below.

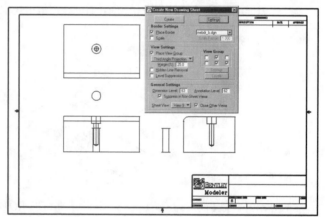

Use the Create New Drawing Sheet tool to create drawing sheets.

4. Click the Create button in the Tool Settings window. The views displaying the model close. View 8 opens with a border attached, as specified in the tool's settings. You are prompted to identify the location of the standard views: front, top, and side.

Once the sheet view is created, you can scale, move, and manipulate the views individually or as a group.

The Sheet Detailer tool frame contains tools to hatch, dimension, and annotate the drawing to communicate the model's design. To see for yourself that the sheet view maintains bidirectional associativity with the solid model, use the Modify Feature tool to change a feature's size in the sheet view. You'll notice that the model also changes.

This concludes the introduction to Modeler, and this chapter. For software developers who want to enhance Modeler or customize it to streamline its use for specific projects, Modeler provides APIs in the MDL language. See the c:\Bentley\Program\Modeler\MDL folder for examples and API libraries.

Part 2

Administering MicroStation

Helping Others Be More Productive

Chapter 14

Setting Drafting Standards

Toward Efficiency and Uniformity

When you're learning or using MicroStation in a production CAD environment, your primary interest is its drawing features and tools. You need to know how to set up a drawing, enter coordinate data, navigate a drawing's views, draw and edit geometric entities, attach reference files, print drawings, link nongraphic data to elements, create and render 3D models, and use the engineering configurations. That was the focus of Part 1, *Using MicroStation*.

The next five chapters, including this one, cover MicroStation setup and implementation issues within an organization. You'll find a CAD manager in firms that recognize the importance of proactive CAD management. At other companies, this role falls on the shoulders of the computer guru who seems to have answers to most user's questions.

The CAD administrator supports the drawing production team by developing standards and implementing tools and procedures to meet business goals and client needs more efficiently. If you're called upon to help streamline production and ensure drawing consistency, this chapter is for you.

When you wear a CAD administrator's hat, you're not creating drawings in MicroStation. You're helping to improve the efficacy of CAD as a mission-critical tool within your organization. You must study and identify the needs, processes, and tools in the context of technology, business goals and client needs.

To be effective in this role, it's important that you have the blessing and support of upper management. As you carry out your duties, you'll need their feedback and the necessary authority to implement the policies, procedures, and tools.

Information in this chapter is organized in two sections, listed below.

- **Why and How to Develop Standards** discusses the benefits of standards and how to develop them. You're introduced to several institutes and agencies that publish CAD standards and guidelines. You also learn about issues you should consider when developing your own standards.

- **Implementation Tools** discusses MicroStation features and tools that can help you implement standards so they are easy to use. Here you learn about the role of level names, sidebar menus, Settings Manager, function key menus, workspaces, macros, and custom application programs to meet your goals.

The first section is CAD platform-neutral. Issues discussed aren't software-specific. If you have an interest in CAD standards as a user, project manager, or business owner, you'll find much of this information useful. Not that the information presented is new; it's the compilation of relevant information in a format that can prod you to develop or improve your own standards.

The second section shows how to use several standardization tools, such as Settings Manager, level names and sidebar menus. It also identifies features, such as workspaces, interface customization tools, macros, and custom application programming you'll learn later.

Why and How to Develop Standards

In the quest to streamline and better manage CAD operations, many organizations and government agencies have developed standards or published guidelines. Several such efforts are listed below.

The American Institute of Architects (AIA) publishes guidelines for naming CAD layers and files. The book *CAD Layer Guidelines, 2nd Edition: Computer Aided Design Management Techniques for Architecture, Engineering & Facility Management* is written by the AIA Task Force on CAD. For details, visit AIA on the Web at the URL:

`http://www.aiaonline.com`

The US Army Corps of Engineers, in 1990, published the four-volume *Standards Manual for US Army Corps of Engineers CADD Systems*, also known as EM 1110-1-1807. It's included on Construction Criteria Base (CCB), a CD-ROM resource of specifications, regulations, and other construction and design-related data available from the National Institute of Building Sciences (NIBS) in Washington, D.C.

Additionally, the NIBS CADD Council is tasked with the development of a National CADD Standard. For details, visit them at the URL:

`http://www.nibs.org`

The Tri-Service CADD/GIS Technology Center publishes CAD and GIS/FM standards. Its CAD standard for the architectural, engineering, and construction projects is called the *A/E/C CADD Standards Manual*. The stated goal of the manual is to "reduce redundant CADD standardization efforts within the Army, Navy, Air Force and Corps of Engineers. The manual is part of an initiative to consolidate existing CADD drafting standards into a format generic enough to operate under various CADD software packages and to incorporate existing industry/national standards." The manual is available for download on the Web at the URL:

`http://tsc.wes.army.mil`

The Construction Specifications Institute publishes *The Uniform Drawing System*. For details, you may visit them at the URL:

`http://www.csinet.org`

Most state departments of transportation (DOTs) and government agencies also publish CAD standards. Their in-house design groups and consultants are required to follow these standards.

Obviously, a significant effort has been expended in standards development. If you're starting out, you may want to review the efforts of others. One of the published manuals may fulfill your needs.

The purpose of developing standards is threefold:

- **Consistency:** Using the details, symbols, seed files, and borders defined in a standard ensures that drawings are consistent from one designer to another.

- **Efficiency:** Tools, such as cell libraries and standard detail files, that accompany a standard help designers place typical graphical elements and details quickly. Additionally, the macro and custom application development effort that typically follows publication of a standard further improves productivity for common tasks.

- **Quality:** The planning and effort expended during standard development pools together the knowledge of many bright minds, resulting in a document that outlines procedures that ensures quality of the standards and the deliverables that adhere to it.

In order to serve these goals, a standard developer makes a checklist of relevant issues and tackles the ones likely to have the most significant impact in improving the organization's use of CAD. For example, a company working on large civil works projects will benefit more from reference file usage guidelines than will a landscaping company that creates single-sheet drawings.

When developing your own standards, use the following checklist of issues you may want to consider.

File Naming Convention

Electronic file names no longer have the eight character limitation with an additional three characters for filename extension that was imposed by earlier PC-DOS and MS-DOS operating systems. However, continuing to use this file naming convention may still be useful when exchanging drawings with others still using older computer systems.

CAD files contain many types of information. They may contain full-scale models, sheet files, standard borders, cell libraries, standard details, text glossaries, and drawing setup information. You may wish to consider a naming convention for each so they are easy to identify.

For example, the first two characters in a model file may designate a design discipline. The next two may designate the type of model, and the remaining characters may designate a user-defined code. Sheet files may use the first four characters to designate a project number, the next character for discipline, the next character for the type of sheet, followed by the sheet sequence number.

Cell library, glossary, and standard detail drawings are better named after materials, disciplines, and specification sections.

Project Directory Structure

Electronic files, especially CAD drawings, are company assets that take significant effort to create. Consequently, they should be routinely archived and saved for several years. Rather than store drawings on individual desktop computers, store them on servers that are backed up daily.

Architectural and engineering firms operate on a project basis. Everything—work hours spent, expenses incurred, and the filing system—are tracked by project number. Consequently, it makes sense to name and organize directories by project number.

Of course, files unrelated to projects and library files, such as cells and glossaries, will need a separate directory tree structure.

Seed Files

Drawing templates, also called *seed files*, contain startup parameters and serve as a basis for new drawings. To ensure drawing consistency among designers, you will want to create and manage them. Because drawing setup requirements can vary from project to project, you may need to create seed files for individual projects.

Seed files can contain attached borders, settings for text, dimensions, and working units, view window layouts, and other settings that are saved when you invoke the Save Settings option from the File menu.

Standard Borders

Many clients dictate the border format for a project. If you're a consultant, the tools you develop to automate standards implementation should be flexible enough to accommodate client needs. If you're an owner agency, you probably maintain a few border formats. The border is determined by the drawing size, type of drawing, or discipline.

Drawing Management Systems

Though not strictly a part of CAD standards, drawing management systems are valuable in tracking and reporting on drawing status. They implement security—a user must log on to access such a system—and require drawings be checked in or out from a server to the local system during a design session. They maintain a history of drawing access and can simplify drawing search and other drawing management tasks.

You can invest in such systems. If you have a database programmer on board, he or she can create one for your specific corporate needs.

Drawing Scales

The type of drawing (plan, elevation, section, or detail), discipline, and paper size will usually determine the drawing scale you use when you plot. Many drawing parameters, such as text and cell size, are determined by this scale. Publishing guidelines on acceptable drawing scales, and how they affect text and cell size will help ensure consistency.

Text Sizes and Fonts

Text size used to annotate drawing components differs from the size used to label drawing sections, building or street names, or notes. Publishing guidelines on acceptable fonts and sizes for various annotation tasks will keep designers from having to guess what to use.

Symbology Tables

This is perhaps the most visible component of a drawing standard. When you read about drawing standards, you perhaps think of the level, color, line weight, and line style assignment for graphic elements.

The following symbology table is reproduced from page 5-6 in the U.S. Army Corps of Engineers EM 1110-1-1807 manual referred to earlier. The table lists level assignment and element symbology for architectural details.

Level	Description	Style	Weight	Color
1	Sheet Border	N/A	N/A	N/A
2	Graphic Scale/North Arrow	N/A	N/A	N/A
3	Sheet Independent Title Block Information	N/A	N/A	N/A
4	Modular Detail Reference Grid (Lines)	0	2	6
5	Modular Detail Reference Grid (Ticks)	0	2	6
10	Column Grids(Centerlines)	2	0	0
11	Column Grid Bubbles	0	1	0
20	Components and Steel Sections	0	1	4
40	Reference Symbols and Text	0	1	3
41	Matchline, Breakline, Centerline, Targets	0	4	2
42	Door Number and Symbols	0	1	3
43	Wall Type Labels	0	1	3
46	Notes and Miscellaneous Text	0	1	3
47	Detail Titles and Scales	0	3	3
50	Dimensions and Leaderlines	0	1	3
54	Default Active	0	0	0
59	Specification Numbers	0	0	0
62	Addenda and Bulletin Bubbles	0	4	0
63	Change Indication Level	0	0	0

Simply listing symbology guidelines for designers doesn't go far enough. You must develop tools, such as menus, to automate their selection. Also, there must be a reason for developing such guidelines. Symbology tables developed for rendering models will focus on separating elements for material assignment by unique level and color combinations. Tables developed by add-on software vendors may assign meaning to the unique combination of level, color, weight, and style for a drawing element so it can be manipulated more intelligently. Tables developed for designers that need to plot the same drawing with different plot parameters for different purposes will focus on the needs of the plot resymbolization process.

The combination of symbology tables and associated automation tools can be very powerful and productive, as is evident by the functionality of many add-on application programs that use it.

Standard Symbols

Every engineering discipline uses symbols on drawings. Schematic drawings use them extensively. A *symbol* is a graphic representation of a component or a concept. Examples include the north arrow, break line, type of structural weld, gate valve, and others. Symbols are usually simple in terms of geometry and small in terms of file size. They are stored in cells so they can be reused easily.

A good CAD standard will document the shape of common symbols for reference. It will also include cell libraries to facilitate their use.

Standard Details

Symbols are simple geometric representations of a component or concept. *Standard details* are a detailed representation, based on past experience, of how designs should be built to avoid common mistakes. For example, an architectural, engineering, and construction firm might have gained valuable experience in the construction of concrete, steel, and timber joints that successfully combat corrosive environmental forces for longer structure life. By documenting this knowledge in standard details with detailed construction notes, junior engineers can learn and benefit from their availability.

Standard details are best organized by material or specification classification category. Each detail should be printed for reference along with its file name. These details can be attached temporarily to a drawing, copied, and then detached. All project-specific edits to the detail then become a part of the drawing.

Plotting Guidelines

In your drafting standard, you'll want to include instruction on how to attach to network plotting devices, which ones to use for what purpose, and what drivers to use for which devices.

If you make use of plot resymbolization, documenting pen tables and their use will also serve designers make the best use of the company's hard copy resources.

Training

Education in the proper use of tools and tips on how to overcome known software limitations are important in any endeavor. Many find that participation in CAD user groups and formal classroom training help sharpen their skills.

If your organization provides such training or has contracts with trainers and consultants, promote their availability in the CAD standard manual so designers can take advantage of them.

Disseminate Standards

After you've researched your standardization needs and compiled the requirements, you'll want to organize them as a document. The purpose of this printed manual is not only to document the specific guidelines and procedures, but also to make the information easy to find when needed.

Web technology has become prevalent on company networks. Many organizations have deployed intranets to disseminate corporate knowledge on the network for online access with a Web browser. If your company has an intranet, consider publishing the CAD standards on it. This will make them widely accessible and help you gather feedback for improvements electronically. MicroStation's HTML authoring tools can help you publish the contents of your cell libraries, macros, and other details.

Standards by themselves do little to promote their use. Tools must be developed to automate the requirements. The next section discusses the tools you'll want to consider implementing.

Implementation Tools

MicroStation includes many tools to help you implement CAD standards. This section introduces those tools. Of course, you may not use them all. Over time you'll develop your own preferences and use the tools MicroStation users at your company find the most convenient.

Level Names

If you're an architect and adhere to guidelines set forth by the AIA, you're probably familiar with the layer naming conventions published by the Institute. MicroStation includes level names in level structure files based on these guidelines in the folder:

`C:\Bentley\Workspace\Projects\Examples\Arch\Data`

In this folder, look for files that start with the characters AIA and have the `.lvl` filename extension. You can assign names to levels in your design file from these level structure files.

To assign names to levels from level structure files:

1. From the Settings menu select Level, then Names. The Level Names dialog box opens.
2. From the File menu on the dialog box, select Open. The Open Level Structure dialog box opens.
3. Navigate to the folder containing the level structure files. Highlight the desired file. Click OK.
4. The Open Level Structure dialog box closes and level names are loaded in the Level Names dialog box, as shown below.

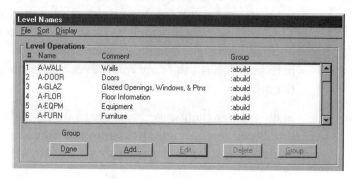

After assigning level names, you can use them in key-ins. For example, to change the active level to one named A-AREA, type `LV=A-AREA` in the Key-in window.

You can use the buttons in the above dialog box to edit level names. You may then save these changes for use in other design files by using the File menu on the dialog box.

The benefit of using level names, other than conforming to standards such as the one published by AIA, is to think of levels in terms of names rather than numbers that can be difficult to associate with components you wish to draw on them. Once you've assigned names to levels, clicking the level field on the status bar opens the Set Active Level dialog box that displays level names, rather than a level map of numbers.

Sidebar Menus

Sidebar menus were introduced in MicroStation Version 3 to invoke commands that could only be picked from tablet menus in the earlier version. They are archaic and supported in MicroStation only for backward compatibility. Bentley recommends you use Settings Manager instead. However, if you receive them from clients who've upgraded to MicroStation since IGDS days, you'll need to know how to use them.

Before Settings Manager, custom sidebar menus were used to facilitate implementation of symbology tables. If you are working on a structural project and want to draw steel details, sidebar menus make the act of switching to the appropriate level and symbology settings just a click or two away.

Sidebar menus are ASCII text files and have the filename extension `.sbm`. To load a sidebar menu, type the following in the Key-in window:

```
AM=menu_filename,SB
```

where `menu_filename` is in the name of the sidebar menu file. A sidebar menu dialog box opens.

Because there are better alternatives to sidebar menus, their syntax is not discussed here. However, a sample sidebar menu is presented so you can examine its structure.

```
MAIN_MENU title=TYMSJ, color=(2,1), width=10, height=1, rows=10, column=1,
border, vline
'Conc', 'E,LV=1;LC=0;CO=0', line
'Steel', 'E,LV=2;CO=0;CO=1', line
'Timber', 'E,LV=3;LC=0;CO=2', line
'CenterLine', 'E,LV=4;LC=4;CO=0', line
'Dims', 'E,LV=5;LC=0;CO=0', line
'Text', 'E,LV=6;LC=0;CO=0', line
'Walls', 'E,LV=7;LC=0;CO=3', line
'Doors', 'E,LV=8;LC=0;CO=4', line
'Windows', 'E,LV=9;LC=0;CO=4', line
'Tree', 'E,LV=10;LC=0;CO=0', line
```

This file is named `tymsj.sbm` and included on the CD-ROM in the
`\Exercise\Ch14` folder. To attach it, in the Key-in window, type:

`AM=tymsj,SB`

The menu dialog box opens, as shown in the figure below.

Sidebar menu dialog box activated by the `AM=` *key-in.*

You must include the path to the menu file unless you copy it in the
`C:\Bentley\Workspace\System\Data` folder. When you click the menu
labeled Conc, the active level changes to 1, style to 1, and color to 0.

Function Keys

You can assign any MicroStation key-in to a function key. MicroStation
supports ninety-six function key combinations. To set up function keys,
use the Function Keys option under the Workspace menu. See chapter
20 for additional details.

The ninety-six function key combinations noted above refer to the
twelve function keys on the keyboard when pressed alone and when
pressed in conjunction with: <Ctrl>, <Alt>, <Shift>, <Ctrl+Alt>,
<Ctrl+Shift>, <Alt+Shift>, and <Ctrl+Alt+Shift>.

You can use function keys to implement symbology tables. For instance, if you need to switch between levels 1 through 10, with separate weight, style and color assignments for each level, you may want to use the function keys F1 through F10 respectively for mnemonic reasons. The text string you will assign to these function keys will resemble the following:

```
LV=5;WT=1;LC=0;CO=3
```

When you press the function key the string is assigned to, it invokes the four concatenated key-ins in one step.

Workspaces

Introduced in Version 5, the concept of workspaces in MicroStation has matured considerably since then. When you start MicroStation, the MicroStation Manager dialog box lets you choose the workspace you wish to use for the design session.

You saw the engineering configurations use it to offer custom menus, access to their default seed files, and other aspects. Add-on application developer vendors use workspaces. You too have control over their creation and implementation.

With workspaces you can set up a custom design environment that includes custom menus, toolboxes, cell libraries, level structure and other data files, seed files, custom line styles and font files. Workspaces can be modified for company, project, and user needs by changing configuration variables accessed from the Workspace menu.

Workspaces are described in detail in chapter 17.

Settings Manager

In contrast to workspaces that let you organize cell libraries, line styles, and other settings, behind the scenes—transparent to the user—the Settings Manager is an interactive tool for switching between different level and symbology settings quickly. Components in the Settings Manager can also invoke drawing commands via key-ins.

Symbology tables in drafting standards are rarely used unless accompanied with tools that automate their selection. You learned about sidebar menus and function keys as tools to implement standards. Settings Manager is another tool. It's far more flexible and was designed especially for implementing standards.

To illustrate how to create settings in Settings Manager, let's take the symbology table for the apartment unit layout exercise in chapter 2, as shown in the table below.

Types of graphic elements	Level	Color	Weight	Style
walls: exterior and interior	1	white	4	0
doors and windows	2	yellow	1	0
labels	3	green	0	0
dimensions	4	red	0	0

We'll organize the settings in this table into two groups: Graphics and Annotation. The first two items will be placed in the Graphics group, the remaining two in the Annotation group. When you create settings in the Settings Manager, it organizes them in groups and components.

To create settings in Settings Manager:

1. Select Manage from the Settings menu. The Select Settings dialog box opens, as shown below.

Select Settings dialog box when Small Dialog is active in the Options menu.

This dialog box is used to activate settings stored in the component list items. You can hide its menus or make it larger by selecting choices from its Options menu. You can also dock this dialog box along the top or bottom edge of the MicroStation application window. When menus are hidden, or the dialog box is docked, you can access its menus by clicking the right mouse button in the dialog box away from any fields.

2. To create new settings, open the Edit Settings dialog box by selecting Edit from the File menu in the Select Settings dialog box. The dialog box is shown below.

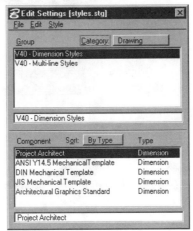

Use the Edit Settings dialog box to create new settings.

3. The Edit Settings dialog box contains a menu bar, two listboxes, an edit field directly below each listbox, and two option buttons to display groups by category and to sort components.

   The menu bar offers choices to manage settings files and to create or edit settings groups and components. The listbox and the edit field at the top are used to list and edit settings group names. The listbox and the edit field at the bottom are used to list and edit names of components corresponding to a highlighted settings group in the upper listbox.

4. Select New from the File menu on the dialog box to open the Create New Settings File dialog box. Navigate to the location where you want to save the new settings file, enter its name and click OK. The new file is created and opened in the Edit Settings dialog box. Its Group and Component listboxes are empty.

5. From the File menu on the dialog box, select Create, then Group. An "unnamed" group is added to the Group listbox.

6. Repeat step 5 to create a second "unnamed" group.

7. Highlight each "unnamed" group in turn and rename it in the edit field under the Group listbox. Name the first group Graphics. Name the second group Annotation, as shown in the figure below.

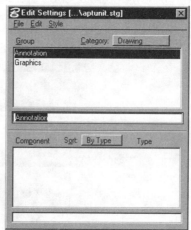

Use the edit field under the Group listbox to edit group names.

8. Highlight the Graphics group and from the Edit menu on the dialog box, select Create, then Linear. An "unnamed" linear component appears in the Component listbox. You'll use this for the interior and exterior walls. Highlight the component and name it Exterior and Interior Walls in the edit box that appears below the Component listbox.

9. Double-click the component. The Modify dialog box opens, as shown below.

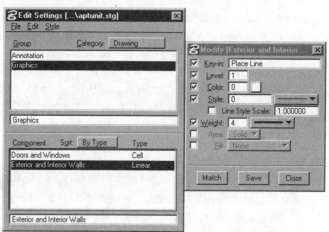

Double-click a component to define its settings.

10. Enable the Key-in, Level, Color, Style, and Weight checkboxes. Enter symbology settings for the component from the symbology table at the beginning of these steps, and Place Line for the key-in. These are shown in the figure above. Click Save to save the component's settings.

11. Highlight the Graphics group and from the Edit menu on the dialog box, select Create, then Cell. An "unnamed" cell component appears in the Component listbox. You'll use this for doors and windows. Highlight the component and name it Doors and Windows.

12. Double-click the Doors and Windows component. The Modify dialog box opens, as shown below.

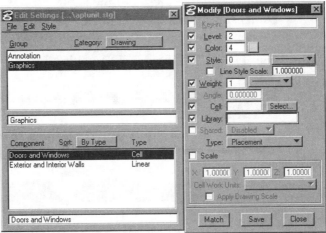

The Modify dialog box displays settings appropriate to component type selected.

13. Enable the Level, Color, Style, Weight, Cell and Library checkboxes. Enter symbology settings from the symbology table, and select the cell library and the default cell for the component. Click Save to close the Modify dialog box and to save the component's settings.

    You could also create separate components for doors and windows. Then, each could be assigned a different default cell.

14. Use steps 8 through 13 as a guide to creating components for the Annotation settings group.

As you've seen, the process of creating settings groups and components is rather straightforward. You create settings groups in the Edit Settings dialog box, and then you create components in the groups. You assign values to settings for each component by double-clicking the component and entering values in the Modify dialog box.

Settings used by the Settings Manager are saved in files with `.stg` as their filename extension.

To use settings you create, users select Manage from MicroStation's Settings menu to open the Select Settings dialog box. It is a nonmodal dialog box that can be left open while you work in your design file. To activate a setting, click its group if it's not already active. Then, select the desired component.

In addition to symbology tables, the Settings Manager is used to save multiple definitions for multi-lines and dimensions. As you learned in chapter 5, multi-line and dimension settings are defined in the Dimension Settings and Multi-lines dialog boxes accessed from the Element menu. However, these dialog boxes have no mechanism to save multiple definitions. Settings Manager to the rescue!

Access these dialog boxes from the Style menu in the Edit Settings dialog box.

To save multiple dimension and multi-line definitions for reuse, define and make the settings active in the Dimension Settings and Multi-lines dialog boxes. Then use the above dialog boxes to name and save them.

Settings Manager is an ideal tool to automate symbology tables and to maintain multiple dimension and multi-line definitions. But it's one of several tools to consider. CAD standards are enhanced immeasurably by macros and custom application programs. The chapters in Part 4, *Programming MicroStation*, introduce you to the many programming languages MicroStation supports.

This concludes the chapter.

Chapter 15

Fixing Corrupt Files

EdG: The Nongraphical DGN File Editor

Though it happens rarely, sometimes MicroStation will refuse to load a specific design file. This is a sign that your design file has become corrupt. There are many reasons why this might happen. A buggy user command, macro, or MDL application that incorrectly processes a graphics element can cause corruption. A bad spot on the hard drive where the file may be stored can cause corruption. A data packet transmission error while sending the file across a network to a file server can cause corruption. A power fluctuation or an unexpected lockup at the computer running MicroStation can cause corruption. The general wear and tear of storage media from which you might restore a file can cause corruption.

No matter how a design file becomes corrupt, it will either refuse to load in MicroStation, or it will display elements that you cannot snap to or manipulate. Other symptoms of a corrupt design file are that existing elements do not display, or display incorrectly.

In order to fix corrupt design files and cell libraries, and to modify design files in a nongraphical environment, Bentley delivers with MicroStation a command-line utility called EdG, an acronym for Edit Graphics. This utility is like EDLIN, the old MS-DOS line editor that you use to edit text files one line at a time in a command-line environment. EdG processes the design file through key-in commands and has no interactive graphical user interface.

This chapter introduces you to EdG. The topics covered in this chapter include:

- Understanding the DGN File Format
- Basic EdG Operations
- More EdG Operations
- Modifying DGN Elements
- Fixing Corrupt DGN Files

This chapter covers a topic that is of interest to power users and CAD administrators. If you are the only MicroStation user at your company, you may be faced with the need to fix a corrupt design file and will find information presented here useful.

If you have been using MicroStation and have heard of EdG but never really knew much about it, this chapter will give you a good idea of what it is and what it does. If you're a CAD administrator and get requests for help in fixing corrupt design files, you'll find step-by-step instructions in this chapter that will help you keep users happy.

Understanding the DGN File Format

The MicroStation DGN file format is binary, sequential, and disk-based. *Binary* means that you cannot open the file in a text editor and display its contents. *Sequential* means that when you create a new element in the design file, MicroStation adds it to the bottom of the file. MicroStation's *disk-based* nature means that when you commit a change to an existing element or create a new one, it is written to disk immediately without an explicit save operation.

A DGN file stores graphical elements and header information as variable length records. This means that the size of information stored about an element depends on its type. Thus the record that stores design file header information would be of a different size when compared to the record for a line element. The first element stored in a design file is normally the Type 9 file header element.

As noted earlier, EdG is also designed to work with cell libraries that normally have the `.cel` filename extension. Cell libraries contain cells which are a collection of graphical elements that behave as a single unit and are identified with a name. The first element in a cell library is a Type 5 file header element. Cells are complex elements that start with a Type 1 cell header followed by component elements. Also, cells can be embedded inside cells, and the cell header for nested cells is a Type 2 element.

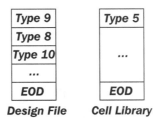

The structure of a design file and a cell library.

As the figure above makes clear, the first three elements in any design file are element types 9, 8, and 10 respectively. The Type 9 file header element specifies the design file's dimensional status, whether 2D or 3D, and its start up parameters. The Type 8 element is not used but exists in MicroStation solely for compatibility with IGDS so it can open newer MicroStation files without a problem. The Type 10 element stores the status of the active level symbology in the design file.

TIP: MicroStation files are compatible across all prior versions, including IGDS. Use the FREEZE command to preserve newer element types when opening a design file in an older version, and the THAW command to unlock the frozen elements when the file is brought back into the newer MicroStation version.

Immediately following the file header information is a list of elements in the design file or cell library. This list consists of graphical and nongraphical elements. Following this list in the design file or cell library is the End Of Design (EOD) marker. This marker signals the end of the file. The EOD marker has 16 bits, each of which is on. Thus, the binary representation of the EOD marker is 1111111111111111. It's hexadecimal representation is FFFF.

Just as there is a Type 9 or a Type 5 file header element, there are many other types of elements: lines, line strings, shapes, arcs, and so on. Each of these element types, whether graphic, nongraphic, setting, or attribute is identified in the design file as an element number. MicroStation uses this element number to determine what type of element it is, how to handle it and what tools will be allowed to manipulate it. The following table lists the various element numbers in numerical order.

Element Number	Element Type/Description
1	complex header for a cell in a cell library
2	complex header for a nested cell, or a cell in a design file
3	line
4	line string
5	group data
6	shape
7	complex header for a text node
8	digitizer setup data needed by IGDS (MicroStation does not use it)
9	design file header designating its dimension, 2D or 3D, among other things
10	level symbology
11	curve
12	complex header for chain
13	conic element in IGDS (MicroStation does not use it)

Element Number	Element Type/Description
14	complex header for shape
15	ellipse
16	arc
17	text
18	complex header for surfaces (valid only in 3D files)
19	complex header for surfaces with end caps (valid only in 3D files)
21	B-Spline pole
22	point string
23	circular truncated cone
24	complex header for B-spline surface
25	B-Spline surface boundary
26	B-Spline knot
27	complex header for B-Spline curve
28	B-Spline weight factor
33	dimension
34	shared cell definition
35	shared cell instance
36	multi-line
37	tag data
38	smart geometry
51	Intergraph AEC application element
66	MicroStation element (IGDS does not use it)
87	complex header for raster elements
88	raster data

In summary, a *design file* is simply a collection of elements (graphic, nongraphic, or header) followed by the EOD marker. An *element* is a variable-length collection of words (a *word* equals 16 bits, or two bytes) of which the first 18 words have the same format regardless of the element type. The remaining words in the design file depend on the type of element they represent.

The first 18 words common to all elements are shown in the following table.

Word Sequence	Description
1	type, level, class, status (complex, deleted)
2	Words To Follow (WTF)
3, 4	X range in UORs (low)
5, 6	Y range in UORs (low)
7, 8	Z range in UORs (low)
9, 10	X range in UORs (high)
11, 12	Y range in UORs (high)
13, 14	Z range in UORs (high)
15	graphic group number
16	index to attributes
17	properties
18	element symbology (color, style, weight)

Because a DGN file contains variable-length records, the record for an element must include a value that can be used to determine its size. The second word in a record is called the *Words To Follow*, or WTF field. It contains the value in words to the beginning of the next record, or element. By reading this value, MicroStation determines where the next element in the design file starts.

We could go on to learn what each bit in every word of an element contains, but that's not necessary for our purposes in this chapter. What you have learned about the design file format up to this point is sufficient to help you use EdG productively.

Basic EdG Operations

EdG provides a command-line environment for you to open design files and cell libraries in and to display, verify, and modify its elements. You can also use EdG to copy elements from the active design file to a new design file. EdG is a design file navigation tool. It has commands to move from one element to another or to set search criteria to locate desired elements. The utility also has commands to let you display words that make up an element, down to the last bit.

In this section you learn the basics of EdG: invoking it, moving from one element to another, displaying the contents of a record that represents an element, setting the search criteria to find only the elements that interest you, and exiting EdG.

Starting EdG

To start EdG from the command line:

1. Open the Command Prompt window on a Microsoft Windows system (or the command shell console in UNIX). On Windows NT 4.0, you do this by clicking the Start button, and selecting Command Prompt from the Programs menu.
2. Use the MS-DOS `chdir` command to change the active directory to the one containing design files you wish to work on.
3. Key in `c:\Bentley\Program\Edg\edg` at the command prompt on a Microsoft Windows system. This assumes MicroStation is installed on your computer's C: drive in the `\Bentley\Program` folder.
4. EdG will start and prompt you to enter a design file name. Because the sole purpose of EdG is to edit a design file, it must have a design file to work with. Unlike MicroStation, EdG is very fault-tolerant. It can open corrupt design files MicroStation refuses to load.

Upon starting, EdG requests a design file name to open.

NOTE: For MicroStation SE and MicroStation 95, the default path to EdG is
`c:\win32app\ustation\edg\edg`.

You can start EdG by also double-clicking its filename in Windows
Explorer. When started by double-clicking the file in Explorer, the
command window is white and its title bar reads WinEdG. When started
from the command prompt, the command window is black and its title
bar reads Command Prompt.

TIP: If you are a CAD administrator and have decided to delve more deeply into
EdG, you will want to create a desktop shortcut to invoke EdG with a simple mouse
button click.

Navigating the Design File

When you open a design file in EdG, it displays its name: Edit Graphics,
followed by the version number and platform you are running it on. The
dimensional status of the design file, 2D or 3D, follows and the name of
the design file, including its full path. This basic information is followed
by a terse description of the first element record in the design file, as
shown in the figure below.

*You key in commands at the **EdG>** prompt to perform all actions on a design file.*

The line you see just above the EdG> prompt in the figure above displays three pieces of information. The first field, which shows the number 1, is the sequence number of the active element in the design file. Because we just opened the file, the active element is the very first element. The first element is the Type 9 design file header. Thus the second field on this line, which has the number 9 in parentheses indicates the element number of the active element, followed by a descriptive name for the element. The third field on this line displays the level the element is on.

Each element has 18 common words followed by many other words that are specific to the element type. Obviously, the three fields displayed on a single line are not everything there is to know about this element. You will be learning how to display the contents of the entire element record a little later.

Let's now learn how to go about moving from one element record to another. When EdG is running, it displays the EdG> prompt that accepts valid commands to navigate, display, and modify design file elements. At any given time, EdG focuses on one and only one element. This element is called the *active element*. Navigating the design file means moving the focus of EdG from one element to another. The navigation commands you will use most often are listed in the table below.

EdG Navigation Command	Action the Command Performs
<Enter>	EdG moves downward by one element sequence number.

EdG Navigation Command	Action the Command Performs
<integer>	EdG makes the element at the sequence number typed active.
TOP	EdG makes the first element in the design file the active element.
END	EdG makes the last element in the design file—the EOD marker—the active element, if the file is not missing it.
NEXT <integer>, or +<integer>	EdG moves forward by the number specified. If no number is specified, the default value of one is assumed.
-<integer>	EdG moves backward by the number specified. If no number is specified, the default value of one is assumed.
<Ctrl+C>	EdG stops an operation in progress.

Exercise: Stepping Through A Design File

In this exercise, you will use the navigation commands to step through from element to element. You can use any design file you like for this exercise. But to be safe, so you don't accidentally damage one of your own files, I included the file **navedg.dgn** on the CD-ROM. You will find this file in the **\Exercise\Ch15** folder.

Use the following steps for the exercise:

1. Start EdG. See the *Starting EdG* section above if you need help.
2. At the **Enter Design File name:** prompt, key in the name of the sample design file **navedg.dgn** supplied on the CD-ROM making sure you supply the entire file path specification.
3. EdG will display the file name, its dimensional status and first element description. Hit the **<Enter>** key a few times and notice that EdG moves focus from the first element to the second, then the third, and so on.
4. Key in **TOP** and EdG moves focus to the first design file element.
5. Key in **END** and EdG moves focus to the last design file element, indicated by the **<<END OF DESIGN>>** description.
6. Key-in the number **2**, and EdG will move focus to the second element in the design file, which is element number 8 for digitizer setup data needed by IGDS.

This concludes our exercise on navigating design files with EdG. However, don't worry about exiting EdG yet. Leave the file open as we continue learning basic EdG commands for displaying element details and searching for specific element types and attributes.

Displaying Element Details

The default display setting in EdG for the active element, upon start up, is to show the contents of the element's first word, which contains the element type, its deletion status, its complex status, and level. As you know, there is more than just one word in any element. There are 18 common words for every element, followed by more element-specific words. In this section you learn how to use the various element detail display commands in EdG. Depending on the element display command you enter, you get to see the various data values stored in the design file for that element.

You can change the active display settings by using the SET DISPLAY command with appropriate options. The following table lists some of the most commonly used element display commands.

Element Display Commands	Action the Command Performs
<.>	EdG displays information about the active element. The amount of information displayed depends on the active SET DISPLAY setting.
FULL	EdG displays all information, header and data, about the active element regardless of the current SET DISPLAY setting.
SET DISPLAY/BRIEF	This is the default. It sets the display of element information to the first word.
SET DISPLAY/HEADER	When this display mode is active, EdG shows the first 18 words that make up the element header.
SET DISPLAY/DATA	When this display mode is active, EdG shows the remaining data words specific to the element type.
SET DISPLAY/FULL	When this display mode is active, EdG displays all the information, header and data, relevant to the active element type.

Element Display Commands	Action the Command Performs
SET DISPLAY/DUMP	When this display mode is active, EdG displays the information in hexadecimal notation. You will not normally use this mode unless you know the DGN file format really well.
TYPE <sequence range>	Same as the <.> command except it can accept a range of element sequence numbers. This command can also accept search and display qualifiers to override current settings temporarily.

Many other SET DISPLAY commands, like SET DISPLAY/SYMBOLOGY, are used to display a subset of what the above commands display. The commands in the above table will suffice for most of your needs. For a list of all commands EdG supports, key in HELP at the EdG> prompt.

To see the active SET DISPLAY setting at any time, you can key in SHOW DISPLAY

Exercise: Viewing Element Details

In this exercise you will use element display commands to view different aspects of information about the active element in the design file. I'm assuming you still have the navedg.dgn file loaded in EdG to perform the following steps. If you had quit EdG, you will want to start it and open a copy of the design file from the CD-ROM in the \Exercise\Ch15 folder.

Use the following steps for the exercise:

1. Ensure you have EdG running with the navedg.dgn file loaded. If you need help with this, see the *Starting EdG* section above, or the previous exercise.
2. At the EdG> prompt, press the period key. EdG will display information about the active element.
3. Key in FULL and EdG will display all information, both header and data, about the active element.
4. Key in SET DISPLAY/HEADER and EdG will set the display mode to header. Now press the period key to display the information contained in the first 18 words of the element record.

5. Try navigating through the file by pressing the `<Enter>` key a few times and notice that the header information displays for each element EdG encounters.

6. Key in `SET DISPLAY/DUMP` and EdG will set the display mode to hexadecimal, rather than the English language translation of the binary values you have thus far seen. Now press the period key to display the information about the active element in hexadecimal notation.

7. Key in `SET DISPLAY/BRIEF` to return EdG to the default brief display mode. Now press the period key to verify that element information is back to the one line display you had seen earlier.

This concludes our exercise. At this point you may exit EdG by keying in EXIT at the command prompt. Or, if you intend to continue reading the next section, you can leave the file open for the element search exercise.

Setting Search Criteria

When you start EdG and begin navigating a design file, you can move from element to element without restriction, because the default search criteria in EdG includes all attributes for all elements. However, if you wanted to restrict EdG to work with just arc elements, you would set the search criteria to only look for Type 16 (arc) elements.

To activate EdG's search criteria to look only for arc elements, you would key in `SET SEARCH/TYPE=16` at the `EdG>` prompt. Now when you use the navigation commands, EdG will move its focus from one arc element to the next arc element. If you were to issue a command to navigate to a specific element sequence number that were not an arc element, EdG would report that the element you want to navigate to is *not in search*.

NOTE: To disable a search criteria specified earlier, use the `SET NOSEARCH` command. EdG will find all elements.

Though I used the example of an arc element, the search criteria need not restrict EdG's operation by only element types. The search criteria can include any data attribute, such as color or level, or other property type.

You set a search criteria in EdG by using the SET SEARCH series of commands. This command must be followed by one or more qualifiers. The following table lists most of the search qualifiers you will need to use. You may obtain a complete list of SET SEARCH qualifiers by keying in HELP SET SEARCH at the EdG> prompt.

SET SEARCH qualifiers	Action the Command Performs
/ALL_ELEMENTS	Returns all elements to the search criteria.
/CASE_SENSITIVE	Specifies that case (upper or lower) of letters matters when using the /CHARCTERS qualifier. Use /NOCASE_SENSITIVE to disable.
/CELLNAME="celnam"	Restricts search to cells that have the cell name specified within quotation marks. The * and ? wildcards are supported. Use /NOCELLNAME to disable.
/CHARACTERS= "text"	Restricts search to text elements with the value specified within quotation marks. The * and ? wildcards are supported. Use /NOCHARACTERS to disable.
/CLASS=<number list>	Restricts search to element class specified. Use /NOCLASS to disable.
/COLOR=<number list>	Restricts search to colors specified. Use /NOCOLOR to disable.
/EXPAND	When a complex element is encountered, all its component elements are also displayed. Use /NOEXPAND to disable.
/FONT=<number list>	Returns text and text nodes with the specified font value(s). Use /NOFONT to disable.
/GROUP=<number list>	Locates elements belonging to graphic group(s) specified. Use /NOGROUP to disable.
/LEVEL=<number list>	Locates elements on the specified level(s). Use /NOLEVEL to disable.
/NEST=<number list>	Locates elements with the specified complex nesting level. Use /NONEST to disable. /NEST=0 finds only primary elements. Valid values for number list are from 0 to 12.
/P_BITS=<keyword list>	Locates elements by value of property bit such as snappable, planar, view independent, etc. Use /NOP_BITS to disable.

SET SEARCH qualifiers	Action the Command Performs
/STATUS=<keyword list>	Locates elements with specified status. Valid keywords are ACTIVE, COMPLEX, DELETED, SIMPLE. Use /NOSTATUS to disable.
/STYLE=<number list>	Locates elements with specified line style. Use /NOSTYLE to disable.
/TYPE=<number list>	Locates elements of type(s) specified. For instance, arcs are of type 16. Use /NOTYPE to disable.
/WEIGHT=<number list>	Locates elements with the weight(s) specified. Use /NOWEIGHT to disable.

The number list accepted by the commands listed in the table above is a list of numeric values separated by a comma. To specify a range, use the dash character between the numbers. Let's use the search commands you have learned in the following exercise.

NOTE: To see the active SET SEARCH setting at any time, you can key in SHOW SEARCH.

Exercise: Controlling Navigation Through Search Criteria

In this exercise you will see how EdG's navigation commands are affected by the active search criteria as you step through a design file from element to element. You will use the same design file, navedg.dgn, we used in the earlier exercises. This design file is located on the enclosed CD-ROM in the \Exercise\Ch15 folder.

Use the following steps for the exercise:

1. Start EdG. See the *Starting EdG* section above if you need help.
2. At the Enter Design File name: prompt, key-in the name of the sample design file navedg.dgn supplied on the CD-ROM, making sure you supply the entire file path specification.
3. EdG will display the file name, its dimensional status, and first element description. Press the <Enter> key a few times and notice that EdG moves focus from the first element to the second, then the third, and so on.

4. Key in TOP and EdG moves focus to the first design file element.

5. Key in SET SEARCH/TYPE=16 to have EdG locate only arc elements. Press the <Enter> key and notice that rather than move to the next sequential element in the design file, you have now located the first arc element.

6. Press <Enter> a few times and see that it skips over all element types except arc elements. Now key in TOP to go back to the top of the design file.

7. Key in SET SEARCH/TYPE=3,4/LEVEL=1-10,25/COLOR=1-4 to restrict your search to only lines and line strings that are on levels 1 through 10 and 25, and have a color from 1 to 4. Press the <Enter> key and notice that EdG has located the element that meets your search criteria.

8. Key in TOP to move to the beginning of the design file. Now key in SET NOSEARCH to clear any active search criteria. Press <Enter> to see that you are now back to the default navigation status.

Pressing **<Enter>** *at the* **EdG>** *prompt locates the next element that meets the search criteria.*

This concludes the exercise on search criteria. The EdG features you learned so far have been non-destructive. You displayed or searched for element information but did not change it. The MODIFY and WRITE commands edit a design file and change element information. We will use these later in the chapter. Now that you know the basics, it's time to terminate your EdG session.

Quitting EdG

To exit from EdG, you can key in **EXIT** or **QUIT**. You can also key in **x**, or press the **<ctrl+z>** key combination. All these commands do the same thing. They close all open files and exit the EdG utility.

More EdG Operations

In addition to the navigation, display, and search commands, EdG supports a variety of auxiliary design file and cell library modification operations. This section introduces these commands to you with a brief description of their purposes. You will use several of these commands in exercises in the next two sections of the chapter.

File Operations

EdG Command	Description
BACKUP	Copies the active design file or cell library to a backup file specified.
EDG	Closes the active design file and opens the new file specified.
OPEN	Creates a blank new secondary file in the background from the active design file. You can then selectively copy elements from the active file to the open file.
WRITE	Writes the current element or range of elements, if specified, to the secondary file opened with the OPEN command.
CLOSE	Closes the file previously opened with the OPEN command.
EXIT	Closes all files and exits EdG.

Reporting Operations

EdG Command	Description
SUMMARY	Prepares a statistical summary of the current element or range of elements if specified.
VERIFY	Checks for errors in the current element or a range of elements. As a default, it stops processing when it encounters a bad element. Use SET VERIFY commands to modify the default behavior.
EVALUATE	Displays the hex, decimal, octal, ASCII, and rad50 translations of the value specified.
FIND	Moves the file pointer to the element sequence or range specified. Also reports the element count if a search criteria is active.

Repair Operations

EdG Command	Description
PATCH	Sets values for the WTF field in an element header. Also used to fix Words-In-Description errors.
REPAIR	Corrects element parameters as specified with SET REPAIR.
DELETE	Marks the current element, or range of elements, for deletion.
UNDELETE	Removes the delete status of the current element or range of elements.
MODIFY	This command is followed by a keyword and a value, such as COLOR=3, followed by an element sequence range.
DEMARCATE	Replaces the element sequence number, or the current element if no element sequence number is specified, with the EOD marker.
UNDEMARCATE	Locates and removes the EOD marker in the design file.

You will have read the term *range of elements* in the description associated with several commands. Many commands take as input a range of elements, or element sequence numbers, to process. If no range is specified, the current element is the only element processed. The command to specify the current element is CURRENT. If you wish to process all elements in the design file, you use the range WHOLE, which is also equivalent to typing BEGIN THRU END_OF_DESIGN. The range BEFORE designates the start of design file to the element before the current element, or BEGIN THRU CURRENT-1. The range AFTER designates CURRENT+1 THRU END_OF_DESIGN. The keyword THRU can also be abbreviated with the ":" symbol. Thus the element sequence range 5:55 designates that the command is to process elements starting with and including the sequence number 5 through and including 55.

The list of commands in the above tables are supplemented by more commands. There are several other SET commands and SHOW commands. You can get a complete listing of these commands and their syntax by typing HELP on the EdG> prompt.

To help you process a design file with a certain series of commands, EdG supports the use of command files. A *command file* is a text file containing a sequence of commands you would normally type at the EdG> prompt. To have EdG execute the commands contained in a command file with the name cmdfile.edg, you would key in @cmdfile.edg at the EdG> prompt.

Bentley also provides a batch file called edgbatch.bat to help you process multiple design files through EdG in a single step. The batch file runs each design file through EdG and executes the list of commands contained in the command file. The syntax for running this batch file is shown below:

```
EDGBATCH cmdfile.edg *.dgn
```

Modifying DGN Elements

This section showcases EdG's ability to manipulate design file elements. You will work through several exercises, each is designed to help you understand how EdG can help solve a different type of problem. You won't fix corrupt files here. You will do that in the next section. Here you will learn how to use EdG to operate upon perfectly good files to make changes that might be either tedious or time-consuming when done in MicroStation's graphical environment.

Exercise: Changing Weight Globally

Suppose your company standards call for drawing all tables in a conference room using line elements on level 4 with color 5 and weight 1. However, while drawing them you accidentally left the active weight to 0. Your task is to change the weight of all tables from 0 to 1. Assume all line elements on level 4 with color 5 are tables. Use the file `tables.dgn` located in the `\Exercise\Ch15` folder on the CD-ROM for this exercise.

Use the following steps for the exercise:

1. Start EdG. See the *Starting EdG* section above if you need help.
2. At the `Enter Design File name:` prompt, key in the name of the design file tables.dgn supplied on the CD-ROM, making sure you supply the entire file path specification.
3. Key in `SET SEARCH /TYPE=3 /LEVEL=4 /COLOR=5` to restrict the search to line elements (type 3) on level 4 with color 5.
4. Key in `MODIFY WEIGHT=1 WHOLE` to change the weight attribute of elements in the entire design that match the search criteria set in the above step.
5. Key in `EXIT` to quit the EdG session.

Exercise: Extracting Elements to Another File

Suppose the conference room layout drawing you have contains chairs that were inadvertently drawn within the design file, rather than as a reference file attachment. You know that all chairs were drawn as **lines** or **closed shapes** on **level 6** with **color 3**. Your task is to extract all chairs from this file into a new file called `chairs.dgn`. Use the file `room.dgn` located in the `\Exercise\Ch15` folder on the CD-ROM for this exercise.

Use the following steps for this exercise:

1. Start EdG. See the *Starting EdG* section above if you need help.
2. At the `Enter Design File name:` prompt, key in the name of the design file `room.dgn` supplied on the CD-ROM, making sure you supply the entire file path specification.

3. Key in OPEN CHAIRS.DGN to create a secondary design file called chairs.dgn in the current directory. EdG creates chairs.dgn by copying the first three elements, type 9 (design file header), type 8 (digitizer setup), and type 10 (level symbology) from room.dgn.

4. Key in SET SEARCH /TYPE=3,6 /LEVEL=6 /COLOR=3 to restrict search to **lines** (Type 3) and **closed shapes** (Type 6) on **level 6** with **color 3**.

5. Key in WRITE WHOLE to write all elements in the design file that meet the search criteria to the secondary design file. Now the design file chairs.dgn contains a copy of all chairs, but so does the design file room.dgn.

6. Key in DELETE WHOLE to delete all elements in the design file that meet the search criteria. The command does sound destructive, but remember: As long as the search criteria restricts searches to chairs, only chairs will be deleted.

7. Key in CLOSE to close the secondary design file.

8. Key in EXIT to quit the EdG session.

Exercise: Dropping All Cell Instances to Component Elements

The conference room layout drawing contains sofa chairs. These were placed in the design file as the cell **sofa**. Suppose that your client has specifically requested that no cells be used in the design files you deliver after project completion. You had used the sofa cell for productivity reasons and now that the project is complete, you must drop all its instances to component elements. Use the file room.dgn located in the \Exercise\Ch15 folder on the accompanying CD-ROM for this exercise.

You can accomplish this task using EdG as shown in the following steps:

1. Start EdG. See the *Starting EdG* section above if you need help.

2. At the Enter Design File name: prompt, key-in the name of the design file room.dgn supplied on the CD-ROM, making sure you supply the entire file path specification.

3. Key in SET SEARCH /TYPE=CELL /CELL="sofa" to restrict search to cell headers with the name sofa.

4. Key-in DELETE WHOLE to delete all sofa cell headers in the design file. Note that only cell headers are deleted with this command, and all component elements will still have their complex bit set. You have now corrupted the file by creating what are known as *phantom elements*—complex elements with no header. The next few steps will fix these elements.

5. Key in SET NOSEARCH to invalidate the previous search criteria.

6. Key in SET SEARCH /TYPE=GRAPHIC to restrict search to all graphical elements.

7. Key in SET SEARCH /STATUS=ACTIVE,COMPLEX to find all graphical elements that are nor marked for deletion but have their complex bit set.

8. Key in SET SEARCH /NEST=0 to restrict search to primitive (non-complex) elements only.

9. Key in MODIFY STATUS=SIMPLE WHOLE to turn off the complex bit of all phantom elements to make them primitive elements.

10. Key in EXIT to quit the EdG session.

Fixing Corrupt DGN Files

The single most common symptom of a corrupt design file is when MicroStation displays an alert dialog box stating that the End Of Design marker is missing and requests permission to repair the file. In my experience, you are always better off denying MicroStation this permission and fixing the file yourself with EdG.

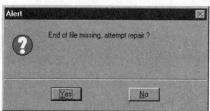

If you see this dialog box, always click the No button and repair the file with EdG.

Corrupt design files you will need to repair most often will have the following types of errors:

- Missing End Of Design Marker
- Elements Beyond the End Of Design Marker

- Phantom Elements
- Corrupt Design File Header
- Bad Value for Words To Follow

No matter what type of file corruption you encounter, there is one thing you must always do. Make a copy of the corrupt file and run the EdG utility on the copy, not the original. This way you will still have the original corrupt file to try and fix again should you accidentally corrupt the corrupted file beyond repair.

In order to fix a file, you first need to identify problems. Do this by using the verify commands. After you locate the problems, you need to fix them one at a time. The following subsections provide step-by-step instructions on how to fix specific types of corrupt design files.

Missing End Of Design Marker

When MicroStation encounters a design file missing an EOD marker, it displays an alert dialog box to that effect. At this point you should exit MicroStation and make a copy of the corrupt design file and open the corrupt copy in EdG.

Use the following sequence of commands to repair a design file that is missing its EOD marker:

1. Load a copy of the corrupt design file in EdG.
2. Key in END to navigate to the end of the file.
3. Key in DEMARCATE to place a EOD marker at the current location.
4. Key in EXIT to quit EdG.
5. Load the design file you just fixed in MicroStation and verify that it behaves properly before replacing the corrupt file with the recovered file.

Elements Beyond End Of Design Marker

When you open a design file and can't believe that it does not display graphics you know exist in the file, you have encountered a corrupt file that has elements beyond the EOD marker.

Use the following steps to recover a design file that has elements beyond its EOD marker:

1. Load the copy of the corrupt design file in EdG.

2. Key in FIND END to locate the EOD marker and move to it.

3. Key in SHOW SIZE to display the size of the design file to the EOD marker and the size of the design file to its physical end. A significantly larger physical design file size (greater than 788 bytes when compared to the size to the EOD marker) implies that there possibly is a large amount of data you will want to invest time in recovering.

4. Key in UNDEMARCATE to overwrite the intermediate EOD marker with a dummy element header that is marked for deletion. This command adjusts the WTF valued of this dummy element to point to the next valid element.

5. Key in EXIT to quit EdG.

After you have fixed the corrupt copy of the design file, you will want to open it in MicroStation to verify that it now behaves properly. Now you are ready to overwrite the original corrupt file with the fixed file.

Phantom Elements

When you encounter elements in your design file that you cannot snap to or otherwise locate, or even delete, you have a corrupt file with phantom elements. This simply means that the phantom elements have their complex bit enabled, indicating they belong to a complex element, but the header for the complex element has been lost.

To fix a design file that contains phantom elements, first make a backup copy of the corrupt design file and then follow the steps shown below.

1. Load the copy of the corrupt design file in EdG.

2. Key in SET SEARCH /STATUS=ACTIVE,COMPLEX to set the search criteria to look for non-deleted that have their complex bit set.

3. Key in SET SEARCH /TYPE=GRAPHIC to further restrict the search to displayable graphic elements.

4. Key in SET SEARCH /NEST=0 to prevent from processing elements that are components of other complex element groups.

5. Key in MODIFY STATUS=SIMPLE WHOLE to change the complex bit status to simple for all elements in the design file that meet our search criteria.

6. Key in DELETE WHOLE to delete all elements that meet above search criteria, which should be none, as all elements meeting the criteria were already modified to simple status. This operation is performed to catch any elements that the MODIFY operation may have had trouble with.

7. Key in EXIT to quit EdG.

After you have fixed the corrupt copy of the design file, you will want to open it in MicroStation to verify that it behaves properly. Now you are ready to overwrite the original corrupt file with the fixed file.

Corrupt Design File Header

When MicroStation does not recognize the file you wish to open as a valid design file, and you know it is a design file, it may have lost its design file header. This simply means that the Type 9 element (or Type 5 for a cell library) is corrupt and needs to be reconstructed.

I use three design file placeholders in the following steps. The placeholder losthead.dgn refers to the corrupt file. The placeholder seed.dgn refers to a good seed file having the same dimensional status (2D or 3D) as the corrupt file you wish to recover. Finally, the placeholder fixed.dgn refers to the new file you will create with the reconstructed file header.

Before fixing the file, make a backup copy and then follow the steps shown below.

1. Start EdG and load the good seed file seed.dgn. Make sure the seed file you select has the same dimensional status as the corrupt file.

2. At the EdG> prompt, key in OPEN fixed.dgn to create a new secondary file from the seed file opened above. EdG only copies the first three elements, types 9, 8 and 10, from the seed file to the new file.

3. Key in EDG losthead.dgn to switch the seed file with the corrupt file as the active file EdG will operate upon. Ignore the message EdG might display about the file not being a design file.

4. Key in PATCH WTF to enter the patch facility in EdG. The prompt will change from EdG> to Patch WTF>. At this new prompt key in the number 0 to fill the element's WTF field with 0.

5. Key in AUTOMATIC 5 to instruct the patch facility to automatically adjust the WTF of the current element. The number 5 instructs EdG to ensure that five successive elements are valid before it computes the WTF value for the corrupt element.

6. Key in SAVE to make the change to WTF value permanent and exit the patch facility.

7. Key in TYPE NEXT to navigate to the next valid element found by the patch facility.

8. Key in WRITE REST to take all elements from here on to the end of design marker and copy them into the secondary file fixed.dgn opened earlier.

9. Key in CLOSE to close the secondary file because all valid elements from the corrupt file are now in the new file.

10. Key in EXIT to quit EdG.

After you have fixed the corrupt copy of the design file, you will want to open it in MicroStation to verify that it behaves properly. Now you are ready to overwrite the original corrupt file with the fixed file.

Bad Value for Words to Follow

To fix a design file with a bad WTF value for an element, first make a backup copy of the design file and then follow the steps shown below.

1. Load the copy of the corrupt design file in EdG.

2. Key in SET ON_BADELE to instruct EdG to stop when a bad element is found.

3. Key in VERIFY WHOLE to start checking all elements in the design file from the beginning. EdG will stop when a bad element is encountered. Note the element sequence number of this bad element, as it will be used later.

4. Key in VERIFY AFTER to check all elements that follow the bad element. If all following elements appear to be valid, return to the bad element by keying in the element sequence number you had noted in the previous step.

5. Key in PATCH WTF to invoke the WTF patch facility within EdG. The prompt will change from EdG> to Patch WTF>. At this new prompt key in the number 0 to fill the WTF value of the corrupt element with the number zero.

6. Key in AUTOMATIC 5 at the patch utility prompt to instruct EdG to automatically adjust the WTF value and make sure that following five elements are also valid.

7. Key in SAVE to save the computed WTF value in the element and exit the patch facility.

8. Key in MODIFY STATUS=DELETED to mark the patched element as deleted, as perhaps it is corrupt. Do note that if the element you just fixed were a complex element header (cell, text node, complex chain, etc.), you should delete the entire complex element.

9. Key in EXIT to quit EdG.

After you have fixed the corrupt copy of the design file, you will want to open it in MicroStation to verify that it now behaves properly. Now you are ready to overwrite the original corrupt file with the fixed file.

This concludes the chapter on fixing corrupt design files.

Chapter 16

Exchanging Drawings with Archive

Keeping Design Files and Resources Together

If you receive design files that include custom fonts and other external resources, you can't re-create them in exact detail on your computer without installing the external resources too. MicroStation doesn't maintain *everything* it needs to display a design file correctly within the design file. Reference files, cell libraries, fonts, custom line styles, material tables, and workspace configuration files are stored outside the active design file. To duplicate a design file's environment on another computer, you must copy these dependent resource files as well.

MicroStation's Archive utility facilitates the exchange of design files, including dependent resource files, so you may re-create them on another system in all respects. Archive compresses selected files into a single archive file. It also implements digital signatures so that design file modifications after submittal may be flagged.

MicroStation archive files have the extension .mar. An *archive file* is like a Microsoft Windows .cab cabinet file or the popular .zip file used in electronic communication—it's a container for other files. Archive compresses several files into a single, smaller archive file. When you receive an archive file, you must extract its contents.

You don't have to identify a design file's dependent resource files when creating archive files. The Archive utility can identify resource files. You can archive a design file with its dependent resources. You can also archive all project design files without dependent resources.

Select Archive from MicroStation's Utilities menu to invoke the Archive dialog box, as shown below.

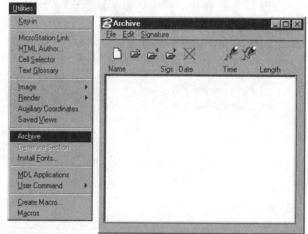

MicroStation Archive bundles design files with dependent external files into a single, compressed archive file to facilitate design file exchange.

This chapter teaches you how to use Archive to:

- Create archive files.
- Add to and delete files from archive files.
- Display and select dependent external files.
- Extract archive file contents.
- Seal design files with a digital signature.
- Determine if design files were modified after being digitally signed.

Creating and Using Archive Files

MicroStation uses the term *resource* to identify external files it uses to set up its design environment. Archive retrieves a resource list by querying MicroStation and the design file it adds to an archive file. The following list identifies the resources Archive can process.

- Reference files (design and raster)
- Cell libraries
- Symbology resources (fonts, custom line styles)
- Images (background, pattern and bump maps, materials)
- Configuration and workspace files

First, create an empty archive file. Then, add design files to the archive file. You select the resources to include in the archive file after identifying the design file.

To create an archive file:

1. Invoke the Archive dialog box by selecting Archive from the Utilities menu.
2. Select New from the File menu in the MicroStation Archive dialog box. The Create Archive File dialog box opens.
3. Navigate to where you wish to save the archive file. Enter a name for the archive file in the Files text field. Click OK.
4. An archive file is created. Archive files have the `.mar` extension.

The archive file created is initially empty.

To add design files to an archive file:

1. Invoke the Archive dialog box by selecting Archive from the Utilities menu.
2. Create or open an archive file by using the File menu in the MicroStation Archive dialog box.
3. Select Add from the Edit menu. The Select Files To Add dialog box opens.
4. Navigate to where design files you wish to add are located. Identify a design file or a group of design files. (To highlight several files, hold Shift or Ctrl while clicking files.) Click the Add button.
5. Design files you selected appear in the lower listbox, as shown below. If you wish to remove a file from the list, highlight the file and click Remove.

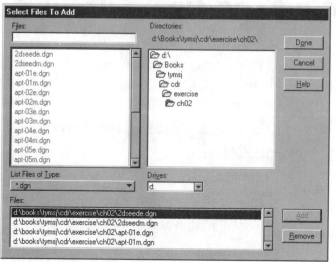

Use this dialog box to add design files to an archive.

6. Click Done. The Add Archive Files dialog box opens, as shown below.

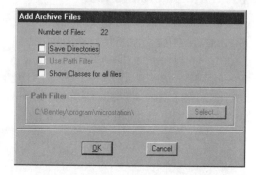

7. Leave the checkboxes in the dialog box unchecked. This is the default. These options are discussed later. Click OK. An Alert dialog box opens asking whether you wish to see class files.

8. Click No to prevent MicroStation from opening each file to display resource classes used by it. Otherwise, click Yes.

9. The selected design files and default resource files are added to the archive file and appear in the MicroStation Archive dialog box.

Having learned the two basic functions of Archive, let's explore its other commands and functions. The following table lists actions available from the File menu in the MicroStation Archive dialog box.

File Menu Options	Description
New	Opens the Create Archive File dialog box for creating archive files.
Open	Invokes the Open Archive File dialog box for opening archive files.
Open URL	Invokes the Open Remote Archive dialog box for opening archive files from intranet and Internet sites. See chapter 12 for details.
Close	Closes an archive file opened earlier.
Save As	Save a copy of an open archive file with a new name or in the new MicroStation/J archive format that supports digital signatures.
Info	Displays archive file and size information in the Archive Information dialog box.
Test	Verifies whether files in an open archive are corrupt.
Create List	Opens the Archive List File dialog box for creating a text file listing archive file information. This file is a catalog of archive files.
View Log	Displays contents of the Archive log file.
Exit	Closes the MicroStation Archive dialog box.

The following table lists actions available from the Edit menu in the MicroStation Archive dialog box.

Edit Menu Options	Description
Add	Opens the Select Files to Add dialog box to add design files to an archive.
Extract	Extracts selected files from an open archive.
Modify	Opens the Modify Archive dialog box for editing the selected file's name and path.
Delete	Deletes the selected file from an open archive.
Select All	Selects all files in an open archive.
Select None	Deselects any file(s) that may be highlighted in an archive.

After you select files to add to an archive and click Done in the Select Files To Add dialog box, the Add Archive Files dialog opens. See the figure accompanying steps describing how *to add design files to an archive file*. The dialog box offers three checkboxes, as described below.

The Save Directories checkbox, when enabled, causes Archive to include path specification with file added to an archive. The Use Path Filter checkbox becomes available when Save Directories is enabled. Use this checkbox to enable the Select button in the Path Filter groupbox. The Show Classes for All Files checkbox is designed to display a list of resource files used by all files in an archive.

After accepting the files to add to an archive, if you click Yes when prompted to see class files in the Alert dialog box, the Select Archive Classes dialog box opens, as shown below.

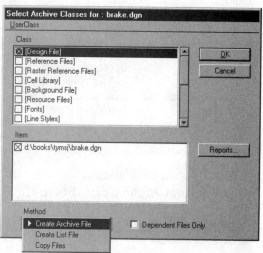

Resource files used by MicroStation and design files are listed in this dialog box.

The above dialog box lists various resource classes and the files in each class. Use the checkboxes next to classes and items to include them in an archive. If you wish to include resources related to design files only (not workspaces), enable the Dependent Files Only checkbox. The Method option button allows you to create a list from or copy selected files to another directory instead of adding them to an archive file.

The resource classes listed in the above dialog box are associated with MicroStation. However, your projects may include files not associated with MicroStation, such as database files. To include such files, Archive supports *user resource class* definitions. Select New from the UserClass menu to open the Create Archive Class dialog box and click the Create button to name the class. Then, click the Files buttons to define files to associate with the class.

To extract files from an archive file:

1. Invoke the Archive dialog box by selecting Archive from the Utilities menu.
2. Open an archive file by selecting Open from the File menu in the MicroStation Archive dialog box. The Open Archive File dialog box opens.
3. Navigate to where the archive file desired is located. Highlight the file. Click OK. Files in the archive display in the MicroStation Archive dialog box.
4. Highlight the files you wish to extract and select Extract from the Edit menu on the dialog box. The Extract Archive Files dialog box opens, as shown below.

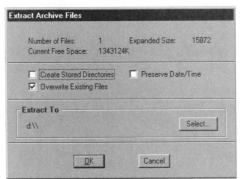

Select options desired and click OK to extract files from an archive.

5. Enable the Create Stored Directories checkbox to re-create the directory structure stored in an archive file. Enable the Preserve Data/Time checkbox if extracted files are to preserve their original date and time attributes. Enable the Overwrite Existing Files checkbox if you wish to overwrite existing files of the same name with files extracted from the archive. Click OK. Files are extracted to the directory you specify in the Extract To groupbox.

This concludes our discussion on the functions of the Archive utility. The next section discusses digital signatures.

Working with Digital Signatures

Architects and engineers apply a seal of professional status and a signature on drawings before submitting them to clients at project completion. Information on these drawings is legally binding. Contractors build projects from them. Project owners save them as a record of what was designed. If modifications are needed during construction, a separate as-built set of drawings is created from them. When the structure needs upgrades in the future, record drawings are used to assess and design upgrades.

Many clients demand electronic CAD files in addition to paper plots because electronic files are easier to modify and serve as background for future upgrades. Sealed and signed paper plots are still required and used during construction. Nevertheless, the design community is concerned about misuse of electronic files they submit. MicroStation addresses these concerns through digital signatures.

With the Archive utility you can mark design files in an archive with a digital signature unique to a designer. Archives can then be inspected for modifications. A digital signature serves two purposes. First, it marks a file with a unique identity. Second, it permits inspection to see whether the file changed. One file can have multiple signatures. A group of files can be signed in one step.

When you inspect a digitally signed file in an archive, you can determine the identity of the person who signed it. You can also determine whether the file in the archive is the original.

A digital signature doesn't prevent a file from being extracted from an archive, nor does it prevent modifications or additional signatures.

The concept of key pairs is central to MicroStation's digital signature capabilities. A *key pair* is a pair of very large numbers, called *keys*, generated from the name and password you supply when creating it. One number is called the *public key*, the other, *private key*. Key pairs are stored in a file with the `.kpf` extension in the `C:\Bentley\Workspace\Users` folder.

To sign a file, your key pair file must be available on the system. The signature in an archive file includes the public key so Archive may verify its authenticity. You can only use the private key in the `.kpf` file if you know the password. You don't need a key pair to verify a file.

To create a key pair:

1. Select Sign from the Signature menu on the MicroStation Archive dialog box. The Load Key Pair dialog box opens.
2. Click Create. The Create Key Pair dialog box opens, as shown below.

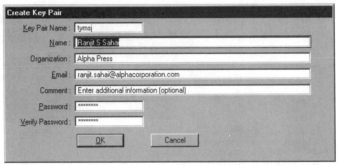

Key Pair Name, Name, Password, and Verify Password are required fields.

3. Enter a name for the key pair file, your name, organization, e-mail, comment, and password. Click OK.
4. The key pair file is created.

To sign files in an archive:

1. Highlight the files you wish to sign in the MicroStation Archive dialog box. Select Sign from the Signature menu. The Load Key Pair dialog box opens, as shown below.

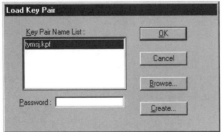

Select key pair, enter password, and click OK to sign highlighted files.

2. Select the key pair you created. Enter your password. Click OK

3. The highlighted files are signed and their signature status in the MicroStation Archive dialog box updates.

To verify files in an archive:

1. Highlight the files you wish to verify in the MicroStation Archive dialog box. Select Verify from the Signature menu.

2. The Signing and Verification Results dialog box opens, as shown below. It reports how many files were signed and how many passed verification.

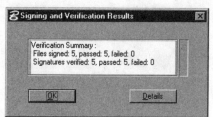

To see the identity of the person who signed the files, click Details.

This concludes our tour of the Archive utility and digital signatures.

Chapter 17
Understanding Workspaces
Customizing MicroStation's Design Environment

Besides being a powerful CAD system, MicroStation is a customizable platform for architectural and engineering design. It uses *workspaces* to deliver a different environment for a specific task. GeoGraphics, TriForma, and Modeler—discussed in chapter 13—implement custom workspaces to modify MicroStation's menu bar and Main tool frame.

Similarly, you can use workspaces to deliver corporate drafting standards in an easy-to-use format. Loading a custom workspace can provide menu-driven access to macros. It can also make cells, details, settings, and project directories you develop, the default.

Setting up a custom workspace requires a double-barreled strategy. First, you compile or develop workspace data components such as menu bar, cells, fonts, and macros. Second, you create configuration files for MicroStation to use that data.

A *workspace* is a named collection of MicroStation resources defined in configuration files. The collection includes seed files, cell libraries, font resource files, custom line styles, menus, and design applications it loads by default. A *configuration file* is a text file containing value assignment statements for MicroStation-defined variables, called *configuration variables*. If you know operating system environment variables and their impact on system configuration, you know configuration variables and how they define workspaces.

MicroStation reads configuration files during startup. Configuration variable values defined in these files determine where MicroStation looks for resources it needs for many tasks. Depending on the files it loads, MicroStation presents the user with a different environment.

Module data refers to the collection of workspace data components such as cell libraries, seed files, level names, and symbology resources. A workspace can share all or only parts of module data with other workspaces.

Workspaces are based on the premise that your needs change based on your work in MicroStation. You need different module data for civil drafting than you do for importing AutoCAD drawings. Workspaces make switching module data a matter of selecting the proper workspace from the MicroStation Manager dialog box before opening a design file.

To help you understand workspaces, MicroStation delivers example configuration files in the `c:\Bentley\Workspace` folder.

This chapter is organized in two sections, as shown below.

- **Configuration Files and Variables** introduces you to the files and variables that define workspaces. You learn the sequence in which configuration files are loaded and their syntax.
- **Customizing Interface Components** discusses the tools to edit MicroStation's menu bar and dialog boxes. You also learn how to create and edit other interface components, such as toolboxes and tool frames.

Information presented in this chapter assumes MicroStation knowledge. A knowledge of operating system environment variables is helpful, but not required. If you've created MS-DOS batch files and edited text files to configure systems, you can master workspaces easily.

Configuration Files and Variables

Configuration files and workspaces go hand in hand. A workspace provides seamless access to interface components and module data for an application, site, project, or user. A configuration file defines the module data a workspace uses.

You can maintain several sets of module data and configuration files on a computer. To choose which to load, a user selects its workspace name in the MicroStation Manager dialog box.

Workspace Hierarchy

MicroStation uses several directories for configuration files and module data. Understanding the directory hierarchy and the types of files stored in them will help you create and manage workspaces better.

When MicroStation starts, it loads the configuration file `mslocal.cfg`, which includes `msconfig.cfg` by reference, from the folder `C:\Bentley\MicroStation\Config`. The latter defines directories for module data and the sequence in which to load other configuration files. Consider the following excerpt from `msconfig.cfg`:

```
_USTN_SYSTEM          : $(MSDIR)config/system/
_USTN_APPL            : $(MSDIR)config/appl/
_USTN_SYSTEMROOT      : $(_USTN_WORKSPACEROOT)system/
_USTN_SITE            : $(_USTN_WORKSPACEROOT)standards/
_USTN_PROJECTSROOT    : $(_USTN_WORKSPACEROOT)projects/
_USTN_USER            : $(_USTN_WORKSPACEROOT)users/
_USTN_USERINTROOT     : $(_USTN_WORKSPACEROOT)interfaces/
```

Each line above is a variable definition. To the left of the colon operator (`:`) are variables; values are to the right. Each variable in the above list refers to a directory. Configuration variables usually define directory locations and filenames. Values can include variables previously defined. When a variable enclosed in parentheses is preceded by a dollar symbol, for example `$(MSDIR)`, its previously defined value is used.

MicroStation predefines many variable names. Applications and users can define others. Never edit system or application configuration files! Do so at your own risk! Incorrectly editing these files can prevent MicroStation from loading.

You assign values to predefined variables to control MicroStation's environment. Variables you create must relate back to MicroStation's predefined variables through variable definition statements. If you develop MDL applications, you can create variables especially for them.

NOTE: Configuration variable names that start with the underscore (_) character are private variables. MicroStation's Configuration dialog box (invoked from the Workspace menu) can't display them.

The following table lists several directories and their purposes in a workspace definition.

Folder	Purpose in Workspace Definition
\Bentley\Program\MicroStation\Config\System	MicroStation processes all .cfg files in this folder first.
\Bentley\Program\MicroStation\Config\Appl	MicroStation processes all .cfg files in this folder second.
\Bentley\Workspace\System	Contains default module data, if none is defined.
\Bentley\Workspace\Standards	MicroStation processes all .cfg files in this folder third. Subdirectories contain module data that is appended to default module data.
\Bentley\Workspace\Projects	Contains subdirectories corresponding to user configuration files which in turn contain .pcf project configuration files and corresponding subdirectories for module data. These appear as project workspace choices.
\Bentley\Workspace\Users	Contains .ucf user configuration files. These appear as user workspace choices in the MicroStation Manager dialog box and are processed last.
\Bentley\Workspace\Interfaces\MicroStation	Contains interface modification files. Subdirectory names appear as interface choices in the MicroStation Manager dialog box.

Subdirectories in the `c:\Bentley\Workspace\Standards` folder are initially empty. Place module data you develop for corporate or site standards here. MicroStation is configured to append contents it finds here to its default module data.

The sequence in which MicroStation reads configuration files during startup depends on their directory location. Configuration files are defined in a five-level hierarchy, explained below.

- *System*: Files in `c:\Bentley\Program\MicroStation\Config\System` are called *system configuration files*. They are processed right after `msconfig.cfg` finishes loading.

- *Application*: Files in `c:\Bentley\Program\MicroStation\Config\Appl` are called *application configuration files*. They are created by MDL applications and are processed after site configuration files.

- *Site*: Files with `.cfg` extension in `c:\Bentley\Workspace\Standards` define company-wide standards. They are processed after application configuration files.

- *Project*: These have the `.pcf` extension for project configuration files and are located in `c:\Bentley\Workspace\Projects`. Each has a corresponding directory tree in the same folder for module data.

- *User*: These have the `.ucf` extension for user configuration files. They can include project configuration files and consequently project module data. These files are processed last and so take precedence over other variable definitions. If the variable MS_DEF is defined by all previous levels, the definition in the user configuration file can overwrite previous definitions because it is loaded last.

The site configuration file `standards.cfg` is delivered with MicroStation. It appends its module data to the default system module data. If your site standards aren't very complex, copy your site module data files in appropriate subdirectories in the `c:\Bentley\Workspace\Standards` folder. MicroStation automatically makes them available. If your needs are complex, you can edit the site configuration file or create new ones.

You'll learn a lot by studying MicroStation's system configuration files. *However, don't modify them lest an incorrect modification cause MicroStation not to load!* Site, project, and user configuration files are an exception. They are meant to be modified by users and system administrators.

 TIP: Should you accidentally corrupt a system configuration file, restore it from a backup or another system. You can also start MicroStation from the command line with the `-debug` switch—see chapter 1—to dump configuration variables in the `msdebug.txt` file for examination and correction.

If you're responsible for corporate CAD standards, use the following table as a guide for placing module data. The folder names listed assume `C:\Bentley\Workspace\Standards` to be the parent directory.

Folder	Site Module Data
Cell	cell libraries
Data	color tables, glossary files, level names, settings files
Dgn	design files
Macros	MicroStation BASIC macros
Materials	material palettes used in rendering
Materials\Bump	bitmap images used as bump maps in material palettes
Materials\Pattern	bitmap images used as patterns in material palettes
Mdlapps\IntelNT	MDL applications for Intel processor-based systems (For Alpha processors use the AlphaNT folder. For Sun SPARC systems use the Sparc folder.)
Seed	seed files
Symb	symbology resources: fonts, custom line styles
Tables\Pen	pen tables for resymbolization of plots

When MicroStation starts, it displays choices in the Workspace groupbox in the MicroStation Manager dialog box, as shown below.

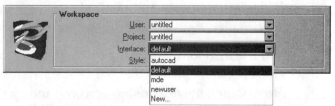

You can select User, Project, and Interface components in the MicroStation Manager dialog box during startup.

The choices you see in the User field are names of user configuration files, except `dfltuser.ucf`, in the `C:\Bentley\Workspace\Users` folder. The Project field lists project configuration files in the folder

`C:\Bentley\Workspace\Projects`. Because user configuration files can redefine the location for project configuration files, the choices in this field can change. Select `examples` in the User field and notice that choices for Project change. This is because `examples.ucf` redefines the variable `_USTN_PROJECT` to `C:\Bentley\Workspace\Projects\Examples`. So, project configuration files in that folder are displayed instead. The directories in `C:\Bentley\Workspace\Interfaces\MicroStation` are listed as workspace interfaces in the Interface field. MicroStation uses interface modification files stored in these directories to modify its menu bar, toolboxes, tool frames, and dialog boxes.

Now that you understand the workspace hierarchy and directory structure, it's time to learn the syntax for defining configuration variables.

Configuration File Syntax

Configuration files, regardless of filename extension—`.cfg`, `.pcf`, or `.ucf`—are text files and use the same syntax. You can edit or create them in any text editor, such as Windows Notepad or MS-DOS Editor, or a programmer's editor such as Visual SlickEdit or Multi-Edit. (Demos of both are included on the CD-ROM.) When you edit configuration variables in the Configuration dialog box accessed from the Workspace menu, changes are saved in the active user configuration file. To edit site or project configuration files, you must use a text editor.

A configuration file consists of statements. A statement can be only one line long by default. Long statements can be continued on another line by ending the previous line with the backslash (\) character. Most statements in a configuration file assign values to variables. A typical statement is shown below.

`_USTN_SYSTEM : $(MSDIR)config/system/`

The colon character, (`:`) is the assignment operator. To the left of the assignment operator is a configuration variable. To the right is its value.

Configuration variables are defined in MicroStation. The Configuration dialog box lists all user-editable configuration variables. Values are filenames or directory locations and can include previously defined variables. The term `$(MSDIR)` is substituted for `MSDIR`'s value.

The following table lists the meanings of valid assignment operators.

Operator	Meaning
=	Assign new value to variable.
:	Assign new value to variable if it doesn't already exist.
>	Append the path separator (;) followed by the value *after* the existing value of the variable.
<	Append value and the path separator (;) *before* the existing value of the variable.
+	Append a space followed by the value after the existing value of the variable.

The following table the meanings of value reference expressions.

Expression	Meaning
$(...)	Expand expression to value of variable in parentheses when it's used.
${...}	Expand expression to value of variable in parentheses when it's defined.

In addition to the assignment operator and value reference expression, configuration files support several directives to control the flow of statements. Directives are always preceded with the percent symbol (%). The `%include` directive is followed by a filename and causes MicroStation to load the variables in the file specified. The `%if`, `%else`, `%elif`, and `%endif` directives provide flow control by evaluating expressions. The `%error` directive prints a string and exits. The `%undef` directive deletes an existing variable. The `%lock` directive locks a variable to its current value so it can't be modified.

Configuration Dialog Box

When MicroStation starts, you choose a user configuration file to set its environment. While the site and project configuration files are the responsibility of the system administrator and project manager, the user configuration file is for users to modify. MicroStation implements the Configuration dialog box, as shown below, to simplify editing user configuration files.

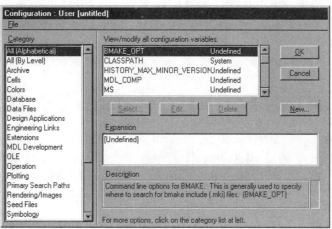

Select Configuration from the Workspace menu to open this dialog box.

This dialog box has three listboxes and several buttons. The listbox to the left is titled Category. Use it to display a list of configuration variables in the upper right listbox. The All (Alphabetical) category lists all configuration variables in alphabetical order. The All (By Level) organizes the list of variables by their hierarchical level—user, project, site, application, and system. The remaining categories list a subset of all variables specified by the category.

When you highlight a variable name, its value appears in the lower right listbox labeled Expansion. A description of the variable and how it affects MicroStation appears in the Description field. When you have time, scroll through the variable list and highlight each in turn to read its description. This is sure to enhance your knowledge of configuration variables tremendously.

The purpose of each button in the dialog box is explained below.

- **Select**: Highlight a variable and click Select to open a dialog box to navigate the hard disk to locate a filename or directory.
- **Edit**: Highlight a variable and click Edit to type a value in the configuration file syntax.
- **Delete**: Highlight a user configuration variable and click Delete to delete it. You can't delete variables defined in other levels.
- **New**: Click it to define a new configuration variable.

When you click OK, the dialog box closes after prompting you to save any changes you made. To close the dialog box without saving changes, click Cancel.

Customizing Interface Components

MicroStation's menu bar, dialog boxes, toolboxes, and tool frames are called its *interface components*. MicroStation comes with several interfaces you can choose from when starting it. You pick the desired interface from the Interface field in the MicroStation Manager dialog box.

The choices listed in the Interface field are directory names in the `C:\Bentley\Workspace\Interfaces\MicroStation` folder. You'll find four subdirectories under this folder, as listed below.

- **AutoCAD**: This interface lists AutoCAD terminology in parentheses next to menu choices. Its folder contains four resource modification files, as they modify four separate dialog and menu resources.

- **Default**: This interface is the default with no modifications. Its folder is blank, as no interface component is modified.

- **MDE**: This interface incorporates menu choices to invoke MDL programming-related tools and dialog boxes.

- **NewUser**: This interface offers a smaller list of choices on menus and is designed for the new user who may feel overwhelmed by the number of choices available in the default interface.

Engineering configuration and other MDL applications deliver custom interfaces. You saw how GeoGraphics, TriForma, and Modeler delivered custom interfaces by modifying the default menu bar and tool frame.

MicroStation provides easy-to-use dialog box-driven tools that allow you to edit its interface. Changes to interfaces are saved in the directory corresponding to the interface in the folder identified earlier. The files that define interface changes are binary. They are called *resource modification files*. The name of the resource modification file is based upon the name of the original resource file is modifies. The filename extension defines whether the resource modification file is processed at the user, project, or site level.

Interface modification tools are accessed from the Customize dialog box. From the Workspace menu, select Customize to open the dialog box, as shown below.

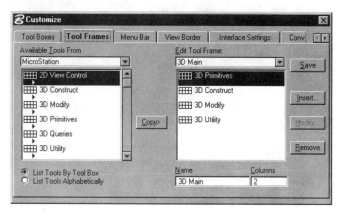

Use the Customize dialog box to modify interface components.

This dialog box has tabs identifying interface components it modifies. If you've edited the interface in other applications, you'll feel at home with the Customize dialog box.

To modify a toolbox:

1. Click the Tool Boxes tab in the Customize dialog box.
2. Select the toolbox to modify from the drop-down list in the Edit Tool Box field and highlight a tool in the listbox below.
3. To copy an existing tool above the tool highlighted in step 2, highlight the existing tool in the listbox under the Available Tools From field and click Copy. To add a new tool by drawing an icon and associating it with a key-in, click Insert. To modify a tool by editing its icon or associated key-in, click Modify. To delete a tool, click Remove.
4. Click Save.

To modify a tool frame:

1. Click the Tool Frames tab in the Customize dialog box.
2. Select the tool frame to modify from the drop-down list in the Edit Tool Frame field and highlight a tool or toolbox in the listbox below.

3. To copy an existing tool or toolbox above the item highlighted in step 2, highlight the existing item in the listbox under the Available Tools From field and click Copy. To insert a new tool by drawing an icon and associating it with a key-in, click Insert. To modify a tool in the tool frame by editing its icon or associated key-in, click Modify. To delete a tool or toolbox, click Remove. To rearrange toolboxes in the tool frame, drag them to new positions. To edit tools in toolboxes in the tool frame, use the controls in the Tool Boxes tab.

4. Click Save.

Toolboxes can contain only tools. However, tool frames can contain tools and toolboxes. You can modify tools and rearrange toolboxes in tool frames in the Tool Frames tab in Customize. To modify tools in toolboxes that appear in the tool frame, use the Tool Boxes tab instead.

To modify the menu bar:

1. Click the Menu Bar tab in the Customize dialog box.
2. Double-click a menu to expand or collapse it in the Menus listbox. When you expand a menu, its menu items appear below it.
3. To copy an existing menu above the highlighted menu in step 2, highlight the existing menu in the listbox under the Available Menus From field and click Copy. To insert a new menu item by typing a label and associating it with a key-in, click Insert. To modify a menu or menu item, click Modify. To delete a menu or menu item, click Remove. To rearrange menus or menu items, drag them to new positions.
4. Click Save.

NOTE: You can create new tool boxes or tool frames with Customize. From the Edit Tool Box or Edit Tool Frame drop down list in the appropriate tab, select Create Tool Box or Create Tool Frame.

This concludes the chapter.

Chapter 18
....
Translating Drawings
Working with AutoCAD's DWG and DXF Formats

If only one CAD software existed, you wouldn't have to worry about translating drawings. The fact is, there are dozens of general purpose and vertical market CAD applications to choose from. Each uses a different file format to store drawing entity and attribute data. Software for different markets from the same vendor often use different file formats.

To acquaint you with the variety of CAD software packages available, I've compiled this partial list: ArchiCAD from Graphisoft US, Inc.; AutoCAD and AutoSketch from Autodesk, Inc.; CADDS, MEDUSA, and ProEngineer from Parametric Technology Corporation; CADKEY from Bay State Technologies, Inc.; Cadra Design System from Adra Systems, Inc.; CATIA and CADAM from Dassault Systemes and IBM Corporation; DataCAD from DATACAD LLC; DesignCAD from ViaGrafix Corporation; DynaCADD from Ditek International; EasyCAD and FastCAD from Evolution Computing, Inc.; HASP from HASP, Inc.; Imagineer Technical and Solid Edge from Intergraph Corporation; IntelliCAD from Visio Corporation; MiniCAD from

Diehl Graphsoft, Inc.; SolidWorks from SolidWorks Corporation; TurboCAD from IMSI; Vellum from Ashlar Corporation; and XCAD from Xitron Software Corporation.

MicroStation saves drawings in the `.dgn` design file format Intergraph originally developed for IGDS. AutoCAD saves drawings in its `.dwg` drawing file format. CADKEY, DataCAD, DesignCAD, MiniCAD, TurboCAD, XCAD, and others, use their own proprietary drawing file formats. If you need to submit your MicroStation drawings in electronic format to those who don't use MicroStation, you must translate the drawings to a format their software will be able to read.

Drawing file formats from vendors are usually proprietary and each stores data in a different way. Simple elements, such as lines and circular arcs, that have similar data structures in different file formats, are easy to translate. Complex elements like multi-lines that may not exist in the other package or are implemented very differently, are difficult to translate perfectly. Other aspects, such as design plane size, attribute data, number of levels, and length of cell names, also determine how well you can translate a drawing from one format to another.

NOTE: Because drawing file formats differ and there may not be one-to-one correspondence between element types and attribute data, translations are never perfect. At best, you can strive to make translations as good as they can be. This chapter introduces you to the tools and options that make this possible.

The CAD industry has standardized on a few drawing exchange formats that are supported by most vendors. DXF/DWG and IGES are the most common. MicroStation supports these and several others. Though other file formats are mentioned, the focus of this chapter is translating between MicroStation's `.dgn` and AutoCAD's `.dwg` file formats, as they are the most common.

This chapter is organized in the following sections.

- **Translating with Default Settings** introduces MicroStation's translation tools and their default behavior. You'll discover why files convert the way they do.

- **Controlling Translation Settings** discusses the alternative to default settings. You learn where to configure settings for translating even the most difficult drawings successfully.

Translating with Default Settings

The simplest way to translate the active MicroStation drawing to another supported format is from the Save Design As dialog box. Select Save As from the File menu. The Save Design As dialog box opens, as shown in the figure below.

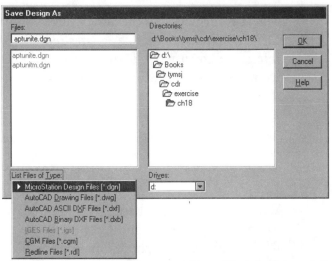

Use the Save Design As dialog box to export files with default translation settings.

From the List Files of Type drop-down list, select the format you wish to use when you convert the active design file. The following table describes each of the available formats.

File Type	Description
.dgn	Use this option to save the file with a new name without translating.
.dwg	Native AutoCAD drawing format. Default is set to version 14.
.dxf	AutoCAD drawing exchange format, ASCII version.
.dxb	AutoCAD drawing exchange format, binary version.
.igs	Disabled. Use the Export option under the File menu for IGES support.
.cgm	Computer Graphics Metafile vector format. (Doesn't process in one step.)
.rdl	MicroStation redline file used by the Redline toolbox in the Tools menu.

After selecting the desired file format and specifying a location and name for the file, click OK. If any of the three AutoCAD formats is selected, the file is translated using default settings with no further prompts. If .cgm is selected, another dialog box opens to let you select translation settings.

The .dgn format saves the design file without translation to another location or under a new name.

The .rdl format saves the design file, without translation, with the .rdl filename extension that designates redline revisions. These files can be referenced to an active design file with the Redline toolbox accessed from the Tools menu and shown below.

Redline On ———— Redline Off

The Redline toolbox.

When you invoke the Redline On tool, it attaches a file with the same name as the active design file, but with the .rdl extension. Clicking Redline Off detaches the redline revision file. MicroStation PowerScope, a separate design review package from Bentley, creates redline revision files.

To import drawings in other formats into MicroStation with default translation settings, use the MicroStation Manager dialog box, as shown below.

To import other formats with default settings, use MicroStation Manager.

When you import an AutoCAD drawing, MicroStation translates it to the `.dgn` format before opening it from the directory defined by the configuration variable MS_DWGOUT.

Regardless of the AutoCAD file format (`.dwg`, `.dxf`, or `.dxb`) you import or export, MicroStation uses the same translator. The translator has default behavior for file export and import that may not be what you want.

The drawing translation tables that define the translator's default behavior are located in the `c:\Bentley\Workspace\System\Tables\Dwg` folder defined by the configuration variable MS_DWGTABLES. The following table lists the file names and what they do.

DWG Translation Mapping Table	Purpose
dwgchar.tbl	Character mapping table
dwgcolor.tbl	Color mapping table
dwgfont.tbl	Font mapping table
dwghatch.tbl	Hatch object mapping table
dwglevel.tbl	Level name to number mapping table
dwgline.tbl	Line style mapping table
dwgwght.tbl	Line weight mapping table
dwgwtco.tbl	AutoCAD color to MicroStation weight mapping table
dwg.bas	MicroStation BASIC macro used by translator to load above mapping tables

Studying the MicroStation BASIC file that controls import and export settings will prove invaluable in understanding the translator's default behavior. It uses mapping tables in ASCII text format that can be read or edited in any text editor. Mapping tables contain rows that correlate values between the two file formats.

When translating a design file to AutoCAD format, the translator by default uses no AutoCAD template file, doesn't use the mapping table for colors, ignores line weights, merges reference files, uses the master unit as a basis of conversion, converts MicroStation shapes to AutoCAD polylines, converts filled shapes to solids, and converts small shapes to polylines.

These settings may work for small and simple drawings. If you want better conversions, you must control translation settings. MicroStation's translator is very flexible. You can control virtually all aspects of the translation. The more you know how elements, attributes, or settings in one should be converted to the other file format, the better equipped you'll be to edit or activate the translation setting.

The next section introduces you to the flexible way of translating drawings between .dgn and .dwg file formats.

Controlling Translation Settings

To take complete control over the conversion of the active MicroStation design file to the AutoCAD file format, use the DWG/DXF Export dialog box. Select Export, then DWG or DXF from the File menu, as shown below.

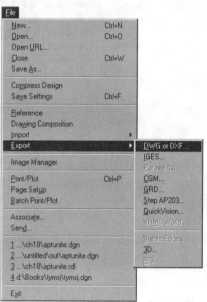

Use the Export submenu for conversion flexibility.

The Save As AutoCAD Drawing File dialog box opens. Specify a location and name for the file you wish to create. Click OK. The DWG/DXF Export dialog box opens, as shown below.

Use the File and Settings menus on this dialog box to control translation parameters.

You can load and edit mapping tables from the Settings menu. You can set, examine, or edit other translation parameters that don't have mapping tables by opening the MicroStation BASIC `dwg.bas` translation settings file from the File menu. The following table describes the options under the File menu.

File Menu Choices	Description
Settings File, Attach	Use to pick the BASIC macro file containing translation settings.
Settings File, Edit	Opens `dwg.bas` in the MicroStation BASIC Editor.
Settings File, Save	Saves changes you make in the dialog box to `dwg.bas`.
Settings File, Save As	Saves the settings file (`dwg.bas`) to another location or name.
Log File	To specify an alternate file to log the conversion process.

The translator reads the conversion settings file, `dwg.bas`, before it starts processing a file for translation. Any changes you make to parameters from the Settings menu are saved in this file.

To map MicroStation cells (six-character name) to specific AutoCAD blocks (thirty-one character name), specify a MicroStation font number for imported text. Specify a value for the AutoCAD LTSCALE variable, or other parameter and edit the well-commented translation settings file.

The following table describes the options under the Settings menu.

Settings Menu Choices	Description
General	Specify AutoCAD version, units, and other basic settings.
Layers	Edit the `dwglevel.tbl` mapping table.
Line Styles	Edit the `dwgline.tbl` mapping table.
Weight Width	Edit the `dwgwght.tbl` mapping table.
Weight Color	Edit the `dwgwtco.tbl` mapping table.
Color	Edit the `dwgcolor.tbl` mapping table.
Character	Edit the `dwgchar.tbl` mapping table.

When you select General from the Settings menu, the Export Drawing File Settings dialog box opens, as shown below.

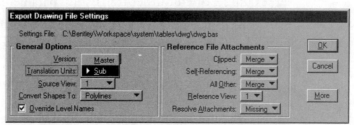

For drawings in English units, select Sub from Translation Units.

In this dialog box, you can select compatibility of the exported file to a specific AutoCAD version. You can also decide on the view to use as a source for view-dependent symbology settings, and how to convert MicroStation shapes (polylines or polyface mesh). It's possible to override level names. You can specify whether to merge, ignore, or create AutoCAD Xrefs from reference files for clipped or self-referenced files.

The one setting in the dialog box that may not be obvious is Translation Units. If working units are defined for English units in feet and inches, select Sub. If working units are for metric units or decimal feet, select Master.

When you select any other option from the Settings menu in the DWG/DXF Export dialog box, a dialog box opens to let you edit the selected mapping table. The dialog box for editing the weight to width mapping table is shown in the figure below.

To edit a row, highlight it and enter a new value in the text field below the listbox.

The MicroStation BASIC language, discussed in chapter 24, implements *objects* for actions. It implements four DWG/DXF translation objects: **MbeBlockNameTable**, **MbeFontNameTable**, **MbeDWGImportSettings**, and **MbeDWGExportSettings**. The first two objects work with mapping tables. The other two are used to set parameters that haven't been implemented as mapping tables—many don't have a dialog box interface.

To import AutoCAD drawings with control over the process, use the Import submenu from the File menu in MicroStation's menu bar.

It helps to know the units set in the drawing you are trying to import so you can set up appropriate working units in the active design file. If the AutoCAD file is set to architectural units, use feet and inch working units. If it's set to engineering units, use a decimal working unit setting.

NOTE: When you translate an AutoCAD drawing from the MicroStation Manager dialog box, a new design file is automatically created. When you translate it from the Import menu, elements in the AutoCAD drawing are imported in the design file you have open.

After you identify an AutoCAD file to import, the DWG/DXF Import dialog box opens, as shown below.

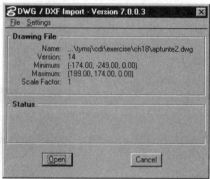

Values in the Minimum and Maximum coordinate fields can help you determine the unit setting in the AutoCAD file.

The File and Settings menu options in this dialog box are identical to those in the DWG/DXF Export dialog box.

If you don't know the units used in the AutoCAD drawing but know the drawing extent, the minimum and maximum coordinate values displayed in the dialog box can help. By subtracting the minimum from the maximum x-coordinate value (189 - (-174) = 363 from the above dialog box) and comparing it with the drawing extent, you can determine whether architectural (inches) or engineering (decimal) units were used in the AutoCAD drawing. This will help you set the proper working units for the active design file.

Some tips follow that may help you convert files successfully:

- If you encounter memory allocation, system fault, or MDL abort errors during translation, try increasing your system RAM and defragment the drive because virtual memory needs contiguous space.

- If a design file won't export, it may have range errors. Use EdG to fix the file and try again. You may also place a fence over its entire contents and use the `FF=filename` key-in to generate a clean copy. Try to export that file. (`FF=` is called the fence file key-in.)

- If an AutoCAD drawing won't import, run Recover and try again. You may also use AutoCAD's WBLOCK command to generate a clean copy and try to import that file.

This concludes the chapter.

Part 3

Customizing MicroStation

Set Preferences and Customize Without Programming

Chapter 19

Setting User Preferences

Optimizing RAM and Other User-controlled Settings

Having come this far in the book, you've learned MicroStation features that help you create drawings and electronic models. You've also learned aspects of MicroStation that can help you support other users by developing and implementing standards, fixing corrupt design files, and archiving and translating drawings. In Part 3, *Customizing MicroStation*, you will learn the settings in the Preferences dialog box, how to create custom lines styles, glossaries, function key menus, cells, and macros in other applications, such as Microsoft Excel, to create drawings.

As an experienced MicroStation user, you know the type and size of drawings you work with. You notice the defaults MicroStation uses, such as tool size and cursor. You also wish these defaults could be changed. At this point, you're a power user. This chapter is written for you. It helps you understand user preference options and where to set them.

As a power user, you know how to draw even the most complex drawings. You are comfortable using MicroStation's drawing and modeling tools. However, you aren't quite sure how computer system resources such as amount of RAM (*random access memory*) might affect your MicroStation environment.

MicroStation maintains settings to help you customize and fine-tune your workspace environment. If you work on projects that have different needs, you can create several user preferences and load the one more suitable for the project. If other users share your computer, each person can maintain their own user preferences.

The more you know about preferences, the better equipped you are to mold MicroStation to your way of working. In this chapter you explore the Preferences dialog box in detail. Select Preferences from the Workspace menu to open the dialog box shown below.

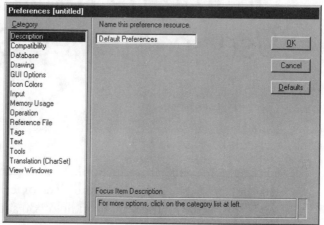

The Preferences dialog box controls many user settings.

On finishing this chapter, you will have learned the following.

- How to compute system RAM for a swap-free environment.
- How to set compatibility with older .dgn file formats.
- How to highlight elements instead of placing handles on them.
- How to configure default reference file attachment settings.
- How to set tool size, grid density, and many other settings.

Unlike some settings you've seen, such as workspace configuration files and translation mapping tables, user preferences are stored in a binary file. You can't view or edit them in a text editor.

When you pick a workspace name from the User drop-down menu in the MicroStation Manager dialog box shown below, MicroStation loads the user configuration file for the workspace and a user preference file, if it exists.

Each user configuration file has an associated user preference file.

When a workspace is opened for the first time, it has no corresponding user preference file. MicroStation creates a new user preference file on the fly, with default settings for such a workspace.

TIP: When MicroStation can't remember your preference settings, the user preference file is probably corrupt. To fix the problem, simply delete the corrupt file. A new one with default settings will be created automatically the next time you use that workspace.

User preference files have the filename extension `.upf` and are stored in the same directory with user configuration files. The default location for them is `c:\Bentley\Workspace\Users`, discussed in chapter 17. I invite you to examine this directory. User configuration files that were used on your computer have corresponding user preference files. They share the same filename but use a different filename extension. User configurations that haven't been used don't have corresponding user preference files.

To create a user preference file, create a user configuration file. Select New from the User drop-down menu in the MicroStation Manager dialog box. The Create User Configuration File dialog box opens, as shown below.

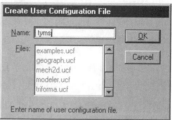

Creating a user configuration file also creates a corresponding user preference file.

Enter a name for the workspace and click OK. Another dialog box opens where you enter a description for the workspace and specify a project configuration file and interface. When you open a design file with this workspace, a user preference file is created.

The design file stores many settings that are available between sessions. Many other settings are kept in the user preference file. MicroStation and MDL applications can read from and write to it.

Let's now begin our journey through the land of user preferences!

The Preferences dialog box displays preference categories to the left and settings associated with the category to the right, as shown below.

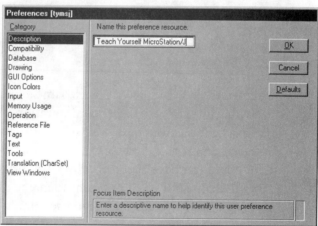

Click a category on the left to display associated settings on the right.

If you're unsure of what a setting does, highlight it and read its description that appears in the Focus Item Description field below.

Description

This category has one field. Use it to enter a description for the user preference file. If you forget the name of the user preference file, look at the title bar. The name appears in brackets.

Compatibility

This category implements four checkboxes and one option button. Here you set design file format compatibility. MicroStation version 3 used the same format as Intergraph's IGDS. Type 33 associative dimension elements, multi-lines, shared cells, and associative patterns didn't exist. Nor did custom line styles, tag data, and smart geometry. Version 4 supported dimension elements, multi-lines, and shared cells, but not associative patterning. MicroStation 95, SE, and /J use the same design file format as version 5.

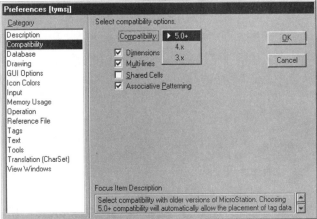

Leave at 5.X unless you exchange drawings with users of an older version.

When the elements in your design file must be compatible with an older version, select that version on the compatibility option button. Checkboxes help you further refine the types of elements you don't want placed in your design file. Enable them as desired.

It's important that you realize that no tool stops working as a result of choices you make here. MicroStation checks your compatibility preferences while creating elements and uses older element types as necessary. For example, the Dimension Element tool uses line, line string, and text elements instead of the dimension element to place dimensions under version 3 compatibility. Existing elements in the design file aren't affected. They remain of the type originally placed. However, new elements placed after a compatibility mode change are compatible with the selected version.

When you open a design file in an older MicroStation version, incompatible elements don't display. For example, dimension elements in a design file won't display in MicroStation version 3. If you wish to retain dimension elements, shared cells, tags, and multi-lines in a design file and want them to display in version 3, freeze them. Key in **FREEZE** and identify elements you wish to freeze. To restore frozen elements to their original state, use the **THAW** or **FENCE THAW** key-ins.

You'll want version 5 compatibility under normal circumstances to benefit from the features of newer element types.

Database

This category implements the following three checkboxes.

- Block Database Undeletes, when enabled, prevents Undo from restoring deleted elements with external database links.

- Use Single AE/MSFORMS Tables, when enabled, prevents MicroStation from using multiple active element and *msforms* tables. Leave it disabled. Enabling this option adds overhead because anytime you switch to an element that is linked to another table, the single active element (AE) table must be cleared and loaded with the data from the new table.

- Use Database Mslink Cache, when enabled, caches entity numbers and data in the *mslink* field for faster database lookups.

These checkboxes are disabled by default. If you link elements to large databases and have sufficient RAM, enabling the last checkbox will improve performance when querying database records.

Drawing

This category lets you specify acceptable grid density in a view for display purposes. In the first field, shown in the figure below, you specify how many grid points in a view you consider too dense for display.

Acceptable values are between 10 and 400. In the second field, you specify how many grid references in a view are too dense. Acceptable values are between 5 and 150. If more grid points than you prefer would appear on the screen even when the Grid checkbox is enabled in the View Attributes dialog box, grid points don't display.

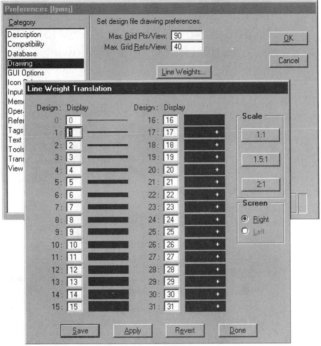

line weight

Clicking the Line Weights button opens the Line Weight Translation dialog box, shown above. Use it to control how line weights display on the screen.

Clicking the 1:1 scale button increments each weight by 1 pixel for display; clicking 1.5:1 divides the line weight by 1.5 and uses the quotient; clicking 2:1 divides the line weight by 2 and uses the quotient. For example, when you the click 2:1 scale button and accept the display weight table, line weights of 10 and 11 will display 5 pixels wide. You can also edit the line weight display fields directly. Normally you want to see line weight differences, and you will use the default 1:1 line weight to display mapping.

Click Apply to see changes without closing the dialog box. Click Save to store changes in the user preference file and close the dialog box. Click Reset to restore fields to default values. Click Done to close the Line Weight Translation dialog box.

GUI Options

Use this category to select interface look and feel preferences. The Dialog Boxes option button offers Motif and Windows as choices. Motif emulates the UNIX Motif windowing environment for the look of dialog boxes. Windows emulates the look of Microsoft Windows dialog boxes.

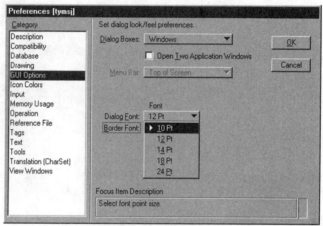

The Open Two Application Windows checkbox is for dual-screen systems.

The Open Two Application Windows checkbox causes MicroStation to open two application windows simultaneously in a session. On computers that use two screens, you can keep an application window in each to make more room for MicroStation's many view windows.

The Dialog Font and Border Font option buttons let you select a font size for the text and borders in dialog boxes.

Icon Colors

To use gray icons select Gray Scale. To specify custom colors, select Custom and specify the colors.

Input

The checkbox Start in Parse All Mode is not as relevant as it was in earlier MicroStation versions when the Key-in window was used to enter commands and tool-specific data. Leave it on, the default. It is the same as keying in SET PARSEALL ON. You can turn it off by keying in SET PARSEALL OFF.

When you drag the mouse in a view window with element placement tools such as Place Line, a data point is placed once when you click the mouse button, and another is placed when you release it. To have MicroStation enter a data point only when you click the button, enable the Disable Drag Operations checkbox.

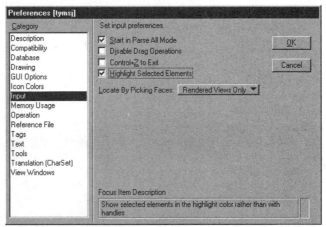

Highlight Selected Elements displays elements in a selection set in highlight color rather than with handles on them.

Users of the UNIX operating system close command windows by entering the Ctrl+Z keyboard shortcut. To use this shortcut to exit MicroStation, enable the Control+Z to Exit checkbox.

When you click elements, they are added to the selection set and handles appear on them. To show selected elements in the highlight color instead, enable the Highlight Selected Elements checkbox.

The Locate By Picking Faces option button lets you specify when to locate elements when you click their faces. Available choices are Never, Rendered Views Only, and Always.

Memory Usage

This category controls how MicroStation uses system RAM. To coax the best performance from MicroStation, you must understand these options well. I've included the Microsoft Excel spreadsheet `ramcalc.xls` in the `\Exercise\ch19` folder on the CD-ROM to help you determine, based on the size of your design files and other parameters, how much RAM you should install on your system for the best performance. More about the spreadsheet later.

How much element cache, in kilobytes, should you set? The default value is 8,000, or about 8 megabytes. It's better to overestimate this number because MicroStation uses only what's needed—not all of it. For better performance, MicroStation stores design file elements in memory because memory access is significantly faster than disk access. Use the Maximum Element Cache field to specify how much memory should MicroStation allocate for your design files. This value can be estimated by adding the size of design and reference files you use. For example, if the largest design file you use is 6 megabytes with reference files totaling another 10 megabytes, the cache value can be set to 16,000 safely.

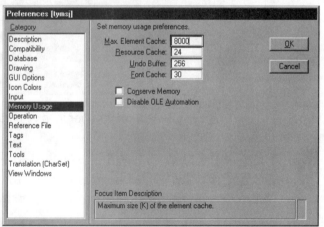

Use the sum of design and reference file sizes for Max. Element Cache.

The default 24 kilobytes for Resource Cache is adequate for most needs. It is the memory used by MicroStation for displaying dialog boxes on screen. Dialog boxes are stored in resource files. Resource files are created in MDL, a topic covered in chapter 25.

Undo Buffer is the memory MicroStation allocates for storing actions it can undo. If an action such as Fence Delete processes more than will fit in the undo buffer, the action can't be undone completely. The value should be set to the largest action you may want to undo.

The default 30 kilobytes for Font Cache is adequate for most needs. This memory is used by MicroStation for displaying text elements.

If your computer has limited RAM, enable the Conserve Memory checkbox. Refer to the `ramcalc.xls` spreadsheet discussion later in the chapter to determine whether you have sufficient RAM.

If you develop or use applications on your computer that use OLE (Object Linking and Embedding) automation technology, leave the Disable OLE Automation checkbox off. Otherwise, enable it. OLE automation services are loaded in memory when MicroStation starts. If you don't need these services, disabling them will conserve memory.

NOTE: The Memory Usage category specifies how MicroStation allocates memory for many tasks when it starts. Changes you make here take effect only after you restart MicroStation.

Other than processor speed, the most important system resource that determines your computer's performance is RAM. Where hard disks have an average seek time of 10 milliseconds, RAM is rated at 70 nanoseconds. This means that your computer can access information nearly 143,000 ($= (10 \times 10^{-3}) / (70 \times 10^{-9})$) times faster from RAM than from the hard disk.

MicroStation will run fastest if it can access all information it needs from RAM. Installing adequate memory on your computer is the best investment you can make. Some guidelines follow to determine the amount you need.

- **Operating System Needs:** Use 8 megabytes for Windows 95/98 and 16 megabytes for Windows NT.
- **Basic MicroStation Needs:** Use 6 megabytes.
- **Undo Buffer:** Use the value discussed earlier in megabytes.
- **Element Cache:** The sum of design and reference file sizes in megabytes.

- **Range Tree:** Element cache times 0.32 in megabytes.

- **Backing Store:** Screen resolution multiplied by color depth in megabytes. For example, a 1024 x 768 screen resolution with 256 colors (a color depth of 8 bits or 1 byte, because $2^8 = 256$) means that backing store needs $1024 \times 768 \times 1 \times 10^{-6} = 0.786$ megabytes. Backing store is discussed under the View Windows category later.

- **Rendering:** Screen resolution times 8 bytes per pixel, in megabytes. For example, a 1024 x 768 resolution means that if you render views, the task will take $1024 \times 768 \times 8 \times 10^{-6} = 6.291$ megabytes.

- **MDL Applications:** Add the file size, in megabytes, of all MDL applications you typically use to estimate this.

- **Other Concurrent Application Needs:** This depends on how you use your computer. If you have several applications open concurrently on your desktop, add the memory needs of each in megabytes.

Add memory for each bullet above for the RAM you need. To help you compute this number more easily I've included the Microsoft Excel spreadsheet `ramcalc.xls` on the CD-ROM. Enter numbers under the column titled *input* in colored cells on the spreadsheet. The result is computed by the embedded formulas.

Operation

Use this category for element selection, cursor size and orientation, level display, and other software operational preferences.

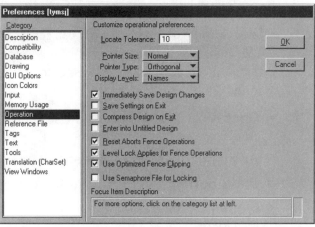

MicroStation's default locate tolerance (area in which it locates elements) is 10 pixels.

The diameter of the circle, in pixels, that tracks the cursor while it awaits element identification is called *locate tolerance*. If you need help in identifying the cursor shape while MicroStation awaits element identification, you may wish to refer to the cursor shapes figure in chapter 1. When you click in a view, elements within the locate tolerance are highlighted. You can change this value as a user preference.

The other options in this category are self-explanatory. Set them to meet your needs. For example, to invoke the Save Settings command automatically when MicroStation exits, enable the Save Settings on Exit checkbox. To invoke the Compress command automatically when MicroStation exits, enable the Compress on Exit checkbox. To let MicroStation finish processing fence contents before it responds to a Reset button click, disable the Reset Aborts Fence Operations checkbox. To have the cursor span across the view window, select Full View from the Pointer Size option button.

Reference File

Use this category to specify preferences related to reference files. Available settings are shown in the figure below.

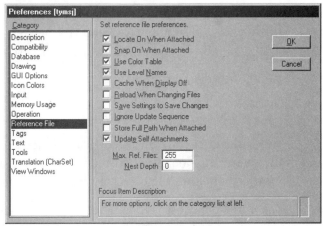

In this dialog box, you can specify the maximum number of reference files that may be attached to an active design file.

When the checkbox Locate On When Attached is enabled, you can identify elements in attached reference files by default.

When the checkbox Snap On When Attached is enabled, you can snap to elements in attached reference files by default.

When the checkbox Use Color Table is enabled, MicroStation uses the reference file's color table to display its elements. Otherwise, the active design file's color table is used. Turning this option off speeds the loading of design files with reference files. However, if reference files use custom color tables, elements will display in a different color.

When the checkbox Use Level Names is enabled, reference file level names are displayed instead of level numbers.

When the checkbox Cache When Display Off is unchecked, reference file elements are not cached when you turn their display off. When you turn its display back on, MicroStation must read the reference file from disk, causing a short delay.

When the Reload When Changing Files checkbox is unchecked, reference files are kept in memory (if element cache permits) when a design file is closed to load another. When you switch between reference files and the active design file, reference files load extremely quickly because they are already in memory.

When the checkbox Save Settings to Save Changes is unchecked, reference file attachment information is saved immediately in the design file. Otherwise, you must select Save Settings from the File menu for a design file to remember which files were attached.

When the checkbox Ignore Update Sequence is unchecked, the update sequence specified in the Reference Files dialog box is used. Otherwise, the standard update sequence is used.

When the checkbox Store Full Path When Attached is unchecked, only the reference filename is stored in the design file, not the directory location. To store the directory location, enable it.

When the checkbox Update Self Attachments is enabled, you can edit self-referenced file elements.

Use the text field Max. Ref. Files to specify the maximum number of reference files that may be attached to an active design file.

Use the text field Nest Depth to specify how many levels of nesting a reference file attachment is to accommodate. The default is zero. When you attach a reference file with attachments, only the reference file—not its attachments—is attached.

Tags

Use this category to specify tag-related preferences.

When the checkbox Prompt on Duplicate Tag Sets is enabled, inserting a cell with a tag set definition that already exists in the design file causes MicroStation to display an Alert dialog box for confirmation. Otherwise, the design file tag set definition is replaced without warning.

When the checkbox Use Design File Tag Sets by Default is enabled, tag sets in cells use design file definitions in case of a conflict.

When the checkbox Place Tags in Same Graphic Group is enabled, all tags are placed in a graphic group. This is the default.

Text

Use this category to specify text-related preferences, as shown in the figure below.

When the Display Text with Line Styles checkbox is unchecked, text displays with the solid line style regardless of its line style.

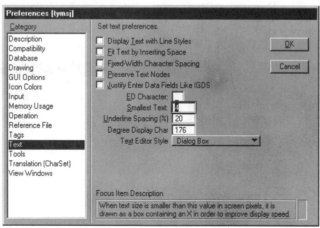

Be sure to check out the WYSWYG Text Editor Style.

When the checkbox Fit Text by Inserting Space is unchecked, text size changes when fitted text is placed. If enabled, the active text size is used and text is fitted by changing character spacing.

When the checkbox Fixed-Width Character Spacing is enabled, character spacing is measured from beginning to beginning of letters. Otherwise, it is measured from the end of the first letter to the beginning of the next.

When the checkbox Preserve Text Nodes is enabled, multi-line text remains a text node when it is edited to a single line. Otherwise, a text node is converted to a text element.

When the checkbox Justify Enter Data Fields Like IGDS is enabled, MicroStation emulates the enter data field justification style of IGDS.

Use the field ED Character to specify a character other than the default underscore character (_) for creating enter data fields.

Use the field Smallest Text to set the size, in pixels, when text is to be displayed as a box, rather than text. If you don't want text to be greeked at any display resolution, set the value to 0.

Use the field Underline Spacing (%) to override the default 20 percent of text height as distance between the text baseline and the underline.

Use the field Degree Display Char to override the default 176 ASCII character used to display the degree symbol.

Use the option button Text Editor Style to select the Text Editor dialog box, the WYSIWYG (What You See Is What You Get) text editor, or the Key-in window when placing or editing text.

The WYSIWYG Text Editor window uses design file fonts instead of dialog box fonts. It also implements a keyboard to simplify entering special characters.

Tools

This preference category lets you control the toolbox, the tool frame, the Tool Settings window, and tool icon settings, shown below.

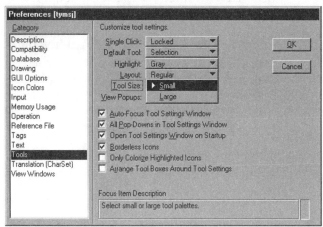

Tool Size lets you select the size of icons displayed in toolboxes.

The Single Click option button has two choices, Locked and Single-shot. A tool restarts—the Locked option—unless you click Reset or select another tool. When Single-shot is selected, the default tool (Element Selector or PowerSelector) activates after a tool completes.

The Default Tool option button specifies the default tool. There are three choices, None, Selection, and PowerSelector. When None is selected, MicroStation reverts to a *null* state.

The Highlight option button is used to change the color of the selection background. There are three choices: Black, Gray, and Color. (The element highlight color is set in the Design File Settings dialog box).

The Layout option button is used to change the size of dialog boxes. There are three choices: Narrow, Regular, and Wide.

The Tool Size option button lets you select the size of tool icons. There are two choices, Small and Large. When you write MDL programs, discussed in chapter 25, that use tool icons you must draw two sizes.

Use the View Popups option button to specify whether to display the Views popup menu when you click Shift-Reset in a view window.

When the Auto-Focus Tool Settings Window checkbox is enabled, the Tool Settings window receives the focus when a tool is selected.

When the All Pop-Downs in Tool Settings Window checkbox is enabled, older MDL programs written for version 5 that used toolbox pop-downs use the Tool Settings window instead.

When the Open Tool Settings Window on Startup checkbox is enabled, the Tool Settings window is opened when MicroStation starts. Otherwise, it opens when a tool needs it.

When the Borderless Icons checkbox is enabled, icons in toolboxes are borderless, as are icons in newer Windows applications.

When the Only Colorize Highlighted Icons checkbox is enabled, only highlighted icons appear in color. Others are gray.

When the Arrange Tool Boxes Around Tool Settings checkbox is enabled, the changing size of the Tool Settings window causes adjacent toolboxes, such as the Key-in window, the Standard toolbox, and the Primary toolbox, to rearrange.

Translation (CharSet)

This category displays a listbox for selecting a character translation table when bringing in text files into MicroStation. For the English language distribution you have two choices: Default and None.

This character translation table is used to convert native (English or another language) single-byte characters to MicroStation's internal DEC multinational ASCII format.

View Windows

This Preferences category lets you control view window settings.

When the Scroll Bars on View Windows checkbox is enabled, view windows display scroll bars used for panning views. If you turn off scroll bars, the View Control bar doesn't display.

When the Black Background->White checkbox is enabled, the default black background turns white.

When the Tile Like IGDS checkbox is enabled, the order of view windows (when four are open) emulates IGDS.

When the Enhanced Dither checkbox is enabled, MicroStation uses enhanced dithering algorithms on systems with lower color depths when rendering models.

When the checkbox Use Backing Store is enabled, MicroStation stores a copy of each view in memory so that obscured areas are refreshed instantly when dialog boxes are moved or views are rearranged.

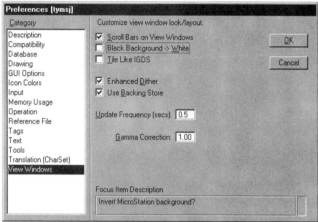

When backing store is enabled, MicroStation stores a copy of each view in memory.

In the Update Frequency field specify the frequency in seconds at which to update the view when rendering models.

In the Gamma Correction field specify a value of gamma correction used to compensate for spectral characteristic differences between mediums, such as screens and plots, used to showcase renderings. The value can vary from 0.1 to 3.0, with 1.0 being the default. Higher values lighten middle shades.

This concludes the tour of MicroStation's preference settings.

Chapter 20

Creating Custom Resource Data

Line Styles, Glossaries, and Other Tools

Workspaces and standards represent concepts, rules, and CAD data organization for consistency, efficiency, and productivity. To ensure the success of standards and implementation of workspaces, you must develop supporting resource data that gives form to the concepts and rules. In this chapter we explore the development of custom symbology resources and other data files that help standards implementation.

Drawings use a variety of line styles to communicate design intent clearly. For example, existing site information may be shown in a dashed line style, while site additions may appear in a solid and thicker line style. Using different line styles clarifies the design unambiguously. Other uses for line styles include the representation of underground utility lines, chemical process flows, and railroad lines. When the eight standard line styles aren't enough, custom line styles can help.

Graphical elements such as lines and arcs are used to create models and drawings. Text notes on drawings support models with annotation that describe generic symbols and other issues, such as construction sequence, that don't have graphical representations. To place standard text notes without typing, MicroStation includes the Glossary utility. It also includes the Font Installer so you can import system and other fonts to enhance drawings.

In addition to custom line styles, text glossary, and Font Installer, this chapter introduces you to function key menus for providing quick access to frequently used key-in sequences.

On finishing this chapter you will have learned the following:

- What are custom line styles?
- How to create custom line styles.
- How to use and modify custom line style parameters.
- How to ensure others can use drawings that use custom line styles.
- What are text glossaries?
- How to create and use text glossaries.
- How to import system and other fonts for use in MicroStation.
- How to ensure others can use drawings that use fonts other than standard fonts that ship with MicroStation.
- How to create function key menus.

You don't need extensive MicroStation experience to follow the tools and steps introduced in this chapter. If you are a CAD administrator who knows but doesn't use MicroStation in a production environment, you can create custom resource data (line styles, glossaries, function key menus, and font resource files) easily.

If you are a user, it's best to discuss needs and implementation issues with other users in your company before creating and using custom line styles and font resource files. If you create your own and use them, others won't be able to display or plot the custom fonts or line styles unless you make your custom resource data files available for their use.

Custom Line Styles

The eight standard line styles, also called *linecodes*, are an internal MicroStation resource. MicroStation requires no external data file to determine the line's pattern.

When you need a line style other than the standard, you can create custom line styles in an external resource file that MicroStation reads when it starts.

What They Are and How to Use Them

Custom line style definitions are stored in the workspace symbology resource directory by convention. Because MicroStation must have access to custom line style definitions to display drawings correctly that use them, storing custom line style definitions on a network site workspace directory eliminates the need to copy these resource data files on individual computers.

The site workspace symbology resource directory for a default MicroStation installation is:

`C:\Bentley\Workspace\Standards\Symb`

The configuration variable that defines a list of workspace symbology resource files is MS_SYMBRSC. MicroStation opens all symbology resource files in the order they are defined. If no resource files are defined by the variable, MicroStation looks for the file `mssymb.rsc`.

Custom symbology resource files are binary and portable across all operating systems. You can share custom resource data files from a network directory in a heterogeneous network that connects Windows and UNIX workstations.

Most MicroStation elements, such as arcs, circles, curves (including B-spline curves), ellipses, lines, line strings, multi-lines, and shapes can use custom line styles. Many custom line styles come with MicroStation. You can use them as they are or add new line styles to default resource files. You can also create new resource files for custom line styles. The last option is the best; it should be undertaken as a company standard for reasons discussed earlier.

To activate a line style, do one of the following:

- In the Key-in window, type `LC=linestylename`, where `linestylename` is a number 0 through 7, or the name of a custom line style.

- In the Key-in window, type `ACTIVE STYLE linestylename`, where `linestylename` is a number 0 through 7, or the name of a custom line style.

- From the Primary toolbox, select a standard line style or Custom to open the Line Styles dialog box.

- From the Element menu, access the Element Attributes dialog box. Select a standard line style or Custom to open the Line Styles dialog box.

NOTE: When keying in line style names, you need not type its name entirely. For example, if you type `LC=DI` in the Key-in window and press enter, the Select Line Style dialog box opens with a list of line styles that contain the letters DI. If the letters you type uniquely identify the line style name in the list, the line style is selected without displaying the dialog box.

The Line Styles dialog box displays all custom line style definitions MicroStation loaded during startup, as shown in the figure below.

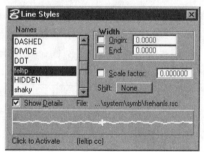

Toggle the Show Details checkbox to resize the dialog box.

Double-click a line style in the Names listbox to activate it. The active line style name appears in the Primary toolbox. When the dialog box opens, only the Names listbox displays. Enable the Show Details checkbox for the larger version of the dialog box, shown above. Custom line styles have many attributes standard line styles don't. This is evident in the larger version of the Line Styles dialog box. During placement, you can define starting and ending widths to create variable-width lines, scale their dash-gap pattern, and shift the origin of a pattern, as shown in the figure below.

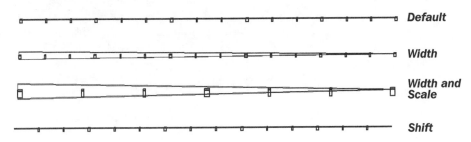

The {Curtain} line style with different width, scale, and shift parameters.

When you need to adjust the width, scale, or origin of custom line styles during their placement, use the Line Styles dialog box with the Show Details checkbox enabled.

TIP: If you prefer keying in numbers for custom line styles, include a unique number in their names. For example, if you name the custom line style that draws tree lines Tree99, you can activate it by keying in LC=99.

To modify custom line style parameters of existing elements:

1. Define desired parameters in the Line Styles dialog box and make the line style active.
2. Activate the Change Element Attributes tool and enable the Style checkbox. You are prompted to identify an element.
3. Click the element. It highlights, and you are prompted to accept or reject. Click a data point to change its style or click Reset to identify another element.

You can drop the status of custom line styles so their components are converted to the primitive element used in their definitions. Use the Drop Line Style tool in the Drop toolbox for this purpose.

To convert a custom line style to primitive elements:

1. Open the Drop toolbox from the Tools menu.
2. Activate the Drop Line Style tool. You are prompted to identify an element.

3. Click the element. It highlights and you are prompted to accept or reject it. Click a data point and the highlighted element is converted to primitive elements or click Reset to identify another element.

TIP: Custom line styles are stored in a symbology resource file that MicroStation loads at startup. If you use custom line styles in drawings you must share with others, send the resource file with the drawing or use the Archive utility to package it.

How to Define Them

A custom line style definition can contain three components: stroke patterns, point symbols, and compound components.

A *stroke pattern* defines the size, width, and sequence of dash and gap patterns in a line style. A line style definition that contains only a stroke pattern may look similar to a standard line style but has all the attributes of a custom line style, such as width, scale, and shift parameters.

A *point symbol* groups several elements into a single unit in the line style resource file. It defines how the symbol repeats, offsets, and scales along the line. Point symbols are like shared cells.

A *compound component* is a combination of stroke patterns, point symbols, and even other compound components.

You define custom line styles in the Line Style Editor dialog box. Select Edit from the Style option button on the Element Attributes dialog box or Primary toolbox. The Line Style Editor dialog box opens, as shown below.

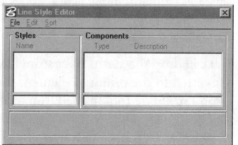

Open the Line Style Editor by selecting Edit from the Line Style option button in the Primary toolbox.

The Line Style Editor dialog box sports offers three menu choices: File, Edit, and Sort.

Use the *File* menu to create, open, close, and save line style resource files. You can also rename or delete line style definitions by selecting Manage from the File menu. When you create a new line style resource file MicroStation loads its standard line styles in the Components section of the dialog box.

Use the *Edit* menu to create, delete, and duplicate line style names and components. You link line style names with components by highlighting them and selecting Link from the Edit menu.

Use the *Sort* menu to sort line style names and components by type or description. Menus in the Line Style Editor dialog box are shown below.

The File, Edit, and Sort menus on the Line Style Editor dialog box.

When a line style resource file is open in the Line Style Editor, line style names appear in the Styles groupbox, and components in the Components groupbox. When a component is highlighted, its graphical representation appears in the preview bar below the Styles and Components groupboxes. The dialog box size changes to display editable fields that define the component.

To create a stroke pattern line style:

1. Open or create a line style resource file for the line style by using the File menu.
2. Select Create, then Name from the Line Style Editor's Edit menu. An unnamed style is created and listed in the Styles groupbox. It is also linked to the active component. Edit its name in the edit field below the listbox.
3. Select Create, then Stroke Pattern from the Edit menu. A component called "new stroke component" is created and listed in the Components groupbox. The dialog box expands, as shown below.

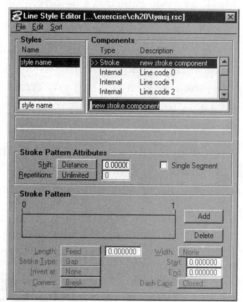

Line Style Editor expands to display editable fields for the selected stroke pattern.

4. Edit the new stroke component name in the edit field below the listbox.

5. Highlight the style name and the stroke pattern name and select Link from the Edit menu. A marker appears next to the component to designate the link.

6. Click the Add button in the Stroke Pattern groupbox as many times as new strokes are desired. One unit long strokes appear in the pattern definition.

7. Highlight one of the strokes and select its Stroke Type as gap or dash. Define its other properties by selecting choices from option buttons.

8. Repeat step 7 for all other strokes. This completes the stroke pattern line style definition. Select Save from the File menu to save the line style resource file.

Before you can create point symbol components, you must create point symbols in the line style resource file.

To create point symbols:

1. Open or create a line style resource file for the point symbol definition.

2. Draw the symbol in the active design file as you would a cell using element placement tools.

3. Add all symbol elements to a selection set, or place a fence around them.

4. Define the symbol origin by activating the Define Cell Origin tool in the Cells toolbox and clicking a data point.

5. Type `CREATE SYMBOL symbolname` in the Key-in window, where `symbolname` is a name, six characters or less, for the symbol. You can also click the Create button in the Line Style Editor when a point component is highlighted.

6. The point symbol is created and added to the active line style resource file.

To create a point symbol line style component:

1. Open or create a line style resource file for the line style by using the File menu.

2. Select Create, then Name from the Line Style Editor's Edit menu. An unnamed style is created and listed in the Styles groupbox. It is also linked to the active component. Edit its name in the edit field below the listbox.

3. Select Create, then Point from the Edit menu. A component called "new point component" is created and listed in the Components groupbox. The dialog box expands, as shown below.

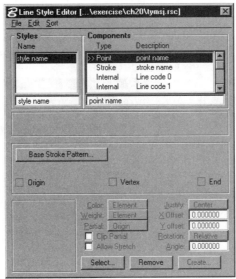

Line Style Editor expands to display editable fields for the selected point component.

4. Edit the new point component name in the edit field below the listbox.

5. Highlight the style name and the point component name and select Link from the Edit menu. A marker appears next to the component to designate the link.

6. Click the Base Stroke Pattern button and select an existing stroke pattern relative to which you will place instances of a point symbol.

7. Click the Select button and select an existing point symbol. The symbol graphic appears. If your line style resource file has no point symbols, an Alert dialog box appears. You must create a point symbol as described earlier before you can define point components.

8. Highlight the stroke in the stroke pattern relative to which you wish to define the point symbol. Define point symbol parameters using the dialog box controls.

9. This completes the point component line style definition. Select Save from the File menu to save the line style resource file.

To create a compound line style component:

1. Open or create a line style resource file for the line style by using the File menu.

2. Select Create, then Name from the Line Style Editor's Edit menu. An unnamed style is created and listed in the Styles groupbox. It is also linked to the active component. Edit its name in the edit field below the listbox.

3. Select Create, then Compound from the Edit menu. A component called "new compound component" is created and listed in the Components groupbox. The dialog box expands, as shown below.

Line Style Editor expands to display options for the selected compound component.

4. Edit the new compound component name in the edit field below the listbox.

5. Click Insert and select a stroke, point, or another compound component.
6. Repeat step 5 to add more components. You may also click Remove to delete a selected component.
7. This completes the compound component line style definition. Select Save from the File menu to save the line style resource file.

As you start creating custom lines styles, you'll want to learn from those delivered with MicroStation. In the Line Style Editor, open the resource file `lstyle.rsc` from the folder `c:\Bentley\Workspace\System\Symb`. Highlight the line style component that interests you and study the options that define it.

Text Glossary

When you submit a project, the drawing set includes a title sheet with a location map, a sheet with lists of abbreviations and drawings, and sheets containing plans, sections, and details. MicroStation's Glossary utility helps you place standard text phrases, such as those found on abbreviation sheets, on plan, section, and detail drawings.

You can place text without typing by picking the phrase from a list and identifying a data point for its location. This ensures consistency of phrases as they are picked from a standard list. It also eliminates typing mistakes.

The default glossary file used by the Glossary utility is `example.gls`, located in the `c:\Bentley\Workspace\System\Data` folder. When you develop your own glossary file for use as a corporate standard, place it in the `c:\Bentley\Workspace\Standards\Data` folder. It will load automatically. The workspace configuration variable MS_GLOSSARY determines which glossary files to load. By default, it is defined to load all files with the `.gls` extension from the two folders listed in this paragraph, the system and site data folders. You can edit the configuration variable if you wish to change the default.

A *glossary file* has a simple format. It is a text file with two lines for each definition. The first line is the alias that appears in the Glossary utility. The second line is the phrase associated with the alias. When you click the alias, the associated text phrase is made ready for placement. The glossary file can contain comments preceded with the # symbol. It can also contain the variables ($date) and ($time). These variables expand to text representing current date and time.

The contents of a sample glossary file are listed below:

```
# TYMSJ
# Sample Glossary Data File
#
# This file has the following format:
# 1) A '#' character in column 1 starts a comment
# 2) The first line is the alias displayed in list
# 3) The second line is the phrase to be placed in the design file
# 4) $date and $time are special variables that represent system date and time
#
TYMSJ
Teach Yourself MicroStation/J
a.b.
anchor bolt
steel
ASTM A-50 structural steel
Date
The date today is $date.
Time
The current time is $time.
```

When Glossary processes this file, it adds five aliases to its list: TYMSJ, a.b., steel, Date, and Time. The lines preceded with the # symbol are comments, and they are not processed. When you select "a.b." from the list, the text "anchor bolt" is placed in the design file.

To place text using the Glossary utility:

1. Start MicroStation if it's not already running.
2. Open a design file in which you wish to place text.
3. Select Text Glossary from the Utilities menu. The Glossary dialog box and the Tool Settings window open.

   The Glossary dialog box contains a listbox displaying aliases from glossary files it loads. A gray pane under the listbox displays the text associated with the highlighted alias. A multi-line text field under the gray pane displays text you build before placing it. Clicking the Build button places text corresponding to the highlighted alias in the multi-line text field.

   The Glossary Tool Settings window is used to control the height, width, font, line spacing, justification, and active angle for text. The Glossary dialog box and the Glossary Tool Settings windows are shown below.

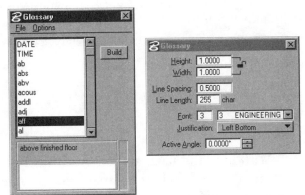

The Glossary dialog box (left) and the Tool Settings window (right).

4. Highlight the desired glossary alias in the listbox. Its corresponding phrase appears in the gray pane below.
5. Click the Build button to enter the text in the multi-line text field below.
6. Feed free to edit the text in the multi-line text field. You can type more text, or append another alias by highlighting it and clicking Build.
7. Change text placement parameters in the Tool Settings window as needed.
8. Click a data point at the desired location in the design file to place the text.

The Glossary utility is a simple and timesaving tool for entering standard text on drawings. I'm sure you will find it useful.

Font Installer

MicroStation uses its own font resource file, not system fonts. Fonts used by CAD software are often called *stick-line* fonts because they are vector fonts made of lines and arcs and were designed for pen plotters that use a vector plotting language.

MicroStation's fonts are stored in a font resource file located in the same folder as custom line style resource files. The configuration variable MS_SYMBRSRC declares the folder name where MicroStation looks for font resource files. By default, it is assigned the value `C:\Bentley\Workspace\System\Symb`. The default font resource file is `font.rsc`.

Here you learn about Font Installer, a font management utility that allows you to add, rename, and delete fonts from MicroStation's font resource files. Font Installer manages fonts in font resource files; it does not create fonts.

NOTE: MicroStation does not use external fonts directly. They must be copied into a MicroStation font symbology resource file (.rsc) before you can use them in your drawings.

With Font Installer, you can use PostScript Type 1, Windows TrueType, font cells, IGDS font libraries, and AutoCAD SHX fonts in your drawings. You do this by importing desired fonts into MicroStation's font resource file. When translating AutoCAD drawings, you can improve font mapping by importing SHX fonts used in the drawing into MicroStation's font resource file.

MicroStation fonts are assigned a unique integer, called the *font number*, used to access the font. MicroStation loads all font resource files it finds in the symbology resource folder. If two font files use the same font number, the font number from the resource file loaded later is used.

To open the Font Installer, select Install Fonts from the Utilities menu. The dialog box is shown below.

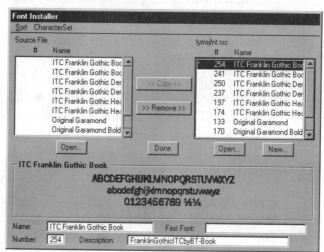

Use the Font Installer to copy and remove fonts in the font resource file.

The Font Installer contains two listboxes, several buttons, a menu bar, a font preview panel, and several text display/edit fields. Open fonts you wish to copy in the left listbox, and the destination font resource file in the right listbox. Open font files, copy and remove fonts, and create a new font resource file by clicking appropriate buttons in the dialog box. The highlighted font is displayed in the font preview pane. If a font is highlighted from the font resource file, you can edit its name, number, and description.

Below is a list of font types you can use as source fonts to import into a font resource file.

- AutoCAD SHX
- IGDS font cell libraries
- IGDS font libraries
- MicroStation font resource file
- PostScript Type 1
- Windows TrueType

To copy a font to a font resource file:

1. Open Font Installer by selecting Install Fonts from the Utilities menu.
2. Open or create a font resource file by clicking Open or New under the right listbox. Fonts in the resource file are listed.
3. Open fonts you wish to copy by clicking Open under the left listbox. The Open Source Font Files dialog box lets you select multiple fonts of the same type in a directory by using the Shift and Control keys when clicking. Click Add, then Done, to copy selected fonts to the left listbox.
4. Highlight the fonts you wish to copy in the left listbox. The Copy button is enabled.
5. Click the Copy button. Selected fonts are copied to the font resource file.
6. Highlight the font you just copied. Its number, name, and description appear in text edit fields. You may edit these values. You may also assign a fast font to use for this font. The display of fast fonts is enabled from the View Attributes dialog box.

TIP: Fonts are stored in font resource files that MicroStation loads at startup. If you use imported fonts in drawings you must share with others, send the font resource file with the drawing or use the Archive utility to package it.

Function Key Menus

MicroStation provides many ways to activate its tools. You can select them from pull-down menus, toolboxes, sidebar menus, tablet menus, and function keys. Of all these methods, function key menus are the easiest to develop.

Use function key menus to provide quick access to frequently used key-in sequences or to activate tools and settings that don't appear on menus or toolboxes.

Function key menus are stored in text files in the workspace interface folder `c:\Bentley\Workspace\Interfaces\Fkeys`. MicroStation determines the function key menu file to load by reading the configuration variable MS_FKEYMNU. By default, it is set to read the file `funckey.mnu`.

To create or edit function key menus:

1. Start MicroStation if it's not already running.
2. Select Function Keys from the Workspace menu to open the Function Keys dialog box, shown below. If the function key menu that opens is not the one you want, use the File menu to select another.

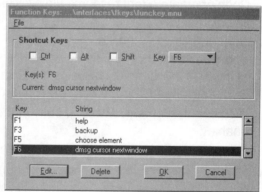

You can assign key-in sequences to function keys in this dialog box.

3. Select the function key you wish to edit or define, F1 through F12, from the Key option button. You may also enable any combination of Ctrl, Alt, and Shift checkboxes to qualify the function key. You can choose from ninety-six combinations. Its definition highlights.

4. Click the Delete button to delete the definition. If you want to define or edit the definition, click the Edit button. The Edit Key Definition dialog box opens, as shown below.

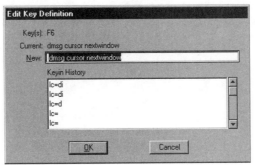

Enter a key-in for the function key and click OK.

5. In the New field, enter a key-in or pick one from the Key-in history listbox. It may not be obvious, but you can enter key-in sequences separated by semicolon (;). For example, to define a function key to change the line style to 3, color to 2, and weight to 2, enter: `LC=3;CO=2;WT=2`.
6. Click OK. The Edit Key Definition dialog box closes.
7. Repeat steps 3 through 6 for other function keys you wish to edit or define.
8. Select Save from the File menu in the Function Keys dialog box to save the function key definition.
9. Click OK to close the dialog box.

Chapter 21

Creating Cells

Managing Symbols with
Cell Libraries

Symbols convey design intent and other information concisely. For example, the weld symbol on structural and mechanical drawings designates weld type and size unambiguously. It would take more room on the drawing if they were explained in text. The north arrow symbol to identify North on maps and plans is known universally. Symbols abound and are used to identify a sport at stadiums, traffic regulation and other information along streets and highways, size and type of gates and valves on process piping drawings, and other things.

To help you reuse graphical elements and manage symbols, MicroStation implements *cell libraries* as a container for symbols, called *cells*. You place cells in a drawing with tools in the Cells toolbox, discussed in chapter 5. In this chapter, you learn how to create cell libraries and cells.

A cell is a way of grouping graphical elements. It's called a complex element because it can contain several primitive and complex elements and yet behaves as a single element. Cells are stored in cell libraries and have a name. You can create cells so text in them can be edited without dropping the cell's complex status. You can also create dimension-driven cells for parametric symbols.

A cell has the following attributes:

- **Name:** Up to a six-character name unique in the cell library.
- **Description:** A description of up to twenty-seven characters.
- **Type:** Point cell or graphic cell. When you want cell elements to be snappable and to retain level and symbology information, create them as *graphic* cells. If cell elements must be placed on the active level with active symbology, create them as *point* cells. You can snap to a point cell's origin, not its component elements. Point cells do not rotate when you rotate a view; graphic cells follow view rotation. The two other types of cells, tablet menu and tutorial cells, are archaic. They are from IGDS days and are not discussed.
- **Origin:** The insertion point about which the cell is placed. The cell origin need not lie on a component element. If you always move a cell a certain distance after placing it, such as a sofa away from a wall, define the cell origin to accommodate this distance so it is placed correctly the first time.

Cell libraries are files with the extension `.cel`. You can maintain any number of cell libraries, but only one can be active at a time. By default, MicroStation looks for cells in `C:\Bentley\Workspace\System\Cell` and `C:\Bentley\Workspace\Standards\Cell` folders declared by the configuration variable MS_CELL. When you place a cell, you must first attach its cell library. You can also place a cell by name without attaching a cell library by specifying the list of cell libraries you want MicroStation to search. This is specified by the configuration variable MS_CELLLIST.

Like design files, cell libraries can be two- or three-dimensional. You can place cells from a 2D cell library in 2D and 3D design files. However, cells from a 3D cell library can only be placed in 3D design files.

This chapter covers the following topics:

- Creating cells and cell libraries
- Embedding enter data fields in cells for editable text
- Using dimension-driven cells

How to Create a Cell

Cells created to serve a standard or discipline are useful to the creator and all within a company who produce similar drawings. By treating cells as a corporate resource, you are likely to create better cells and protect them from inadvertent or unauthorized modifications.

TIP: When learning to create cells, create them on your local computer rather than in corporate cell libraries.

Before you create a cell, you have to create a cell library for the cell. Like design files, you create cell libraries from seed files. MicroStation delivers 2D and 3D blank cell libraries for you to *seed* your own cell libraries.

To create a cell library:

1. Start MicroStation if it's not already running.
2. Select Cells from the Element menu to open the Cells dialog box, shown below.

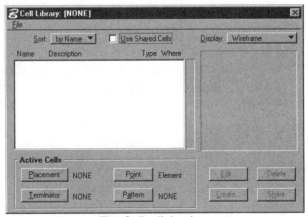

The Cells dialog box.

3. Select New from the File menu in the Cells dialog box. The Create Cell Library dialog box opens.
4. Verify the dimensional status of the seed file in the Seed File groupbox on the bottom of the dialog box. To change the default 2D cell seed file, click the Select button.

5. Enter a name for the cell library. You need not type an extension. The `.cel` extension is added automatically.

6. Click OK. The cell library is created and its name appears in the Cells dialog box title bar. No cells appear in the dialog box because the cell library is initially empty.

NOTE: If you are responsible for maintaining corporate cell libraries, consider the needs of those who will use them. What names will be intuitive? Will they know the symbol types contained in a library by its name? It is better to create multiple cell libraries that address specific needs rather than storing all cells in a large library.

To create a cell, you must first draw it using element placement tools like you would any geometry. When creating 2D cells, open a 2D design file to draw it in. Similarly, open a 3D design file in MicroStation when creating 3D cells.

Cells can contain any element, including arcs, circles, complex chains, lines, shapes, text, and others. Though you can include cells in cells—that is, create nested cells—it is discouraged, as nested cells waste disk space. To incorporate existing cells in new cells, drop them to primitive elements before creating new cells. When you draw cell elements, take their symbology and levels into consideration.

To include editable text in a cell, embed enter data fields in the cell definition. To create a parametric cell, draw its geometry with dimension-driven design tools discussed in chapter 9. You will create cells incorporating enter data fields and dimension-driven geometry in exercises later.

To create a cell:

1. Start MicroStation if it's not already running. Open a 2D design file to create 2D cells, and a 3D design file for creating 3D cells.

2. Draw the symbol you wish to add to a cell library. Use standard element placement, modification, and manipulation tools. Cells can include enter data fields and dimension-driven geometry.

3. Select Cells from the Element menu to open the Cells dialog box.

4. Open or create a cell library from the File menu on the Cells dialog box.

5. Switch to the design file and place a fence around the elements you wish to create a cell from. You can also group them in a selection set with the Element Selection or PowerSelector tools.

6. Activate the Define Cell Origin tool from the Cells toolbox and click the location to use as the origin. The letter **O** appears to confirm your action and the Create button on the Cells dialog box becomes active.

7. Click the Create button on the Cells dialog box. The Create New Cell dialog box opens, as shown below.

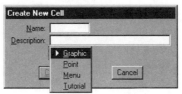

Select type of cell from the option button.

8. Select the cell type, point or graphic, from the option button. Enter a name and description.

9. Click Create. The cell is added to the cell library and a confirming message appears on the status bar.

Let's practice what we've learned in the next exercise. You'll start with a design file that contains geometry for three cells. The first will be a graphic cell that contains enter data fields, the second will be a point cell, and the third a dimension-driven cell.

Exercise: Adding Cells to a Cell Library

This exercise uses the design file `cellgeom.dgn` and the cell library `tymsj.cel` in the `\Exercise\Ch21` folder on the CD-ROM. Copy these files to your computer's hard drive. Once copied, clear their read-only attributes. Otherwise, you won't be able to write to the files.

These steps guide you through the exercise:

1. Start MicroStation with the design file `cellgeom.dgn`.

   The design file contains three symbols. The one to the left is a note bubble made of a line and a circle with two data fields entered as the underscore character with the Place Text tool. The one in the middle is an elevation symbol. The one to the right is the dimension-driven geometry you created in chapter 9. These symbols are shown in the figure below.

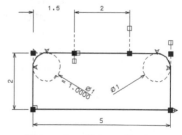

| *Note Bubble* | *Elevation Symbol* | *Dimension-Driven Geometry* |

Cells you will add to the cell library.

2. Invoke the Cells dialog box from the Element menu.
3. Attach the cell library `tymsj.cel` using the File menu in the Cells dialog box.
4. Select the Note Bubble geometry with the Element Selection tool or place a fence around it.
5. Activate the Define Cell Origin tool from the Cells toolbox and click the tentative button in the center of the circle followed by a data point. The letter **O** appears where you click.
6. Click the Create button on the Cells dialog box. The Create New Cell dialog box opens.
7. Select Graphic for cell type, enter `NOTEBL` for name and `Note Bubble` for description.
8. Click Create. The cell is added to the cell library.
9. Repeat steps 4 through 6 for the Elevation Symbol geometry.
10. Select Point for cell type, enter `ELSYMB` for name and `Elevation Symbol` for description.
11. Click Create. The cell is added to the cell library.
12. Repeat steps 4 through 6 for the Dimension-Driven Geometry. Identify the lower left corner as its origin.
13. Select Graphic for cell type, enter `DDGEOM` for name and `DD Geometry` for description.
14. Click Create. The cell is added to the cell library.

This completes the exercise. To continue your exploration of cells, place the `NOTEBL` and `ELSYMB` cells in the design file. You'll notice that the graphic cell geometry retains its symbology while the point cells takes on active symbology settings. Rotate the view and see how the graphic cell rotates but the point cell retains its original orientation. Additionally, use the Fill in Single Enter Data Field tool from the Text toolbox and enter text in the Note Bubble cell.

Creating parametric cells is no different than creating any other cell type. You can also place them in the design file with standard cell placement tools. After placement, you can use the Modify Value of Dimension or Variable from the Modify Constraint toolbox in the DD Design tool frame. However, if you wish to specify parameter values *before* you click a data point to place a dimension-driven cell in a design file, you must use the DDCELL application. The steps below describe how to use this application.

To place dimension-driven cells:

1. Start MicroStation if it's not already running.
2. Open the Cells dialog box from the Element menu.
3. Attach the cell library containing the dimension-driven cell.
4. Make the dimension-driven cell active by highlighting it in the Cells dialog box and clicking the Placement button.
5. Load the DDCELL application by typing MDL LOAD DDCELL in the Key-in window. Then, key in Place Cell Dimensions. The Dimension-Driven Design dialog box opens, as shown below.

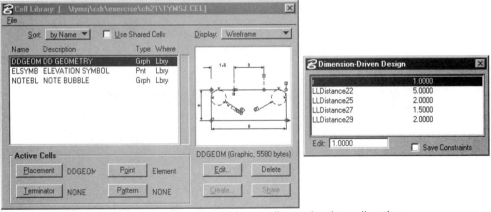

To place dimension-driven cells, make the cell active, load DDCELL, and key-in `Place Cell Dimensions`.

6. Highlight the dimensional parameter you wish to edit and enter a value in the Edit field. Do this for all parameters you wish to change.

7. Enable the Save Constraints checkbox if you wish to place constructions along with cell geometry in the design file. You'll be able to modify constraints later with DD tools. Uncheck the Save Constraints checkbox if you don't want to place constraints with cell geometry in the design file. Instances of cells in the design file placed with Save Constraints unchecked are no longer dimension-driven and can't be modified with DD tools.

NOTE: Be aware of these facts and cautions about cells. Cells are limited to 128 kilobytes. Avoid nesting cells and including graphic groups in cells. When creating cells, draw them in a design file with the same working units as the design file they'll be placed in; else, you'll have to scale them every time after placement.

This concludes the chapter.

Chapter 22

Using the Clipboard, OLE, and DDE
Interacting with Other Applications

The migration of CAD from mainframe and mini-computers to desktop computers has opened doors to inter-application communication that weren't previously possible. Earlier, IGDS ran on mini-computers and business productivity applications ran on other systems. Now, most users run MicroStation with several other applications on the same computer. MicroStation can communicate with other applications using data communication protocols Microsoft Windows supports.

Why would you want MicroStation to communicate with other applications? This feature is used to integrate tasks, such as calculations and specifications, with drawing production. Many engineers use spreadsheet and database software to solve problems. The applications include Microsoft Excel, Corel Quattro Pro, Lotus 1-2-3 for Windows, Microsoft Access, Corel Paradox, and Lotus Approach. By using

Microsoft Windows' data exchange protocols, you can embed linked drawings in your design documents. You can also send data to create MicroStation sketches from design results.

In Microsoft Windows, applications can communicate with each other in several ways. The Clipboard allows data transfer by selecting Cut and Paste from the Edit menu. Object Linking and Embedding (OLE) uses the Clipboard to transfer data along with a link to the application that generated the data. Dynamic Data Exchange (DDE) permits data transfer by using data exchange functions in a macro programming language where you control what to do with the data before and after sending it.

This chapter introduces you to each of the three data exchange protocols—Clipboard, OLE, and DDE. We also discuss the various ways in which you might use it.

This chapter is organized in the following sections:

- **Data Exchange Protocols** describes the Clipboard and how to manage Clipboard data with ClipBook Viewer. The OLE section covers how to exchange data between MicroStation and another application. The DDE section contains instructions on how to initiate communication from a macro programming environment.

- **A Dynamic Data Exchange Example** discusses situations where you might use data exchange. You learn DDE by developing an example macro in Microsoft Excel to compute coordinates and draw geometry in MicroStation.

If you know your spreadsheet or database software well and have written macros to automate tasks within it, you can use that knowledge to extend their reach and communicate with MicroStation. A macro can send commands and coordinate data computed from design results to create a drawing in MicroStation. This is demonstrated with a macro that draws a stair elevation in MicroStation from input to a spreadsheet.

Even if you don't write spreadsheet macros or develop databases, you can benefit from learning the various data exchange interfaces MicroStation supports. You might discover a method that solves a problem you didn't think could be addressed easily. You might also discover that writing macros isn't all that difficult.

Data Exchange Protocols

Microsoft Windows is a multitasking operating system. It allows multiple applications to run concurrently. From its inception, Windows has allowed you to copy data from one application to another. The data exchange between applications was static, initially. Copy of the data in the target application remained unchanged when data was modified in the source application. The ability to send data with an attached link came later, making data exchange dynamic.

In this section we discuss the Windows Clipboard for static data exchange. Then, we look at dynamic data exchange using OLE. This is followed by a discussion on DDE.

Clipboard

When you select data in an application and invoke the Copy command from its Edit menu, a copy of the data is placed on the Clipboard. The term *Clipboard* refers to system memory set aside by Windows to hold data temporarily so it can be copied elsewhere.

The Clipboard can hold data in various formats such as text, images, audio, and video.

There is room for only one piece of data on the Clipboard at a time. When you select Copy from the Edit menu in an application, existing Clipboard data is overwritten.

To copy data from an application to the Clipboard:

1. Start or switch to the application that has the data you wish to copy. The application can be a word processor, graphics program, sound, or another.
2. Select the desired data. In some cases the entire file is the data.
3. Select Copy from the application's Edit menu. A copy of the data is placed on the Clipboard.

To help you see and manage data on the Clipboard, Windows includes the ClipBook Viewer application. From the Start button, select Programs, then Accessories, followed by Clipboard Viewer. The ClipBook Viewer application window opens, as shown below.

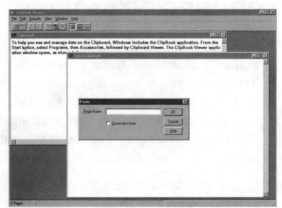

The ClipBook Viewer helps you manage Clipboard data.

The ClipBook Viewer application contains two windows: Clipboard and Local ClipBook. Whatever you copy to the Clipboard appears in this window. The Local ClipBook is used to save copies of Clipboard data for later use. It's like a scrapbook containing Clipboard data.

To copy Clipboard Data to the ClipBook:

1. Select Paste from the ClipBook Viewer's Edit menu. The Paste dialog box opens.
2. Specify a name for the ClipBook page in the Paste dialog box. To make this data available to other users on the network, enable the Share Item Now checkbox.
3. Click OK. The page is added to the ClipBook.

You can use data in your ClipBook by selecting the desired page and selecting Copy from the Edit menu to place it on the Clipboard. You can use data from the ClipBook on your computer or sharable data from ClipBooks on other networked computers. Use the tools in the tool bar under the menu bar for this purpose.

To paste data from the Clipboard to an application:

1. Start or switch to the application, such as MicroStation, that is to receive Clipboard data. You can copy data to the application where it originated.
2. Move the insertion point to the desired location in the application.
3. Select Paste from the Edit menu. Clipboard data is placed.

Data transferred this way is *static*. It's a snapshot that doesn't change when the source data changes.

When you paste text in MicroStation from a word processor, the Place Text tool is activated automatically. Note that Clipboard and application data size limitations may prevent you from pasting all the data you might want. For example, if a long paragraph of text is pasted in MicroStation as a single text element that has a limit of 255 characters, text will be truncated.

Not all applications can accept all data types. For example, if you copy a selection set from MicroStation to the Clipboard, you can't paste it in Windows Notepad, but you can in Windows WordPad.

Object Linking and Embedding

Object Linking and Embedding is an enhancement to the Clipboard's static data exchange mechanism. With OLE, a link to the application is included with the data.

When you copy data to the Clipboard, an application sends more than just the data. The application sending data determines the type and content of information that accompanies data. When you select Paste from the Edit menu, the application only retrieves data. When you select Paste Special from the Edit menu, the application prompts you for the type of link you wish to establish with the source application.

Selecting Paste Special from MicroStation's Edit menu opens this dialog box so you can select data type and whether to link or embed.

You can embed the data, or you can link it. When you *embed*, the data is copied in the target application, increasing file size. When you *link*, only a link to the data, such as source filename, is stored. When data changes in the source application, linked data updates automatically if both applications are running concurrently. Otherwise, you are prompted to open the source application to update the link when you open the target application. To edit embedded data, double-click the data and it loads in the application that created it.

Not all applications support all aspects of OLE. Software vendors determine the extent to which their application supports this data exchange protocol.

MicroStation supports a link from any OLE compliant application and has special support for data from Microsoft Excel. When you paste cells from Excel into MicroStation, contents are placed as MicroStation elements with cell borders.

You can embed or link text, graphics, sound, and video in a MicroStation design file. You can also embed a MicroStation view in other OLE-compliant applications. When you change the contents in a view window, the linked view in another application updates automatically.

To insert data in a design file, the source application need not be open. You can use the Insert Object dialog box, shown below. This dialog box is accessed from the Edit menu.

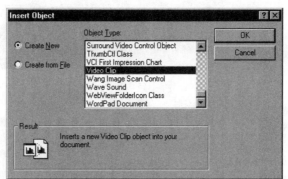

Use the Insert Object dialog box to insert data in a design file from any OLE-compliant application on your computer.

To insert an OLE object:

1. Start MicroStation if it's not already running.
2. Select Insert Object from the Edit menu. You are prompted for the object origin.
3. Identify two diagonally opposed data points for the object. The Insert Object dialog box opens.
4. If creating a new object, select the Create New radio button. From the Object Type listbox, select the source application.

   If creating an object from an existing data file, select the Create From File radio button. Enter the filename in the File text field, or click Browse to locate it. To embed the file, uncheck the Link checkbox.
5. The source application opens if you are creating a new object. As you create the data, it updates in the design file.

MicroStation is an OLE container and an OLE server. An application that permits OLE objects to be inserted in its data files is called an *OLE container*. An application that can publish its data so it can be linked by other applications is an *OLE server*.

> **NOTE:** MicroStation uses the MDL application `olecntr.ma` to provide OLE container support and `oleserve.ma` to provide OLE server support. MicroStation loads OLE container support automatically. To serve views for other applications to link, you must load oleserv.ma by typing `MDL LOAD OLESERVE` in the Key-in window.

To place a MicroStation view OLE object on the Clipboard:

1. Start MicroStation if it's not already running.
2. Arrange objects in a view as you would like them in the target application.
3. In the Key-in window, type `MDL LOAD OLESERVE`. The status bar displays a confirming message.
4. In the Key-in window, type `OLESERVE VIEWCOPY`. You are prompted to identify a view.
5. Enter a data point in the view you prepared in step 2. The view is copied to the Clipboard as an OLE object. An OLE container application can embed or insert it.

The OLESERVE application has one other function. After loading it, you can also type `OLESERVE UPDATE` in the Key-in window to force an update of the MicroStation view in an OLE container application.

Dynamic Data Exchange

The Clipboard and OLE let a user exchange data as static or dynamic objects. You use the Copy, Paste, and Paste Link options under the Edit menu. In addition to data exchange protocols discussed earlier, MicroStation supports exchange of data from a macro programming environment.

MicroStation can send DDE messages to other applications. It can also respond to DDE messages from other applications.

An application that sends a DDE message to initiate a link is called a *DDE client*. An application that responds to DDE messages from other applications by sending data or commands is called a *DDE server*. MicroStation is a DDE client and a DDE server. It can send and receive DDE messages. To send DDE messages from another application to MicroStation, use the other application's macro programming language. To send DDE messages to another application, use MicroStation BASIC or MDL.

In a DDE conversation, MicroStation accepts key-ins in text messages from other applications. Because a key-in can invoke every tool and pass coordinate data, you can draw or create 3D models in MicroStation from other applications.

A DDE conversation between applications can be of three types:

- **Cold:** The source application doesn't inform the target of data changes. The target must poll the source application for changes.
- **Warm:** The source application informs the target when data changes, but doesn't send the data. The target must request the data in a separate message.
- **Hot:** The source application sends data as soon as it changes. Updates are automatic.

To initiate a conversation, a DDE client broadcasts a message to Windows identifying the application it seeks and the *topic* within that application it will communicate with. Windows tries to establish the link, and when it succeeds, it assigns the conversation a unique channel number. The DDE client uses this channel number for all communication.

To start a DDE conversation with MicroStation from Microsoft Excel:

1. Use the function `Application.DDEInitiate("USTN", "KEYIN")` to initiate the link. This function returns an unique integer, the *DDE channel number*, to identify the link.

   The parameter `USTN` designates MicroStation as the OLE server application Excel seeks. The `KEYIN` parameter designates that communication will use key-ins.

2. Use the function `Application.DDEExecute` followed by the channel number and a string containing key-ins to send commands and coordinate data to MicroStation.

3. Use the function `Application.DDETerminate` followed by the channel number to terminate the link established in step 1. Terminating links that are no longer needed frees system resources for other uses. It is a wise practice.

To communicate with other applications, MicroStation BASIC includes the following functions:

- DDEExecute to send a message to the other application.

- DDEInitiate to initiate a conversation with another application. The application is started automatically if not already open.

- DDEPoke to set a value for a data item.

- DDERequest to retrieve a value as a text string for the specified data item in another application.

- DDESend to start a conversation with another application. The application must already be running.

- DDETerminate to terminate the link with a DDE server specified by its channel number.

- DDETerminateAll to terminate the link with all applications.

- DDETimeOut to specify the time within which a response must be received from the DDE server. If not response is received within the time specified, a timeout message is generated.

To manage DDE links, select DDE Links from the Edit menu. If no links exist, a message box pops up indicating that. Otherwise, the DDE Links dialog box opens with a list of links you may have established.

A Dynamic Data Exchange Example

Exchanging data between MicroStation and other applications is useful for many reasons. It can add value to drawings by incorporating relevant design data. It can also facilitate drawing reviews. For example, you can attach a sound file describing issues the reviewer can listen to by double-clicking it in a design file.

Spreadsheets are a popular computation tool used by many engineers for design tasks. By storing standard part dimensional data, a spreadsheet can facilitate the designer's search for a specific part and also draw the shape on-the-fly in MicroStation.

In the rest of this section, you'll learn how to create a spreadsheet in Microsoft Excel that uses a macro to draw a stair in elevation. You'll learn how to use range names for cells that accept input. You'll also learn how to associate range names with variables in an Excel macro, perform computations, and send key-ins to MicroStation using DDE functions.

Creating an Input Form in a Spreadsheet

The application you create is called the Stair Generator. It draws steps in elevation. You enter values for the following three variables:

- Floor Height (ft) to specify the distance in feet between floors in a building.
- Tread Width (in) to specify the width in inches of a step.
- Riser Height (in) to specify the height in inches of a step.

The application you create is to determine the number of steps that can be drawn between floors by dividing the floor height with the riser height. Then, it must use the tread and riser dimensions to draw the steps in elevation view.

Your first task is to create an interface for the user. In a spreadsheet, this is easier than creating an interface in MicroStation BASIC or MDL. Type the name of the application, and other information you might want in cells. For a professional look, you may want to use appropriate fonts, colors, and cell borders. Also, declare names, called *range names*, for cells that will be used to accept input data.

Use the following figure as a guide to creating the user input form. I used cells D2, D3, and D4 for input and named them **Floor_Height**, **Tread_Width**, and **Riser_Height**, respectively. In Excel, you name a cell by clicking it and selecting Name, then Define from the Insert menu.

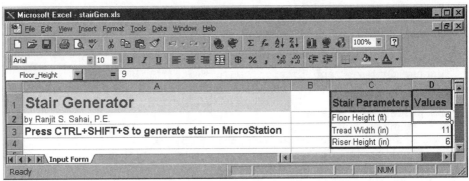

The Stair Generator input form in Microsoft Excel.

Though the use of range names is optional, I recommend them highly. Should you need to change input cell location, naming a cell saves you from having to revise cell addresses in the macro.

NOTE: By creating the above spreadsheet and the macro code explained next, you'll learn all the nuts and bolts of macro creation. However, if you run into problems, feel free to copy the file `stairGen.xls` from `\Exercise\Ch22` on the CD-ROM.

Writing the Spreadsheet Macro

Once the input form is ready and you've named the input cells, you are ready to write the macro that crunches numbers and communicates with MicroStation.

To write macro code:

1. Select Macro, then Macros from the Tools menu in Excel. The Macros dialog box opens.
2. Enter `stair_Generator` in the Macro Name field and click Create. The Microsoft Visual Basic window opens.
3. Type the code Visual Basic code listed below.

```
Sub Stair_Generator()

Dim Flr, Ris, Trd As Double
Dim Count, Steps As Integer

Flr = Range("Floor_Height").Value
Ris = Range("Riser_Height").Value
Trd = Range("Tread_Width").Value

Steps = CInt(Flr * 12 / Ris)
Count = 0

channelNumber = Application.DDEInitiate("USTN", "KEYIN")
Application.DDEExecute channelNumber, "PLACE LSTRING;XY=0,0"

Do While Count < Steps
    Count = Count + 1
    Application.DDEExecute channelNumber, "DL=0,:" + Trim(Str(Ris))
    Application.DDEExecute channelNumber, "DL=:" + Trim(Str(Trd)) + ",0"
Loop

Application.DDEExecute channelNumber, "reset"
Application.DDEExecute channelNumber, "move;xy=0,0"
Application.DDETerminate channelNumber

End Sub
```

The first and last statements designate the start and end of the
Stair_Generator() subroutine.

The two lines starting with Dim declare variables of type double and
integer. The macro variables Flr, Ris, and Trd represent floor height, riser
height, and tread width. They are double-precision floating point numbers.

The next three lines use the Range().Value method to capture the value
of cells by specifying their names and assigning the values to the macro
variables.

The CInt() function is used next to convert the number of steps calculated
into an integer value. The loop counter Count is initialized to zero.

The function Application.DDEInitiate("USTN", "KEYIN") initiates the
link with MicroStation and returns a channel number.

The function Application.DDEExecute sends the key-in Place Lsting to
MicroStation along with the coordinate XY=0,0 as the starting point for the
steps.

Then the Trim and Str functions are used to convert numbers to text
strings and to concatenate with the DL key-in to pass distance values to
MicroStation in a Do...Loop statement.

Finally, after the line string is drawn, a `Reset` terminates the tool. The `Move` command is used to attach the steps to the cursor from their original `XY=0,0` location. When the user clicks a data point, the steps will be placed there.

4. From the Visual Basic window, select Close and Return to Microsoft Excel from the File menu. This completes the macro definition.

Running the Macro

You will find it helpful to assign a shortcut to the macro so it can be activated quickly.

To assign a shortcut to the macro:

1. Select Macro, then Macros from Excel's Tools menu to open the Macro dialog box.
2. Highlight the **Stair_Generator** macro and click Options. The Macro Options dialog box opens, as shown below.

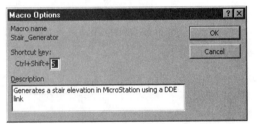

Define a shortcut and description for the macro.

3. Click the data field and simultaneously press the Ctrl, Shift, and S keys. This associates the Ctrl+Shift+S keystroke to the macro.
4. Enter a description for the macro in the Description field.
5. Click OK to save the information and close the Macro Options dialog box. You can also close the Macros dialog box.

The Stair Generator application is now ready to run.

To run Stair Generator:

1. Start MicroStation if it's not already running.
2. Start Microsoft Excel if it's not already running.

3. Load the `stairGen.xls` spreadsheet in Microsoft Excel if it's not already loaded.

4. With focus in Excel, press `ctrl+shift+s` to activate the **Stair_Generator** macro.

5. Switch focus to MicroStation. The steps are drawn and attached to the cursor.

6. Click a data point in a view window to place the steps. Click Reset to terminate the Move command.

7. Repeat steps 4 through 6 for different values in the Excel input cells. Notice how the step drawing changes.

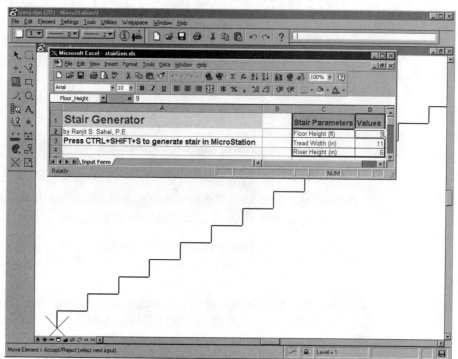

The Excel Stair Generator application drawing steps in MicroStation.

The example spreadsheet application you developed is a glimpse of what you can accomplish with DDE macro applications. I'm sure you can think of many more.

This concludes the chapter.

Part 4

Programming MicroStation

Making MicroStation Do What It Otherwise Can't

Chapter 23

The User Command Language
Still Supporting the Legacy

User Commands predate MicroStation. When Intergraph's IGDS software ran on DEC VAX computers, users were looking for ways to automate repetitive tasks. To meet their needs, Intergraph created the User Command language that uses predefined memory storage areas called *registers* and provides access to special variables in the design environment. The language implements keywords to capture user input, display messages, and sequence commands.

When Bentley wrote MicroStation version 2.0 (Version 1 was never released commercially.) in the mid-1980s, User Command support was implemented for compatibility. IGDS users migrating to MicroStation would be secure in knowing their investment in User Commands (UCMs) was safe. IGDS users had developed a vast library of UCMs that automated many routine tasks. If the ability to run their field tested macros were taken away, their productivity would suffer and they wouldn't upgrade to MicroStation.

User Commands were the only means of programming in MicroStation until 1991, when Bentley introduced MDL with version 4. (I know many of you may have used script files, but scripts are not a programming language.) Consequently, users developed a wealth of UCMs for use within their organizations. Old-time IGDS and MicroStation users continue to maintain a library of UCMs and actively use them. This latest release of MicroStation continues to support the legacy programming language.

If you have programmed a calculator, you will have little trouble understanding how to write User Commands. The language is terse but easy enough to learn for the motivated non-programmer. All you need to start UCM programming is an ASCII text editor such as Windows Notepad, MS-DOS Editor, or others.

The purpose of this chapter is to:

- Introduce you to the User Command language.
- Show you where to find free UCMs.
- Help you start writing UCMs.

Introducing User Commands

For purposes of this chapter I assume you have never written or used UCMs before. In this section you are introduced to UCMs: what they are, their purpose, where to obtain UCMs, and, once you have them, how to invoke them.

What Are User Commands?

User Commands are *macros*, or command sequences, written in an ASCII text file that follow the UCM language syntax. Their purpose is to automate routine tasks. Macros written in the UCM language can run only within MicroStation.

Compared to modern programming languages, the UCM language is limited. It provides 34 native operators and predefined registers for all data storage. Nevertheless, because of its ability to access the scores of settings and hundreds of MicroStation commands, it has enough flexibility to let you develop powerful and useful applications. It may interest you to know that in earlier days Intergraph created sophisticated discipline-specific technical applications entirely in the UCM language.

The UCM language implements flow control operators to conditionally branch to other statements. It implements statements to display messages and capture user input. There are operators to send data points and key-ins to MicroStation. UCMs also have the ability to read from and write to design files. They can also read and write data from linked databases.

Being plain text files, UCMs are independent of the computer platform you run MicroStation on. This means that if a UCM were created on a DOS platform, you will be able to run it without modification on another platform, such as Windows or UNIX.

NOTE: User Commands can also be compiled to byte code to protect the source code from modifications and for faster processing. You compile UCMs by keying in `UCC=ucmname`, where `ucmname` is the name of the User Command file.

Characteristics of User Commands

User Commands are procedural programs that run sequentially from start to finish without deviating from the sequence of code statements. While MicroStation is processing a UCM, almost no other process is allowed to interrupt it. This is in stark contrast to MicroStation's event-driven environment where almost any user-initiated event, such as a click or tool selection, can be executed at any time.

User Commands are effective when a structured set of commands must be executed completely for a specific task.

User Commands can receive user input via key-ins, data point and reset button clicks, and archaic tutorial menus. They can also display messages in the various fields of the Status bar. However, they can't generate or interact with dialog boxes and other interactive tools.

User Commands use predefined memory registers to save input data and other values that need to be recalled during processing. UCMs can't use arbitrary variables or create new data types.

Free User Commands

Bentley introduced the MicroStation BASIC macro programming language with the release of MicroStation 95. Since then UCMs have been on the sidelines and are mentioned only out of necessity. The UCM language hasn't been enhanced for many years. Nevertheless, examples of its use are still available, though not as many as you will find for BASIC or MDL. MicroStation also includes several examples. Yet another resource is Bentley's FTP site.

UCM Directory

Nearly a dozen macros written in the UCM language come with MicroStation. These macros are located in the following directory:

`C:\Bentley\Workspace\System\UCM`

The macro source code is written in an ASCII text file that has the extension `.ucm`. You can examine the code in any text editor.

The following table lists the UCMs that are shipped with MicroStation.

UCM	Description
autoplot.ucm	Demonstrates how to create plots without using the Plot dialog box.
blockpat.ucm	Places a patterned block.
branch.ucm	Teaches how to control program flow by branching to other statements.
chgattr.ucm	Changes symbology of identified element to active settings.
digz.ucm	Permits user to change active depth while performing 3D digitization.
dispchng.ucm	Displays elements that have been changed in a design file by highlighting them.
hilite.ucm	Highlights elements satisfying fence criteria.
mscb.ucm	Builds a cursor button menu.
mscm.ucm	Builds a command menu.
msmm.ucm	Builds a matrix menu.
mstut.ucm	Builds control information needed when creating tutorial menus.

UCM	Description
template.ucm	Template for use in creating new UCMs.

UCMs on the Internet

Another source of UCMs is the Bentley FTP site at:

`ftp://ftp.bentley.com/pub/tools/ucms/`

Point your browser to this location and you will see the file `00index.txt`. This index document lists nearly twenty files with the `.ucm` or `.zip` extension, along with a short description of each.

The following table lists some of the UCMs from this collection:

Macro	Description
attach.ucm	Demonstrates how to attach database linkages to complex elements.
celiso.ucm	Places a cell in an isometric plane.
chgtxtfn.ucm	Changes the font of a text string.
datetime.ucm	Demonstrates the use of date and time operators.
fencfont.ucm	Changes the font of text elements in a fence to the active font.
fenggv2.zip	Creates a graphic group from elements in a fence.
fenlocx.zip	Demonstrates the use of fence locate in UCMs.
txtset.ucm	Changes the height and width of text to active settings.

MicroStation Manager Magazine

MicroStation Manager is a monthly publication from Bentley. It is distributed to all Bentley SELECT program subscribers. It is also available through a subscription. Many articles published in the magazine are user-contributed and contain tips and tricks fellow MicroStation users have discovered.

The magazine has published several articles on User Commands over the years. *MicroStation Manager* also maintains a Web site for its readers where code published in the magazine is made available for download. The Web site can be found at the following URL:

`http://www.msmonline.com`

Invoking UCMs

There are two ways to run User Commands: from the command line in the Key-in window, or from the Run User Command dialog box.

From Command Line

Invoke User Commands from inside MicroStation by keying in:

`UC=ucmname`

where `ucmname` is the filename of the user command. MicroStation expects macros to be located in a directory defined by the MS_UCM configuration variable. This variable has a default value of `C:\Bentley\Workspace\System\UCM` on a Microsoft Windows NT system.

You can invoke macros in another directory by specifying the complete path along with the filename in the `UC=` key-in, shown below.

`UC=C:\Standards\Company\UCM\ucmname`

TIP: You can assign your UCM directory to a configuration variable, such as **MY_UCMS**, to facilitate invoking them from the command line. To invoke the macro **ucmname** stored in a directory defined by the configuration variable **MY_UCMS** you would key in `UC=MY_UCMS:ucmname`.

From Run User Command Dialog Box

Another way to run UCMs is from the Run User Command dialog box. Invoke the dialog box by selecting User Commands, then Run from the Utilities menu. A standard file navigation dialog box opens.

The Run User Command dialog box lists available UCMs.

The Run User Command dialog box allows you to navigate your local hard drive or a mapped network drive to locate User Commands not in the default UCM directory.

To run a UCM, select it from the Run User Command dialog box and click the OK button.

The User Command Language

The only tool you need to write User Commands is an ASCII text editor. MS-DOS Editor, Windows Notepad, or any other programmer's editor, such as those on the CD-ROM, will serve you well.

When writing User Commands, you must adhere to the following rules:

- Each UCM statement can have only one operator.
- Statements are not case sensitive. Uppercase and lowercase letters are treated identically.
- Many operators need operands that must be separated by a comma or a blank.
- Statements can span multiple lines by ending the incomplete line with a comma.
- Statement labels can be alpha-numeric but must begin with an alphabet.

- Statements without labels must be indented with a space or tab.
- A semicolon must precede a comment line.
- The END operator must be the last statement in a UCM.

A typical statements has the following syntax:

```
LABEL: OPERATOR OPERAND,OPERAND,...,OPERAND ;COMMENT
```

This section lists all UCM operators with a brief description of what they do. It also lists UCM registers used to store data. Later in the chapter you will see code for several User Commands that will help you learn the syntax for many commonly used operators.

NOTE: For complete syntax details of all operators and descriptions of register variables and terminal control block variables you must refer to the MicroStation Reference Guide that comes in electronic PDF format with MicroStation on the product CD.

UCM Operators

Think of operators as verbs. They command MicroStation to take action. UCM operators can be grouped into several categories by the type of action they perform. There are flow control operators, interface operators, math operators and design file operators.

Flow Control Operators

These operators define how statements branch to other statements. Statements can branch conditionally or unconditionally. Available operators are listed in the table below.

Name of Operator	Action Performed
CAL	Calls another User Command but does not restore register contents upon return.
CLS	Calls another User Command and restores register contents upon return.
END	Exits the User Command.
GO	Unconditionally branches to another statement.

Name of Operator	Action Performed
PAUSE	Suspends the UCM for a specified time, or until the user presses a key.
TST	Branches to another statement depending on the result of a logical test.
UCM	Executes another User Command.

User Interface Operators

These operators display messages or wait for user input. Available operators are listed in the table below.

Name of Operator	Action Performed
MSG	Displays a message on the Status bar. The first two characters of the message specify where on the status bar to display the message. Valid letters for the first two characters in a message string are: cf, pr, er, st, and ms for command, prompt, error, status, and message fields, respectively.
TOT	Displays a message in a tutorial menu. If you don't know what a tutorial menu is, you don't need this operator! (Trust me, you do not even want to know. However, to satisfy your curiosity, this short definition should suffice. Tutorial menus are a poor man's version of interactive dialog boxes saved as *tutorial cells*. They were introduced in IGDS and their only role in MicroStation is to support menus you may have created while you were using IGDS.)
GET	Waits for the user to supply input. The operator is followed by an array of two-part parameters; the first part specifies the type of input, and the second part specifies the label to branch to.

NOTE: The word MSG is both an operator and the name of a register. Refer to the *Registers and Variables* section that follows.

MicroStation Interface Operators

These operators send input to MicroStation for processing. Available operators are listed in the table below.

Name of Operator	Action Performed
CMD	Activates an IGDS primitive command.
KEY	Sends a string to MicroStation as a key-in. If no parameter follows, the contents of the KEY register are sent.
PNT	Sends a data point to MicroStation. Operands specify data point location and search criteria.
RST	Sends a reset to MicroStation.
SLI	Sends the last input retrieved by the GET operator to MicroStation for processing.

NOTE: Do not confuse the dual meaning of the word KEY. It is both an operator and the name of a register.

Design File Input/Output Operators

These operators read from and write to design files. Available operators are listed in the table below.

Name of Operator	Action Performed
RDF	Reads into DGNBUF a design file element without transforming reference file coordinates.
RED	Reads into DGNBUF a design file element. Reference file elements are transformed to the active design file coordinate system.
WRT	Writes element in DGNBUF to design file at location specified by parameters to the operator.
STO	Writes the contents of the specified TCB variable to the design file's Type 9 element.

Mathematical, Conversion, and Assignment Operators

These operators perform computations, convert between string and numeric variables, and assign values to variables. Available operators are listed in the table below.

Name of Operator	Action Performed
ATN	Computes an angle in degrees from supplied sin and cos values.
CVT	Converts between working units (string) and UORs (numeric).
SCS	Computes the sin and cos values from the supplied angle.
SET	Assigns the value of an expression to a register.
SQR	Computes the square root of a number in a register.

Matrix Operators

These operators perform computations on matrices. Available operators are listed in the table below.

Name of Operator	Action Performed
CCM	Converts cell transformation matrix to a double-precision floating point format.
CQM	Converts a rotation matrix to a double-precision floating point format.
MML	Multiplies matrices or transforms a series of points.
MTN	Transposes square matrices.

MicroCSL Interface Operators

These operators interact with applications developed in C or FORTRAN using Bentley's MicroCSL object code library. Available operators are listed in the table below.

Name of Operator	Action Performed
TSK	Starts a MicroCSL application with specified parameters.

Name of Operator	Action Performed
WT	Waits for data from specified MicroCSL application.

Database Interface Operators

These operators interact with a database connected to MicroStation. Available operators are listed in the table below.

Name of Operator	Action Performed
DBADD	Adds a row to a database.
DBDELETE	Deletes a row from a database.
DBREAD	Reads one or more columns from a database row.
DBWRITE	Writes to specified columns in a database row.

Registers and Variables

There are three types of storage areas accessible to UCMs: Registers, Terminal Control Block (TCB) variables, and DGNBUF variables. This section covers each of the three variable types.

Registers

These are general purpose memory registers used to store values needed by UCMs. There are 32 integer registers, 16 long integer registers, 16 character registers, 16 double-precision floating-point registers, and many other read-only registers you can query to determine coordinates and attributes. The following table lists the UCM registers.

Register Name	Description
R0 through R31	Integer.
I0 through I15	Double-precision integer.
A0 through A15	Double-precision floating point.
C0 through C15	Character.

Register Name	Description
ERR	Stores error code prior to branching to EXITUC, a special label in your UCM.
NUM	Stores number of characters input from keyboard.
XDT, YDT	Coordinates on digitizing tablet for last data point.
XUR, YUR, ZUR	UORs for last data point clicked by user.
VNO	View number in which last data point was clicked.
KEY	Stores user key-ins. Also usable for value storage. Do not confuse with the KEY operator.
KO	Stores number of characters in the KEY register.
MSG	Character. Typically used to build text strings to display with the MSG operator.
MO	Stores number of characters in the MSG register.
NO through N15	Stores the number of characters in C0 through C15, respectively.
FNO	Stores menu and tutorial command information.

TCB Variables

The Terminal Control Block (TCB) is an area of memory where MicroStation maintains variables that define active settings. Most TCB variables are saved in the design file when you select Save Settings from the File menu, but some are not. Saved variables are called Type 9 and Type 66 variables, and include locks, working units, text settings, graphics group number, and others. They are stored in the design file header, a Type 9 element. Variables that are not saved in the design file include design file name, fence points, and current element buffers.

You use TCB variables in User Commands to determine or change active settings and to manipulate elements in the design file. Though UCMs allow you to change values of TCB variables, no error-checking takes place, which can lead to erroneous values that can cause design file corruption. Thus, when you need to change values of TCB variables, always use a MicroStation key-in whenever possible, as they are checked for errors.

Rather than using the statement:

```
SET ACTLEV=5
```

to change the active level, it is recommended that you use:

```
KEY 'LV=5'
```

The first statement does not check whether the level is on or off, or if an invalid level, such as 0, is assigned. The second statement uses a standard MicroStation key-in ensuring that MicroStation checks for the validity of the level, thus preventing errors.

There are over a hundred TCB variables. You will find a list of all TCB variables in the online Reference Guide in PDF format that comes on the software CD. Some common ones you will encounter are listed below.

TCB Variable	Description
ACTANG	Active angle.
ACTLEV	Active level.
CAFONT	Active font number.
CELFIL	Cell library name.
CHHGT	Character height in UORs.
CHWID	Character width in UORs.
GRAFIC	Highest graphic group number + 1.
IDPROP	Active element properties.

Some TCB variables, though referencing the same memory location, have different names so their value can be extracted in the format desired. For instance, UCWRD, UCINT, UCDPF, UCDPV, UCASC, UCRAD, and UCBYT reference the same variable but can extract its value as a word, integer, double-precision floating point, double-precision VAX, ASCII, Radix-50 or byte format, respectively.

TIP: To turn off message display on the status bar, use the statement SET CONTRL = CONTRL ! 256 in the beginning of the program. To turn message display on, use the statement SET CONTRL & -257 just before the END statement.

DGNBUF Variables

Whenever you locate elements by using the LOCELE MicroStation primitive command or the RED operator, the elements are placed into a buffer called DGNBUF. Here they can be manipulated and written back to the design file. The TCB element pointers CUREBL and CUREBY point to the element currently stored in the buffer DGNBUF.

You use DGNBUF variables to access and to modify attributes of elements stored in DGNBUF. DGNBUF variables are of two types: general and element-specific. Names of element-specific DGNBUF variables start with a two character prefix followed by a period and attribute. The two character prefix designates the type of element the variable applies to. For example, the AR prefix refers to an arc element, the CL prefix refers to a cell, the EL prefix refers to an ellipse, and TX refers to text.

The following statement:

```
SET I0 = AR.STA
```

assigns the start angle of the arc in DGNBUF to the integer register I0. Of course, variables with the prefix AR are valid only if DGNBUF contains an arc.

There are nearly a hundred general purpose and element-specific DGNBUF variables. You can find them listed in the MicroStation Reference Guide included in PDF format in the DOCS directory of the product delivery CD that accompanies MicroStation.

Writing User Commands

This section covers User Command examples. Here you see how the language keywords you learned are used. Source code for several examples is presented and explained. These examples are provided in a ready-to-execute form on the CD-ROM in the \Dev\UCM directory. You may either write the UCMs from scratch in your text editor by following the code printed in these pages, or you may copy the examples from the CD-ROM to your default UCM directory. In either case, you should run the examples and study the code to better understand how to write your own UCMs.

The User Commands presented in this section are listed in bullet form below.

- **DispMsg.ucm:** Demonstrates the use of the MSG operator to display messages on the status bar.
- **PlaceROW.ucm:** Demonstrates how to send a sequence of commands to change active settings and an element placement command using the KEY operator.
- **CirArray.ucm:** Copies an element you identify in a circular array by using the Rotate Copy command. It prompts you for an angle, the element to copy, and the location of the center. Based on the angle you specify, it computes the number of elements it can draw and uses a loop to draw rotated copies of the element.
- **StairGen.ucm:** Draws steps in elevation by prompting the user for the number of steps, and the start and end points of the staircase.
- **ChgLvFen.ucm:** Changes the level of elements enclosed in a fence. It requests the destination level, makes the level the active level, and uses the Fence Move command to accomplish its goal. It ends by restoring the active level to the state it was in before invoking the UCM.

DispMsg.UCM Displays Messages on Status Bar

This example helps you understand the various status bar message fields and how you can display a message in a specific field. The status bar has five message fields listed in the table below.

Status Bar Field (MSG prefix)	Typical Contents of Field
Command (cf)	Name of active command.
Prompt (pr)	Prompts requesting input from user.
Message (ms)	Messages such as active element attributes.
Error (er)	Error messages.
Status (st)	Status of MicroStation environment, such as locks.

Because the status bar is smaller than the Command Window interface that was the default in MicroStation V4 and V5, the same status bar area is used to display different message fields. The GET operator is used in the following DISPMSG.UCM macro to wait for a data point to illustrate how the status bar gets overwritten by other message fields.

```
; DISPMSG.UCM
;
; Display text strings in Command, Prompt and Message fields
    MSG 'cfDisplay Message UCM'
    MSG 'prClick data point and watch Status bar'
    MSG 'msMessage goes here'
; Wait for data point and display Error and Status strings
WAIT:
    GET P, GOTDP
    GO WAIT
GOTDP:
    MSG 'erError string overwrites Command and Prompt fields'
    MSG 'stStatus string overwrites Message field'
    END
```

You will use the MSG operator, as shown here, in all your UCMs to interact with the user. The GET operator is shown with a single pair of operands. The first element of the pair **P** waits for the data point, the second element of the pair **GOTDP** refers to a label in the UCM to branch to when a data point is received. The GO operator cycles back to the GET statement if something other than a data point is clicked.

This UCM is included on the accompanying CD-ROM. You may either copy it, or type the contents shown above in a text editor and save it to your default UCM directory. Then invoke it with the uc=DISPMSG key-in to see it run.

| Display Message UCM > Click data point and watch Status bar | | Message goes here |

The status bar before a data point is clicked.

| Error string overwrites Command and Prompt fields | | Status string overwrites Message field |

The status bar after a data point is clicked.

PlaceROW.UCM Sets Symbology for ROW Line

This macro changes the active symbology before placing a right-of-way (ROW) line in a design file. It's useful for implementing symbology standards for design file elements. Assume that your company's CAD symbology guidelines require that ROW lines be drawn with weight 2, color 2 (green) and line code 3 on level 5. To implement this guideline, you could write the User Command shown below.

```
; PLACEROW.UCM
;
; Store necessary key-ins in character registers
   SET C0 = 'WT=2'
   SET C1 = 'CO=2'
   SET C2 = 'LC=3'
   SET C3 = 'LV=5'
; Send register contents to MicroStation
   KEY C0
   KEY C1
   KEY C2
   KEY C3
   MSG 'msROW symbology set'
   KEY 'Place Line'
   END
```

This is a simple macro that only uses the SET, KEY, MSG, and END operators. The first operator assigns text strings to character registers. The second sends the contents of the registers to MicroStation as key-ins. The third displays a message in the status bar, and the last is a mandatory statement that indicates the completion of the UCM.

This UCM is included on the CD-ROM. You can either copy it, or type the code shown above in a text editor and save it in your default UCM directory. To invoke the UCM, key in UC=PLACEROW in the Key-in window.

NOTE: If no operand is given with the KEY operator, the content of the KEY register is used as the default.

CirArray.UCM Copies Element in Circular Array

This macro makes multiple copies of an element and arranges them in a circular array. First, it requests the rotation angle. Then, it prompts you to identify the element to rotate and copy. Finally, when you identify the center of rotation, the UCM loops through the computed number of copies to complete a circular path.

```
;CIRARRAY.UCM
;
    KEY 'NOECHO'
START:
    MSG 'cfConstruct Circular Array'
    MSG 'prEnter rotation angle'
; Save active angle to register R0
    SET R0=ACTANG
; Wait for angle Key-in or Reset
GETANG:
    GET K,CHKANG, R,EXIT
    GO GETANG
CHKANG:
; Save angle keyed to register R1
    SET R1=KEY
; Check angle keyed in is between 0 and 180
    TST R1 LE 0, GETANG
    TST R1 GT 180, GETANG
; Save number of times to copy in register R2
    SET R2=360 / R1
    SET C0='msNo. of times to copy element: '+R2
    MSG C0
; Change active angle to value keyed-in
    SET C0 = 'AA='+R1
    KEY C0
; Invoke Rotate Copy command
    KEY 'Rotate Copy'
GETELE:
MSG 'prIdentify element'
    GET P,FOUND, R,START
    GO GETELE
FOUND:
; Pass data point to Rotate Copy command
    PNT
CHKELE:
    TST RELERR NE 0, GETELE
    MSG 'prLocate point to rotate about'
LOCCTR:
; Locate center of rotation
    GET P,DOIT, R,RESET
    GO LOCCTR
```

```
RESET:
    RST
    GO CHKELE
DOIT:
; Check if more copies to make
    SET R2 = R2-1
    TST R2 EQ 0, EXIT
; Continue passing center of rotation data point
    PNT
    GO DOIT
EXIT:
    KEY 'Choose Element'
    MSG 'pr '
    MSG 'msCircular array completed'
EXITUC:
; Restore active angle stored in register R0
    SET ACTANG = R0
    KEY 'ECHO'
    END
```

This is a relatively more complex macro than those discussed earlier. It uses many operators such as TST, PNT, GET, RST and the RELERR and ACTANG variables. The TCB variable ACTANG contains the value of the active angle. The TCB variable RELERR contains an error code and is used above to check if an element is located or not by the data point clicked.

 NOTE: The + operator is used to add numbers and concatenate strings.

When your macro changes active symbology settings you'll want to save their state on entry into the User Command and restore them before exiting. In the user command above, the active angle is changed to rotate an element. Thus the angle is saved in an integer register and restored upon exit. If an error occurs during the processing of a User Command, or an operator selects a new menu command while the User Command is active, MicroStation branches to a special label EXITUC, if one exists. To ensure your macro has a chance to restore active symbology settings even if interrupted by an error, you must use the EXITUC label and restore settings with statements that follow this special label.

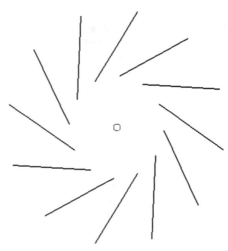

The Circular Array UCM copies and rotates an element around a data point.

StairGen.UCM Draws Steps in Elevation

The purpose of this macro is to draw steps in elevation. You are first requested to enter the number of steps to draw, then to identify the start and end points for the steps. The UCM extracts the X and Y coordinates of the points clicked, computes the riser and tread values by dividing the height and span of the stairs with the number of steps desired, and proceeds to use the **Place Lstring** command with the DL= key-in to draw the steps.

```
; STAIRGEN.UCM
;
BEGIN:
   MSG 'cfPlace Steps'
   MSG 'prKey in no. of steps to place'
; Request number of steps to draw
   GET K,NUMSTEPS, R,EXITUC
   GO BEGIN

NUMSTEPS:
; Store number of steps in register R0
   SET R0 = KEY
   MSG 'prEnter start point for first riser'

STARTPT:
; Wait for start point
   GET P,ENDPT, R,EXITUC
   GO STARTPT
```

```
ENDPT:
; Extract X and Y coordinates of start point
    SET I0 = XUR          ;X for start point
    SET I1 = YUR          ;Y for start point
    MSG 'prEnter end point for last tread'
; Wait for end point
    GET P,COMPUTE, R,EXITUC
    GO ENDPT

COMPUTE:
    SET I2 = XUR          ;X for end point
    SET I3 = YUR          ;Y for end point
    SET A1 = I2 - I0      ;A1 = Delta X
    SET A2 = I3 - I1      ;A2 = Delta Y
    SET A3 = A1 / R0      ;Tread width
    SET A4 = A2 / R0      ;Riser height

DRAW:
    KEY 'PLACE LSTRING'
    PNT I0,I1

LOOP:
    SET C0='DL=0,::'+A4
    KEY C0
    SET C0='DL=::'+A3+',0'
    KEY C0
    SET R0 = R0 - 1
    TST R0,GT,0,LOOP

FINISH:
    KEY 'RESET'
    KEY 'NULL'
    MSG 'cf '
    MSG 'pr '
    MSG 'msStairGen user command finished'

EXITUC:
    END
```

This macro illustrates how to extract coordinate values by using the XUR and YUR registers. Otherwise the macro is pretty straightforward and uses statements illustrated in earlier examples.

The figure below illustrates what MicroStation draws under the control of the macro.

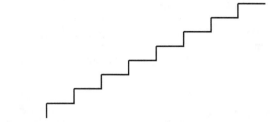

The Stair Generator UCM requests the number of steps to draw and draws them between the two data points specified.

ChgLvFen.UCM Changes Level of Elements In Fence

This macro moves elements inside a fence to a level specified by the user. The UCM first checks if a fence is active. If no fence exists, the macro terminates; otherwise, it prompts the user to key in a level number. Then it changes the active level to the level specified, and uses the Fence Move key-in to accomplish its goal.

```
; CHGLVFEN.UCM
;
; Save active level
    SET R0 = ACTLEV
    MSG 'cfChange Level Fence'
    MSG 'st'
    TST FENCE EQ 0, NOFENCE
GETLV:
    MSG 'prKey-in level to move fence contents to'
    GET K,CHKLV, R,EXITUC
    GO GETLV
CHKLV:
    SET R1 = KEY
    TST R1 LE 0, GETLV
    TST R1 GT 63, GETLV
    SET C0 = 'LV='+R1
WAIT:
    MSG 'prData point to accept, Reset to exit'
    GET P,CHGLV, R, EXITUC
    GO WAIT
CHGLV:
    MSG 'prMoving fence contents'
    KEY 'Lock Fence Inside'
    KEY 'Fence Move'
    PNT
    KEY C0
    PNT
```

```
        CMD NULCMD
        MSG 'msChanged level of fence contents'
        GO EXIT
NOFENCE:
        MSG 'erNo fence defined'
        MSG 'stExiting command'
        GO EXIT
EXITUC:
        CMD NULCMD
        MSG 'msCommand aborted'
EXIT:
        SET ACTLEV = R0
        KEY 'LV='
        END
```

The macro illustrates how to check the presence of a fence, check the validity of the value keyed in, and how to branch to different areas of the code based on the mouse button clicked, or the result of the TST operator. The figure below shows a fence around an area in a design file ready to be moved to another level by the macro.

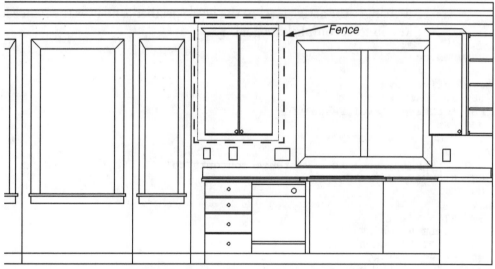

The Change Fence Level UCM is ready to change the level of a wall-hung cabinet that is shown enclosed inside a fence.

Beyond User Commands

This chapter introduced you to User Commands despite the fact they are now considered obsolete. There is a reason for this. If you inherit UCMs that do the job well but need just a little work to enhance them, your knowledge of the UCM language will help you get the job done. For some simple command sequencing tasks, you may find you can create UCMs more easily than another language.

Another point in favor of User Commands is they offer direct access to MicroStation internals through the use of TCB variables. Such a level of access is not available in MicroStation BASIC. Of course, MDL and JMDL offer even more control, but these languages are geared to professional programmers and many of you may not have the need to use them at length.

User Commands help you automate many routine MicroStation tasks, but they have limitations.

Limitations of User Commands

User Commands cannot:

- Request user input through dialog boxes, which are now a standard interface component.
- Create variable names. You must use existing registers to store data.
- Create user-defined data types.
- Provide dynamics, also called rubberbanding.
- Respond to events as they operate in a procedural, not event-driven, environment.

User Commands are useful, but the language is now dated. When writing new macros, take the time to learn MicroStation BASIC. Even though this new macro language does not provide dynamics or an event-driven operating environment, it provides modern flow control constructs, lets you create variable names and user-defined data types, offers several standard dialog boxes, and lets you build custom dialog boxes for user interaction.

Moving User Commands to BASIC

When Bentley introduced MicroStation BASIC in MicroStation 95, their goal was to offer an environment that was superior and easier than User Commands. They succeeded. And to help users who continue to rely on old User Commands, Bentley has written a User Command porting tool named UCM2BAS, an MDL application that can read User Commands and generate a MicroStation BASIC template you can use to re-create the macro in the newer macro language. It's not a complete porting tool, but a porting template. This means that the BASIC code it generates is likely to work for simple User Commands only. For more complex macros, the code will need to be examined and modified.

The UCM2BAS application is invoked by keying in MDL LOAD UCM2BAS. This opens the application dialog box shown in the figure below.

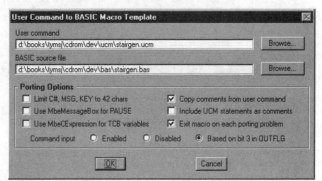

The UCM2BAS application generates BASIC code for the selected UCM.

You select the User Command to process in the User command text field, and the MicroStation BASIC source file to generate in the BASIC source file field. The User Command to BASIC Macro Template dialog box also lists six checkboxes and a set of three radio buttons to control Porting Options. These options are described below.

- **Limit C#, MSG, KEY to 42 chars:** The UCM character registers C0 to C15, MSG, and KEY are limited to storing 42 characters. If the UCM you are porting uses logic that makes use of this 42 character limit, turn this option on. It is off as a default.

- **Use MbeMessageBox for PAUSE:** When this option is turned on, the PAUSE operator in the UCM is translated to use the MbeMessageBox function to display a message box that prompts "Press Enter to resume." The default translation uses the MbeGetInput function to wait for a key-in. It is off as a default.

- **Use MbeCExpression for TCB variables:** When this option is turned on, TCB variables used in the UCM that have no equivalent MicroStation BASIC properties are translated using MbeCExpression functions. It is off as a default.

- **Copy comments from user command:** This option is turned on as a default. Turn it off if you do not want comments in the UCM to be ported to the BASIC macro.

- **Include UCM statements as comments:** This option is turned off as a default. Turn it on if you want to all UCM statements to be incorporated as comments in the BASIC macro.

- **Exit macro on each porting problem:** For every line that poses a porting problem, UCM2BAS inserts code to invoke an Alert box and exit the macro. You can turn off this safety feature.

- **Command input:** When a UCM is waiting for input and the user selects another command, MicroStation uses bit 3 of the TCB variable OUTFLG to determine whether to accept the command as input or to exit with an error. As a default, UCM2BAS checks bit 3 of OUTFLG to determine treatment of command input. To always include command input select Enabled. To always exclude command input select Disabled.

The next chapter introduces you to MicroStation BASIC.

Chapter 24

Creating Macros In MicroStation BASIC
Automating Repetitive Tasks With Macros

In the mid-1960s Dartmouth College professors John Kemeny and Thomas Kurtz created the BASIC programming language to teach their students the concepts of programming. They never imagined the popularity the language would gain. BASIC has been included, in one form or another, with the PC-DOS and MS-DOS operating systems on every IBM-compatible PC. Microsoft deserves credit for popularizing the language and improving its functionality in Visual Basic.

In keeping with the language's popularity and its easy-to-learn structure and syntax, Bentley chose it as the macro language for users. Bentley licensed the macro language from Summit Software and extended it to support MicroStation-specific features and functions.

Given the language's popularity, many good books on the market teach you BASIC. MicroStation BASIC is patterned after Microsoft's Visual Basic. Consequently, if you've never programmed in BASIC and wish to learn the language, you'll want to pick up a good book on BASIC.

I assume you either have some understanding of BASIC or have access to books you can refer to for syntax and other questions. Of course, you will also want to refer to the MicroStation BASIC Guide that comes with the software and the online help file `basichlp.hlp` on the Windows platform in MicroStation's `C:\Bentley\Program\MicroStation\Docs` directory.

The purpose of this chapter is to:

- Introduce you to the MicroStation BASIC environment.
- Show you where to find free macros.
- Help you start writing MicroStation BASIC macros.

Introducing MicroStation BASIC

This section discusses the MicroStation BASIC programming language, assuming you've never used it before. You are introduced to the macro recording facilities and the BASIC code editor and debugger included with MicroStation. A discussion of the benefits of writing macros is followed by a look at several sources you can tap to locate free MicroStation BASIC applications. You also learn how to request input from, and how to display messages to users of your macros.

What is MicroStation BASIC?

MicroStation BASIC is a nearly complete superset of the popular BASIC programming language that includes MicroStation-specific extensions to query and interact with elements and variables in MicroStation's graphical environment. Programs written in this language can only run within MicroStation.

The language is simple and flexible and is especially designed to let you automate repetitive tasks fairly easily. Macros can:

- Sequence MicroStation commands.
- Perform mathematical computations.
- Control program flow.

- Request user input and generate output.
- Read from and write to external files.
- Query environment settings.
- Display messages and request user input in standard dialog boxes.
- Request user input in custom dialog boxes.

You do not have to write MicroStation BASIC code from scratch. MicroStation includes a macro recorder that translates actions to MicroStation BASIC code. Letting the macro recorder generate code saves you from looking up function names. You focus on changes to code to improve its functionality. If you have an existing library of User Commands, the UCM2BAS application discussed in chapter 23 can help you port UCM macros to the BASIC language.

MicroStation BASIC macros are independent of the computer hardware platform and operating system. Macro created on the PC will run without modifications on another platform, such as Windows or UNIX.

Comparing MicroStation BASIC to User Commands

User Commands were first introduced by Intergraph for IGDS. This macro development environment was implemented in MicroStation when Bentley created the software for the PC. Bentley introduced MicroStation BASIC in MicroStation 95 as a replacement for User Commands.

The bulleted list below compares the two macro languages.

- **Language Design:** User Command language is akin to a calculator programming language. It uses predefined registers to store variables and includes primitive flow control. MicroStation BASIC, on the other hand, is a modern programming language. It lets you define variables and data structures at will.

- **Program Size:** User Commands, theoretically, can be of any size. MicroStation BASIC programs can be large, but the source file has a limit of 64 kilobytes.

- **User Interface:** User Commands are limited in the type of user input they understand. They can process key-ins and mouse button clicks, such as data points and reset. They can also display short messages on the status bar. MicroStation BASIC supports all of these and includes the ability to capture input via standard and custom dialog boxes, file browser, and item lists. MicroStation BASIC can also display messages on the status bar and in dialog boxes.

- **Programming Model:** Both languages are procedural and support only the top-down, or sequential, paradigm. Macros start running from the first line and go down one line at a time. When the macro pauses for input, you can't do anything else in MicroStation until the macro finishes. This is in stark contrast to the event-driven programming model of modern windowing environments, and that of MDL and JMDL.

Free MicroStation BASIC Code

Most people learn best by studying existing examples. Since its release, MicroStation BASIC has become increasingly popular. Many people have written programs and made them available for you to study and learn from. In addition to the examples that come with MicroStation, Bentley maintains an Internet site to gather and disseminate macros contributed by its own staff and by users.

Macros Directory

Bentley has written nearly two dozen macros that demonstrate various concepts in MicroStation BASIC. These macros are located in the following directory:

```
C:\Bentley\Workspace\System\Macros
```

Macro source code is written in ASCII text files that have the extension .bas. You can examine this code in any text editor, such as MicroStation's Basic Editor or the programmer's editor demos included on the CD-ROM.

The following table lists several macros delivered with MicroStation and describes what you can learn by studying them. If you are serious about learning MicroStation BASIC, you should study each of these examples to discover how they do what they do.

Macro	Description
cmd.bas	Demonstrates how to pass command line arguments to a macro.
currtran.bas	Demonstrates how to use the MbeCurrentTransform object to rotate objects during placement.
fopen.bas	Demonstrates how to use the File Open dialog box.
inputbox.bas	Demonstrates how to get user input using a standard dialog box.
msgbox.bas	Demonstrates how to use the standard message box.
refinfo.bas	Demonstrates how to query reference file information.
table.bas	Demonstrates how to read a delimited text file and place it in the design file as a table with symbology controlled by a custom dialog box.
widget.bas	Demonstrates how to draw many elements with a single click.

BASICware on the Internet

Another useful source of MicroStation BASIC macros is the Bentley FTP site:

`ftp://ftp.bentley.com/pub/tools/basicwar/`

Point your browser to this location, and you will see the file `00index.txt`. This index document lists nearly a hundred files with the `.bas` extension along with a short description for each. These useful utilities are archived into a file called `basicwar.zip`. Be sure to download the file, extract its contents, and study the code for utilities that interest you.

The following table lists some of the utilities from the BASICware collection:

Macro	Description
accugo.bas	Demonstrates how to start AccuDraw from within a macro.

Macro	Description
align.bas	Aligns elements by moving and rotating them.
clouds.bas	Places drawing revision clouds.
dfrang.bas	Determines the extents of a design file.
cal.bas	Draws the current month's calendar in the design file.
histogram.bas	Draws a histogram in the design file.
refdet.bas	Detaches all reference files from the active design file.
vitext.bas	Replaces text in design file to become view-independent.

MicroStation Manager Magazine

MicroStation Manager is a monthly publication from Bentley. It is distributed to all Bentley SELECT program subscribers. It's also available by subscription. Many articles are user-contributed and contain tips and tricks that fellow MicroStation users have discovered.

Many articles are included on MicroStation BASIC programming, including the popular "Macro of the Month" series.

The magazine also maintains a Web site for its readers where macro source code published in the magazine is made available for download. The Web site can be found at the following URL:

http://www.msmonline.com

Invoking Macros

MicroStation BASIC macros have the extension .bas and are stored in ASCII text files. When you first run a macro, the .bas file is compiled into a .ba binary file.

You can keep macro source and compiled macro files in the same directory. But if you wish to protect your macros from modifications by others, you'll want to keep the macro source files to yourself and make the compiled macro files available on the network for others to use.

If you keep macro source and compiled macro files in the same directory, MicroStation checks to see if the time and data stamp on the source file is more recent than that on the compiled macro file. When that happens, it compiles the macro again before running it.

MicroStation expects macros to be located in a directory, or directories, defined by the MS_MACRO configuration variable. This variable has a value of `C:\Bentley\Workspace\System\Macros` for system macros and `C:\Bentley\Workspace\Standards\Macros` for user macros. Keep your library of macros in the user macros directory.

From the Command Line

To load a macro from the MicroStation Key-in window, type the following command:

`MACRO macname`

where `macname` is the name of the MicroStation BASIC macro you wish to run. As long as the macro is located in directories defined by the MS_MACRO configuration variable, you do not have to append the path name to the macro. If the macro is located in a directory other than those defined by the MS_MACRO configuration variable, you will need to type the complete path to the macro, as shown below:

`MACRO c:\standards\company\macros\macname`

TIP: You can store macros in a directory associated with a configuration variable other than MS_MACRO and still invoke it from the command line easily. Here's an example. To invoke the macro MACNAME, stored in a directory defined by the configuration variable CFGVAR, you would key in `MACRO CFGVAR:MACNAME`.

From Macros Dialog Box

You can load macros through the Macros dialog box. Invoke the dialog box by selecting the option Macros from the Utilities menu. The left side of the dialog box lists all macros located in the macros directory. The right side of the dialog box has several action buttons.

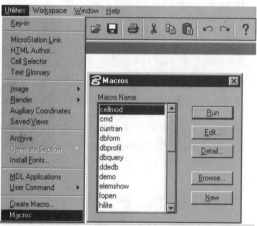

The Macros dialog box displays a list of available macros and lets you manage them.

The Browse button in the Macros dialog box lets you navigate your local hard drive, or a mapped network drive, to locate applications not in the default macros directory.

To load and run a macro, select it from the Macro Name section of the Macros dialog box and click the Run button. If the macro loaded successfully, you will see a message to that effect on the status bar.

Recording and Editing Macros

The easiest way to create macros is to use the macro recorder. Start the macro recorder and perform actions in MicroStation to create a macro source file. The macro source generated by the recorder consists of statements written primarily in MicroStation BASIC extensions to the standard language. That's because MicroStation actions can only be represented by extensions, not the core language.

The next step is to edit the source file by adding functions to make it interactive and more useful. Your knowledge of the BASIC language will help you in this phase of development.

Of course, the recorder is also an excellent tool to determine code syntax for specific MicroStation actions. Simply start the recorder and perform the desired task. Then go back and study the macro code.

Create Macro

To record a macro, select Create Macro from the Utilities menu. This opens the Create Macro dialog box.

The Create Macro dialog box initiates the macro recorder after you supply a name for the macro and click the OK button.

The option button titled Location in the Create Macro dialog box displays a list of directories associated with the MS_MACRO configuration variable. You choose the location for the macro source file with this option button. If only one directory is associated with the MS_MACRO configuration variable, you have no choice but to save it there.

Select the location for the macro source file, and enter a name for the macro and an optional description. Then, click OK. A dialog box with macro recorder controls appears, as shown below. The macro name appears in its title bar.

The appearance of a dialog box with recorder controls indicates that MicroStation is now recording your actions.

The bulleted list below describes the three recorder control buttons.

- **Play:** When the recorder starts, the Play button is selected by default and your actions are recorded in the macro source file.

- **Pause:** During a macro recording session, you may want to perform actions you don't want recorded. Click the Pause button to temporarily stop the recorder. After completing the actions you did not want recorded, click the Play button to resume macro recording.

- **Stop:** When you're finished performing actions you want recorded, click the Stop button to end macro recording. Optionally, you can select End Macro from the Utilities menu. The Create Macro menu option changes to End Macro when a macro recording session is underway.

If you don't wish to use the macro recorder and want to write macros from scratch, click the New button in the Macros dialog box. The MicroStation BASIC Editor window opens. (Invoke the Macros dialog box by selecting Macros from the Utilities menu.)

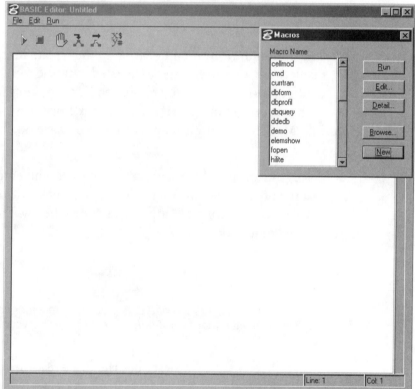

Clicking the New button on the Macros dialog box invokes the BASIC Editor.

 NOTE: You can also invoke the BASIC Editor by keying in **MACRO DEBUG** in the Key-in window.

The BASIC Editor is an ASCII text editor. Its menu bar lets you perform file operations, such as opening existing macros to edit or saving source files. The Edit menu offers common text editing actions and access to the *dialog box builder* application, so you can incorporate custom dialog boxes in macros. The Run menu lets you run the macro and step through it line by line for debugging purposes. The icons above the text edit window are debug controls to let you single-step through code, step into subroutines, view and edit values of variables, set breakpoints, run the macro, or stop the debugger.

TIP: You can create toolboxes for your macros by using MicroStation's Customize dialog box. Associate custom icons with key-ins that invoke macros, as shown below.

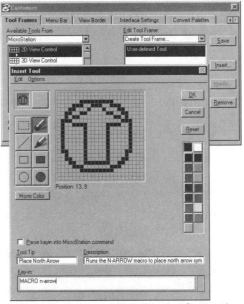

Icons in a custom toolbox created with the Customize dialog box can be associated with key-ins that invoke your macros.

Understanding Macro Syntax

In order to understand the syntax of commands and functions saved by the macro recorder, let's create a macro that draws a north arrow symbol and examine its code. Then, we'll edit this code to make the macro more useful.

Follow along with the sequence of steps listed below to create the N-ARROW macro.

1. Select Create Macro from the Utilities menu in MicroStation to invoke the Create Macro dialog box.

2. Key in `N-ARROW` in the Name field and `Place the North Arrow symbol` in the Description field. Note the location where the macro will be saved and click the OK button.

3. The N-ARROW dialog box with macro controls opens with the Play button selected, ready to record your actions.

4. Invoke the Place SmartLine command. Click the Segment Type option button and select Lines. Click the Vertex Type option button and select Sharp. Do this even if the option buttons display the desired choices. This will ensure that the act of selecting these tool settings is recorded and played back when the macro is run.

5. Click a data point to identify the first vertex and key in the following relative distances to draw the outline of the arrow:

   `DL=0,3`

   `DL=-.5,0`

   `DL=1.5,2.5`

   `DL=1.5,-2.5`

   `DL=-.5,0`

   `DL=0,-3`

   and snap to the first point to close the arrow symbol.

6. Invoke the Place Circle command. In the tool settings window, select Edge from the Method option button.

7. Snap to the top vertex of the arrow followed by the lower two vertices to draw a circle around the arrow. This completes the north arrow symbol.

8. Click the Stop icon on the macro control dialog box, or choose End Macro from the Utilities menu.

   This ends macro recording and saves the macro code in the `n-arrow.bas` file.

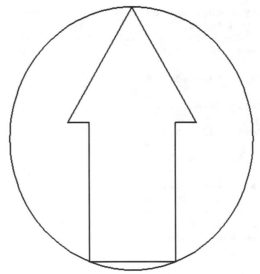

The north arrow symbol recorded by Create Macro.

Now open the Macros dialog box by selecting Macros from the Utilities menu and browse the Macro Name list to find the **n-arrow** macro. Highlight it and click the Edit button. This will open the BASIC Editor with the macro code. The macro code listing is shown below.

```
' Place the North Arrow symbol.

Sub main
    Dim startPoint As MbePoint
    Dim point As MbePoint, point2 As MbePoint

'   Start a command
    MbeSendCommand "PLACE SMARTLINE "

    MbeSendCommand "SMARTLINE SEGMENT LINES "

    MbeSendCommand "SMARTLINE VERTEX SHARP "

'   Coordinates are in master units
    startPoint.x = 0.460344#
    startPoint.y = 628.451687#
    startPoint.z = 0.000000#

'   Send a data point to the current command
    point.x = startPoint.x
    point.y = startPoint.y
    point.z = startPoint.z
    MbeSendDataPoint point, 1%
```

```
'     Send a keyin that can be a command string
      MbeSendKeyin "dl=0,3"

      MbeSendKeyin "dl=-.5,0"

      MbeSendKeyin "dl=1.5,2.5"

      MbeSendKeyin "dl=1.5,-2.5"

      MbeSendKeyin "dl=-.5,0"

      MbeSendKeyin "dl=0,-3"

'     Send a tentative point
      point.x = startPoint.x + 0.062792#
      point.y = startPoint.y + 0.059677#
      point.z = startPoint.z
      MbeSendTentPoint point, 1%

      point.x = startPoint.x
      point.y = startPoint.y
      point.z = startPoint.z
      MbeSendDataPoint point, 1%

'     Set a variable associated with a dialog box
      MbeSetAppVariable "IGEN", "msToolSettings.igen.placeCircleMode", 1&

      MbeSendCommand "PLACE CIRCLE ICON "

      point.x = startPoint.x + 0.219771#
      point.y = startPoint.y - 0.059677#
      point.z = startPoint.z
      MbeSendTentPoint point, 1%

      point.x = startPoint.x
      point.y = startPoint.y
      point.z = startPoint.z
      MbeSendDataPoint point, 1%

      point.x = startPoint.x + 1.067469#
      point.y = startPoint.y + 5.310990#
      point.z = startPoint.z
      MbeSendTentPoint point, 1%

      point.x = startPoint.x + 1.000000#
      point.y = startPoint.y + 5.500000#
      point.z = startPoint.z
      MbeSendDataPoint point, 1%

      point.x = startPoint.x + 1.977948#
      point.y = startPoint.y + 0.268531#
      point.z = startPoint.z
      MbeSendTentPoint point, 1%
```

```
    point.x = startPoint.x + 2.000000#
    point.y = startPoint.y
    point.z = startPoint.z
    MbeSendDataPoint point, 1%

    MbeSendReset
End Sub
```

All lines that begin with an apostrophe are comments. The statement `sub main` signals the beginning of the main subroutine where all macro processing starts. All macros end with the `End Sub` statement that designates the end of the subroutine where processing stops.

The two lines following the `sub main` statement declare that variables `startPoint`, `point`, and `point2` are of type `MbePoint`. The data type `MbePoint` is specific to MicroStation BASIC as evidenced by the prefix `Mbe`. This data type is used to store data point coordinates. You access the x, y, and z coordinates of a data point `startPoint` with the syntax `startPoint.x`, `startPoint.y`, and `startPoint.z`. Notice the use of this syntax throughout the code listing.

The two statements `MbeSendCommand` and `MbeSendDataPoint` send a key-in and a data point, respectively. Other statements used in the above listing are `MbeSetAppVariable`, `MbeSendTentPoint` and `MbeSendReset` which set the state of a Tool Settings window variable, send a tentative point, and a reset button click, respectively. Other MicroStation BASIC statements generated by the macro recorder you are likely to use include `MbeSendDragPoints`, which sends points from a mouse drag operation, and `MbeSendAppMessage`, which initiates an application-specific event.

BASIC supports many variable data types. In addition to explicit data type declaration, BASIC supports the declaration of data types implicitly. You can use special characters as a suffix to variable names to declare them implicitly. The following table shows the special characters you can use to declare simple data types.

Data Type	Special Character for Data Type
integer	%
long integer	&
string	$

Data Type	Special Character for Data Type
single precisions floating point number	!
single precisions floating point number	#

In addition to the built-in data types, MicroStation BASIC supports the definition of user-defined data types. The data type `MbePoint` is an example of this. This user-defined data type is defined as:

```
Type MbePoint
    x as Double
    y as Double
    z as Double
End Type
```

With this introduction to syntax you are well equipped to understand the code for the recorded macro. You may find it instructive to see how the macro works without any modifications. Close the BASIC Editor and delete the north arrow symbol in the view window. Invoke the `n-arrow` macro and see what happens. The north arrow symbol is drawn at exactly the same location where you had drawn it while recording the macro. Normally, you will want the symbol drawn at a location the user clicks.

Edit Macro

As you can see, a macro created by recording actions is functional but needs modifications to improve its usability. We will modify the macro source code so it prompts for a data point and waits for input before drawing the north arrow symbol.

To display a prompt on the status bar, use the `MbeWrite` series of functions. To wait for a data point, use the `MbeGetInput` function. The code listing below incorporates such revisions to the macro.

```
' Place the North Arrow symbol.

Sub main
    Dim startPoint As MbePoint

    MbeSendCommand "NOECHO"
    MbeWriteCommand "Place North Arrow"
    MbeWritePrompt "Identify location for symbol, Reset to abort"
```

```
'Wait for data point, reset or command input
MbeGetInput MBE_DataPointInput, MBE_ResetInput, MBE_CommandInput

While MbeState.InputType <> MBE_ResetInput AND _
      MbeState.InputType <> MBE_CommandInput

'Start Place SmartLine with Line segments and Sharp Vertices
MbeSendCommand "PLACE SMARTLINE "
MbeSendCommand "SMARTLINE SEGMENT LINES "
MbeSendCommand "SMARTLINE VERTEX SHARP "

    'Store data point into variable startPoint
    status=MbeState.getInputDataPoint(startPoint)

    MbeSendDataPoint startPoint
    MbeSendKeyin "dl=0,3"
    MbeSendKeyin "dl=-.5,0"
    MbeSendKeyin "dl=1.5,2.5"
    MbeSendKeyin "dl=1.5,-2.5"
    MbeSendKeyin "dl=-.5,0"
    MbeSendKeyin "dl=0,-3"
    MbeSendKeyin "dl=-2,0"

MbeSetAppVariable "IGEN", "msToolSettings.igen.placeCircleMode", 1&
MbeSendCommand "PLACE CIRCLE ICON "

    MbeSendDataPoint startPoint
    MbeSendKeyin "dl=1,5.5"
    MbeSendKeyin "dl=1,-5.5"

'Wait for data point, reset or command input
MbeGetInput MBE_DataPointInput, MBE_ResetInput, MBE_CommandInput
Wend

If MbeState.InputType = MBE_ResetInput Then
    MbeSendCommand "ECHO"
    MbeWriteStatus "Macro exited"
    MbeStartDefaultCommand
End If

If MbeState.InputType = MBE_CommandInput Then
    MbeSendCommand "ECHO"
    MbeSendLastInput
End If

End Sub
```

In the modified code listing shown above, the three variables
startPoint, point, and point2 the macro recorder defines by default as
data type MbePoint have been reduced to just one variable because

coordinates for all other points can be determined from this single data point. Thus, the modified code uses `startPoint` as the only variable of data type `MbePoint`.

The next three statements enhance usability by displaying messages on the status bar, much like MDL applications do. The functions `MbeWriteCommand` and `MbeWritePrompt` display messages in the command field and the prompt field of the status bar respectively. The `MbeGetInput` function is used next to wait for a data point, a reset, or a key-in command.

The `While ... Wend` loop that follows, keeps executing until the user clicks the reset button or selects another command. This loop initiates the Place SmartLine command, stores the data point coordinates to the variable `startPoint` and passes it on to MicroStation for drawing the arrow using `DL=` key-ins. This is followed by the Place Circle command to draw the bounding circle that passes through the `startPoint`, and the top vertex and the lower right vertex of the arrow. The macro then waits for another data point, a reset button, or a key-in command before continuing the loop.

The next two `If ... End` statements take care of the reset button click and command input.

Make the changes outlined above to the macro you recorded and try executing it again. Isn't the macro more user-friendly now? Also, the Place North Arrow command keeps on repeating, as most MicroStation commands do, until you terminate it by clicking the Reset button.

During the creation of the above macro, you saw some MicroStation BASIC extensions at work. Many more extensions let you access data and variables within the MicroStation environment. Most of these extensions are implemented as objects with properties and methods.

NOTE: You get to the properties and methods within an object by using the dot operator. The statement `startPoint.x` is an example of extracting the `x` coordinate from `startPoint`.

The following table lists the MicroStation BASIC extensions you are most likely to use as a macro programmer.

MS-BASIC Extension	Description
MbeElement	Design file element objects.
MbeElementSet	Collection of elements with a selection set or a fence.
MbeLocation	Allows generation of element selection and location information.
MbeDgnInfo	Active design file information.
MbeSettings	Active MicroStation settings and locks.
MbeState	Current input and output states of MicroStation.
MbeView	Design view information.
MbeRefFile	Reference file attributes such as name, display mode, description, and others.

With what you have learned so far, you can start creating useful macros. But something tells me you are not content with that. You need to learn more and do better. The next section is designed to help you do just that. It shows you how to improve your macros by exploiting your knowledge of the BASIC language and by incorporating custom dialog boxes.

Creating Better Macros

Macro programming is designed to be easy. That is why a macro recorder is included in MicroStation to minimize the need to write code. Granted, the recorder is useful and gets the job done; however, it has limitations.

The following list outlines the limitations of code generated by the macro recorder:

- The macro recorder saves coordinates of data points you click. This is a limitation because you don't usually want the macro to enter the saved data point when you run it. You learned how to resolve this in the N-ARROW macro discussed earlier.

- The macro recorder can't generate control flow statements, such as `While ... Wend`, `If ... End If`, `Do ... While`, and others, that cycle through sections of code. Such statements must be added manually to improve the code.

- The macro recorder cannot generate macros that need to perform computations. The BASIC language has a rich set of mathematical operators and functions that can perform almost any computation you may want. To use this power, you must write code.

- To invoke standard dialog boxes that are used to request input or display alert, warning, or information messages, you must write code.

- To invoke custom dialog boxes that can include option buttons, color picker, level map, and other types of controls, you must write code.

I am sure there are other items that can be added to the above list, but these are the most prominent.

Like any craft, building better macros takes practice and perseverance. Tackling chores you and your users face that would save time when automated, may be all the challenge you need to further your understanding of MicroStation BASIC that will allow you to create better macros.

In this section you learn about conventions used in good MicroStation BASIC programming, using standard dialog boxes, custom dialog boxes, and language extensions that Bentley has implemented for you to exploit.

Determining Need

The first step to writing macros that are truly useful in your organization is to talk to users. Find out what tasks in MicroStation they find repetitive. What processes and procedures would they like automated. The importance of this step cannot be overstated. After all, of what use would a meticulously crafted macro be if it did not solve the problem users face?

It is not always easy to determine true user needs. You may elicit such information by holding informal user meetings and encourage them to record things they repeat often enough and pass on the recorded macro for modification and enhancement.

Another way to convince users about the time-saving potential macros provide and why they should communicate their needs for automation would be to install existing macros you download. These could be made available on a network and users made aware of their presence with a brief description of what each does. As they begin using the macros, they will come up with suggestions for new ones or improvements to existing ones. Many times users are not aware of the benefits macros provide and how easy it is to record actions.

The following list provides reasons why problem definition from a user's perspective is very important.

- Determining user needs ensures that macro functionality is driven by users rather than by the macro programmer.

- An explicit set of requirements keeps the macro programmer focused, ensuring quicker development. Without explicit requirements, the programmer may unnecessarily spend time exploring options that users may not need.

- Users are more likely to use time-saving macros if they specified the requirements to begin with.

- Formally agreed-to user needs protect you if you develop macros for clients. Documented user needs can resolve arguments in case of a disagreement.

Coding Practices

Creating powerful and interactive macros takes more effort than simply recording actions with the macro recorder. Of all the tasks you will perform as a macro writer, the one task that will determine the ultimate quality of your macro is the code you write. By following simple coding conventions, you will improve code readability and avoid subtle mistakes that can easily go unnoticed. Of course, you will also do well to learn as much as you can about the language you will be writing in.

Names of constants, variables, functions, objects and procedures can be up to 40 characters long. They can contain alphanumeric characters `a-z`, `0-9` and the underscore character (_). Names must begin with an alphabetical character.

The BASIC language is not case sensitive. This means that the same word (constant name, variable name, or a function name) can be written in uppercase, lowercase, or mixed case without fear of ruining the macro. Thus, the words myFunc, MyFunc, and MYFUNC refer to the same thing. Nevertheless, you will want to use case to improve code readability and to differentiate between constant and variable data types.

Constants. There are many predefined constants in MicroStation BASIC. For example the constant MBE_Success refers to the number 0 (zero). Most predefined constants begin with the characters MBE_. By always naming constants with a set of uppercase prefix characters followed by the underscore character you make them easy to spot in the code. You declare constants with the CONST keyword. The following statement defines a math constant:

```
CONST DGN_uor% = 4294967296
```

Variables and Objects. Because variable names can be up to 40 characters long, you should use descriptive names that help you remember the type of value they are designed to hold. Built-in objects use names such as MbeSettings and MbeRefFile that are easy to relate to. When you use variable names such as startPoint, endPoint, and dgnMastPerSub, you will reduce the chance of plugging the wrong variable in an expression. It is much easier to misplace variables in expressions when using cryptic names such as x, y, or z. You may wish to begin all variable names in lowercase.

Subroutines. Most small macros can be written entirely inside the Sub Main ... End Sub routine while retaining their readability. As your macros get larger, you will find it helpful to organize your macros into smaller subroutines that perform well defined tasks. You may wish to begin all subroutine names with an initial uppercase letter.

Such practices are not mandatory, but they go a long way in improving your ability to understand the code when it is time to update the macro. Also, be sure to comment your code wisely, with the sole purpose of making it easily maintainable.

Standard Dialog Boxes

Earlier you learned how to edit recorded macro code to insert statements that make the macro pause for user input by way of a data point click, a reset, or a key-in. Macros can also pause for other types of input, such as element color, level number, or file name. Many standard dialog boxes are available for this purpose. These dialog boxes are invoked through a simple statement that accepts parameters to customize some of its elements such as title.

The following table lists the types of standard dialog boxes available and the BASIC statement used to invoke them.

Dialog Box Type	BASIC Statement
File Open	MbeFileOpen (filename$, suggest$, filter$, directory$, title$)
File Create	MbeFileCreate (filename$, suggest$, filter$, directory$, title$)
Message Box with Buttons and Optional Icon	MbeMessageBox (msg$, buttonType& or iconType&)
Input Dialog Box	MbeInputBox (prompt$, defaultText$, title$)
Selection List	MbeSelectBox (prompt$, itemArray$(), title$)

For details on which parameters are optional, and the values the above BASIC statements return, refer to MicroStation BASIC online help.

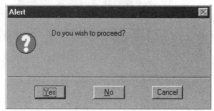

A message box with Yes, No, and Cancel buttons and the Question icon.

The following code fragment shows how to invoke a message box with Yes, No and Cancel buttons and how to process the button clicked.

```
msg$ = "Do you wish to proceed?"
Button% = MbeMessageBox (msg$, MBE_YesNoCancelBox or MBE_QuestionIcon)

SELECT CASE Button
    CASE MBE_BUTTON_YES
        CALL subYesPressed
    CASE MBE_BUTTON_NO
        CALL subNoPressed
    CASE MBE_BUTTON_CANCEL
        CALL subCancelPresed
END CASE
```

The first line assigns a message string to the variable msg$. The second line assigns an integer value to the variable Button% depending on the button the user clicks in the message box invoked by the MbeMessageBox function. The Select Case ... End Case block of statements checks the value of the Button% variable and processes it accordingly. If the user clicks the Yes button, the subroutine subYesPressed is called. If the user clicks the No button, the subroutine subNoPressed is called. If the user clicks the Cancel button, the subroutine subCancelPressed in called.

Let's now take another complete working example to showcase how to use the Input dialog box. This macro prompts the user for the number of steps to draw in elevation and waits for two data point clicks to draw the steps through.

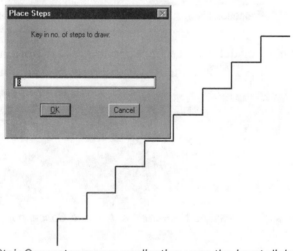

The Stair Generator macro application uses the input dialog box to request the number of steps the user wants to draw.

To create the macro application shown in the figure above save the code listed below in the file `stairgen.bas`.

```
' Place steps in elevation

SUB Main
    DIM numSteps    AS Integer
    DIM startPoint AS MbePoint
    DIM endPoint    AS MbePoint
    DIM riser       AS Double
    DIM tread       AS Double
    DIM vertex      AS MbePoint

'   Prompt for the number of steps to draw
    MbeWriteCommand "Place Steps"
    MbeWritePrompt "Key in no. of steps to draw"
    chrSteps$ = MbeInputBox("Key in no. of steps to draw:", "8", "Place Steps")
    numSteps = val(chrSteps)

    IF numSteps = 0 THEN
        GOTO UserCancelledCmd
    END IF

'   Prompt for start and end points
    MbeWritePrompt "Enter start point for first riser"
    MbeGetInput MBE_DataPointInput, MBE_ResetInput
    IF MbeState.inputType = MBE_ResetInput THEN End
    status = MbeState.getInputDataPoint(startPoint)
    vertex = startPoint
    MbeWritePrompt "Enter end point for last tread"
    MbeGetInput MBE_DataPointInput, MBE_ResetInput
    IF MbeState.inputType = MBE_ResetInput THEN End
    status = MbeState.getInputDataPoint(endPoint)

'   Compute riser and tread
    x# = endPoint.x - startPoint.x
    y# = endPoint.y - startPoint.y
    riser = y#/numSteps
    tread = x#/numSteps

'   Draw the steps as a line string
    MbeSendCommand "PLACE LSTRING"

    MbeSendDataPoint startPoint

    FOR counter = 1 TO numSteps
       vertex.x = vertex.x
       vertex.y = vertex.y + riser
       MbeSendDataPoint vertex

       vertex.x = vertex.x + tread
       vertex.y = vertex.y
       MbeSendDataPoint vertex
```

```
    NEXT

UserCancelledCmd:
'    End macro by invoking Element Selector
     MbeSendReset
     MbeSendCommand "CHOOSE ELEMENT"
END SUB
```

The two statements that invoke the input dialog box and process the value supplied by the user are listed below.

```
chrSteps$ = MbeInputBox("Key in no. of steps to draw:", "8", "Place Steps")
numSteps = val(chrSteps)
```

The first line assigns the user key-in to the string variable chrSteps$. The second line converts the string to a number using the BASIC val function and assigns it to the variable numSteps. The standard input dialog box can only capture a string variable. If the requested input is a number, the string captured must be explicitly converted to a number as shown here.

Custom Dialog Boxes

The standard dialog boxes discussed above will let you address the needs of many macros. And if your macro needs happen to be more complex, you can always design custom dialog boxes. You use the Dialog Builder to interactively draw the custom dialog boxes needed by your macro. And you use the function MbeOpenModalDialog to invoke custom dialog boxes.

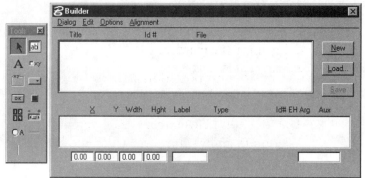

*The Dialog Builder and the associated Tools
toolbox let you draw custom dialog boxes.*

The Dialog Builder contains a menu bar, three buttons, two list boxes, and four text edit fields. Each of these components is briefly described below.

Menu Bar

The menu bar offers four choices: Dialog, Edit, Options, and Alignment.

Use the Dialog menu to create a New dialog box, Load an existing one, Close it, Save (to file, over an existing one, or to a new file), and Delete an existing dialog box from a file.

The Edit menu offers options to Cut, Copy, Paste, Delete, Select All, Bring to Front, or Send to Back dialog items you add to a dialog box.

The Options menu lets you test a dialog by switching it between edit and test modes, display or hide the Preferences window, display or hide the Tools toolbox, and Dialog Attributes or Item Attributes dialog boxes.

The Alignment menu offers choices to help align dialog items inside a dialog box.

Buttons

The three buttons in Dialog Builder provide one-click access to the most commonly used menu options, namely create new, load existing, or save dialog boxes to file.

List Boxes

The top list box contains the names and details of custom dialog boxes defined for the macro.

The bottom list box contains a list of items that belong to the selected custom dialog box.

The four edit fields under the bottom list box are used to revise the location (x and y) and size (width and height) of dialog items.

Tools Toolbox

The table below lists the various dialog items available for placement on custom dialog boxes from the Tools toolbox. Also listed next to the type of dialog item is the type of variable the dialog item can communicate with.

Type of Dialog Item	Valid Access String Variable Types
Text Field	String, Long, Integer, Single, Double
Label	None
Checkbox	Long, Integer
Groupbox	None
Option Button	Long, Integer
Push Button	None (Uses action button value)
Color Picker	Long, Integer
Level Map	Long, Integer (Active Level); Array of 4 integers (Access string)
Slider/Scale	Single, Double
Radio Button	Long, Integer

NOTE: Your macro code communicates with dialog items through a variable, called an access string, that you assign to the item using the Item Attributes window. Double click an item in the bottom list box to display its Item Attributes window.

To create a custom dialog box:

1. Invoke the Dialog Builder and its associated Tools toolbox by selecting Custom Dialog, then Edit from the BASIC Editor's Edit menu.
2. Select New from the Dialog Builder's File menu. This creates a blank custom dialog box with the title *Untitled* and the OK and Cancel buttons.
3. Double click the new custom dialog box entry in the Dialog Builder to open the Dialog Box Attributes window. Change the Title field from *Untitled* to a desired text string. Optionally you can enable other attributes, such as Sinkable or Growable, by enabling the appropriate checkbox.
4. From the Tools toolbox select a desired dialog item and click a location for it on the dialog box. The new dialog item appears in the bottom list box of the Dialog Builder.

5. Double-click the dialog item to open the item attributes window. Change the label of the dialog item to a desired text string.

6. Assign the dialog item to an access string variable in the macro source. This is done by typing the variable name in the access string field in the dialog item attribute window. The dialog item attributes window offers other choices depending on the type of dialog item being edited. For instance, when defining an option button, the dialog item attributes window for it contains a list box for storing the options it is to display.

NOTE: Custom dialog box definitions are stored in `.ba` files corresponding to your macros. If you delete the `.ba` file, the dialog boxes defined for the macro will also be deleted. To salvage the custom dialog boxes, you have no choice but to draw them again.

From all the macro examples that come with MicroStation, my favorite is `TABLE.BAS`. It is a well written, professional-quality macro. Print it and study it; you will learn a lot. This macro reads a comma delimited ASCII text file and places the content in a neat table. It effectively uses a custom dialog box to let the user choose the color, weight, style and other settings for the table to be drawn. As you might expect, a compiled version of the macro with the `.ba` extension is included because it contains a custom dialog box definition. See the screenshot below for the custom dialog box used by the TABLE macro.

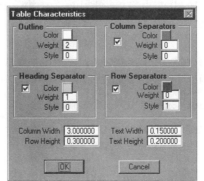

The TABLE macro uses a custom dialog box to let users select table attributes.

The macro declares two user-defined data types, namely `TableSymbology` and `TableParams`. The code fragment that implements the type declaration is shown below.

```
Type TableSymbology

    color  as Integer

    weight as Integer

    style  as Integer

End Type


Type TableParams

    columnWidth as Double

    rowHeight   as Double

    textHeight  as Double

    textWidth   as Double

    wantHdgSep  as Integer

    wantColSep  as Integer

    wantRowSep  as Integer

    lineSymb(1 To 5) as TableSymbology

End Type
```

Note that the five element array `lineSymb()` is of data type `TableSymbology` and is incorporated into the `TableParams` data type. To have the code communicate with settings the user chooses in the custom dialog box, the macro need use a single user-defined data type. The function `table_getTabeParams()` listed below illustrates this.

```
Function table_getTableParams (table as TableParams)

    Dim status      as Integer

    Dim buttonVal   as Long


    table.wantHdgSep  = 1

    table.wantColSep  = 1

    table.wantRowSep  = 1
```

```
table.columnWidth = 3.0

table.rowHeight   = 0.3

table.textHeight  = 0.2

table.textWidth   = 0.15


table.lineSymb(OUTLINE).color = 0

table.lineSymb(HDGSEP).color  = 4

table.lineSymb(COLSEP).color  = 2

table.lineSymb(ROWSEP).color  = 5


table.lineSymb(OUTLINE).weight = 2

table.lineSymb(HDGSEP).weight  = 1

table.lineSymb(COLSEP).weight  = 0

table.lineSymb(ROWSEP).weight  = 0


table.lineSymb(OUTLINE).style  = 0

table.lineSymb(HDGSEP).style   = 0

table.lineSymb(COLSEP).style   = 0

table.lineSymb(ROWSEP).style   = 1


buttonVal = MbeOpenModalDialog (1)


If (buttonVal < 0) Or (buttonVal = MBE_BUTTON_OK) Then

    table_getTableParams = MBE_Success

Else

    table_getTableParams = CANCELLED

End If

End Function
```

To understand the role of access strings in dialog items, call up the code of the TABLE macro in MicroStation's BASIC Editor. Then invoke the Dialog Builder from the Editor's Edit menu by selecting Custom Dialog, then Edit. Then double-click a color picker item on the dialog box and examine the value of the access string assigned to it. You will recognize it from the above listing.

The following excerpt from the macro shows how the dialog settings are used. The `MbeSettings` object is first invoked to change the active symbology settings to correspond to those in the dialog box. This is followed by calling another function to draw the table outline.

```
MbeSettings.color     = table.lineSymb(OUTLINE).color

MbeSettings.lineStyle = table.lineSymb(OUTLINE).style

MbeSettings.weight    = table.lineSymb(OUTLINE).weight

.

.

.

Call table_drawOutline (origin, view, totalWidth, totalHeight)
```

With the background you have now gained in recording macros, editing the syntax, calling up standard dialog boxes and creating custom dialog boxes, you can craft interactive macros users will appreciate.

Beyond Macros

The more you learn about the BASIC language and the extensions Bentley has added to MicroStation BASIC, the better equipped you will be to handle complex tasks and meet user demands for automation. Following are some macro language functions I have found helpful while writing macros.

BASIC Function	Purpose
FileExists	Checks whether the file specified exists. Useful for trapping errors while opening files.
FileList	Populates a string array with names of files meeting specified criteria. Useful for macros that need to process multiple files.
FileParse	Extracts the desired component of a filename such as drive, path, extensions.

BASIC Function	Purpose
DDEInitiate	Initializes a dynamic data exchange (DDE) link to another application. Only for the Windows environment. Useful for having your macro communicate with a spreadsheet or database software.
DDEExecute	Sends a command string to another application for execution.

For a user-command programmer, MicroStation BASIC is heaven. The depth of the language by way of the number of functions it makes available, support for user-defined data types, and modern flow-control constructions offers power that is truly incredible. Despite all this power, macros are limited in some ways in what they cannot do.

Limitations of Macros

Macros cannot:

- Communicate directly with external dynamic link modules.
- Implement dynamic dialog boxes that change depending on an option selected.
- Implement non-modal dialog boxes.
- Provide dynamics, also called rubberbanding.
- Respond to events as they operate in a procedural, not event-driven, environment.

If you need to overcome any of these limitations, you will need to hone your programming skills and move to the more professional development environments offered in MicroStation, namely MicroStation Development Language (MDL) and Java MicroStation Development Language (JMDL).

Moving to MDL and Java

Most third-party applications that extend the functionality of MicroStation are written in MDL. MDL is a professional C language based environment that offers all the tools needed to create truly integrated applications that operate upon the DGN file format. The next chapter introduces you to MDL programming.

Java (and JMDL, the superset of Java as implemented in MicroStation/J) is the latest professional language to be supported by the software. The purpose of this language is to support MicroStation's ProActiveM object technology that goes beyond the limitations of the DGN file format. To develop enterprise-wide applications that offer the ability to model engineering components as simulations of real-world objects, you will need to move to JMDL. This language is introduced after the chapter on MDL.

Chapter 25

Developing MDL Applications

Creating Sophisticated Programs for MicroStation

Of the many levels of customization MicroStation offers, one of the most powerful is MDL, or MicroStation Development Language. With MDL you can create add-on applications that extend the software's functionality by implementing new commands with an interface indistinguishable from MicroStation's own. Best of all, the MDL compiler is included at no extra charge with every copy of MicroStation.

The purpose of this chapter is twofold. It introduces you to the MDL tools so you can recompile existing MDL source code for your platform. It also introduces you to MDL programming so you can create custom applications. Though a basic knowledge of the C programming language is assumed, no previous knowledge of MDL is required to follow this chapter.

The most potent tools in your tool kit are the thousands of built-in MDL functions. To understand better why the built-in MDL functions behave the way they do, you must have a good working knowledge of MicroStation. In other words, you must be familiar with the software you will be customizing.

This chapter is not intended to replace MDL documentation that comes with MicroStation. It is designed to jump start your learning curve and help you exploit Bentley's documentation as a reference resource.

You will want to keep the following Bentley documentation handy as you learn programming in MDL:

- MicroStation 95 Reference Guide, chapter 18, titled *Intergraph Standard File Formats*. It discusses the DGN file format and the various MicroStation element types.

- MDL Programmer's Guide. It discusses the development tools, the dialog box manager, and the graphical user interface resources.

- MDL Function Reference Manual. This is your definitive reference to the various built-in MDL functions.

- MDL Supplement Guide. This book discusses the recent enhancements and changes implemented in MDL.

All the above guides and manuals are included on your MicroStation CD-ROM in PDF (Portable Document Format) that can be read, and printed as necessary, by Adobe's Acrobat Reader. You also have access to the latter three manuals via on-line help.

The highlights of this chapter include:

- Introduction to MDL tools

- Where to get free MDL source code

- How to setup and use the MDL development tools

- MDL programming practices and its event-driven nature

- Liberal use of code fragments to reinforce what you learn

- Introduction to the bonus *RSTools LE*, MDL application included free with this book

Introducing MDL

This section discusses the MDL programming language from a beginner's point of view. You are introduced to MDL as a C language-based environment for customizing MicroStation. A discussion of the benefits of programming with MDL is followed by a look at several sources you can tap to locate free MDL applications. You also learn how to load and unload MDL applications and display key-in commands supported by them.

What Is MDL?

MDL is an ANSI C-based programming language created by Bentley to develop professional-quality custom applications that run inside MicroStation. It is an almost complete implementation of ANSI C with access to a couple of thousand MicroStation-specific prebuilt MDL functions.

When Bentley created MDL, its goal was twofold. First, it wanted to implement a programming environment that would make it relatively easy for its own developers to extend MicroStation's functionality. Second, it wanted to empower its customers, MicroStation users, to go beyond the customizability offered by User Commands (UCMs) and script files. In fact, a significant set of MicroStation's native commands is implemented using MDL. As testimony, just peek at the number of MDL application files (these have the extension `.ma`) in the `mdlsys\asneeded` subdirectory under the base MicroStation directory.

Just as you would use a C compiler to create executable programs for an operating system such as DOS, Windows, or UNIX, you use an MDL compiler to create programs for MicroStation.

To determine whether the MDL development tools are loaded on your system, check your base MicroStation directory to see if the MDL subdirectory exists. The MDL tools, on a default Windows NT installation, are located in the following directory:

```
C:\Bentley\Program\MicroStation\MDL\Bin
```

To build MDL applications, you will want to append this directory to your system PATH statement so you have access to the tools no matter what your source code directory.

If the MDL directory tree does not exist on your system, a typical install without MDL was selected during installation. You will need to run MicroStation Setup again and select the MDE Programming tools checkbox from the MicroStation/J Installation dialog box.

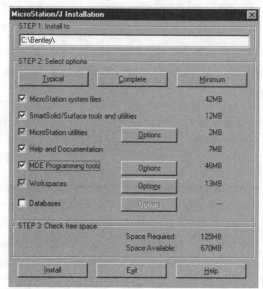

Run MicroStation Setup to add MDE Programming tools if they are not already installed on your system.

Keep in mind that MDL programs are platform-dependent. This means that an MDL program you compile for one platform, such as Windows, will not run as is on another platform, such as UNIX. You will need to recompile your source code with the MDL compiler for the platform on which you need your program to run.

Though, strictly speaking, MDL should refer only to MicroStation's programming language, the term will be used loosely here to refer to the MicroStation Development Environment (MDE) also.

Why Program in MDL?

Now that we know what MDL is and that it is used to develop tightly integrated custom applications for MicroStation, let's take a quick look at the benefits of programming with it:

- **Consistency.** MDL offers the same tools on all supported hardware platforms. You do not have to learn a different set of tools if you migrate to different platforms.

- **Graphical Interface.** MDL offers tools to build for your application a graphical interface that is indistinguishable from MicroStation's own. This frees you from having to code an interface from scratch.

- **Internationalization.** MDL simplifies the translation of your application to foreign languages by using message and string lists in separate resource files.

- **Portability.** MDL source code is easily portable to different hardware platforms. All it takes in most cases is a recompile on the desired platform.

- **User-Friendly.** MDL is event-driven, like all modern graphical environments, thus putting the user in control. Contrast this with the procedural nature of User Commands (UCMs) and MicroStation BASIC programs, which must follow a structured code sequence.

Free MDL Code

There is no better way to learn MDL than to start with examples someone else has written. Plenty of examples are available for experimenting, learning, and using MDL. Your first source is the examples that come with MicroStation. And of course, you have the Internet.

MDL Examples Directory

When you perform a complete install of MicroStation, an MDL *examples* folder is created on your hard disk. The default location of the MDL examples is:

```
C:\Bentley\Program\MicroStation\MDL\Examples
```

This directory contains several dozen subdirectories, each containing source code demonstrating a different MDL programming concept. For example, the code in the *adrwdemo* subdirectory (AccuDraw Demo) shows how to write applications that communicate with AccuDraw, and the code in the basic subdirectory shows how to create basic dialog boxes in MDL.

If you are serious about learning MDL, you most definitely will want to compile all of these examples and work with them to get a sense of what they do. Then you will want to read through the code carefully to understand the application logic and its implementation.

NOTE: The process of compiling existing source code is covered later in this chapter. It is also covered in chapter 7, *Building Applications*, in the MDL Programmer's Guide, and in the online version of the manual.

MDLware on Internet

Another very useful source of MDL code is the Bentley FTP site at:

`ftp://ftp.bentley.com/pub/tools/mdl/ware`

Point your browser to this location and you will see a list of nearly one hundred files with the `.zip` extension. Most of these are working examples with MDL source code. Many were written for MicroStation versions 4 and 5 and may require minor modifications to compile under the current MicroStation version.

After logging on to the site, be sure to print out the file `00index.txt`. This file contains a brief description of what each file contains. Some of my favorites from this collection are:

Application	Description
cellutil	Tool to batch process cells in a cell library.
drftools	Tools to automate the creation of common drafting symbols (now integrated into MicroStation as Annotation tools).
steel	Tools to draw AISC (American Institute of Steel Construction) standard structural steel shapes.

These aren't commercial applications. Use them at your own risk!

Another source of useful information is the Internet newsgroup `comp.cad.microstation.programmer`.

MicroStation Manager Magazine

High Mountain Press started this magazine in 1990 as a forum for MicroStation users to exchange tips and tricks, and as a vehicle for advertisers to market their MicroStation-related products. It has undergone a few ownership changes over the years and is now under Bentley's control. The magazine was and still is focused on the user community.

Many articles on MDL programming have appeared in the magazine over the years. Much of this chapter is based on my articles published by the magazine.

MicroStation Manager maintains a web site for its readers where MDL source code related to articles is made available for download. The web site can be found at the following URL:

`http://www.msmonline.com`

Invoking MDL Programs

Once you understand what MDL is and have downloaded several free programs that appear promising, you will want to know how to run them. This section shows you the two ways available.

As you might guess, the quality of programs you download for free will vary greatly. Some programs may have good accompanying documentation, while others may not even list the commands they implement. In this section you will learn how to deal with the latter type of programs as well.

MicroStation expects MDL programs to be located in a directory defined by the MS_MDLAPPS configuration variable by default. This variable has a default value that includes two folders, `c:\Bentley\Program\MicroStation\MdlApps` and `c:\Bentley\Workspace\Standards\MdlApps\IntelNT`. The first directory contains system applications. The second allows you to separate your MDL programs from those delivered with MicroStation.

If you keep your MDL applications in another folder, you will want to add that folder to the definition of the MS_MDLAPPS variable. This way, you need not type the application's full path to load it.

Loading from Command Line

To load a compiled MDL application (these have .ma as their filename extension), enter the following command at the MicroStation Key-in window:

```
MDL LOAD appname
```

where appname is the name of the MDL application you want to load, assuming it is located in the directory defined by the MS_MDLAPPS configuration variable. If the application is located in directories other than those defined by the configuration variable, you will need to type the complete path to the application, as shown below:

```
MDL LOAD C:\Standards\Company\MDLapps\appname
```

You can also load programs from a directory assigned to a configuration variable, say pathvar, by typing:

```
MDL LOAD pathvar:appname
```

NOTE: If you have typed the command and filename correctly—with no typing mistakes—and get an error message regarding platform compatibility, the application was compiled for a different operating system than the one you are currently running. To run the application on your computer, you will need to recompile the program source code for your operating system.

Loading from MDL Dialog Box

Another way to load compiled MDL applications is from MDL dialog box. Open the dialog box by selecting MDL Applications from the Utilities menu. The top section of this dialog box displays all MDL applications currently loaded in memory. The bottom section displays available MDL applications that reside in the directory defined by the MS_MDLAPPS configuration variable.

*The MDL dialog box displays applications loaded in memory;
it also lets you load available applications.*

The Browse button in the MDL dialog box allows you to navigate the computer's hard drive, or a mapped network drive, to locate applications not in the default MDL applications directory.

To load an application, select it from the Available Applications section of the MDL dialog box and click the Load button. If the application loads successfully, you see a message to that effect on the status bar.

Determining Supported Key-Ins

Many MDL applications you load announce their presence by opening a dialog box or a toolbox that you use to activate commands. However, many applications may do nothing. In case the application does not invoke a dialog box or a toolbox, and does not prompt with a helpful message, you will want to enlist the help of the Key-in window.

The Key-in window implements a Command Table browser. This browser can display all the key-ins supported by MicroStation and all loaded MDL applications, or just the key-ins supported by a specific MDL application.

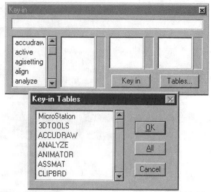

*The Key-in window can display key-ins
supported by a specific MDL application.*

To display the key-ins supported by an MDL application loaded in memory, use the following steps:

1. Select Key-in from the Utilities menu. This opens the Key-in window.

2. If the Key-in window displays the command line only, or is docked, drag it so it floats. Then, resize it by dragging its bottom edge so the Key-in and Tables buttons display.

3. Click the Tables button. This will open the Key-in Tables dialog box that lists MicroStation and all loaded MDL applications.

4. Select the desired MDL application and click OK.

5. The Key-in Tables dialog box closes and the key-ins supported by the MDL application selected in step 4 display. Select the first command keyword in the left listbox, its dependent commands display in the listbox to the right.

Using the MDL Development Tools

The previous section explained MDL concepts and tools and identified locations you can look up for sample code. You also learned how to start existing MDL applications and how to discover the key-ins supported by them.

This section introduces you to the development tools you will use to write MDL applications. Here you learn about tools such as the MDL source compiler, the resource compiler, the librarian, and the *make* utility. You also learn how to set up your system environment for the tools. Filename extensions and the tools directory tree are discussed as well.

MDL Tools

If you have programmed in a compiled language, whether Pascal, C, BASIC, FORTRAN, or other, you will relate immediately to the development tools that come with MicroStation. There is a source and resource compiler, a linker, a librarian, a debugger, and a make utility. In addition, there are graphical tools to help you design your application's interface.

For a default MicroStation installation, MDL tools can be found in the `C:\Bentley\Program\MicroStation\MDL\Bin` directory. To develop MDL programs, you will want to place this directory on your system's PATH statement, so you have access to these tools no matter what your development directory.

Following is a list of the MDL development tools and what each does.

- **BMAKE:** This utility is referred to as Bentley Make and is very similar to make utilities you may be familiar with on other compilers. Its purpose is to define the compilation rules for different file types and interdependencies between source files. For every program you develop, you will create a make file for use by this utility to generate your completed application.

- **DLMSPEC:** The Dynamic Link Module Specification compiler is for advanced programmers who need to load and link portions of code with MicroStation at run time. This is one instance where you need tools, such as a compiler and linker for the host operating system, other than those provided with MicroStation.

- **MCOMP:** The MDL compiler that takes your source files and converts them to object code. Typically, the BMAKE utility will take care of invoking MCOMP to compile your code.

- **MLIB:** The MDL librarian for maintaining and managing compiled object code.

- **MLINK:** The MDL linker that creates project files from object files created by MCOMP. Project files are the functional portion of the applications you create and must be combined with the interface portion to build MDL executables.

- **RCOMP:** The resource compiler for managing the data portion of your application. It generates compiled resource files from resource source files.

- **RDUMP:** The resource dump utility is used to display resource IDs from a compiled resource file. It can be helpful when debugging a problematic resource file.

- **RLIB:** The resource librarian that combines functional program files from MLINK with interface resource files from RCOMP to generate executable MDL applications.

- **RSCTYPE:** A type generator that creates a special resource file. Anytime you need to interact with the user of your application via a dialog box interface, you will use RSCTYPE to relate dialog items with variables in your application.

The directory, `C:\Bentley\Program\MicroStation\MDL`, that contains MDL tools and examples, includes several subdirectories listed below. The following table includes a brief description of subdirectory contents.

Directory	Contents
BIN	MDL development tools
EXAMPLES	MDL source code examples that demonstrate concepts
INCLUDE	Function definition **.fdf**, header **.h**, and make include **.mki** files
LIBRARY	Library of MDL functions in object code **.ml** format

In addition to the development tools discussed above, MicroStation includes a Resource Development Environment (RDE). The RDE is used to manage application resources such as command tables, string lists, and dialog boxes.

Invoke RDE by keying in MDL LOAD RDE in MicroStation's Key-in window.

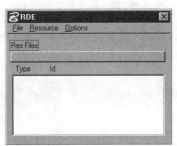

RDE lets you manage your application's resources.

I realize that I have introduced a couple of terms you may not yet understand. The terms are: *command table* and *string list*. Command table refers to the list of commands you can type in the Key-in window to invoke an action in MicroStation. String list is a list of messages. An application retrieves messages from it to display on the status bar. We will discuss these resources in more detail later.

TIP: To invoke the Command Table Editor, key in MDL LOAD CMDTEDIT. To invoke the Dialog Box Builder, key in MDL LOAD BUILDER. To invoke the String List Editor, key in MDL LOAD STRGEDIT.

One other tool you will not be able to do without is the Icon Editor. Use this tool to draw icons for toolboxes. Invoke the Icon Editor by typing **MDL LOAD ICONEDIT** in MicroStation's Key-in window.

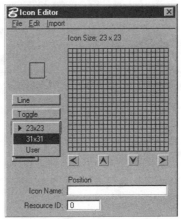

Icons for toolboxes come in two sizes: 23X23 and 31X31 pixels.

Filename Extensions

Let's take a look at the filename extensions, in alphabetical order, used in MDL development.

Extension	File Type
.c	C language source code to create dynamic link libraries and modules
.dll	dynamic link library
.dlm	dynamic link module
.dlo	compiled DLS file
.dls	function and variable declaration file for communicating between .ma and dynamic link libraries and modules
.fdf	function definition file to declare function prototypes
.h	header files that define constants and function declarations and are included by .mc, .r, and .mt files
.ma	executable MDL application files created by RLIB or MLINK by combining .mp and .rsc files
.mc	MDL source files that impart functionality to your application and are used by MCOMP
.mke	make file containing rules that define how to build your application and are operated on by BMAKE
.ml	object-code library files created by MLIB
.mm	map files generated by MLINK
.mo	object-code files generated from .mc files by MCOMP
.mp	project files created by MLINK by combining .mo and .ml files
.mt	source files for publishing structures and unions you create
.r	resource source files
.rsc	compiled resource files generated from .r files by RCOMP

Setting Up BMAKE

A typical development cycle involves the use of RCOMP to compile dialog box and toolbox resources (.r to .rsc), MCOMP to compile MDL source files (.mc to .mo), RSCTYPE to publish structures and unions (.mt to .r), MLINK to link compiled MDL object files with standard library functions (.mo and .ml to .mp), and finally, RLIB to combine resource and source objects to an application (.mp and .rsc to .ma). Rather than invoke each needed MDL tool separately, BMAKE automates their invocation by defining rules based on filename extensions.

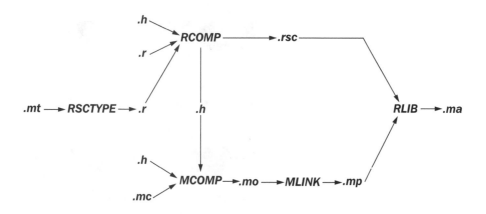

The MDL development cycle.

BMAKE is the primary tool you use to build MDL applications. But before you can use BMAKE, you will need to set up your system environment to declare two variables: MS and BMAKE_OPT. The former defines the MicroStation base directory, and the latter specifies the command line switches for BMAKE.

To set these two system environment variables under Windows NT, you use the System icon in Control Panel. To set them up under Windows 95, Windows 3.1, and DOS, you edit the autoexec.bat file. Under UNIX, you edit your login script file.

Whatever your development platform, your system environment will need to define the following variables for BMAKE to work:

`MS = C:\Bentley\Program\MicroStation`

`BMAKE_OPT = -Ic:\Bentley\Program\MicroStation\MDL\Include`

Of course, you should modify the value of the variable MS to reflect your base MicroStation directory. The -I switch for BMAKE_OPT specifies the location of make include, namely `.mki`, files so BMAKE can find them. Note that there is no space between the letter I and the directory name. BMAKE_OPT supports an optional switch, `-ddebug`, that can be specified if you wish to include debugging information in your program file.

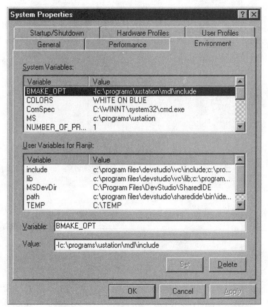

Use the Environment tab on the System dialog box under Windows NT to set the MS and BMAKE_OPT system variables.

NOTE: MicroStation/J includes a batch file to automate shell configuration for developing MDL and JMDL applications. From the Windows Start button, select Programs, then MicroStation_J, followed by MicroStation Development Shell. A command shell window opens. This window eliminates the need to setup system environment variables manually, as discussed above. Use it to call up development tools.

Using BMAKE

The Make utility, BMAKE, won't run properly unless you have:

1. Added the MDL tools directory on your system path.
2. Defined the system environment variable MS as outlined in the previous section.
3. Defined the BMAKE_OPT system environment variable also outlined in the previous section.

NOTE: Invoking the MicroStation Development Shell from the Start button automatically takes care of the above issues.

Exercise

To practice using BMAKE to compile an MDL application, let's use an example file already on your hard disk. No coding is required for this one! Work through the following steps and you will have compiled the DIMLINE application that places a line, a circle, or an arc with dimensions in one step.

Use the following steps for this exercise.

1. Start the MicroStation Development Shell window, and switch to the `C:\Bentley\Program\MicroStation\Mdl\Examples\DimLine` directory on a Windows NT machine.
2. Invoke the Bentley Make utility: `BMAKE DIMLINE`.

    Your screen should scroll with messages similar to those shown below:

```
MicroStation Resource Compiler
    Generating header file (c:\...\mdlexmpl\objects\dimlcmd.h) ... done.
MicroStation Development Language Compiler
MicroStation Development Language Linker
MicroStation Resource Librarian
MicroStation Resource Compiler
MicroStation Resource Librarian
Bentley Systems Make Utility. Version 7.13, Mar 14 1998

[** MDL Examples: c:\...\mdlexmpl\objects\dimlcmd.h <--
C:\...\mdl\examples\dimline\dimlcmd.r **]
c:\...\mdl\bin\rcomp @c:\...\mdlexmpl\objects\temp.cmd

[** MDL Examples: c:\...\mdlexmpl\objects\dimline.mo <--
c:\...\mdl\examples\dimline\dimline.mc **]
c:\...\mdl\bin\mcomp @c:\...\mdlexmpl\objects\temp.cmd
```

```
[** MDL Examples: c:\...\mdlexmpl\objects\dimline.mp <--
c:\...\mdlexmpl\objects\dimline.mo **]
c:\...\mdl\bin\mlink @c:\...\mdlexmpl\objects\temp.cmd

[** MDL Examples: c:\...\mdlexmpl\intermed\dimline.mi <--
c:\...\mdlexmpl\objects\dimlcmd.rsc **]
c:\...\mdl\bin\rlib @c:\...\mdlexmpl\objects\temp.cmd

[** MDL Examples: c:\...\mdlexmpl\rscobj\dimlmsgs.rsc <--
C:\...\mdl\examples\dimline\english\dimlmsgs.r **]
c:\...\mdl\bin\rcomp @c:\...\mdlexmpl\objects\temp.cmd

[** MDL Examples: c:\...\mdlapps\dimline.ma <--
c:\...\mdlexmpl\intermed\dimline.mi **]
c:\...\mdl\bin\rlib @c:\...\mdlexmpl\rscobj\make.opt
```

TIP: If you receive error messages and the application does not compile, you may have a typographical error in your PATH statement, or in the values assigned to either the MS or the BMAKE_OPT environment variables.

After BMAKE runs successfully, you will have the DIMLINE application created in your MDLAPPS subdirectory under the MicroStation base directory.

3. To check out the newly created application, start MicroStation and in the Key-in window type MDL LOAD DIMLINE and the status bar will state that the application loaded successfully.

When DIMLINE is loaded in your MicroStation environment, it makes the following three commands available:

Command	Purpose
Place Arc Dimension	Draws a dimensioned arc by three points
Place Circle Dimension	Draws a dimensioned circle by center point and radius
Place Line Dimension	Draws a dimensioned line

4. Try the commands listed in the above table by entering them in the Key-in window.

DIMLINE is not a polished application. It does not include interactive icons or dialog boxes. However, by compiling it, you've learned what to do to create MDL applications when you download source code.

Understanding the Makefile Syntax

When you start writing MDL applications, you too will write .mke make files. Let's continue using the DIMLINE example code to help you understand the makefile syntax.

On opening the make file ...\mdl\Examples\DimLine\dimline.mke in any ASCII text editor, you will see the code listed below:

```
#-----------------------------------------------
#Define constants specific to this example
#-----------------------------------------------
%if defined (_MakeFilePath)
BaseDir    = $(_MakeFilePath)
%else
BaseDir    = $(MS)/mdl/examples/dimline/
%endif
privateInc = $(BaseDir)

dimlineObjs  = $(o)dimline.mo \
            $(mdlLibs)mdllib.dlo

dimlineRscs  = $(o)dimlcmd.rsc \
            $(o)dimline.mp


#-----------------------------------------------
#   Include mki files for default rules and definitions
#-----------------------------------------------
%include mdl.mki


#-----------------------------------------------------------------------
# Create needed output directories if they don't exist
#-----------------------------------------------------------------------
$(o)$(tstdir): $(o)$(tstdir)

$(rscObjects)$(tstdir): $(rscObjects)$(tstdir)

$(reqdObjs)$(tstdir): $(reqdObjs)$(tstdir)


#-----------------------------------------------
#Compile Dialog Resources
#-----------------------------------------------
$(genSrc)dimlcmd.h     : $(BaseDir)dimlcmd.r

$(o)dimlcmd.rsc: $(BaseDir)dimlcmd.r

$(o)dimline.mo: $(BaseDir)dimline.mc $(privateInc)dimline.h \
  $(genSrc)dimlcmd.h

$(o)dimline.mp: $(dimlineObjs)
$(msg)
> $(o)temp.cmd
```

```
-a$@
-s6000
$(linkOpts)
$(dimlineObjs)
<
$(MLinkCmd) @$(o)temp.cmd
~time

$(reqdObjs)dimline.mi    : $(dimlineRscs)
    $(msg)
> $(o)temp.cmd
-o$@
$(dimlineRscs)
<
$(RLibCmd) @$(o)temp.cmd
    ~time

%include $(BaseDir)dimlrsc.mki
```

The first five lines in the above code check to see if a system environment variable _MakeFilePath exists. If it exists, the variable BaseDir is assigned that value; if not, the variable BaseDir is assigned the value $(MS)/mdl/examples/dimline/.

Note the syntax used to expand a variable's value: namely, $(MS). This syntax is identical to that used when defining configuration variables for workspaces. The operator $(...) expands the value of the variable enclosed in parentheses. Thus, if the variable MS is defined with the value shown in the *Setting Up BMAKE* section in this chapter, the statement $(MS) expands to the value c:\Bentley\Program\MicroStation.

The next statement defines the variable PrivateInc as having the same value as BaseDir. Following this, the variable dimlineObjs is defined as a set of two object files, dimline.mo and mdllib.ml. And the variable dimlineRscs is defined as a set of two resource files, dimlcmd.rsc and dimline.mp.

Note that variables o and mdlLibs are defined in the mdl.mki file located in the directory c:\Bentley\Program\MicroStation\mdl\Include. Also, note the use of the backslash (\). The backslash character designates continuation. Thus, the backslash at the end of the line defining the variable dimlineRscs implies that the definition continues past the current line to the next line. Paths are specified with the slash (/) character.

When you write make files, you will always include the `mdl.mki` file. The easiest way to create your own make files is to make a copy of an existing make file first. Then edit it to fit your application's needs.

Next, a group of statements defines dependencies between files. The syntax for such statements is:

```
list of target files : list of dependent files
      build commands
```

Thus, the statement `$(genSrc)dimlcmd.h : $(BaseDir)dimlcmd.r` means that the file `dimlcmd.h` is derived from `dimlcmd.r`. The build commands use the operator `>` to open a file to write to, and the `<` operator to close the file previously opened. Thus, the statement `>$(o)temp.cmd` creates a file `temp.cmd` in the directory pointed to by the variable `o` and writes the lines that follow the statement into the file, until the `<` operator is encountered.

When header filenames are included on the same line with source filenames, the source file is recompiled, if the header file changes. This happens even if the source file doesn't change. For example, in the following statement:

```
$(o)myline.mo : $(baseDir)myline.mc $(privateInc)mylntxt.h
```

`myline.mc` is compiled if `mylntxt.h` changes.

When a dependency statement in a make file is not followed by build commands, the default rules in the `mdl.mki` file, which tell BMAKE how to generate one type of file from another, are used.

NOTE: Chapter 7 in the MDL Programmer's Guide, also available online as the Windows Help file `MDEHELP.HLP`, is your definitive resource to the syntax of the make file. The time you spend reading and understanding it will be rewarded by a keen understanding of what goes on when BMAKE is run.

MDL Environment Changes

In this section we focus on the changes that have been made to the MDL development environment when compared to previous versions of MicroStation. I assume you have been developing MDL programs before. If MDL programming is new to you, you may safely skip this section.

The MDL interpreter, or virtual machine, in MicroStation/J is almost completely compatible with earlier versions. All existing MDL programs should continue to work unchanged. Only exceptions may be those programs that reference external dynamic link libraries, or DLLs. The external DLLs may need to be recompiled with Microsoft Visual C++ 5.0 for the Windows platform. This is because Bentley switched from using Microsoft Visual C++ 2.0 to version 5.0 when compiling MicroStation/J on Microsoft Windows.

A few changes have been made to the *make* environment in MicroStation/J. These are listed below.

- BMAKEWIN has been renamed BMAKE on the Windows platform. If you were using a batch file to invoke the make process, you will need to change the word BMAKEWIN to BMAKE for the batch file to work.

- If your make file uses the macro definition `linkCmd` that invokes the MDL linker, you will need to replace it with the macro `MLinkCmd` because of changes in the `mdl.mki` file.

- If your make file uses the macro definition `rscLibCmd` that invokes the MDL resource librarian, you will need to replace it with the macro `RLibCmd` because of changes in the `mdl.mki` file.

- If your make file invokes a command to link your application with `mdllib.ml` you will need to change the library file to `mdllib.dlo`. This is because the statically linked library (`.ml`) has been changed to a dynamically linked shared library (`.dlo`).

- If your make file invokes a command to link your application with `rdbmslib.ml` you will need to change the library file to `rdbmslib.dlo`. This is because the statically linked library (`.ml`) has been changed to a dynamically linked shared library (`.dlo`).

Because a new solid modeling kernel is included in MicroStation/J, a new library of functions has been introduced to help you manipulate these elements. This new library of solid modeling functions is `mdlSolid_....` This library of functions includes solid modeling, B-rep topology query, and conversion functions to let you convert between the new Parasolid element type and the older MicroStation element type.

Do you use any undocumented MDL calls in your applications? If so, you will certainly want to test your application in MicroStation/J to make sure it still runs. Does your external DLL file use file functions such as `fopen`, `fclose`, `fwrite`, etc.? If so, you will have to recompile your DLL. If memory allocation functions such as `malloc` and `calloc` in your DLLs are resolved by MicroStation rather than by the Visual C++ run time library, you will have to recompile your application for MicroStation/J.

Programmer's Editor

As noted earlier in this chapter, MicroStation comes with all the tools needed to build MDL applications but one: a programmer's editor. Though you can use MS-DOS Editor or Windows Notepad that come standard on your PC, if you plan to develop seriously with MDL, you will do well to invest in a third-party programmer's editor.

For the Microsoft Windows environment on the PC, the three most prominent editors are: *CodeWright from Premia Corp.* (800-547-9902 or `www.premia.com`); *Multi-Edit from American Cybernetics* (800-899-0100 or `www.amcyber.com`); and *Visual SlickEdit from MicroEdge* (800-934-EDIT or `www.slickedit.com`).

Of the three listed above, SlickEdit runs on the most operating system platforms. There are versions for DOS, Windows, Windows NT (all four hardware platforms: Intel, MIPS, Alpha AXP, PowerPC), OS/2, and several flavors of UNIX.

The key benefits of using a programmer's editor for MDL development are listed below:

- One-keystroke interface to BMAKE for building applications.
- Color coding of MDL language syntax for improved readability.

- Support for version control software.
- Emulation of BRIEF, vi, and Emacs keystrokes for text editing and manipulation.
- Line, column, and character selection.
- Syntax expansion and automatic indenting.
- Programmable language for extending the editor.
- Ability to process compiler error messages.
- Support for function templates to simplify filling parameters to standard functions.
- Ability to invoke online MDL help on desired function from within the editor.

The figure below is a screen shot of Visual SlickEdit with the DIMLINE application source loaded. Though this is a black-and-white shot, you can still see, through shades of gray, how the MDL language syntax is color-coded for significantly improved readability.

Programmer's editors offer such niceties as chroma coding to improve code readability.

This color syntax highlighting, called *chroma coding*, for MDL can be implemented easily in programmer's editors because they all support the C language syntax, and MDL is based on the ANSI C standard. To configure your programmer's editor for MDL chroma coding, specify that it treat files with the .r and .mc extensions as C language source files.

Writing MDL Code

If you have stayed with me thus far, and have successfully compiled the example DIMLINE application, you have made excellent progress in understanding the MDL application compile process. The next step is to understand the event-driven nature of MDL and the coding practices used in most Bentley examples and other sources.

This section is devoted to just these topics. It also presents two simple working MDL applications that you will write from scratch. This will be followed by a discussion of the two resources, command tables and string lists, that you will always use in your applications. Finally, you will be introduced to toolboxes and tool frames.

MicroStation's Event-Driven Nature

If you look back at the structure and syntax of MicroStation User Commands discussed earlier in this book, you will recall that the programs were procedural, or top-down in nature. The programs queried the user for all needed input up front and then proceeded to sequence commands one after another, from top to bottom, in the same exact order, time after time. This is procedural programming reminiscent of the teletype interface.

Contrast the above mode of interaction with how MicroStation works. For example, when you invoke the Place Line command either from the menu bar or the toolbox, and anchor the first point, you receive dynamic feedback via rubber banding on how the line will look. In addition, if you change an active attribute, such as color or weight, using the Primary toolbox or a key-in, the dynamic line changes to reflect your choice right away, without interrupting the active command.

Writing an application that responds to events initiated by a user, such as the data point button click, or text typed in the Key-in window, requires you to think differently from how traditional programs were written. Rather than structuring code monolithically, from top to bottom, the event-driven nature of MicroStation means that you write short functions that are declared as handlers for events. When your application is loaded, it does not take complete control of the system. Instead, it waits for the user to initiate an event and then proceeds to handle it.

In other words, think of MicroStation as a state handler, or an event-driven environment. You decide what user events your application should handle, and how. Then you write functions to handle each event and declare your intentions to MicroStation. When a user initiates an event your application needs to handle, MicroStation invokes the appropriate function from your application. Rather than making the user answer all prompts for data input first, as in a User Command or a MicroStation BASIC program, an MDL application extends MicroStation by registering its functionality as an event handler.

To illustrate this concept, let's create a simple MDL program titled watchme.ma. This application will set up the state handlers in MicroStation to watch you key in a string in the Key-in window, click a data point, or click the Reset button. When you type a string, click a data point or Reset button, it displays a message to that effect on the status bar. Though a simple application, it really explains MicroStation's event-driven nature well.

To create the **watchme** application, use an ASCII text editor to create two files: watchme.mke and watchme.mc. The first file contains the compilation rules. The second contains the MDL source to handle events.

File watchme.mke

```
#************************************************************************+
#                                                                       |
#    Filename:  watchme.mke                                             |
#    Subject:   Make file for the WatchMe application                  |
#    Author:    Ranjit S. Sahai                                        |
#    Publisher: Alpha Press                                            |
#    Book:      Teach Yourself MicroStation/J                          |
#                                                                       |
#    Copyright 1998 Ranjit S. Sahai, All rights reserved               |
```

```
#                                                                       |
#*********************************************************************/

#*********************************************************************+
#    Include files                                                    |
#*********************************************************************/
%include mdl.mki

#*********************************************************************+
#    Application specific variables                                  |
#*********************************************************************/
baseDir      = ./
privateInc   = $(baseDir)
watchMeObjs  = $(o)watchme.mo

#*********************************************************************+
#    Use MCOMP to generate object code                               |
#*********************************************************************/
$(o)watchme.mo:                      $(baseDir)watchme.mc

$(mdlapps)watchme.ma:                $(watchMeObjs)
                                     $(msg)
                                     > $(o)temp.cmd
                                     -a$@
                                     $(linkOpts)
                                     $(watchMeObjs)
                                     <
                                     $(MLinkCmd) @$(o)temp.cmd
                                     @$(deleteCmd) $(o)temp.cmd
                                     ~time
```

File watchme.mc

```
/*********************************************************************+
|                                                                    |
|   Filename:  watchme.mc                                            |
|   Subject:   Demonstrate MDL's event driven nature                 |
|   Author:    Ranjit S. Sahai                                       |
|   Publisher: Alpha Press                                           |
|   Book:      Teach Yourself MicroStation/J                         |
|                                                                    |
|   Copyright 1998 Ranjit S. Sahai, All rights reserved              |
|                                                                    |
+*********************************************************************/

/*********************************************************************+
|   Include Files                                                    |
+*********************************************************************/
#include    <mdl.h>
#include    <mselems.h>
#include    <global.h>
#include    <scanner.h>
#include    <msinputq.h>
```

```
#include    <userfnc.h>

#include    <msoutput.fdf>
#include    <mssystem.fdf>
#include    <msstate.fdf>

/************************************************************************+
|    Function Declarations                                              |
+************************************************************************/
Private void watchEvent_datapoint (Dpoint3d  *, int);
Private void watchEvent_reset (void);
Private void watchEvent_keyin (char *);
Private void watchme_cleanup (void);
Private int  watchme_unload (int);
Private int watchme (void);


/************************************************************************+
|    Function:    main                                                  |
|    Type:        userSystem_loadProgram                                |
|    Purpose:     Initialize the application                            |
|    Description: Display copyright and declare cleanup event handler   |
+************************************************************************/
Private int main (void)
{
    mdlOutput_command ("WatchMe");
    mdlOutput_prompt ("To start, key-in MDL COMMAND watchme");

    mdlSystem_setFunction (SYSTEM_UNLOAD_PROGRAM, watchme_unload);

    return (SUCCESS);
}

/************************************************************************+
|    Function:    watchme_unload                                        |
|    Type:        userSystem_unloadProgram                              |
|    Purpose:     Display message that application unloaded             |
|    Description: Invoked when application is unloaded                   |
+************************************************************************/
Private int watchme_unload
(
    int unloadType      /* => how application unloaded */
)
{
    mdlOutput_error ("WatchMe unloaded");
    return (SUCCESS);
}

/************************************************************************+
|    Function:    watchme                                               |
|    Type:        command handler                                       |
|    Purpose:     declare events to handle                              |
|    Description: Invoked when user keys-in "MDL COMMAND watchme"       |
+************************************************************************/
cmdName watchme (void)
```

```
{
    mdlState_setFunction (STATE_DATAPOINT, watchEvent_datapoint);
    mdlState_setFunction (STATE_RESET, watchEvent_reset);
    mdlState_setFunction (STATE_KEYIN, watchEvent_keyin);
    mdlState_setFunction (STATE_COMMAND_CLEANUP, watchme_cleanup);

    mdlOutput_command ("WatchMe");
    mdlOutput_prompt ("Ready to monitor events  . . .");
    return (SUCCESS);
}

/**********************************************************************+
|   Function:     watchme_cleanup                                     |
|   Type:         userState_commandCleanupEvent                       |
|   Purpose:      display message and turn off dynamics flag          |
|   Description: Invoked when the command is terminated               |
+**********************************************************************/
Private void watchme_cleanup (void)
{
    mdlOutput_error ("WatchMe interrupted and cleanup invoked");
}


/**********************************************************************+
|   Function:     watchEvent_datapoint                                |
|   Type:         userState_datapointEvent                            |
|   Purpose:      display message that datapoint clicked              |
|   Description: Invoked when user clicks datapoint                   |
+**********************************************************************/
Private void watchEvent_datapoint
(
    Dpoint3d  *dpt,      /* <= coordinates of data point clicked */
    int       view       /* <= view number in which data point clicked */
)

{
    mdlOutput_printf (MSG_PROMPT, "You clicked (%g, %g)", dpt->x, dpt->y);
}

/**********************************************************************+
|   Function:     watchEvent_reset                                    |
|   Type:         userState_resetEvent                                |
|   Purpose:      display message that reset clicked                  |
|   Description: Invoked when user clicks reset button                |
+**********************************************************************/
Private void watchEvent_reset (void)
{
    mdlOutput_prompt ("You clicked the Reset button");
}


/**********************************************************************+
|   Function:     watchEvent_keyin                                    |
|   Type:         userState_keyinEvent                                |
|   Purpose:      display keyin string on status bar                  |
|   Description: Invoked when user enters something in Key-in window   |
```

```
+*****************************************************************/
Private void watchEvent_keyin
(
    char *stringP        /* <= string keyed in the Key-in window */
)
{
    /* When nothing is keyed in and <Enter> is pressed */

    if (!*stringP)
        mdlOutput_prompt ("You just pressed <Enter>");

    /* Display the keyin string in ERROR field */

    else
        mdlOutput_printf (MSG_PROMPT, "You keyed-in: %s", stringP);
}
```

Compiling watchme

Though you can save the two files you created above in a directory of your choosing, I have a recommendation. On a hard drive available to you, whether local or network, create a directory tree as shown below.

`\tymsj\dev\mdl\watchme`

It is a good idea to create a directory structure that helps you organize your files in a manner that lends itself to easy retrieval later. Here the root directory name (`tymsj`) is an acronym for this book's title. The next level represents development (`dev`) files, followed by the development language (`mdl`) and the application name (`watchme`). You would store both files `watchme.mke` and `watchme.mc` in this directory.

For those of you who would rather not type the code, I have included the two files for the watchme application on the CD-ROM. The files are located in the `\dev\mdl\watchme` directory. You can copy the two files to your hard drive.

To compile "watchme," take the following steps:

1. Open the MicroStation Development Shell. On Windows NT and Windows 95/98 you do this from the Windows Start button.
2. Navigate to the directory on your hard drive where you saved the two **watchme** application files. You do this by keying in
   `cd c:\tymsj\dev\mdl\watchme` if you followed my suggestion about directory organization.

3. Type BMAKE watchme. If you receive an error message, your system environment has not been properly setup to run BMAKE. See the Setting Up BMAKE section earlier in this chapter.

4. Upon compilation, the application file watchme.ma will have been placed in the directory defined by your MS_MDLAPPS configuration variable. It is now ready to run.

Understanding and Running watchme

To understand how watchme operates, start MicroStation and in the Key-in window type MDL LOAD watchme. This will load the application in memory and prompt you with a message on the status bar. Type MDL COMMAND watchme in the Key-in window to start the application. This needs some explaining.

When you load watchme, MicroStation immediately executes the function called main() in the application. Examine the source code for the main() function in watchme.mc and notice that it uses the mdlOutput_command() and mdlOutput_prompt() functions to display text strings in the command and the prompt areas, respectively, of the status bar. It also declares the watchme_unload() function as the one to invoke when the application is unloaded from memory. Beyond this, the application is not ready to do anything else.

When you key in MDL COMMAND watchme in MicroStation's Key-in window while watchme is loaded, MicroStation looks for a function named watchme() to execute. It knows to do this because the function name has the keyword cmdName preceding it in watchme.mc.

NOTE: The function name that follows MDL COMMAND is case sensitive. It must be typed in exactly as it is defined in the application source code.

When you invoke the function watchme() by keying in MDL COMMAND watchme, the function sets up MicroStation's state handlers to handle four events using the mdlState_setFunction() function. Read the watchme.mc file to notice that in the watchme() function we are declaring that MicroStation use the functions watchEvent_datapoint(), watchEvent_reset(), watchEvent_keyin(), and watchme_cleanup() when the user clicks a data point, the Reset button, keys in a string, or switches to another command. Each of these four functions in turn uses either the `mdlOutput_prompt()` or the `mdlOutput_printf()` function to display appropriate messages on the status bar.

Play with the application. Click a data point, a Reset button, or key in something in the Key-in window and watch the status bar while examining the code in `watchme.mc` to understand why the message displays the way it does. Also, try clicking another tool in MicroStation's Main tool frame and keying in `MDL UNLOAD watchme`.

The real value of **watchme** is to help you understand the event-driven nature of MDL programming. In MDL you do not write code that gets executed sequentially from top to bottom as in User Commands or MicroStation BASIC. You set up the MicroStation state handler such that it associates a function with an event. And you decide what events your application needs to handle and write functions to handle them. When a particular event occurs, the designated function will activate to handle it.

MDL Coding Practices

You will wade through many code examples as you continue to learn MDL programming. Without a knowledge of MDL coding conventions found in most sample code, you will spend more time than you should have to, in understanding code you might download. First, this section discusses software engineering principles and guidelines to help you become a better programmer. Then it introduces coding practices and conventions.

Software engineering principles and coding practices such as those described here are important for obvious reasons. They help you create useful applications and generate understandable, consistent, quality code that is easier to maintain over the long haul.

You typically follow these steps when embarking on a software development project:

- **Define Problem.** This entails describing in detail the problem that needs to be solved. You identify key users and interview them to understand all facets of the problem they are trying to solve. It is important to not even think of a potential solution; just explore the problem in detail. Once you and the user are satisfied with the problem definition, an exploration of alternative solutions and development of a set of requirements that they must satisfy follows.

- **Gather Requirements.** During this phase you develop functional specifications for the proposed software. One approach is to sketch storyboards, or to develop a prototype using demo software, of the proposed software's interface and successively refine it until it clicks with the user. This leads to documenting the requirements the software must meet. Now detail design work that defines the software architecture can begin.

- **Develop Architecture.** Here you define the organization of the program, the modules that will comprise it, and how each will interact with the other. You also define the structure of all data the software will need to use. Other issues you consider during this stage include user input, program output, error handling, memory management, and robustness. You study alternatives and clearly identify reasons for choices made. The architecture developed becomes the foundation for the construction of the software application.

- **Code Modules.** The steps outlined above deal with design issues. This step represents the software construction phase. Here you code and debug functions that perform tasks that solve the problem by meeting requirements identified earlier. This task is obviously the most vital; without it, there can be no software. Because coding takes the most time and is the core asset of your software, you should make it as easy as you possibly can to navigate and understand. Effort you invest in formalizing coding guidelines and following them will pay back handsomely when the time comes to maintain the code. After coding is complete, you perform testing and maintenance.

The steps described above are a broad overview, not an exhaustive list by any means, of the software development process. The sections that follow are concerned exclusively with the last step, that of writing code, also referred to as coding practices.

Directory Name

Your MDL application typically will be made up of several files. Though we used just a source and a make file in our watchme example, you usually will create source, resource, type, header, help, make, and function definition files. It makes sense to keep all files belonging to an application in a separate directory dedicated to that application.

Let us assume you develop applications in several languages, say MDL and Java. One way to organize your code data drive D: is shown below.

```
d:\dev\mdl\appnameA ... d:\dev\mdl\appnameZ

d:\dev\java\appnameA ... d:\dev\java\appnameZ
```

Here the directory d:\dev contains subdirectories mdl and java, which in turn contain subdirectories for individual applications. Code files reside in the appropriate application subdirectory, which in turn may contain other subdirectories. Most sample MDL code you come across will reside in the application root directory, with the string list resource file and the text header file residing in a language-specific subdirectory (English) and the help file in another (Help) subdirectory. Thus, for the hypothetical application **roadtool**, the string list and text header files would be located in:

```
d:\dev\mdl\roadtool\english\
```

and the help files would be located in:

```
d:\dev\mdl\roadtool\help\
```

and all other source, resource, type, header, make, and function definition files would be located in:

```
d:\dev\mdl\roadtool\
```

Maintaining string lists in a separate language-specific directory makes them easy to find and edit for another language when you decide to port your application to go international.

File Names

The names of files in the MDL examples directory (c:\Bentley\Program\MicroStation\MDL\Examples) follow a convention used within Bentley. The convention is logical and you can adopt it for your own code. When writing an application, come up with two names for it: a regular name of eight characters or fewer, and a short name of five characters or fewer. So, for the hypothetical application you could use the regular name of appname and a short name of **appnm**. You then build file names, depending on their content, from the regular and short names as shown in the table below:

Content of File	Type	File Name
Compilation rules	Make	appname.mke
MDL source	Source	appname.mc
Command Table (CMD)	Resource	appnmcmd.r
Text string definitions (TXT)	Header	appnmtxt.h
String list (MSG or STR)	Resource	appnmmsg.r or appnmstr.r
Type (TYP)	Resource	appnmtyp.mt
Dialog box definitions (DLG)	Resource	appnmdlg.r

The above table covers the most frequently used file types. Though such naming is not required, (i.e., the code will compile and work just fine even if you follow no such convention) by following it you ensure consistency and gain the ability to tell the contents of a file simply by looking at its name.

The eight character limit imposed by DOS for filenames is no longer a concern. Dominant operating systems, such as Windows and UNIX, support long filenames. Feel free to revise the above suggestions to accommodate long filenames.

Function Names

The MDL application you develop is likely to have multiple tools. Consider MicroStation's Linear Elements toolbox. It implements several tools: Place SmartLine, Place Line, Place Multi-Line, and others. Each tool, in turn, requires the services of several functions.

A first small step in organizing code is to keep together in sequential order all functions that service a tool. Of course, you should include comment headers at the beginning of each function. This lets you navigate more readily to a desired function as you enhance or debug a tool. A more significant step in organizing code is to formulate and use a function naming guideline.

Charles Simonyi of Microsoft created the Hungarian naming convention that is widely used in C, especially in Windows programming. This convention defines names with three components: base type, prefix, and qualifier.

The standard MDL functions Bentley developed have two major parts separated by the underscore character. The first part in turn has two components. The first component is an `mdl` prefix that designates the function as belonging to the standard library. The second component designates type (`state` for state functions, `Level` for level functions, etc.). There are over a hundred function types in MDL. The second part of a standard MDL function that follows after the underscore character describes what the function does and is usually named with a verb followed by a noun.

For example, the function `mdlState_startPrimitive()` tells us that it is a standard MDL function (the `mdl` prefix) and it belongs to the `state` group of functions. Further, its purpose is to start the primitive element placement state in MicroStation. Note the use of case to separate words.

By formulating a similar set of guidelines for your own MDL development you will:

- Facilitate consistency between projects leading to code that is more readily obvious to others who may later have to revise it.

- Reduce the mental effort you put in while naming new functions.

- Make obvious relationships among related functions, as they will share the same prefix.

- Reduce the chance of invoking the wrong function for a task, as its name will help eliminate obvious errors.

In the spirit of the above discussion, you may wish to adopt the following guidelines to be used in MDL code you write:

- **First and Last Name.** Break function names into two parts separated by the underscore (_) character. This convention is consistent with how standard MDL functions are named.

- **Change Case between Words.** Start each part of a function name in lower case and make upper case the initial letter of the following word.
- **Tool Name as Prefix for First Name.** Let the first word of a function name designate the tool it services. For functions that service several tools, use the application name instead.
- **Service Type as First Name.** Let the type of service the function provides the tool be included in the first part of its name.
- **Action as Last Name.** Let the specific task the function performs, or the data it returns, be the second part of its name. Typically, this will be in the form of a verb followed by a noun. Do recognize that there will be exceptions to this rule.

Let us see how the above guidelines can be put to work. Suppose you are writing code for the Change Elevation tool and have decided on `chel` (for CHange ELevation) as its abbreviation for use as a prefix for function names. Following are some function names you might use:

Function Name	Comments
chelEnv_initCmd	Sets MicroStation environment; initial command
chelQuery_determineCurrElev	Queries element; determine current elevation
chelWrite_setElev	Writes to design file; set elevation
chelDialog_getElev	Interacts with dialog box; get value in elevation field

If you wish to explore the ideas on software engineering presented in this section further, I highly recommend the book, *Code Complete*, by Steve McConnell (Microsoft Press, 1993, $35, ISBN 1556154844). The book is extremely well researched, tightly edited, and written with a passion for the subject that shows.

MDL Function Library

When you write an MDL application, you rely on the over 2,000 built-in functions the MicroStation environment provides. All built-in MDL functions start with the letters `mdl` and let you access the entire functionality of the MicroStation graphics engine.

Because of the sheer number of functions available, they are organized into function groups. Each function group is designated by a group name followed by the underscore (_) character, which is followed by word(s) that describe its functionality. Let's consider an example. The function `mdlArc_create` is a built-in function, as designated by its initial letters `mdl`. It belongs to the `Arc` group of functions, as designated by the word following `mdl` and preceding `_`. Finally, as its name suggests, the purpose of this function is to `create` an arc.

To see a complete listing of all functions, use online help. When you open the file `mdlhelp.hlp` located in `c:\Bentley\Program\MicroStation\Docs` with the Windows Help engine, you will see the MDL Function Index. Click it to list all available MDL functions as shown in the figure below.

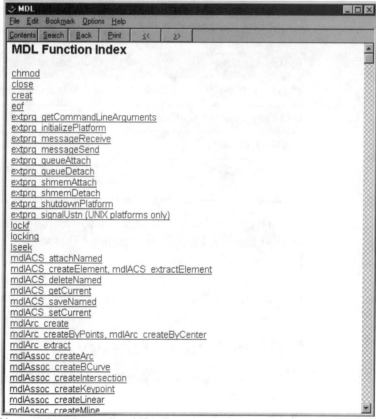

You will find the on-line MDL Function Index invaluable while coding.

Command Tables and Message Lists

Virtually all MDL applications you write will consist of three components: resource files, functional code, and a make file. The application `watchme` was an exception. It did not implement a resource file. Had we wanted to create a toolbox for the application, we would have created a resource file. Resource files have the filename extension `.r` and implement user interface components such as command names for key in, message prompts, toolboxes, dialog boxes, and pull-down menus.

In this section we discuss the basic MDL application resource files. Of the different types of resources you create in an `.r` file, the command table and the message list are the most basic and will be our focus here. Though you can write an application without either a command table or a message list, as we did with `watchme`, it is not good practice to do so. Why? Because you want your users at least to invoke your application commands via a key-in and you want to prompt them for steps they need to take to accomplish the task your command implements.

A command table declaration in a resource file makes available a key-in string to the user so s/he can invoke a command from your application. Essentially, the command table is a hierarchical definition of an application's command syntax that starts from one table and branches out to other tables. A message list is a list of text strings for use as command names, command prompts, error messages, copyright notices, and any other types of messages for display on the status bar, or the Command window, to the user.

Command Tables

The best way to illustrate a command table definition is to look at one. The following code fragment implements the command *Place myLine*:

```
/*
 * Command Table IDs
 */
#define CT_NONE    0
#define CT_LEVEL1 1
#define CT_LEVEL2 2

/*
 *First level of command table
```

```
 */
Table CT_LEVEL1 = {
    {1, CT_LEVEL2, PLACEMENT, REQ, "Place"},
};


/*
 * Second level of command table
 */
Table CT_LEVEL2 = {
    {1, CT_NONE, INHERIT, NONE, "myLine"},
};
```

The #define statements above essentially substitute easy-to-remember text strings for integer IDs required by the Table declaration.

The rest of the code fragment implements two-command words that declare a syntax for key in by user as: *Place myLine*. If we wanted to implement three commands: *Place theirLine*, *Place myLine*, *Place yourLine*, we would need to add just two more lines to the Table CT_LEVEL2 declaration as follows:

```
/*
 * Second level of command table
 */
Table CT_LEVEL2 = {
    {1, CT_NONE, INHERIT, NONE, "myLine"},
    {2, CT_NONE, INHERIT, NONE, "theirLine"},
    {3, CT_NONE, INHERIT, NONE, "yourLine"},
};
```

As you will have noticed, we use MDL's Table resource structure to define an application's command table. This resource structure is defined in the include file rscdefs.h that can be found in MicroStation's mdl/include subdirectory. Consequently, you must #include it in your .r file that defines a command table.

Let's now examine the array of statements that define command words in a table declaration. Each command word statement is enclosed in curly brackets and contains five elements. The first four are of type unsigned long and the fifth is of type char. The following table summarizes each of the five elements:

Element	Description
NUMBER	Used to construct a unique command number for the command implemented.

Element	Description
SUBTABLE ID	Specifies the ID of another command word table, or 0 if no table, to look up for the next word in the command.
COMMAND CLASS	Stores the class of command implemented. The classes are declared in the **cmdclass.h** file in the MDL/INCLUDE subdirectory of MicroStation.
OPTIONS	Declares the bit-field flag for the command word. Commonly used options are DEF for default word from this table, REQ for requires a lookup from a subtable, and NONE for no additional words are needed for command.
COMMAND WORD	Name of command word enclosed in quotation marks as it is to appear in the Tool Settings window.

For complete syntax details of command tables, you are referred to the *MDL Programmer's Guide*, which is also available online as a help file with MicroStation. Look for the section *Building Applications*.

Once you have written the command table syntax for your application in an `.r` file, it is compiled by `rcomp` with the `-h` command line option to generate a header file to be included in your `.mc` file. For example, to compile the `myline.r` file directly with `rcomp`, you would need to be in the directory where the file resides and key in:

`rcomp -h -ic:\ bentley\program\ustation\mdl\include myline.r`

This command will generate the `myline.h` header file and compile the resource code into the `myline.rsc` file. You will notice that the base name of the `.h` and the `.rsc` output files is the same as the `.r` input file. The `myline.h` file generated contains command numbers assigned using the `#define` statement to `CMD_...` text strings from your command table. The content of the `.h` file is:

```
#define CMD_PLACE              0x01000000  /* PLACEMENT */
#define CMD_PLACE_MYLINE       0x01010000  /* PLACEMENT */
```

Now that you have command numbers for your applications commands, how do you use them? Much like we used the keyword `cmdName` in the `watchme` application, MDL implements a keyword `cmdNumber`. You will see an example of this just a little later. You use the keyword `cmdNumber` to tie in a command number that represents a command entry syntax to a function in your application.

Message Lists

As its name suggests, a message list is a list of messages. MDL implements a separate resource class called `MessageList` for managing messages you need to display in your application. You can create as many message lists as you need and each will have its own unique integer ID. Within a message list is an array of text strings, each with an associated integer message number. Of all message lists you define, one can be declared as a command name list, and one as a prompt message list. Following is a code fragment that defines three message lists:

```
/*
 * Message list for application command names
 */
MessageList CMD_NAMES = {
    {
        {CMDID_PlaceLine, "Place Line"},
        {CMDID_DeleteElement, "Delete Element"},
    }
};


/*
 * Message list for prompts
 */
MessageList PROMPTS = {
    {
        {PRID_Line_fv, "Enter first vertex"},
        {PRID_Line_nv, "Enter next vertex or reset to start over"},
        {PRID_Delete_sel, "Identify element to delete"},
        {PRID_Delete_accept, "Accept with Data point or Reset to reject"},
    }
};


/*
 * Message list for general messages
 */
MessageList GEN = {
    {
        {GENID_copyright, "Copyright (1998) Ranjit S. Sahai"},
        {GENID_appName, "My Application loaded"},
    }
};
```

In the above code, CMD_NAMES, PROMPTS, and GEN are message list identifiers, and CMDID_PlaceLine, CMDID_DeleteElement, PRID_Line_fv, PRID_Line_nv, PRID_Delete_sel, PRID_Delete_accept, GENID_copyright, and GENID_appName are message number identifiers. These are assigned integer values in a separate .h file that must be included in the .r message list resource file and the .mc application code file. Again, you will see this in the next application we build.

To register CMD_NAMES as the command names MessageList and PROMPTS as the command prompt MessageList you would use the following statement in your application's main() function:

```
mdlState_registerStringIds(CMD_NAMES, PROMPTS);
```

Once thus registered, you can simply provide the message number identifiers from the two lists to MDL State functions such as mdlState_startPrimitive and mdlState_startModifyCommand. If you need to display a message in a specific field on the MicroStation Command window or the status bar, you can use the mdlOutput_rscPrintf function with message list and message number identifiers as parameters.

Toolboxes and Tool Frames

All MDL application you write should include at least the two basic resources discussed above: command tables and message lists. The next type of resource you will want to learn are toolboxes and tool frames. Toolboxes used to be known as tool palettes or icon palettes in MicroStation version 4 and version 5. Toolboxes will be the user's primary means of invoking commands from your applications. Tool frames are nothing more than a collection of toolboxes. MicroStation's Main tool frame is an example.

There are three steps to creating a toolbox. First you create icons. Then you define a toolbox resource. Finally, you invoke the toolbox from within your MDL code. In keeping with these steps, this section is organized into three subsections.

Creating Icons

The best way to illustrate how you create icons is to demonstrate it. You will want to load MicroStation on your computer at this point. It does not matter which design file you open while loading MicroStation. Of course, to be safe, you will want to open a scratch design file.

Once MicroStation is loaded, key in MDL LOAD ICONEDIT in the Key-in window. This will open the Icon Editor.

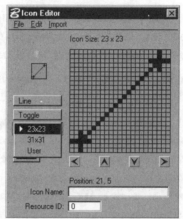

Use the Icon Editor to create icons for toolboxes.

Another way of invoking the Icon Editor is by choosing the MDE workspace when loading MicroStation, and then selecting Icon Editor from the Tools menu of that workspace.

Before you draw your first icon, you will want to create an empty container resource file for it. You do this by selecting New File from the Icon Editor's File menu. This opens up the New Resource File dialog box. In this dialog box navigate to your application's directory, for example, c:\dev\mdl\myline. Once in the directory, assign the name icons to the resource file you are about to create by keying it in the Files field of the dialog box. On clicking the OK button, the dialog box closes and the name of the new resource file appears in the title of the Icon Editor. Now you have the ability to save icons you draw with the Icon Editor.

As you will notice in the figure above, there are two standard sizes for MicroStation icons: 23X23 and 31X31. These sizes are in pixels and correspond to the Small or Large option for Tool Size in the Preferences dialog box you invoke from MicroStation's Workspace menu. When you draw icons for your applications, make sure you draw both the small

(23X23) and large (31X31) versions so your application can accommodate any preference setting for the Tool Size a user may have selected.

Let's draw two icons: one small and one large for the *Place myLine* command. You are free to draw the icons in any way you want. It might be helpful for you to know that Icon Editor includes the ability to capture onscreen graphics or cells in a design file using the Import menu. Once you draw an icon, save it before moving to the next one. The figure below shows the pattern I drew for the small icon for the *Place myLine* command. The figure also shows the icon name and resource IDs I assigned to the icons.

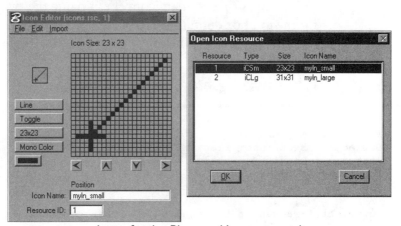

Icons for the Place myLine command.

To create consistent and meaningful icons, you do need some graphic design background. If you work for a commercial developer, a designated person probably designs icons. For purposes of this chapter, do not worry about your drawing skills. No matter what you draw, it will be fine. Our purpose is simply to understand how to create toolboxes, not to worry about the look of icons.

Once you have drawn the icons and saved them in the `icons.rsc` file, you use the application `sourcer.ma` to generate code for the icon definitions. You do this by keying in MDL LOAD SOURCER, or by selecting Generate Resource Source from the Tools menu of the MDE workspace. This opens the Generate Resource Source dialog box. Navigate to the directory where you saved the `icons.rsc` file. Highlight the file and click the Add button to add the resource to the list of files to process. When you click the OK button in the dialog box, Sourcer generates from `icons.rsc` three files: `icons.h`, `icons.r`, and `iconstxt.h`.

Feel free to browse through the three files generated by Sourcer using your text editor. In the next section, we see how to use this source in a toolbox resource definition.

Defining the Toolbox Resource

From a programmer's standpoint, a toolbox resource definition is no different from a dialog box resource definition. Toolboxes are essentially dialog boxes that contain icons. Let's name the two new files we create for the toolbox definition as: `mylndlg.h` and `mylndlg.r`. The code for the two files is presented below.

File mylndlg.h

```
/*********************************************************************+
|                                                                    |
|    Filename:  mylndlg.h                                            |
|    Subject:   Header for Place MyLine dialog resource             |
|    Author:    Ranjit S. Sahai                                     |
|    Publisher: Alpha Press                                         |
|    Book:      Teach Yourself MicroStation/J                       |
|                                                                    |
|    Copyright 1998 Ranjit S. Sahai, All rights reserved            |
|                                                                    |
+*********************************************************************/

/*********************************************************************+
|    Local Defines                                                   |
+*********************************************************************/

/* --- Dialog Box Resource IDs for Toolboxes --- */
#define DIALOGID_Toolbox                1

/* --- Icon Ids --- */
#define ICONID_Place_myLine             1
```

File mylndlg.r

```
/*********************************************************************+
|                                                                    |
|    Filename:  mylndlg.r                                            |
|    Subject:   Dialog resource file for Place MyLine               |
|    Author:    Ranjit S. Sahai                                     |
```

```
|    Publisher: Alpha Press                                            |
|    Book:      Teach Yourself MicroStation/J                          |
|                                                                      |
|    Copyright 1998 Ranjit S. Sahai, All rights reserved              |
|                                                                      |
+**********************************************************************/


/**********************************************************************+
|    Include Files                                                     |
+**********************************************************************/
#include <rscdefs.h>
#include <cmdclass.h>
#include <dlogbox.h>
#include <dlogids.h>
#include <keys.h>

#include "mylndlg.h"
#include "mylntxt.h"
#include "myline.h"

/**********************************************************************+
|    Dialogbox Resources                                               |
+**********************************************************************/
DialogBoxRsc DIALOGID_Toolbox =
{
   DIALOGATTR_TOOLBOXCOMMON, 0, 0,
   NOHELP, MHELP, NOHOOK, NOPARENTID, "",
   {
   {{0, 0, 0, 0}, ToolBox, DIALOGID_Toolbox, ON, 0, "", ""},
   }
};

/**********************************************************************+
|    Toolbox Item Resources                                            |
+**********************************************************************/
DItem_ToolBoxRsc DIALOGID_Toolbox =
{
   NOHELP, MHELPTOPIC, NOHOOK, NOARG, 0, "Place myLine",
   {
      {{0, 0, 0, 0}, IconCmd, ICONID_Place_myLine, ON, 0, "", ""},
   }
};

/**********************************************************************+
|    Icon Command Item Resources                                       |
+**********************************************************************/
DItem_IconCmdRsc ICONID_Place_myLine =
{
   NOHELP, MHELP, 0,
   CMD_PLACE_MYLINE, OTASKID, "", "",
   {
   }
}
extendedAttributes
```

```
{{
    /* extended attribute type Text for balloon and flyover help */
    {EXTATTR_FLYTEXT, "Place myLine simulates the Place Line command"},
    {EXTATTR_BALLOON, "Place myLine"},
}};

/***********************************************************************+
|    Icon Resources                                                     |
+***********************************************************************/
IconCmdSmallRsc ICONID_Place_myLine =
    {
    23,    23,    FORMAT_MONOBITMAP,    BLACK_INDEX, ìicsm_placeMyLineî,
        {
        0x00, 0x00, 0x00, 0x00, 0x00, 0x08, 0x00, 0x00,
        0x20, 0x00, 0x00, 0x80, 0x00, 0x02, 0x00, 0x00,
        0x08, 0x00, 0x00, 0x20, 0x00, 0x00, 0x80, 0x00,
        0x02, 0x00, 0x00, 0x08, 0x00, 0x00, 0x20, 0x00,
        0x00, 0x80, 0x00, 0x02, 0x00, 0x00, 0x08, 0x00,
        0x00, 0x20, 0x00, 0x04, 0x80, 0x00, 0x0a, 0x00,
        0x00, 0x18, 0x00, 0x01, 0xfc, 0x00, 0x00, 0x40,
        0x00, 0x00, 0x80, 0x00, 0x01, 0x00, 0x00, 0x00,
        0x00, 0x00, 0x00,
        }
    };

IconCmdLargeRsc ICONID_Place_myLine =
    {
    31,    31,    FORMAT_MONOBITMAP,    BLACK_INDEX, ìiclg_placeMyLineî,
        {
        0x00, 0x00, 0x00, 0x00, 0x00, 0x00, 0x00, 0x08,
        0x00, 0x00, 0x00, 0x20, 0x00, 0x00, 0x00, 0x80,
        0x00, 0x00, 0x02, 0x00, 0x00, 0x00, 0x08, 0x00,
        0x00, 0x00, 0x20, 0x00, 0x00, 0x00, 0x80, 0x00,
        0x00, 0x02, 0x00, 0x00, 0x00, 0x08, 0x00, 0x00,
        0x00, 0x20, 0x00, 0x00, 0x00, 0x80, 0x00, 0x00,
        0x02, 0x00, 0x00, 0x00, 0x08, 0x00, 0x00, 0x00,
        0x20, 0x00, 0x00, 0x00, 0x80, 0x00, 0x00, 0x02,
        0x00, 0x00, 0x00, 0x08, 0x00, 0x00, 0x00, 0x20,
        0x00, 0x00, 0x00, 0x80, 0x00, 0x00, 0x02, 0x00,
        0x00, 0x00, 0x08, 0x00, 0x00, 0x01, 0x20, 0x00,
        0x00, 0x02, 0x80, 0x00, 0x00, 0x06, 0x00, 0x00,
        0x00, 0x7f, 0x00, 0x00, 0x00, 0x10, 0x00, 0x00,
        0x00, 0x20, 0x00, 0x00, 0x40, 0x00, 0x00, 0x00,
        0x00, 0x00, 0x00, 0x00, 0x00, 0x00, 0x00, 0x00,
        0x00,
        }
    };
```

In `myIndlg.h` we `#define` two text strings as integer IDs for a toolbox and an icon. In `myIndlg.r` we first define a `DialogBoxRsc` as containing a toolbox item. Then we define the `DItem_ToolBoxRsc` as containing an icon command. Then we define the `DItem_IconCmdRsc` as tied to the command table entry *Place myLine* (CMD_PLACE_MYLINE). Finally, we define the small and large icon item resource definitions. You will notice that these are copied from the icons.r file that Sourcer had generated.

To understand the dialog box, toolbox, and icon resource definition syntax used above, you will want to read chapter 16 from the *MDL Programmer's Guide*. Also, chapter 1 from the *MDL Supplement Guide* will help you understand the extended attributes for flyover help and balloon text implemented in MicroStation 95 and later (SE and /J).

Invoking the Toolbox

With the toolbox resources defined, it's now available for use in your application code. To have the toolbox opened the moment your application is loaded, you will use the mdlDialog_open function in your application's main() function. See the following code fragment from mymline.mc:

```
Private void main ()
{
    RscFileHandle rfHandle;

    if((mdlParse_loadCommandTable (NULL)) == NULL)
        mdlOutput_error ("Could not load the Command Table");

    mdlResource_openFile (&rfHandle, NULL, RSC_READONLY);
    mdlState_registerStringIds(ML, ML);
    mdlDialog_open (NULL, DIALOGID_Toolbox);
}
```

Now when myLine is loaded, a toolbox displaying the icon you had drawn opens, making it much easier for the user to invoke the *Place myLine* command.

The Place myLine tool in action.

Defining the Tool Frame Resource

In this section, we examine the structure of a tool frame. But before we move on, let us spend a little time on the difference between a toolbox and a tool frame.

A *toolbox* is a rectangular array of icons in which all icons are visible at all times. It is also resizable. A *tool frame*, on the other hand, is a rectangular array of toolboxes in which only one icon from each toolbox is visible. It is fixed in height and width. Actually, a tool frame can contain a combination of icons and toolboxes. The tiny arrowhead on the bottom right-hand corner of an icon in a tool frame indicates that this icon represents a toolbox that can be torn away by dragging it. If you click such an icon and hold the mouse button down, a row of icons pops up from it.

If you pull down MicroStation's Tools menu, you will notice that the menu entries Main, 3D, and DD Design have little black triangles next to them. This implies that each of these offers a cascading submenu. It also means that each of these three is a tool frame.

Main, 3D, and DD Design are tool frames, as
indicated by the presence of cascading submenus.

For MDL utilities that perform a dozen or fewer functions, a toolbox is all you need. But if your application is substantial and you need to implement multiple toolboxes, you will want to create a tool frame in which to pack your toolboxes. The primary benefit of a tool frame is its compact size, despite the very large number of icons, or tools, that it can make accessible. MicroStation's Main tool frame is a perfect example of this concept; it incorporates seventeen toolboxes and one icon.

Obviously, before you create a tool frame, you need to have designed toolboxes for your application.

To create a tool frame, you first define a dialog box resource for it using the DialogboxRsc structure, much like we did for a toolbox. The difference between the two is in the dialog box attributes used and the item type (IconCmdFrameX as opposed to ToolBox) included in its declaration. Refer to the two code fragments below for the code used to define a tool frame and a toolbox, and note the differences in the definition of each.

Code Fragment Defining a Tool Frame Resource

```
/********************************************************************+
|    Dialogbox Resource for a Toolframe                              |
+********************************************************************/
DialogBoxRsc DIALOGID_Toolframe =
{
   DIALOGATTR_DEFAULT | DIALOGATTR_NORIGHTICONS | DIALOGATTR_DOCKABLE, 0, 0,
   NOHELP, MHELP, NOHOOK, NOPARENTID, "Main Toolframe",
   {
   {{0, 0, 0, 0}, IconCmdFrameX, DIALOGID_Toolframe, ON, 0, "", ""},
   }
};

/********************************************************************+
|    Toolframe to have 2x1 size for 2 toolboxes                      |
+********************************************************************/
DItem_IconCmdFrameXRsc DIALOGID_Toolframe =
{
   2, 1, NOHELP, MHELP, 0, "",
   {
      {Toolbox, DIALOGID_Toolbox1, ""},
      {Toolbox, DIALOGID_Toolbox2, ""},
   }
};
```

Code Fragment Defining a Toolbox Resource

```
/***********************************************************************+
|    Dialogbox Resources for two toolboxes                              |
+***********************************************************************/
DialogBoxRsc DIALOGID_Toolbox1 =
{
    DIALOGATTR_TOOLBOXCOMMON, 0, 0,
    NOHELP, MHELP, NOHOOK, NOPARENTID, "",
    {
    {{0, 0, 0, 0}, ToolBox, DIALOGID_Toolbox1, ON, 0, "", ""},
    }
};

DialogBoxRsc DIALOGID_Toolbox2 =
{
    DIALOGATTR_TOOLBOXCOMMON, 0, 0,
    NOHELP, MHELP, NOHOOK, NOPARENTID, "",
    {
    {{0, 0, 0, 0}, ToolBox, DIALOGID_Toolbox2, ON, 0, "", ""},
    }
};


/***********************************************************************+
|    Toolbox Item Resources                                             |
+***********************************************************************/
DItem_ToolBoxRsc DIALOGID_Toolbox1 =
{
    NOHELP, MHELPTOPIC, NOHOOK, NOARG, 0, "Toolbox1",
    {
        {{0, 0, 0, 0}, IconCmd, ICONID_icon1, ON, 0, "", ""},
        {{0, 0, 0, 0}, IconCmd, ICONID_icon2, ON, 0, "", ""},
        {{0, 0, 0, 0}, IconCmd, ICONID_icon3, ON, 0, "", ""},
    }
};

DItem_ToolBoxRsc DIALOGID_Toolbox2 =
{
    NOHELP, MHELPTOPIC, NOHOOK, NOARG, 0, "Toolbox2",
    {
        {{0, 0, 0, 0}, IconCmd, ICONID_icon4, ON, 0, "", ""},
        {{0, 0, 0, 0}, IconCmd, ICONID_icon5, ON, 0, "", ""},
        {{0, 0, 0, 0}, IconCmd, ICONID_icon6, ON, 0, "", ""},
    }
};
```

Putting It All to Work (Example: Place myLine)

In this section we will walk through the creation of a simple MDL application, let us call it myLine, to help tie in all the basics we have learned so far. This application, as its name suggests, emulates MicroStation's *Place Line* command. Though myLine adds no additional functionality to MicroStation, understanding how it is written is vital to your being able to build your own custom MDL programs.

When you take on the task of creating original MDL applications, you typically will go through several steps described here. The first task is, of course, to identify what it is your application is supposed to do, along with the objects it will need to create and manipulate. At this time, you are thinking from a user's perspective. The more user oriented your approach, the more likely your application will get used.

Next, you must identify which MicroStation elements and settings your application objects are to use, and the commands your application needs to implement. At this time, you also will want to identify user interface elements to be used by your application.

Finally, you will write the code for the various resources (command table, message lists, toolboxes, menus, and dialog boxes) and the functional aspects of your application. Then it is build and test. If your application is for in-house use, you will be able to get by without creating documentation and help. But if you wish to market your application, you will need to write documentation and incorporate online help capabilities.

Identify Functionality

The purpose of the application myline.ma is to draw a line from the first data point to the second data point. Upon invocation it should open a toolbox containing its icon. When the user clicks this icon, the application should prompt for the start point of the line. When the start point is clicked, it should prompt for the end point and display the line in dynamics. When the second data point is clicked, a line element passing through the first and second data points should be added to the design file. The command should continue asking for the next data point until the user clicks the Reset button, at which point the command will start over.

Design Structure

To provide the above functionality, we could design a four-function structure for the application.

The first function would be invoked when the user clicked the icon, or keyed in a command. This function basically would declare to MicroStation the names of functions you have written to handle data point and reset events.

The second function would process the first data point event, which is to store the coordinates of the start point of the line. It also would declare functions to process the next data point and cursor movements for display of dynamics.

The third function would process all mouse movements, after the first data point event, to provide the rubberbanding effect.

The fourth function would process the second data point, or the accept event, by adding a line element to the design file.

myline_placeCmd()
> *responds to the key-in "Place Myline"*
> *declares itself as the handler for the Reset button*
> *declares "myline_getStartPoint()" as the handler for the first data point*

myline_getStartPoint()
> *responds to the first data point*
> *stores the first data point coordinates*
> *declares "myline_rubberband()" as the handler for cursor movements*
> *declares "myline_acceptEndPoint()" as the handler for the next data point*

myline_rubberband()
> *responds to cursor movements*
> *creates a line element by calling "myline_create()" and draws it onscreen*

myline_acceptEndPoint()
> *responds to the next data point*
> *creates a line element by calling "myline_create()"*
> *adds the line element to the design file*

Application myline.ma relies on four functions to provide needed functionality.

As far as resources go, we will implement only a single icon toolbox linked to the key-in command: Place myLine. So a command table resource is required. The standard MDL function mdlLine_create() will be used to draw the line element.

Write Code and Build Application

To follow along with the coding process, I suggest you create a new directory on your hard drive for this application. In conformance to the directory naming concept discussed earlier, you may want to use the following directory name:

c:\tymsj\dev\mdl\myline

The myline.ma application will have five source files and one make file. Code for each file is listed below.

Header File mylntxt.h

```
/*
 * File: mylntxt.h
 * Description: Define informative text strings for use in
 *              lieu of integer IDs in mdlState_... functions
 * Subject: Code for the "MDL Class 101 Part 4 of 4" article
 * Author: Ranjit S. Sahai, PE
 */

/*
 * Descriptive text strings for command IDs
 */
#define TXTCMDID_myLine                 1
#define TXTCMDID_startPrompt            2

/*
 * Descriptive text strings for prompt IDs
 */
#define TXTPROMPTID_firstPoint          101
#define TXTPROMPTID_secondPoint         102

/*
 * Descriptive text strings for message Lists
 */
#define ML                              1
```

Resource File mylncmd.r

```
/*
 * File: myline.r
 * Description: Command Table and Message List definitions
```

```
 *                  for the MYLINE application
 * Subject: Code for the "MDL Class 101 Part 4 of 4" article
 * Author: Ranjit S. Sahai, PE
 */

/*
 * Process command table related header files from the MDL/INCLUDE
 * directory and the base code directory
 */
#include <rscdefs.h>
#include <cmdclass.h>

#include "mylntxt.h"

/*
 * Command Table IDs
 */
#define CT_NONE    0
#define CT_LEVEL1  1
#define CT_LEVEL2  2

/*
 *First level of command table
 */
Table CT_LEVEL1 = {
    {1, CT_LEVEL2, PLACEMENT, REQ, "Place"},
};

/*
 * Second level of command table
 */
Table CT_LEVEL2 = {
    {1, CT_NONE, INHERIT, NONE, "myLine"},
};
```

Resource File mylnstr.r

```
/*
 * Message list
 */
MessageList ML = {
    {
        {TXTCMDID_myLine, "Place myLine"},
        {TXTCMDID_startPrompt, "Key in PLACE MYLINE to start"},
        {TXTPROMPTID_firstPoint, "Enter first vertex"},
        {TXTPROMPTID_secondPoint, "Enter next vertex or reset to start over"},
    }
};
```

Resource File mylndlg.r

```
/*
```

```
 * Message list
 */
MessageList ML = {
    {
        {TXTCMDID_myLine, "Place myLine"},
        {TXTCMDID_startPrompt, "Key in PLACE MYLINE to start"},
        {TXTPROMPTID_firstPoint, "Enter first vertex"},
        {TXTPROMPTID_secondPoint, "Enter next vertex or reset to start over"},
    }
};
```

MDL Source File myline.mc

```
/*
 * File: myline.mc
 * Description: This MDL application simulates the Place Line command
 * Subject: Code for the "MDL Class 101 Part 4 of 4" article
 * Author: Ranjit S. Sahai, PE
 */

/*
 * Standard header files from the MDL/INCLUDE directory
 */
#include <mdl.h>
#include <mdlerrs.h>
#include <mselems.h>
#include <rscdefs.h>
#include <userfnc.h>

#include <msstate.fdf>
#include <mselemen.fdf>
#include <msparse.fdf>
#include <msoutput.fdf>
#include <msrsrc.fdf>
#include <ditemlib.fdf>

/*
 * Local header files for Command Table (cmd) and text string IDs (txt)
 */
#include "myline.h"
#include "mylntxt.h"

/*
 * Declare endPoints as a Dpoint3d array for storing end-points of the line
 */
Private Dpoint3d endPoints[2];

/*
 * Declare functions used in the application
 */
Private void mylinePlaceCmd (void),
            mylineGetStartPoint (Dpoint3d *firstP),
            mylineRubberband (Dpoint3d *cursorP),
```

```
                    mylineAcceptEndPoint (Dpoint3d *nextP);

/*
 * Load the command table and prompt user how to start myLine
 */
Private void main ()
{
   RscFileHandle rfHandle;

   if((mdlParse_loadCommandTable (NULL)) == NULL)
      mdlOutput_error ("Could not load the Command Table");

   mdlResource_openFile (&rfHandle, NULL, RSC_READONLY);
   mdlState_registerStringIds(ML, ML);

   mdlOutput_rscPrintf(MSG_COMMAND, NULL, ML, TXTCMDID_startPrompt);
}


/*
 * When user keys in "Place myLine" in the key-in window, declare functions
 * to handle data point and reset button events
 */
Private void mylinePlaceCmd ()
cmdNumber CMD_PLACE_MYLINE
{
   mdlState_startPrimitive (mylineGetStartPoint, mylinePlaceCmd,
                            TXTCMDID_myLine, TXTPROMPTID_firstPoint);
}


/*
 * Store line start point and declare functions to handle next data point
 * and cursor movement, i.e. dynamic update
 */
Private void mylineGetStartPoint (Dpoint3d *firstPoint)
{
   endPoints[0] = *firstPoint;
   mdlState_setFunction (STATE_DATAPOINT, mylineAcceptEndPoint);
   mdlState_dynamicUpdate (mylineRubberband, FALSE);
   mdlOutput_rscPrintf (MSG_PROMPT, NULL, ML, TXTPROMPTID_secondPoint);
}


/*
 * Display line from first data point to cursor location for
 * rubberband line effect
 */
Private void mylineRubberband (Dpoint3d *movingCursor)
{
   endPoints[1] = *movingCursor;
   mdlLine_create (dgnBuf, NULL, endPoints);
}


/*
 * The second data point function to accept line creation
 */
```

```
Private void mylineAcceptEndPoint (Dpoint3d *nextPoint)
{
    MSElement el;
    endPoints[1] = *nextPoint;
    mdlLine_create (&el, NULL, endPoints);
    mdlElement_display (&el, NORMALDRAW);
    mdlElement_add (&el);
    endPoints[0] = endPoints[1];
}
```

Make File to Build Application myline.mke

```
#-------------------------------------------------
#      Define constants specific to myLine
#-------------------------------------------------
BaseDir    = ./
privateInc = $(BaseDir)

myLineObjs = $(o)myline.mo

myLineRscs = $(o)myline.rsc \
             $(o)myline.mp


#-------------------------------------------------
#   mdl.mki include file for default rules and
#   definitions, such as:
#      genSrc = $(MS)/mdl/objects/
#          o = $(MS)/mdl/objects/
#-------------------------------------------------
%include mdl.mki

#-------------------------------------------------
#                Compile Resources
#-------------------------------------------------
$(genSrc)myline.h      : $(BaseDir)myline.r

$(o)myline.rsc         : $(BaseDir)myline.r


#-------------------------------------------------
#            Compile Functional Code
#-------------------------------------------------
$(o)myline.mo          : $(BaseDir)myline.mc \
                         $(privateInc)mylntxt.h \
                         $(genSrc)myline.h

$(o)myline.mp          : $(myLineObjs)
$(msg)
> $(o)temp.cmd
-a$@
$(linkOpts)
$(myLineObjs)
<
$(linkCmd) @$(o)temp.cmd
```

```
~time

#--------------------------------------------
#                Build Application
#--------------------------------------------
$(mdlapps)myline.ma    : $(myLineRscs)
$(msg)
> $(o)make.opt
-o$@
$(myLineRscs)
<
$(rscLibCmd) @$(o)make.opt
~time
```

Understanding myline.ma

The application header file mylntxt.h defines two text string IDs,
TXTCMDID_myLine and TXTPROMPTID_firstPoint, for use in the message
list definition and by message display functions. The purpose is simply
code readability. You might as well have used the integers the string IDs
are defined as, thus obviating the need for this header file.

The application resource file myline.r defines the application command
table (the Place myLine key-in) and the message list to be used for
display of command name and prompt on the status bar. A mix of both
hard coded strings and message list IDs have been used in myline.mc for
illustration purposes. If you plan to port your application to other
languages, you will do well to use message lists exclusively. Do note that
a second application header file myline.h that defines constants for the
command table is generated during the compile process by BMAKE.

The application code in myline.mc implements five functions. The main
function is used for initialization tasks such as loading the command
table and informing the user what to do to initiate a command. The
mylinePlaceCmd function is assigned to the Place myLine key-in, as seen
by the syntax cmdNumber CMD_PLACE_MYLINE. All it does is declare
functions to handle the data point and the Reset button events. The
mylineGetStartPoint function stores the coordinates of the data point
clicked, prompts the user for the next data point, and declares two other
functions as data point and dynamics handlers. The mylineRubberband
function, being the dynamics handler function, is called whenever the
cursor moves. It invokes the mdlLine_create function to draw a line on
the screen between the start point stored and the moving cursor point.

The `mylineAcceptEndPoint` function stores the second data point coordinates and invokes MDL functions to create a line element, display it, and store it in the design file.

> **NOTE:** `dgnBuf` is a MicroStation global variable of type `MSElement`. It stores the currently displayed element.

Finally, the make file `myline.mke` is used to automate the process of building the application. Simply key in `BMAKE MYLINE.MKE` while in the source code directory and the compiled application will be saved automatically in MicroStation's MDLAPPS subdirectory. If you have trouble, ensure that the proper system environment variables are set as outlined in the second installment of this series.

Once you have built the application, load it by keying in `MDL LOAD MYLINE` in MicroStation's Key-in window. Watch the status bar for prompts to understand where message from your code display. Key in `PLACE MYLINE` to activate the command.

Introducing RSTools LE

Your background in C language programming, along with the concepts and details presented in this chapter empower you to venture out on your own. Also, you are in a better position to read and understand code you download or inherit.

In this section, you are introduced to an MDL application called *RS Tools LE*. It is a general-purpose drafting utility that automates several routine tasks. A compiled version of the application for the Microsoft Windows platform is included free in appreciation for your investment in this book. The application is located on the CD-ROM in the following directory:

`\mdlapps`

If you like the application and want the source code to learn from or to modify for your needs, order it from Alpha Press. An order form is included in the back.

To install *RS Tools LE* on your computer, copy the file `rstools.ma` from the CD-ROM to MicroStation's MDLAPPS subdirectory on your computer. To load the application, key in `MDL LOAD RSTOOLS`, or use the MDL dialog box from the Utilities menu.

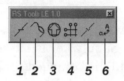

1. *Place BreakLine*
2. *Place Pipend*
3. *Place North*
4. *Place Grid*
5. *Place Utility*
6. *Change Case*

The RS Tools LE application is included free with this book.

The rest of this section introduces you to each tool. You learn the purpose of the tool and its options in the Tool Settings window. You may find the tools useful in your day-to-day design tasks.

Place BreakLine

If the word breakline is unfamiliar, looking it up in a dictionary will most likely prove fruitless. But if you've been working with drawings in the AEC (architecture, engineering, and construction) industry, you probably use the word all the time.

What exactly is a breakline? In the technical drafting industry, *breakline* refers to a symbol that designates the uninterrupted continuation of an object past the break shown. The breakline symbol is a straight line with a squiggle in its center. The symbol is typically drawn perpendicular to and extending slightly past the limits of a long object to designate that the object continues past the breakline.

You may see the breakline symbol on the plan view of a long retaining wall, the elevation of a long structural beam, or another situation. See the figure below for the typical use of a breakline. The breaklines on each end of this retaining wall elevation imply that the wall continues past the break and is not completely shown.

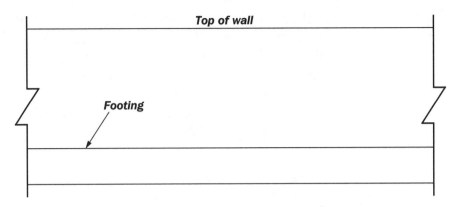

The breakline symbols designate that the wall continues past the breaks shown.

The size or shape of the squiggle in the center of the breakline is not defined by a standard. Almost everyone draws it a little differently.

By using the *Place BreakLine* tool, you can standardize how the symbol is drawn throughout your company. Also, the tool will make the symbol's placement an efficient two-click task.

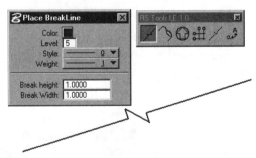

Click the Place BreakLine icon or key in PLACE BREAKLINE to invoke it. The size of the break symbol is determined by the text height field in the Tool Settings window.

Compare the two data points used by the tool with the six data points required to draw the breakline components individually. Not to mention the computations required to ensure the symbol is symmetrical and drawn neatly.

Some of you may be using cells to place breakline symbols. You either scale the cell to fit between data points, or insert it within a line, rotate it, and trim the line around it. The first approach leads to breakline symbols of varying sizes within your drawing. The second approach requires cleanup after cell placement. Either way, I urge you to examine the approach taken by *Place BreakLine*. Notice how a breakline can be placed elegantly with a simple MDL tool that also provides rubberbanding as you move the cursor.

Place Pipend

This tool helps MicroStation users place pipe-end symbols consistently, so they look the same no matter who draws them. In addition to consistency, the tool makes the pipe-end symbol placement an efficient, two-click task.

Pipe-end symbols are placed at the ends of circular pipes. They indicate that the pipe continues past the symbol.

Invoke the tool by clicking its icon, or by typing PLACE PIPEND in the Key-in window after loading *RS Tools LE*. The Tool Settings window allows you to change the symbol's color, weight, style, and level.

On activating the tool, you are prompted for a data point. Snap to an endpoint of the pipe and accept it with a data point. The pipe-end symbol tracks cursor movements dynamically. Snap to the other endpoint of the pipe and accept it with a data point to place the pipe-end symbol.

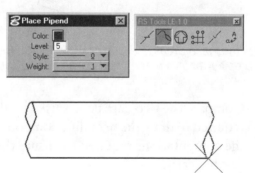

The Place Pipend tool prompts you to click two data points to place it.

Place North

The history of navigation is fraught with stories of great captains lost at sea. Their best navigational aids could not accurately determine the north direction. Without an accurate sense of direction, no wonder they got lost. Similarly, if the plan view on an engineering drawing is missing the north arrow symbol, the contractor won't know how to orient the project during construction. Obviously, placing a north arrow symbol on plan drawings is vital.

Use the *Place North* tool draw a north arrow symbol in your design files. After loading *RS Tools LE*, invoke the tool by clicking its icon in the toolbox or typing PLACE NORTH in the Key-in window.

On activating the tool, a north arrow symbol appears on the screen and moves with the cursor. To draw the symbol, simply click a data point.

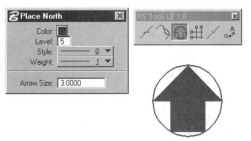

The Place North tool needs a single data point to place the symbol.

The symbol size is determined by the text height setting in the Tool Settings window. Its orientation is determined by the active angle. You can also change its symbology in the Tool Settings window. The symbol is placed as a graphic group. If a view's Fill attribute is enabled, the arrow appears filled.

Place Grid

The *Place Grid* tool draws regularly spaced horizontal and vertical gridlines using distances entered in the Tool Settings window. After loading *RS Tools LE*, invoke the tool by clicking its icon in the toolbox or typing PLACE GRID in the Key-in window.

On activating the tool, a grid appears on the screen and moves with the cursor. To place the grid, simply click a data point.

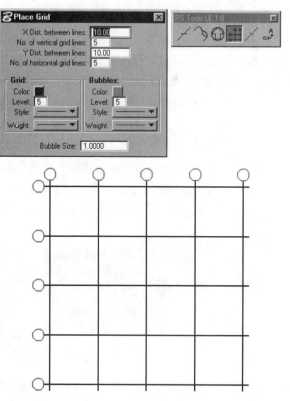

The Place Grid tool simplifies the placement of gridlines and lets you adjust line spacing through parameters in the Tool Settings window.

You have the option of modifying the number of lines and their spacing before committing the grid to the design file with a data point. The size of the bubbles is determined by the text height in the Tool Settings window. To adjust the bubble size, change its diameter in the Tool Settings window.

Gridlines are placed as a graphic group, so you can move or delete them in a single step if the graphic group lock is enabled.

Place Utility

Do you draw utility lines on civil engineering site plans? If so, you'll love the *Place Utility* tool.

A utility pipe on a site layout drawing is drawn as a line broken at regular intervals to accommodate a letter designating its type. An electric utility line may use the letter **E** and a sanitary sewer line may use the letter **S** embedded at regular intervals along its length.

Here's how a utility line might be drawn manually. First, draw a line using the Place Line tool. Next, use the Partial Delete tool to break the line at several locations. Finally, use the Place Text tool to insert the appropriate letter at the breaks created in the previous step. This is a tedious process. I haven't even mentioned the need to rotate the text to be perpendicular to the line. The *Place Utility* tool makes this entire process a two-click operation!

A custom line style definition for utility lines is a viable two-click alternative, but it has limitations. Each utility designation letter requires that you create a separate custom line style. Additionally, the spacing between embedded letters in utility lines can't be changed. So, to accommodate a dozen different letters and varying distances between letters, you must maintain a large library of custom line styles that must be shared with those who need to use your design file. The *Place Utility* tool takes all these issues away.

Place Utility allows you to enter the utility designation letter and the spacing between letters in the Tool Settings window. You don't have to worry about a custom line style resource file. I think *Place Utility* is much more flexible.

The *Place Utility* tool is straightforward in its use. After loading *RS Tools LE* (`MDL LOAD RSTOOLS`), click the *Place Utility* icon in the application's toolbox and identify the start and end points for the utility line. The default utility designation letters are *10" Water* and the default spacing between letters along the line is twenty feet. If you need to change these defaults, change them in the Tool Settings window before clicking the second data point that commits the line to the design file.

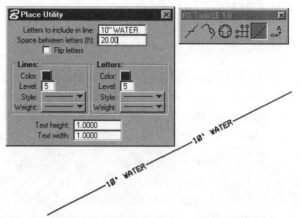

The Place Utility tool allows you to specify the utility designation letters and adjust the spacing between breaks.

The size of the utility designation letters is dictated by the text height and width fields in the Tool Setting window. I'd also like to point out that utility lines are placed as a cells with the name UTLTY. You can delete, copy, rotate, or move a utility line in a single step.

Change Case

Your project mandates that design file text be uppercase, but the designer typed it in lowercase. Typing it all over again in uppercase is out of the question; there is not enough time. Besides, even if there were time, typing the text again might cause spelling errors. What do you do?

Change Case to the rescue! The *Change Case* tool simplifies the conversion of text case in MicroStation design files. After loading *RS Tools LE*, invoke the tool by clicking its icon in the toolbox or typing **CHANGE CASE** in the Key-in window. The Tool Settings window allows you to choose *uppercase*, *lowercase*, or *word caps*. Identify a text element and accept it with a data point to convert the case of the text to conform to your choice in the Tool Settings window.

The benefit of a tool such as *Change Case* is twofold: efficiency and accuracy. You can change the case of text with a click. Also, you avoid introduce new spelling errors because you don't retype text.

```
RS  Tools  LE

RS  TOOLS  LE  (UPPERCASE)

rs  tools  le  (lowercase)

Rs  Tools  Le  (Word  Caps)
```

The Change Case tool allows you to change the case of letters in a design file.

In closing, I'd like to mention that *RS Tools LE* saves options you choose for each tool in the user preference file. When you invoke the application during another session, each tool reads the user preference file to determine the values you used last.

This concludes the chapter. Next, you're introduced to JMDL.

Chapter 26

Programming in JMDL
Creating Enterprise Engineering Applications

JMDL is an acronym for Java MicroStation Development Language. It is a superset of Sun's Java programming language and development environment. Bentley added pointers, structures, C arrays, transaction management, and other features to Java to create JMDL. Bentley's enhancements to Java in JMDL are discussed later.

When Bentley announced JMDL, several users asked if MicroStation/J would be rewritten in Java. The answer is no. MicroStation continues to be written in the C/C++ programming language. Java-based JMDL is a new application development environment in MicroStation.

The release of JMDL is a milestone in MicroStation's evolution. You will use it to create a new class of applications. Until now, MicroStation applications manipulated elements in design files. With JMDL, you will create applications that manipulate engineering components in ProjectBank. By using the DGN Package, JMDL can also create applications that manipulate design file elements.

MicroStation/J incorporates the Sun Java Virtual Machine. Any Java applications you write or download will run in MicroStation/J without modifications.

To run the Java application *myJavaApp* in MicroStation/J:

Type `java myJavaApp` in the Key-in window.

You would type the same statement at the operating system command line if you were using Sun's Java Development Kit (JDK). Java applications are source code and byte-code compatible between *100% Pure Java* platforms and MicroStation/J.

The JMDL development environment consists of many tools. The three you will use most are:

- `javac.exe`: This is Sun's Java compiler. It takes Java source code files as input and creates binary byte-code files (or applications) as output.
- `java.exe`: This invokes the Java and JMDL virtual machines to run Java and JMDL applications.
- `jmdl.exe`: This is Bentley's JMDL compiler. It compiles JMDL source code (Java with extensions) to create JMDL applications.

The following table summarizes the filename extensions and the tools you will use to work with them.

Filename Extension	Description
.java	An ASCII text file containing Java source code.
.class	A Java program created by `javac.exe` from a `.java` file.
.mjava	An ASCII text file containing JMDL source code.
.mclass	A JMDL program created by `jmdl.exe` from a `.mjava` or `.java` file.

It's important that you not think of JMDL as simply a Java-based object-oriented programming (OOP) language that creates MicroStation add-on applications. It's also an interpreted, portable, secure, and network-aware distributed programming environment with an active programming tool vendor community that will enrich your JMDL programming experience.

JMDL programmers benefit immediately from Java interfaces such as JDBC (Java DataBase Connectivity) and RMI (Remote Method Interface). With JDBC, JMDL applications can interact with any corporate database. With RMI, Java applications can invoke methods (i.e. functions) from an active MicroStation/J instance anywhere on the network.

By itself, Java does not recognize the MicroStation `.dgn` file format. It can't communicate with MDL applications either. Bentley extended Java so it would support transaction management required by engineering components in the ProjectBank. Bentley also created the *DGN Package* to allow JMDL programs to manipulate design file elements.

Applications that use DGN Package methods must be compiled with the JMDL compiler, not Sun's Java compiler. Such applications can run only inside MicroStation/J.

Following is a list of OOP definitions you may find helpful, especially if your programming experience has revolved exclusively around MDL.

- **Variables** are data attributes of an object.
- **Methods** are functions that define the behavior of an object.
- **Objects** are extensible, independent, conceptual representations of a well-defined set of abilities. To a programmer, it's a collection of variables and methods that represent these abilities.
- **Classes** are application modules that contains objects.
- **Subclasses** are child classes of existing classes.
- **Schema** is a collection of classes designed to meet the needs of a specific application domain.

The next several paragraphs discuss how and why Bentley chose Java. This will be followed by a discussion of JMDL extensions to Java.

Bentley has been working on MicroStation/J for three years. The software was originally christened Objective MicroStation to stress the object-oriented programming environment it would include. As work on the design of Objective MDL progressed, Sun Microsystems released a new programming language called Java. Java quickly captured the imagination of developers as a network-aware, enterprise-wide, platform-independent application development environment.

The goals Bentley had for Objective MDL were very similar to those Sun had implemented in Java. With the momentum Java had picked up, Bentley began to consider licensing Java to integrate within MicroStation.

It was a tough choice. Drop Objective MDL in favor of Java-based JMDL. The cost would be formidable. Over a year of language design effort would have to be repeated and the release of MicroStation/J would have to be delayed. The promise of Java and a vibrant tool vendor community that supports it convinced Bentley that Java would serve MicroStation application developers better.

JMDL Extensions to Java

Java avoids pointers altogether. MDL uses pointers extensively throughout its library of standard functions. Java objects are not persistent. (*Persistence* refers to an object's ability to maintain its state between sessions.) MicroStation has a need for its objects to be persistent. Java doesn't support structures and unsigned data types. MicroStation requires them. These language design issues meant that Bentley had to extend Java to create JMDL. Bentley's John Gooding who designed the MDL language in 1990, was again asked to design JMDL.

NOTE: You can compile 100% Pure Java code within MicroStation/J with the Java compiler and the JMDL compiler. The Java compiler produces .class file extensions and the JMDL compiler produces .mclass file extensions by default.

The following list identifies the most significant extensions to Java in Bentley's implementation of JMDL. For a complete list and a more detailed explanation of each, I refer you to the online JMDL documentation in the `c:\Bentley\Program\MicroStation\JMDL\Docs` folder.

- **C Arrays:** Everything in Java is an object, including arrays. Java arrays are dynamic, and consequently have a memory overhead. In JMDL, static C language style arrays are also supported.

- **Pointers:** In MDL, you pass variables between functions by value and by reference. To pass variables by reference or memory address, you use pointers. Java doesn't support pointers, and all variables are passed by value. Because MDL uses pointers extensively, Bentley had to extend Java to support pointers in JMDL.

- **jmdl_const:** This keyword is similar to the `const` keyword in the C and C++ programming languages. This keyword is required to support the use of pointers and transaction management. It declares data as read-only.

- **Structures:** Structures are used in MDL extensively but are not supported in Java. JMDL incorporates structures because they are simpler than objects and don't require as much memory. They also make it easier to integrate native platform code with JMDL code. In JMDL, structures do not support instance methods, constructors, or initializers for instance members. However, they do support static methods and inheritance.

- **Unsigned Data Types:** Java does not support unsigned data types. The C language-based MDL supports them. JMDL adds support for them to simplify conversion of existing code logic (UORs are unsigned data types) and the integration of platform native function libraries.

NOTE: This chapter makes no attempt to teach Java. It is assumed you know Java or have access to books on Java to learn its concepts and syntax.

If your code includes JMDL extensions to Java or classes from the DGN Package, you must use the JMDL compiler.

Next, let's discuss the DGN Package.

DGN Package

Bentley created the DGN Package so JMDL programs could manipulate design file elements. It is a collection of JMDL classes that allow your programs to manipulate the `.dgn` file format by calling functions from MicroStation's MDL interpreter.

Rather than pattern the DGN Package after the MDL library function groups, Bentley took this opportunity to develop a logical class, field, and method hierarchy consistent with Java conventions.

All JMDL interaction with design files begins with the `DgnKernel` class. This class contains MicroStation kernel information and implements methods to register key-ins for JMDL applications. You can also use it to display messages on the status bar and to start commands.

The `com.bentley.dgn.DgnKernel` class extends the `java.lang.Object` class as can be seen from its definition listed below:

```
public final class DgnKernel extends java.lang.Object
```

The `DgnKernel` class implements fields such as `int ACTIONBUTTON_NO`, `int MSGBOX_ICON_QUESTION`, `DgnProject project`, and `DgnSession session`. The word *field* in Java corresponds to data type declarations in MDL. It also implements methods such as `void exit()`, `String getProductVersion()`, and `void messageBoxOk(String, int)`. The word *method* in Java corresponds to functions in MDL. Again, online documentation that accompanies JMDL is your definitive resource on all fields and methods implemented in the class.

In addition to the traditional data types such as `int`, the `DgnKernel` class implements the `DgnProject` and `DgnSession` fields. The following table lists these descendent fields.

Field	Description
DgnKernel.project	This field contains information about the current project.
DgnKernel.session	This field contains additional fields relevant to the current session.
DgnKernel.session.settings	This field contains settings applicable to the current session.
DgnKernel.session.view	This field contains information about view windows for the currently open model.
DgnKernel.session.model	This field contains information about the currently open model.
DgnKernel.session.model.level	This field contains information about levels in the currently open model.
DgnKernel.session.model.scanner	This field is used to scan elements in the currently open model.

Field	Description
DgnKernel.session.model.selection	This field is used to scan elements in the current selection set.

The DGN Package includes many more classes, such as `com.bentley.dgn.Element`, that you will use when querying and changing attributes and properties of design file elements.

Setting Up JMDL

Setting up the development environment is the first step to compiling JMDL applications. Instead of using the MicroStation JMDL folder `C:\Bentley\Program\MicroStation\Jmdl` to store JMDL source files, I suggest you store them in a folder, such as `D:\Dev\Jmdl`. Development tools and DGN Package examples are located in the former folder.

When you install MicroStation/J with development tools, an icon for the MicroStation Development Shell is added to the MicroStation_J Program group on the Windows Start button. This shell invokes `msstndevvars.bat` in the `C:\Bentley\Program\MicroStation\Jmdl\Bin` folder. Examine this batch file to see the values assigned to the PATH and CLASSPATH variables.

Edit the CLASSPATH variable in the batch file to include your JMDL source code folder, such as `D:\Dev\Jmdl`. You can edit the CLASSPATH variable on a Windows NT system in the System Properties dialog box invoked by double-clicking the System icon in the Control Panel. On a Windows 95/98 system, edit the `autoexec.bat` file.

Let's create a JMDL source file to test your setup. Use Notepad or a programmer's editor to create the file `HelloTYMSJ.mjava` listed below.

```java
public class HelloTYMSJ
{
    public static void main
    (
    String[] args
    )
    {
        System.out.println("Hello TYMSJ Readers!");
    }
}
```

Let's examine the previous code. Notice that the filename uses mixed case. Filenames are case-sensitive in Java and JMDL. Also, the class you define in a file must be the filename as well. Thus the file `HelloTYMSJ.mjava` defines the class *HelloTYMSJ*. Notice that the first line of code reads `public class HelloTYMSJ`. The curly brace pair on the second and tenth line in the file define the body of the class, which contains the only method in this class called `main()`. The `string` object argument `args` captures command line options.

The `main ()` method is the class entry point and is executed first. This method contains a single line of code that prints a text string on the screen using the `System.out.println()` method. To run the program, you must compile it.

To compile the *HelloTYMSJ* class:

1. Click the MicroStation Development Environment icon in the MicroStation_J program group on the Start button in Windows. The system command prompt opens.
2. Make your JMDL source code directory active by using the CD command.
3. Invoke the JMDL compiler to compile the class, as shown below.

`JMDL HelloTYMSJ`

Notice that the JMDL compiler assumes the `.mjava` extension.

4. The compiler creates the class `HelloTYMSJ.mclass` in the development directory.

To run this class file, type:

`Java HelloTYMSJ`

NOTE: You must type the statement exactly as shown above. In Java and JMDL, filenames are case-sensitive.

This statement invokes the Java Virtual Machine and executes the HelloTYMSJ class. The program greets you with the statement *Hello TYMSJ Readers!*

Let's create a similar program that runs inside MicroStation and displays messages on the status bar and in a dialog box. We'll call this program *HelloUstn*. The CD-ROM contains this file in the `\Dev\Jmdl` folder.

```
import com.bentley.dgn.DgnKernel;

public class HelloUstn
extends Object
{
    public static void main
    (
    String[] args
    )
    {
    String strCommand = "Click the OK button to see a message in the Command
name field.";
    String strPrompt  = "Click the OK button to see a message in the Prompt
field.";
    String strStatus  = "Click the OK button to see a message in the Status
field.";
    String strError   = "Click the OK button to see a message in the Error
field.";
    String strReset   = "Click the OK button to clear the status bar.";

    DgnKernel.messageBoxOk(strCommand, DgnKernel.MSGBOX_ICON_INFORMATION);
    DgnKernel.showCommand("My Command message");

    DgnKernel.messageBoxOk(strPrompt, DgnKernel.MSGBOX_ICON_INFORMATION);
    DgnKernel.showPrompt("My Prompt message");

    DgnKernel.messageBoxOk(strStatus, DgnKernel.MSGBOX_ICON_INFORMATION);
    DgnKernel.showStatus("My Status message");

    DgnKernel.messageBoxOk(strError, DgnKernel.MSGBOX_ICON_INFORMATION);
    DgnKernel.showError("My Error message");

    DgnKernel.messageBoxOk(strReset, DgnKernel.MSGBOX_ICON_INFORMATION);
    DgnKernel.sendKeyin("Reset");
    }
}
```

The first line of code above imports the DgnKernel class in your source file. All JMDL interaction with MicroStation begins with the *DgnKernel* class defined in the DGN Package. This class contains information about the MicroStation kernel. It also implements methods to register key-ins for JMDL applications, to display messages on the MicroStation status bar, and to start a command.

The second line of code in HelloUstn.mjava defines the class *HelloUstn* with the statement public class HelloUstn that extends the base Java Object class. This class also contains a single method called main() with a single String object argument args to capture command line options.

The `main ()` method in turn defines several `string` objects that are to be displayed in a MicroStation dialog box. These string definitions are followed by a pair of statements that invoke the `messageBox` and the `show...` methods to invoke a dialog box and to display a message on the status bar.

The last line of code before the two closing curly braces uses the `sendKeyin()` method to send the Reset command to MicroStation.

To compile the *HelloUstn* class from the MicroStation Development Shell you opened for the previous example, invoke the JMDL compiler as shown below:

```
JMDL HelloUstn
```

The JMDL compiler creates the `HelloUstn.mclass` file that can be run within MicroStation.

To run this program, type:

```
Java HelloUstn
```

in the Key-in window.

This program displays a dialog box requesting you to click the OK button. Then, it displays messages in the Command, Prompt, Status, and Error fields. Finally, it clears all messages from the status bar.

Parallels Between MDL and JMDL

MDL and JMDL are different development environments. Nevertheless, they have many common attributes. Both were designed for modern windowing environments that are inherently event-driven. In this section, we explore the parallels between MDL and JMDL.

The Event-Driven Parallel

Both MDL and JMDL are event-driven. Both implement a mechanism to declare functions (MDL) or methods (JMDL) to handle events such as cursor movement, data point click, and reset button click.

In MDL, you use state functions, such as `mdlState_startPrimitive()`, to designate event handlers. For example, the following MDL statement:

```
mdlState_startPrimitive(dataFunc, resetFunc, cmdNameID, promptID);
```

specifies that the function `dataFunc()` handles the data point event and `resetFunc()` handles the reset button click. This statement also displays the command name on the status bar from a message list with the integer ID `cmdNameID`, and a prompt from a message list with the integer ID `promptID`.

In JMDL, for DGN-mode applications use the method `DgnKernel.startCommand()` to start a registered command. Use the `PrimitiveCommand()` class to create design file elements. Use the `LocateCommand()` class to identify elements for modification.

In JMDL you to create objects or class instances. To create design file elements, extend the `PrimitiveCommand()` class. Creating such a class automatically empowers it to handle the method names listed in the table below.

Method Name	Description
dataPoint()	Invoked by a data point click in a view under the control of this command.
dynamics()	Invoked when the cursor is moved in a view under the control of this command.
reset()	Invoked by a reset button click in a view under the control of this command.
start()	Invoked when DgnKernel.startCommand() makes this command active.
stop()	Invoked when this command is not active and another command starts.

Your application class must use these method names exactly to handle the specified events.

The Code Parallel

The following code listing from the file `BreakLine.mjava` located in the `\Dev\Jmdl` folder on the CD-ROM draws a breakline just like the *Place BreakLine* tool in *RS Tools LE*.

The code logic in the `calcVertexList()` method from the JMDL BreakLine application listed below is virtually identical to the MDL code I used to create *Place BreakLine*.

```
/*-----------------------------------------------------------------+
 |                                                                 |
 | Copyright (1999) Ranjit S. Sahai, All rights reserved.          |
 |                                                                 |
 | This JMDL program accompanies my book "Teach Yourself           |
 | MicroStation/J" published by Alpha Press. Its purpose is to help |
 | you draw a breakline with two simple clicks. It requires        |
 | MicroStation/J. Key-in "java BreakLine" to start the compiled   |
 | ".mclass" file.                                                 |
 |                                                                 |
 +----------------------------------------------------------------*/
/* -----------------------------------------------------------------+
 | This is the JMDL source file for the BreakLine program          |
 |                                                                 |
 | File:   BreakLine.mjava                                         |
 | Author: Ranjit S. Sahai, PE                                     |
 |                                                                 |
 +----------------------------------------------------------------*/


/* -----------------------------------------------------------------+
 |                                                                 |
 | Imports                                                         |
 |                                                                 |
 +----------------------------------------------------------------*/
import com.bentley.dgn.DgnKernel;
import com.bentley.dgn.PrimitiveCommand;
import com.bentley.dgn.View;
import com.bentley.dgn.LineElement;
import com.bentley.dgn.DPoint;
import com.bentley.settings.ISettingGroup;
import java.lang.Math;

/* -----------------------------------------------------------------+
 |                                                                 |
 | BreakLine class starts                                          |
 |                                                                 |
 +----------------------------------------------------------------*/
public class BreakLine extends PrimitiveCommand {
    private DPoint          m_oFirstPoint;
    private DPoint          m_oSecondPoint;
    private LineElement     m_oBreakLine;

/* -----------------------------------------------------------------+
 |                                                                 |
 | constructBreakLine()                                            |
 |                                                                 |
 +----------------------------------------------------------------*/
    private LineElement constructBreakLine
    (
```

```
   DPoint oFirstPoint,
   DPoint oSecondPoint
   )
   throws LineElement.Exception {
      DPoint[] oVertexList = calcVertexList(oFirstPoint, oSecondPoint);
      return new LineElement(null, oVertexList, 6);
   }

/* ----------------------------------------------------------------+
|                                                                  |
| calcVertexList()                                                 |
|                                                                  |
+----------------------------------------------------------------*/
   private DPoint[] calcVertexList
   (
   DPoint oFirstPoint,
   DPoint oSecondPoint
   ) {
      ISettingGroup  oSettings = DgnKernel.session.settings;
      double   dTextHt = oSettings.getDouble ("text.height");
      double   dTextWd = oSettings.getDouble ("text.width");
      DPoint[] oVertexList = new DPoint[6];
      double   dDistance = oFirstPoint.distance(oSecondPoint);
      double   dAngle    = Math.atan2 ((oFirstPoint.y - oSecondPoint.y),
                                       (oFirstPoint.x - oSecondPoint.x));
      dAngle += Math.PI;

      double x0 = oFirstPoint.x - Math.cos(dAngle)*dTextWd*0.5;
      double y0 = oFirstPoint.y - Math.sin(dAngle)*dTextWd*0.5;
      double z0 = oFirstPoint.z;
      oVertexList[0] = new DPoint(x0, y0, z0);

      double x1 = oFirstPoint.x + Math.cos(dAngle)*(dDistance*0.5 - dTextWd);
      double y1 = oFirstPoint.y + Math.sin(dAngle)*(dDistance*0.5 - dTextWd);
      double z1 = oFirstPoint.z;
      oVertexList[1] = new DPoint(x1, y1, z1);

      double x4 = oVertexList[1].x + Math.cos(dAngle)*dTextWd*2.0;
      double y4 = oVertexList[1].y + Math.sin(dAngle)*dTextWd*2.0;
      double z4 = oFirstPoint.z;
      oVertexList[4] = new DPoint(x4, y4, z4);

      double x5 = oFirstPoint.x + Math.cos(dAngle)*(dDistance + dTextWd*0.5);
      double y5 = oFirstPoint.y + Math.sin(dAngle)*(dDistance + dTextWd*0.5);
      double z5 = oFirstPoint.z;
      oVertexList[5] = new DPoint(x5, y5, z5);

      double x2 = oVertexList[1].x - Math.sin(dAngle)*dTextHt;
      double y2 = oVertexList[1].y + Math.cos(dAngle)*dTextHt;
      double z2 = oFirstPoint.z;
      oVertexList[2] = new DPoint(x2, y2, z2);

      double x3 = oVertexList[4].x + Math.sin(dAngle)*dTextHt;
      double y3 = oVertexList[4].y - Math.cos(dAngle)*dTextHt;
```

```
        double z3 = oFirstPoint.z;
        oVertexList[3] = new DPoint(x3, y3, z3);

        return oVertexList;
    }

/* ------------------------------------------------------------------+
 |                                                                   |
 | start() invoked when DgnKernel.startCommand used in main()        |
 |                                                                   |
 +------------------------------------------------------------------*/
    public void start(String oStrUnparsed) {
        DgnKernel.showCommand ("Draw BreakLine");
        DgnKernel.showPrompt ("Enter start point");
    }


/* ------------------------------------------------------------------+
 |                                                                   |
 | stop() invoked when BreakLine finishes                            |
 |                                                                   |
 +------------------------------------------------------------------*/
    public void stop() {
        m_oBreakLine   = null;
        m_oFirstPoint  = null;
        m_oSecondPoint = null;
    }


/* ------------------------------------------------------------------+
 |                                                                   |
 | dataPoint() invoked when data point is clicked                    |
 |                                                                   |
 +------------------------------------------------------------------*/
    public void dataPoint(DPoint oPoint, ViewoView) {
        if (null == m_oFirstPoint) {
            m_oFirstPoint = oPoint;
            DgnKernel.showPrompt("Enter end point");
            startDynamics();
        }
        else {
            try {
               m_oBreakLine = constructBreakLine(m_oFirstPoint, oPoint);
              DgnKernel.session.redrawElement (m_oBreakLine, View.NORMALDRAW);
              DgnKernel.session.model.addElement (m_oBreakLine);
            }
            catch (LineElement.Exception e) {
        }
            catch (java.io.IOException e) {
            }

            m_oFirstPoint  = null;
            m_oSecondPoint = null;
            m_oBreakLine   = null;
            restart ();
        }
```

```
    }

/* ----------------------------------------------------------------+
|                                                                  |
| reset() invoked when reset button is clicked                     |
|                                                                  |
+----------------------------------------------------------------*/
   public void reset() {
       m_oFirstPoint  = null;
       m_oSecondPoint = null;
       m_oBreakLine   = null;
       restart ();
   }

/* ----------------------------------------------------------------+
|                                                                  |
| dynamics() invoked when curosr is moved                          |
|                                                                  |
+----------------------------------------------------------------*/
   public void dynamics(DPoint oPoint, View oView, boolean bDrawMode) {
       try {
          m_oBreakLine = constructBreakLine(m_oFirstPoint, oPoint);
          DgnKernel.session.redrawElement (m_oBreakLine, View.XORDRAW);
       }
       catch (LineElement.Exception e) {
       }
   }

/* ----------------------------------------------------------------+
|                                                                  |
| main()                                                           |
|                                                                  |
+----------------------------------------------------------------*/
   public static void main(String args[]) {
       BreakLine oTymsjBreakLine = new BreakLine();
       oTymsjBreakLine.setKeyin("tymsjbreakline");
       DgnKernel.registerCommand(oTymsjBreakLine);
       DgnKernel.startCommand(oTymsjBreakLine);
   }

} // BreakLine class ends
```

JMDL statements will look familiar to MDL programmers because Java uses many C++ language keywords and syntax. By convention, JMDL class names begin with uppercase initial letters, like the Math class.

Compiling and Running BreakLine.mclass

The compiled version of the BreakLine class is included on the CD-ROM. If you wish to compile it from the source file yourself, make sure your JMDL environment is set up properly as explained earlier. At the operating system command prompt, type:

`JMDL BreakLine`

You need not type the `.mjava` extension because the JMDL compiler assumes it by default. The compiler will create the class file `BreakLine.mclass`. Place this file in the JMDL directory or another defined by the CLASSPATH variable. To run the class file from MicroStation, type the following in the Key-in window:

`Java BreakLine`

This statement invokes the Java Virtual Machine and executes the *BreakLine* class. The status bar displays the application's command name, prompts you for data points, and creates a breakline symbol.

NOTE: You must type the statement exactly as shown above. In Java and JMDL, filenames are case-sensitive.

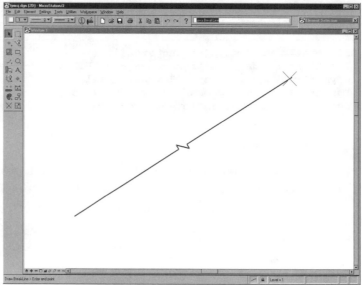

The JMDL BreakLine application drawing a breakline symbol.

The JMDL *BreakLine* tool is very similar to the *Place BreakLine* tool in *RS Tools LE*. However, it lacks the symbology settings in the Tool Settings window. In its current implementation, the DGN Package has limited support for interaction with MicroStation's Dialog Manager. This means that you must use the Java AWT frame or Java's Swing GUI interface for dialog-based interaction with users.

Many other aspects of MDL, such as Auxiliary Coordinates, Associations, Cell library modifications, Constraints, Current Transforms, and License Management, are not supported in JMDL's DGN Package. Consequently, MDL remains the premier development tool for DGN-mode applications.

Why should you learn JMDL?

If JMDL were designed to emulate MDL application development, I'd have a hard time convincing you that your effort in learning JMDL would be worthwhile. The real value of JMDL lies in its ability to create engineering component models for ProjectBank.

Let's explore engineering component modeling concepts by analyzing the BreakLine application in the next section.

Analyzing BreakLine

From a user's perspective, *BreakLine* simplifies drafting tasks because it makes the placement of a breakline symbol a two-click process. It also ensures that the breakline symbol is consistent in shape and size from one drawing to another, or even one instance to another in the same drawing. The active text height determines its size.

From a programmer's perspective, the tool is easy to implement. It needs only two data points to define it completely. Based on the two data points a user clicks, you compute the six vertices that define the breakline symbol, and use the predefined method to create line strings (a Type 4 element) in the design file.

Despite its usefulness, the breakline symbol the application draws is inherently a *dumb* geometric element. Should you query it with the Analyze Element tool in the Primary toolbox, you'll be told that the element is a line string with six vertices at specific coordinates in the design plane—Nothing more.

By using the Modify Element tool, you can easily extend one of its endpoints, thus disrupting its geometry. If you modify the part the breakline represented a break in, the breakline symbol won't adjust automatically. You'll need to delete the old breakline symbol and place a new one at the new endpoints of the modified part. I'm sure you can think of many other scenarios where the geometric nature of the breakline, and its lack of associativity with the breaking element, can make you wish for a more *intelligent* breakline.

The following bulleted list summarizes the most significant limitations of the breakline application when implemented as a geometric element (the DGN and MDL world), despite being written in JMDL:

- MicroStation treats it as just another line string, not a breakline that has a specific purpose.
- Modifying a vertex of the breakline disrupts its geometric symmetry.
- It is not associated with the element it creates a break in.

MDL is a mature development environment for creating geometric models. But if you're thinking of intelligent components or objects, JMDL can help you build them on a foundation far more solid than what most vertical market applications use today—user data attachments to geometric elements with custom MDL applications.

The limitations in *BreakLine* identified above lead to possibilities of a more useful breakline object. If you move the breakline, the associated part moves to maintain model integrity. If you extend the part, the breakline adjusts automatically. If you extract a 2D section from a 3D model, the model calls upon the breakline to attach to it at appropriate section cuts.

Such applications are possible today in MicroStation's DGN-mode, the only mode currently enabled in MicroStation/J, with MDL or JMDL by attaching user data to elements. In ECM-mode, that will coincide with the release of ProjectBank and the component modeling software development kit later this year, such applications will only be possible in JMDL. The latter will provide a far more elegant environment with capabilities that are difficult, if not impossible, to model otherwise.

The following paragraphs discuss component modeling concepts, and JMDL's object-oriented model which makes it suitable for creating component modeling applications.

If you were to create a component breakline, you would need to define a schema for the component. A *schema* is a collection of rules, data structures, and dependencies that define the component and its behavior.

In the component world, the breakline would no longer be an element type, such as a line string, from a limited set of supported element types. It would be a unique component with its own identity as defined by the application schema. In turn, it would have rules defining its interaction with other components, and data structures containing parameters that define its geometry in a drawing, or other property in another form or representation.

JMDL, being object-oriented, implements concepts like constructors, fields, and methods that fit well with the needs of component modeling.

Constructors are methods or functions that define how to create the object, based on supplied parameters. *Fields* are data structures relevant to the object. *Methods* are functions that define and encapsulate the object's behavior.

JMDL will also support transaction management, when ProjectBank becomes available. In ProjectBank, the transaction manager notifies objects when dependent objects change.

In the absence of ProjectBank, and the component modeling software development kit that will pave the way to ECM-mode, the best way to prepare for such development is to create DGN-mode geometry and tag it with user data. This will let you think about geometry in more intelligent terms and identify the constructors, fields, and methods you need to develop in JMDL to support the desired intelligence.

Therefore, if you wanted the breakline to maintain its symmetry and height when modified, you would save the size as user data and implement a method for its modification.

In the world of component modeling you define components and their behavior, data structure, relationships to other components, and representations. JMDL was designed for such modeling. If component modeling is in your future, you have no choice but to embrace JMDL.

JMDL has just been introduced. Its target development platform, the ProjectBank, is still a few months away. I hope this discussion has clarified the role JMDL will play in MicroStation/J development as the software evolves.

It's been a long journey, and you've reached the end. I hope you've enjoyed reading and learning from this book.

Index

MicroStation (*continued*)

    controlling toolboxes and tool frames, 583–584

    controlling view window settings, 584–585

    correcting registration information, 39t

    corrupt user preference file, 569t

    design file format compatibility, 571–572

    directory structure, 40–42

    and EdG, 512n

    engineering components, 29, 761

    exchanging design files with older versions, 77n

    exporting drawing files, 557–558

    freeze command, 507t

    HTML authoring tools, 443–444, 495

    importing drawing files into, 558–560

    installing, 37–39

    interacting with, 63–69

    interface, 51–52, 574

    interface components, customizing, 552–553

    intersection snap mode, 158t

    memory usage guidelines, 576, 577n, 578

    modifying a toolbox, 553

    modifying a tool frame, 553–554

    modifying the menu bar, 554

    mouse buttons, 65

    and OLE, 618

    OLE container and server support, 619n

    online help, 70–72

    origin, 6–9

    placing OLE object on the Clipboard, 619

    precision key-ins supported by, 68

    ProActiveM object technology, 690

    quitting, 78

    registering, 39–40

    restarting, with debug switch, 547t

MicroStation (*continued*)

    saving changes between sessions, 140n

    SGML help engine, 73

    specifying grid density, 572–574

    specifying reference file related preferences, 579–581

    specifying text-related preferences, 581–582

    starting, 42–48

    starting DDE conversation with, 621

    storing geometric shapes, 116n

    THAW command, 507t

    translation table, 584

    verifying .dgn filename extension, 45n

    versions, 9–10, 14

    web-aware aspect of, 436

    See also IGDS

MicroStation Archive dialog box, 537

MicroStation BASIC

    code, 659, 660–662

    comparing to UCMs, 659–660

    defined, 658

    and Dynamic Data Exchange, 620, 621

    extensions, 674, 675

    and UCM language, 632

    and User Commands, 654–655

    See also macro(s); UCMs

MicroStation Development Environment, 694

MicroStation Development Language. *See* MDL

MicroStation/J Installation dialog box, 37, 694

MicroStation Manager, 633–634, 662, 697

MicroStation Manager dialog box, 49–50

Mirror tool, 259–260

modal dialog box, 133

Modeler, 24, 360, 423, 446

    creating assemblies, 481–483

    creating drawing sheet, 483–484

    creating solid model, 478–480

    and dimension-driven cells, 480n

O

Objective MicroStation Development Language (OMDL), 28

Object Linking and Embedding, 614, 617–618
  inserting an OLE object, 619
  placing OLE object on the Clipboard, 619

object oriented programming (OOP), 27, 28, 762, 763

ODBC. *See* Open DataBase Connectivity

ODBC Data Source Administrator dialog box, 452

ODBC Microsoft Access 97 Setup dialog box, 396

OLE. *See* Object Linking and Embedding

Open Archive File dialog box, 539

Open/Close Dialog box, 164–165

Open DataBase Connectivity, 394, 395, 452, 453, 456

Open Level Structure dialog box, 496

Open Palette File dialog box, 427

Open Source Font Files dialog box, 601

openview.dgn, working with views, 164e–166e

Orientation toolbox, 464

Origin, 339
  Default, 355
  Floating, 353

over-constrained, 362

P

Page Setup dialog box, 322

palettes, material, 426, 427

Pan View command, 172

Parameter Constraints toolbox, 366

parametric, 363, 475
  cells, 608, 611
  design, 360

Parametric Solids toolbox, 479

Parasolid, 476

Partial Delete tool, 101e, 266–267, 283e

partial.dgn, partially deleting elements, 282e–283e

Part Manager dialog box, 465

Parts Manager dialog box, 460

Paste dialog box, 616

PATH
  statement, 694, 701, 708t
  variables, 767

Pattern Area tool, 213

pattern(ing), 211, 212n, 214n
  associative, 211
  maps, 426
  methods, 212
  snappable, 211
  stroke, 592

Patterns toolbox, 210–212

PCL. *See* Printer Control Language

persistence of engineering components, 29

phantom elements, 526, 528–529

Phong rendering modes, 432

Photomatch tool, 431

Place Active Cell Matrix tool, 238

Place Active Cell tool, 105e, 237–238

Place Active Line Terminator tool, 239

Place Active Point Tool, 197

Place Arc tool, 218–219

Place Block tool, 216, 345e

Place BreakLine tool, 752–754

Place Circle tool, 221–222, 374e, 412e

Place Cylinder tool, 423

Place Ellipse tool, 222–223, 224, 346e

Place Fence tool, 152

Place Grid tool, 755–756

Place Half Ellipse tool, 219

Place Line tool, 91e, 130e–131e, 202–203, 273e–276e, 344e, 349e, 374e

Place Lstring command, 649

Place Multi-line tool, 203–205, 206

Place myLine
  command, 735
  design structure, 744–745
  example, 743
  functionality, identifying, 743–744
  myline.mc, 747–749

SQL
    command, 395
    queries, 453
    standard, 394
    window, 395, 399, 400
SQL Query Builder dialog box, 458
Stair Generator, 622, 623, 624, 625–626
StairGen.UCM, draws steps in elevation, 649–651
Standards Manual for US Army Corps of Engineers CADD Systems, 489
Standard toolbox, 59–60
statements, configuration files and, 549, 550
static data exchange, 615, 617
status bar, 54–55
Step AP203, 476
stick-line fonts, 599
STL file format, 476
Story of Mankind, The, 2
stream setting, 136
string list, 703
String List Editor, 703t
stroke pattern, 592
    creating, 593–594
style attribute, 127
sub unit, 138
Summit Software, 657
Sun Microsystems, 763
Sun's Java Development Kit, 762
surface and 3D primitive element, 126
Surface Modeling tool frame, 421–422
Sutherland, Dr. Ivan, 4, 14
SVF, 443
switches, command line, 47–48
symbology
    changing, of existing elements, 58n
    resource files, 589, 592t, 600n
    tables, 492–494, 500, 504
Systems Properties dialog box, 767

T

tables.dgn, changing weight globally, 524e
tablet menu cells, 606

tagoffce.dgn
    creating tags, 383e–386e
    tagging elements, 386e–388e
    using tag values to select elements, 389e–390e
tag(s)
    attaching, 386e–388e, 389e–390e
    creating, 383e–386e
    data, 382, 383
    editing and reviewing, 388–389
    related preferences, 581
    reports, creating, 391–393
    sets, 383, 384
Tag Sets dialog box, 383
Tags Toolbox, 387, 442
TCB variables, 641–642, 641–642
Teach Yourself MicroStation/J (Book)
    about the author, vi–vii
    acknowledgements, x
    companion CD-ROM, ix
    credits, x
    dedication, xi
    how book is organized, vii–viii
    notes and tips, ix
    praise for, i
    preface, xiii
    trademarks, v
    typographical conventions, viii, ix
    warning and disclaimer, v
TeamMate, 30
tentative
    cursor, 130n
    point, 156n
tentative button, 64–67, 130n, 156t
    and active depth, 414–416
text
    element, 126, 231n
    glossary, 597–599
    importing, 226n
    line spacing, 225
    node element, 126
    placement methods, 228–229
    related preferences, specifying, 581–582
    size, changing, 227n

Window menu, 164–167, 169n
window(s)
AccuDraw, 337–338
Command, 54–55
Key-in, 699, 700, 721
tool settings, 60–61
view, 61–63, 163–170
Windows 95/98, 42
Windows Explorer, 44, 45
Windows Notepad, 549, 617, 630, 635
Windows NT, 42, 44, 767
Windows Paint, 117, 119
Windows WordPad, 617
wireframe, 425, 426, 431
wiremesh, 431
witness lines. *See* extension lines
Words to Follow, 510
bad value for, 530–531
workgroup collaboration, reference files
and, 289–290, 291

working units, 86, 89–90, 137–138, 139
workspace(s), 141–142, 499, 543
command line switch, 48
configuration file hierarchy, 547
defined, 544
directory structure, 545–546
groupbox, 548–549
workunit.dgn, setting working units,
139e–140e
WT=, 128, 499, 603
WTF. *See* Words to Follow

X
XY=, 68, 189, 625

Z
Zoom In command, 171
Zoom Out command, 171

Alpha Construction & Engineering Corporation (Alpha Corporation) is celebrating **Twenty Years** as a full-service consulting firm offering a wide array of engineering, construction management, and information technology services across the nation. Since 1979, Alpha Corporation has worked with a broad spectrum of clientele, including but not limited to; government agencies, municipalities, private enterprises and contractors. Alpha Corporation's primary areas of expertise in engineering are transportation (highways, bridges, tunnels), civil (facilities design, airports and land development), structural (building renovations), and CAD consulting (training, custom programming, standards development). With offices in Virginia, Maryland, North Carolina, Massachusetts, and Alpha Corporation can offer services to clients throughout the United States.

Alpha Corporation has compiled a diverse team including professional engineers, surveyors, cost estimators, schedulers, construction managers, inspectors, and programmers. Each offering a solid background of technical knowledge and experience to every project, earning Alpha Corporation an outstanding reputation in a very competitive industry.

Alpha Corporation delivers practical, cost-effective, viable solutions to their client's needs. Their hands-on experience encompasses the entire realm of construction engineering: planning, design and management. After years of steady growth and active involvement in the construction industry, Alpha Corporation is confident of their ability to excel in technical knowledge and leadership.

For additional information, please fill out the coupon below and mail to:

Alpha Corporation, 45665 Willow Pond Plaza, Sterling, Virginia 20164.
Phone: 1.703.709.2206; Fax: 1.703.709.0643;
E-mail: mail@alphacorporation.com; URL: *www.alphacorporation.com*

Name: _____

Title: _____

Company: _____

Address: _____

City, State, ZIP: _____

Telephone: _____

AJ, Services Incorporated (AJ, Incorporated), is an Authorized Primavera Dealer for the United States and Canada. Primavera Systems produces the world's leading line of high-end project management software. Unlike other Primavera dealers, A,J Incorporated is a full-service dealer.

AJ, Incorporated provides:

- Primavera Software: Expedition, P3 Project Planner, and SureTrak.

- Public Classroom Training on all software packages offered by Primavera System.

- On-site Private Training and Consulting.

AJ, Incorporated has a staff of certified trainers that work with clients at a designated location creating a training environment customized toward that client's needs. Public Classroom training sessions are also taught by certified trainers at AJ's offices in North Carolina, Maryland, and Virginia.

AJ, Incorporated also offers government agencies the opportunity to receive training covered by a GSA Schedule. AJ, Incorporated can provide all Public and Private Classroom Training, as well as ADP Services such as, System Analysis, System Installation, Programming, Data/Records Management, Resource & Facilities Management and Database Planning & Design through **GSA Contract Number GS-35F-4430G.**

For additional information, please fill out the coupon below and mail to:

AJ, Incorporated, 45665 Willow Pond Plaza, Sterling, Virginia 20164.
Phone: 1.709.709.9046; Fax: 1.703.709.0643;
E-mail: mail@ajinc.com; URL: *www.ajinc.com*

Name: _____

Title: _____

Company: _____

Address: _____

City, State, ZIP: _____

Telephone: _____

AC Software, Incorporated, (AC Software) is the publisher of TimeWizard. TimeWizard is a dynamic labor tracking system that enables an entire company to save money by sharing valuable time accounting data.

AC Software provides its clients with the TimeWizard line of labor tracking and time accounting applications that collect real-time business information for companies—independent of geography.

TimeWizard™, a client-server application, and **TimeWizard.enterprise**™, a Web-enabled application, both enable companies to save money by sharing valuable time accounting data by utilizing enterprise-wide integration, project control, customizable timesheets, enforceable business rules and exception reports, automated notification system, and remote access.

TimeWizard is used by 25,000 individuals at more than 40 companies worldwide. Clients span various industries ranging from Financial Services to Information Technology to Medical/Pharmaceutical. TimeWizard is distributed worldwide via direct sales, original equipment manufacturer partners, value-added resellers, and technology brokers. Channel Partners are located in the United States, Belgium, Germany and the United Kingdom. AC Software has offices in Maryland, North Carolina, Pennsylvania, California, and Virginia to help meet their client's needs.

For additional information, please fill out the coupon below and mail to:

AC Software Inc., 2901 Riva Trace Parkway, Annapolis, Maryland 21401.
Phone: 1.410.224.0841; Fax: 1.410.224.8518;
E-mail: sales@timewzrd.com; URL: *www.timewzrd.com*

Name: _____

Title: _____

Company: _____

Address: _____

City, State, ZIP: _____

Telephone: _____

Alpha Press is the publishing division of Alpha Corporation. It is dedicated to meeting the educational, training, and implementation needs of MicroStation users world-wide. Its goal is to be the leading provider of information and consulting services to companies that use CAD in a mission-critical environment.

Alpha Press' flagship book, **Teach Yourself MicroStation/J**™ by the acclaimed industry author and trainer Ranjit S. Sahai, P.E., was born out of a commitment to quality and value in serving the educational needs of Bentley's MicroStation line of software products. Teach Yourself MicroStation/J™ is the most comprehensive MicroStation book on the market offering unmatched value for the price. It is a cost-effective way to learn all aspects of MicroStation at a fraction of the cost of classroom training.

Alpha Press is looking forward to releasing two more MicroStation books in the coming months: **75 BASIC Macros for MicroStation/J**™ and **3D Modeling in MicroStation/J**™. Alpha Press also carries several other titles from authors throughout the world, also dedicated to the serving the CAD community with books for today's programs!

For additional information, please fill out the coupon below and mail to:

Alpha Press, 45665 Willow Pond Plaza, Sterling, Virginia 20164.
Phone: 1.703.709.9883; Fax: 1.703.709.0643;
E-mail: books@alphacorporation.com;
URL: *www.alphacorporation.com/press.*

Name:_____

Title:_____

Company:_____

Address:_____

City, State, ZIP:_____

Telephone:_____

Books, Software, and Services from Alpha Press

Product or Service ID	Title or Description	List Price (USD)
1-892658-00-3	Teach Yourself MicroStation/J by Ranjit Sahai	$49.95
1-892658-01-1	75 Basic Macros for MicroStation/J by Ranjit Sahai	$75.00
1-892658-02-X	3D Modeling in MicroStation/J by Ranjit Sahai	$49.95
RSTL 1.0	RS Tools LE 1.0	$25.00
RSTL 1.0-SRC	RS Tools LE 1.0 Source Code for Internal Use	$295.00
PRGMDL	MDL and JMDL Programming	call
TRGBMS	Basic MicroStation Training	call
TRGIMS	Intermediate MicroStation Training	call
TRGAMS	Advanced MicroStation Training	call
TRGMDL	Programmer Training (UCM, BASIC, MDL, and JMDL)	call

Note: Above prices do not include shipping and handling.

Alpha Press
45665 Willow Pond Plaza
Sterling, Virginia 20164
Phone: 1.703.709.9883
Fax: 1.703.709.0643
E-mail: books@alphacorporation.com
URL: www.alphacorporation.com/press

(*continued from reverse*) ments or that operation of the Software Program will by uninterrupted or error-free. This limited warranty does not cover any Software Program that has been altered or changed in any way by anyone other than Vendor. Vendor is not responsible for problems caused by changes in the operating characteristics of computer hardware or computer operating systems that are made after the release of the Software Program, nor for problems in the interaction of the Software Program with other software. To obtain warranty service during the 90 day warranty period, you may return the Software Product, postage prepaid, with a description of the problem to Vendor. The defective media in which the Software Product is contained will replaced at no additional charge to you by Vendor.

THE WARRANTIES SET FORTH ABOVE ARE EXCLUSIVE AND IN LIEU OF ALL OTHER WARRANTIES, INCLUDING WITHOUT LIMITATION, ANY WARRANTIES OF MERCHANTABILITY OR FITNESS FOR A PARTICULAR PURPOSE, WHETHER EXPRESSED OR IMPLIED. EXCEPT AS EXPRESSLY SET FORTH ABOVE, VENDOR DISCLAIMS AND EXCLUDES ALL OTHER WARRANTIES.

3.2   Some states do not allow the exclusion of implied warranties, so the above exclusion may not apply to you. The warranty provided by Vendor gives you specific legal rights, and you may also have other rights which vary from state to state.

4. LIMITATION OF REMEDIES AND LIABILITY

4.1   *Exclusive Remedy.* Vendor will replace any defective disk without charge to you if the defective disk is returned to Vendor, postage prepaid, within ninety (90) days from the date of purchase, together with a copy of proof of purchase. However, except for claims for personal injury caused by our sole negligence, replacement of the defective disk shall be your sole and exclusive remedy against Vendor for any breach of warranty claim or any other claim based on contract, tort, statute or otherwise.

4.2   *Limitation of Liability.* ALPHA PRESS AND THE AUTHORS OF THE SOFTWARE PROGRAM SHALL NOT UNDER ANY CIRCUMSTANCES BE LIABLE FOR SPECIAL, INCIDENTAL, CONSEQUENTIAL, INDIRECT, OR OTHER SIMILAR DAMAGES, INCLUDING WITHOUT LIMITATION LOST PROFITS, EVEN IF VENDOR OR ITS AGENT HAS BEEN ADVISED OR OTHERWISE HAS KNOWLEDGE OF THE POSSIBILITY OF SUCH DAMAGES. UNDER NO CIRCUMSTANCES SHALL THE LIABILITY FOR DAMAGES OF VENDOR AND THE AUTHORS OF THE SOFTWARE PRODUCT EXCEED THE PURCHASE PRICE PAID BY YOU.

5. TERMINATION

5.1   This Agreement is effective until terminated. You may terminate it at any time by destroying the Software Product, including all computer programs and documentation, and erasing any copies thereof residing on computer equipment. This Agreement also shall terminate if you do not comply with any of the terms or conditions of this Agreement. Upon such termination you agree to destroy the Software Product and erase all copies residing on computer equipment.

6. U.S. GOVERNMENT RESTRICTED RIGHTS

6.1   The Software Product is provided to the United States Government only with restricted rights and limited rights. Use, duplication, or disclosure by the Government is subject to restrictions set forth in FAR Sections 52-227-14 and 52-227-19, or DFARS Section 52.227-7013(C)(1)(ii), as applicable.

7. GENERAL

7.1   You are solely responsible for the installation, management and operation of the Software Product.

Software License Agreement

1. DEFINITIONS

1.1 *Software Product.* The term *Software Product* includes all copies of the enclosed software and the documentation related thereto. The Software Product is licensed (not sold) to you. Vendor owns all copyrights, trade secrets, trade names, and other proprietary rights in the Software Product, and no such rights are being transferred to you either expressly or implicitly by Vendor.

1.2 *You, Your, Licensee and End User.* The terms *You, Your, Licensee* and *End-User* refer to the purchaser of the book and related materials within which the Software Program is included, together with his assigns, transfers, and legal representatives and successors in interest.

1.3 *Vendor.* The term *Vendor* refers to Alpha Press and Ranjit Sahai, the author of RS Tools LE, exercise files, cell libraries, and example program code. It also refers to MicroEdge, Inc. for the Visual SlickEdit demo and American Cybernetics, Inc. for the Multi-Edit demo.

2. SOFTWARE LICENSE

2.1 *Authorized Use.* Vendor grants you a nonexclusive license to use the Software Product on a single computer (whether a single CPU, part of a licensed network, or a terminal connected to a single CPU). You may make one (1) copy of the Software Product's computer program for back-up purposes only.

2.2 *Restrictions.* You shall not: (1) copy (other than for back-up purposes), distribute, rent, assign, lease, or sublicense all or any portion of the Software Product; (2) modify or prepare derivative works of the Software Product; (3) use the Software Product in a computer-based services business; (4) transmit the Software Product over a network, by telephone, or electronically using any means; (5) reverse engineer, decompile, or disassemble the Software Program; or (6) distribute or otherwise place the Software Product on any electronic Bulletin Board Systems or Online Services.

2.3 *Transfer.* You may transfer the Software Product, but only if you make sure that the transferee agrees to accept the terms and conditions of this Agreement. If you transfer the Software Product, you must transfer all computer programs and documentation and erase any copies residing on computer equipment. Your license is automatically terminated if you transfer the Software Product.

3. LIMITED SOFTWARE PRODUCT WARRANTY

3.1 For a period of ninety (90) calendar days from the date of purchase, Vendor warrants that the enclosed computer disk will be free of material defects in materials and workmanship under normal and proper use. Vendor does not warrant the contents of the Software Product or that it will be error free. The Software Product is furnished *AS IS* and without warranty as to the performance or results you may obtain by using the Software Product. The entire risk as to the results and performance of the Software Product is assumed by you. Vendor does not warrant that the Software Program will meet your require- (*continued on reverse*)